Provincial Museum of Alberta
Natural History
Occasional Paper No. 23
1996

# PROCEEDINGS OF THE FOURTH PRAIRIE CONSERVATION AND ENDANGERED SPECIES WORKSHOP

**February 1995**

At

**The University of Lethbridge**

and

**Lethbridge Community College**

**Lethbridge, Alberta**

Edited by:

Walter D. Willms

Johan F. Dormaar

Published by:

Curatorial Section
Provincial Museum of Alberta
12845-102 Avenue
Edmonton, Alberta
T5N OM6

# NATURAL HISTORY OCCASIONAL PAPER SERIES

Occasional Papers are published by the Provincial Museum of Alberta on subjects pertaining to the natural history of Alberta. Potential contributors are requested to submit manuscript proposals to the Manager, Curatorial and Collections Administration, Provincial Museum of Alberta, 12845-102 Avenue, Edmonton, Alberta T5N OM6.

**Canadian Cataloguing in Publication Data**

Prairie Conservation and Endangered Species Workshop (4th : 1995 : University of Lethbridge and Lethbridge Community College)

Proceedings of the fourth Prairie Conservation and Endangered Species Workshop, February 1995 at the University of Lethbridge and Lethbridge Community College, Lethbridge, Alberta

(Natural history occasional paper / Provincial Museum of Alberta ; no. 23)
Includes bibliographical references.
ISBN 0-7732-1906-4

1. Nature conservation--Prairie Provinces--Congresses. 2. Endangered species--Prairie Provinces--Congresses. I. Willms, W.D. (Walter David), 1944- II. Dormaar, J.F. (Johan Frederik), 1930- III. Provincial Museum of Alberta. Curatorial Section. IV. Title. V. Series: Natural history occasional paper ; no. 23.
QH77.C2P74 1995            333.95'09712            C96-910176-7

Cover photo: Swift Fox (*Vulpes velox*). Courtesy Ludwig N. Carbyn

# ACKNOWLEDGEMENTS

## ORGANIZING COMMITTEE

The workshop is the result of the labours of the organizing committee. The committee held over a dozen meetings, commencing in the fall of 1993. Subcommittees on finance, registration, posters and displays, program, volunteer recruitment, publicity, logistics and awards were struck to facilitate business. The organizing committee is:

**Barry Adams,** Regional Range Manager, Public Lands Services, Southern Region, Alberta Agriculture, Food and Rural Development
**Cheryl Bradley,** Volunteer, Environmental Consultant (secretary)
**Adrien Corbiere,** Volunteer, Lethbridge Naturalists Society
**Ian Dyson,** Regional Environmental Coordinator, Prairie Region, Regional Coordination Services, Alberta Environmental Protection (chair)
**Lorne Fitch,** Fisheries Biologist, Natural Resources Service, Alberta Environmental Protection
**Pat Herzog,** Chair of the Department of Environmental Science, Lethbridge Community College
**Geoffrey Holroyd,** Research Scientist, Canadian Wildlife Service, Environment Canada
**Andrew Hurly,** Assistant Professor, Department of Biological Sciences, University of Lethbridge
**Elizabeth Savoy,** Coordinator, Helen Schuler Coulee Centre, City of Lethbridge
**Walter Willms,** Range Ecologist, Agriculture and Agri-Food Canada, Research Centre
**Craig Wood,** Area Soil Conservationist, PFRA, Agriculture and Agri-Food Canada

## FINANCIAL SPONSORS

Sharing the Prairies is made possible as a result of generous financial support from:

Agr Evo
Agriculture and Agri-Food Canada
Alberta Agriculture, Food and Rural Development
Alberta Cattle Commission
Alberta Environmental Protection
Alberta Native Plant Council
Alberta Society of Professional Biologists
Alberta Wilderness Association
Antelope Creek Ranch
Axys Environmental Consulting Ltd.
Big Rock Brewery
Canadian Association of Petroleum Producers
Canadian Cattlemen's Association
Canadian Forces Base Suffield
Canadian Parks and Wilderness Society
Cottonwood Consultants Ltd.
Ducks Unlimited Canada
Energy Resources Conservation Board
Environment Canada - Canadian Wildlife Service
EnviroScapes
Federation of Alberta Naturalists
Foothills Pipelines Ltd.
Komex International Ltd.
Nature Conservancy Canada
North American Waterfowl Management Plan
Nova Gas Transmission Ltd.

Oldman River Regional Planning Commission
PanCanadian Petroleum Limited
Prairie Conservation Forum
Proven Seed/United Grain Growers
Saskatchewan Environment and Resource Management
Shell Canada
Southern Alberta Grazing Association
Special Areas Board
TERA Environmental Consultants (Alta) Ltd.
TransCanada Pipelines Limited
D. A. Westworth and Associates
Wildlife Habitat Canada
World Wildlife Fund, Canada


## SUPPORTERS

Significant support and in kind services have also been provided by:

Alberta Agriculture, Food and Rural Development
Alberta Environmental Protection
Agriculture and Agri-Food Canada
City of Lethbridge
Ducks Unlimited Canada
Environment Canada, Canadian Wildlife Service
Helen Schuler Coulee Centre Volunteers and Teen Naturalists
Institute for Renewable Resource Management, Lethbridge Community College
Lethbridge Naturalists Society
University of Lethbridge
World Wildlife Fund Canada


## VOLUNTEERS

Thank you to everyone who volunteered to help with registration, the coat checks, the airport shuttle, recording sessions, chairing and facilitating sessions and making presentations. The workshop could not succeed without such tremendous volunteer contributions.


## PROGRAM

Illustrations - Elizabeth Savoy
Typesetting - Marilyn Danish


**SPECIAL RECOGNITION** is extended to Craig Wood who willingly accepted the task of editing these proceedings but was forced to relinquish the duties because of illness. Members of the organizing committee thank him for his thoughtful advice and wish him a speedy recovery.

# TABLE OF CONTENTS

# PROGRAM AGENDA

OPENING WELCOME  - Ian W. Dyson, Organizing Committee Chairman.

PLENARY ADDRESS
> Canadian agricultural policies and other "land mining" initiatives for prairie agriculture  - Ken A. Rosaasen and James S. Lokken.

OPENING PANEL: OVERVIEW OF WORKSHOP THEMES
> Prairie conservation action plan - Monte Hummel.
> Ecosystem management - Rod Heitshmidt.
> Policies and programs affecting prairie conservation - Richard Laing.
> Endangered species - Geoff Holroyd.

HUMAN/NATURE TRANSACTIONS: A SURVEY  - Don Gayton.

PRAIRIE ECOSYSTEM MANAGEMENT: AN ALBERTA PERSPECTIVE
> Presented by: Barry Adams and Lorne Fitch.

THE PRAIRIE CONSERVATION ACTION PLAN - PAST, PRESENT AND FUTURE
> Session Co-Chairs: Steve Kearney and Syd Barber.
> Presenters: Ian W. Dyson, Greg Riemer, and Barry Verbiwski.

ECOSYSTEM MANAGEMENT
> Session Chair: Carole "Kniffy" Hamilton.
> Sustainable agriculture and ecosystem management - Rod Heitschmidt.
> Ecosystems then and now: A historical-ecological approach to ecosystem management - Charles E. Kay.

POLICIES AND PROGRAMS AFFECTING PRAIRIE CONSERVATION
> Session Chair: Derek Bjornback.
> A strategy for sustainable development in agriculture - Allen Tyrchniewicz.
> Policy instruments to maintain habitat - Richard Gray and Kim S. Rollins.
> Applying planning and decision-making tools to the threatened/endangered species issue: An Alberta experience - John Thompson.
> Environmental citizenship programs of government and endangered species - Jim Martin and Bev Yee.

ENDANGERED SPECIES CONSERVATION ISSUES -  Session Chair: Geoff Holroyd.
> Presenter: Simon Nadeau.

ALBERTA PEREGRINE FALCONS  - Gordon S. Court.

WHOOPING CRANES  - Brian Johns.

LIVESTOCK - WILDLIFE INTERACTIONS -  Session Chair: Don Gayton.
> Presenters: Harry Hargraves, Wayne Harris, and Garry Trottier.

USING NATIVE PLANTS IN RESTORATION  - Session Chair: Donna Lawrence.
> Restoration of grassland ecosystems: Agronomy or ecology? - R.E. Redmann.
> Reclamation and restoration: What's the difference in dollars and sense? - Stephen McCanny.

SHARING THE PRAIRIES: BY WHOSE WORLD VIEW?  - Session Chair: John F. Dormaar.
> Presenters: John F. Dormaar and S. Knowlton.

AGRICULTURE PRODUCTION AND PRAIRIE CONSERVATION SYSTEMS  - Session Chair: Craig Wood.
Presenters: Gaylen Armstrong and Graham Dorn.

PESTICIDES  - Session Chair: Dan Johnson.
Effects of herbicides on prairie wildlife - Doug Forsyth
Research on pest control methods that minimize environmental impact - Dan Johnson.
Indirect impacts of insecticides on wildlife - Pamela Martin, Doug Forsyth, Dan Johnson, and Bernie Hill.

NATURE CONSERVANCY, PRAIRIE INITIATIVES  - Larry Simpson.

WATER AND RIPARIAN SYSTEMS  - Kevin van Tighem.

CONSERVATION INITIATIVES  - Session Chair: Richard Laing.
Presenters: Peter Lee and Gerald Mckeating.

BEING RURAL ON THE PRAIRIES: THE PAST AND THE FUTURE  - Jerome Martin.

CROWN LAND CONFLICTS  - Session Co-Chairs: Chris Mills and Cliff Wallis.
Presenters: Karl Block, Hugh Lynch Staunton, Lorne Scott, and Darrell Rowledge.

INTEGRATED FARM CONSERVATION PLANNING  - Session Chair: Ernie Ewaschuk.
Presenters: Paula Brand, Les Wetter, Bob Johnson, and Jim Stutzman.

NATIVE CROWN LAND RANGELANDS  - Session Chair: Peggy Strankman.
Presenters: Keith Lyseng, Greg Haase, and James Bezan.

SUFFIELD NATIONAL WILDLIFE AREA: ECOLOGICAL INVENTORY  - Garry Trottier.

MOVING FROM REACTIONISM TO CONSTRUCTIVE EDUCATION: AN ASSESSMENT OF THE
CANADIAN ENVIRONMENTAL LOBBY  - Peter Jonker.

PROTECTED AREAS GAP ANALYSIS  - Session Chair: Gaile Whelan-Enns.
Presenters: Allan Appleby, Dawn Mitchell, and Gaile Whelan-Enns.

IMPLEMENTING THE PRAIRIE CONSERVATION ACTION PLAN. ARE COMMITTEES USEFUL?  -
Session Co-Chairs: Bob Schuler and Larry Simpson.
Panelists: Roger Creasey, Chris Mills, and Gary Stewart.

DOMINANT USE OF PUBLIC LAND  - Session Chair: Larry Hamilton.
Presenters: Bill Milton, and Tom France.

ALBERTA DRAFT PRAIRIE CONSERVATION ACTION PLAN  - Session Chair: Lynda Paterson.
Panelists: Bill Dolan, Dug Major, and Miles Scott-Brown.

PIPING PLOVER CONSERVATION  - Paul Goossen.

RICHARDSON'S GROUND SQUIRRELS: FRIEND OR FOE?  - Gail R. Michener.

AMPHIBIANS AND REPTILES  - Session co- chairs: Steve Brechtel and Andy Diduck.
Presenters: Ron Larche, Andrew Didiuk, and Larry Powell.

SAGE GROUSE  - Session Chair: Wayne Harris.
Presenters: Harry Vriend and Charlie Eustache.

BURROWING OWL RECOVERY: IS IT POSSIBLE? - Session Chair: Ken De Smet.
Presenters: Dale Hjertaas and Josef Schmutz.

PLANTS - Session Chair: Peter L. Achuff.
Presenters: Peter L. Achuff, Joyce Gould, Sheila Lamont, and Liz Punter.

SWIFT FOX - Session Chair: Lu N. Carbyn.
Presenters: Erika Klausz and Axel Moehrenschlager.

WORKSHOP SESSIONS
Prairie Conservation Action Plan Workshop
Session Reporter: Syd Barber.
Facilitator: Cheryl Bradley.
Ecosystem Management Workshop
Session Reporter: John Dormaar.
Facilitator: Lorne Fitch.
Policies And Programs Workshop
Session Reporter: Richard Laing.
Facilitator: Sam Wirzba.
Endangered Species Workshop
Session Reporter: Geoffrey Holroyd.
Facilitator: Stewart Rood.

CONCLUDING PLENARY
Session Chair: Ian W. Dyson.

REPORTS:
Prairie Conservation Action Plan Theme - Syd Barber.
Ecosystem Management Theme - John Dormaar.
Policies And Programs Theme - Richard Laing.
Endangered Species Theme - Geoffrey Holroyd.

QUESTIONNAIRE
Summary: Andy Hurly.

POSTERS AND DISPLAYS
(Available for viewing throughout the workshop; authors were all present at a special viewing session)

BANQUET SPEAKER - Charlie Russell's Yarns by Raphael Cristy
The workshop participants experienced a glimpse of the "pre-civilized" old west; the period of early European settlement, that brief period of frontier life before the prairie landscape was transformed by homesteaders and the development boom. The acclaimed one man show explores the life and works of C.M. Russell, the great American painter/sculptor/yarn-spinner, in his own words. The presentation is the product of years of study by Raphael Cristy who is presently completing his PhD in the life and work of Russell at the University of New Mexico, in Albuquerque. Expressed in rural grammar and his own cow-boy jargon, with straight forward western views, Russell's unique wisdom, sharp verbal characterization, and wry social observations have a strong impact today. The two hour performance shared a broad range of Russell's paintings and some special anecdotes about periods of the painters life in southern Alberta. Cristy ably imparted to the audience Russell's deep respect for Native Americans, his deep love of the land, and a longing for what has been lost.

# 2.0 OPENING SESSION

# CHAIRMAN'S OPENING REMARKS

## Ian W. Dyson, Chair of the Organizing Committee
*Alberta Environmental Protection, Bag 3014, YPM Place, 530 - 8th Street South,*
*Lethbridge, Alberta T1J 4C7*

The Chairman welcomed participants to Lethbridge, noting that the Prairie Conservation and Endangered Species workshops have now completed one full cycle and have returned to their Alberta roots.

Welcoming and introductory comments were provided by the following dignitaries:

- Howard Tennant, President of the University of Lethbridge.

- Tim Coleman, Canadian Wildlife Service on behalf of Sheila Copps, Minister of the Environment.

- Clint Dunford, MLA, Lethbridge West, on behalf of Ty Lund, Minister of Alberta Environmental Protection.

- Leah Waters, Deputy Mayor, on behalf of Mayor David Carpenter and the City of Lethbridge.

- Monte Hummel, President of World Wildlife Fund Canada.

The chairman then thanked members of the organizing committee individually and expressed appreciation to the financial sponsors and volunteers.

The dominant theme of the first Prairie Conservation and Endangered Species Workshop in Edmonton (1986) was endangered species. The Regina (1989) and Brandon (1992) workshops focused on implementing World Wildlife Fund Canada's Prairie Conservation Action Plan (1989 to 1994) and explored partnerships between the agricultural and wildlife communities. The Lethbridge (1995) workshop is broadening in scope to include consideration of ecosystem management and new policies and programs affecting prairie conservation.

The key themes of the workshop are:

- Progress achieved on the Prairie Conservation Action Plan (1989 to 1994) and a revised plan for the next five years;

- Principles of ecosystem management and practical application on the prairies;

- Existing and proposed policies which have implications for prairie conservation, such as agricultural subsidies, grazing fee structures, use of public lands, protected area initiatives and biodiversity conservation; and

- Progress made on recovery efforts of endangered species and the need for new initiatives.

The workshop is structured to provide participants with the opportunity to focus on their area of particular interest whilst also ensuring everyone gets some exposure to each theme—on Saturday, the theme sessions run concurrently to ensure this mixing takes place and to totally frustrate those of you who, for example, just want to attend the endangered species sessions.

The program also includes a survey on our relationship with nature, a poster session, eight public talks, a banquet featuring the national prairie conservation awards and entertainment by Raphael Christy, and concluding 'hands on' working sessions on each of the key workshop themes.

The chairman concluded his introductory comments with a number of logistical and informational items pertaining to the program.

# CANADIAN AGRICULTURAL POLICIES AND OTHER "LAND MINING" INITIATIVES FOR PRAIRIE AGRICULTURE[1]

## Ken A. Rosaasen and James S. Lokken

*Department of Agricultural Economics, University of Saskatchewan, Saskatoon, Saskatchewan. S7N 0W0.*

## ABSTRACT

The Canadian Prairies became the *Breadbasket of the World* in the 1920's, and they remain a major grain exporting region. But at what cost? Soils and related natural resources have been "mined" during both "booms and busts." Farmers, policy makers and scientists generally have viewed droughts, resource degradation, and prolonged low wheat prices as temporary setbacks. This view can be traced to the European-rooted paradigms underlying prairie agricultural society: man with technology has dominion over land and beast; and, land should be systematically divided, privately owned, and cultivated. Terms such as *improved* (cultivated) versus *unimproved* and *waste* land (native prairie) indicate the gulf between the dominant philosophy and environmental awareness. Major agricultural policies reflect this bias, promoting annual cultivation and grain exports while largely ignoring environmental considerations. How does society achieve sustainable land management (SLM), including a productive agriculture, which does not impoverish future generations? Various interest groups view the issue from narrow, fragmented perspectives. Policies tend to placate the most powerful. Scientists must break down barriers between disciplines. Physical scientists concentrate on physical changes in production and the soil. Economists focus on profitability, perhaps conveying an impression of a singularly dollar-driven *Homo economicus*. SLM, however, is interdisciplinary. Environment must be a recognized dimension in production decisions, even though imperfect information, externalities, input substitutability and option values make determining sustainable activity difficult. Perhaps rates of resource use should be determined explicitly by deciding how many years a resource should be sustainable. Using money as the measure over time is inexact—a *rubber ruler*. Future uncertainty does not translate necessarily into high discount rates and a devalued future. Positive option values suggest low societal discount rates. The requirements for human sustainability and environmental sustainability are rapidly converging.

## INTRODUCTION

For a brief period between the two World Wars, Canada became the *Breadbasket of the World*—the world's largest exporter of wheat. This position was achieved through the mono-culture production of wheat over vast areas of the prairie region, and was dependent on the rich bank of nutrients built up in the soil during thousands of years under native grass.[2]

The mass conversion of the native grasslands and parklands to wheat production within this century was the foundation of the modern prairie economy. Livestock production has always been important in some areas of the region, and both crop and livestock diversification are occurring today. However, wheat production for export remains the cornerstone of prairie agriculture, if no longer of the entire economy.[3] This is especially true in the province of Saskatchewan, where wheat is still *King*.

What have been the costs of developing this *wheat economy*? Prairie agriculture sometimes has been characterized as "land mining" (Thompson 1976) because it has emphasized immediate returns from land-extensive, extractive production. This type of production has taken a toll on prairie soils and related natural resources. Thompson (1976) described the process as "permanently wasteful but immediately profitable."

Coupland (1981) observed that "land use is probably more intensive in the unforested prairie region of southern Manitoba, Saskatchewan and Alberta than anywhere else on the planet, as judged by the proportion of total land surface that is cultivated annually."[4] A 1984 government study found that after only a century "as much as 40 to 60 percent of the organic matter present in [the surface horizons of] virgin prairie soils has been 'used' up by farm production" (Senate of Canada 1984). Prevailing agricultural practices threaten the existence of a number of native plant and animal species (Saskatchewan Data Collection Centre 1993).

Today, the prairie wheat economy, more recently a grains economy, is of questionable viability despite the protection and encouragement provided by a variety of agricultural policies. Wheat-based agriculture has continuously lost ground to other industries as the driving force in the prairie economy. It has not been able to support the majority of individual prairie farmers or prairie communities, either economically or socially, even over relatively short time periods. Deserted farmsteads, dying towns, a declining rural infrastructure and a degraded environment testify to this. Crop, economic and environmental failures have been as much a part of agriculture on the prairies as have been the acclaimed production successes. Prairie agriculture, as it exists today, has not proven itself to be an environmentally, economically or socially sustainable use of the land.

Prairie development has been fundamentally influenced by the belief that agriculture should dominate and improve an unfriendly and featureless environment. Evidence of this perceived struggle with the environment can be found in farming practices, in the contributions of science to agriculture, and in the government policies that have been influential in determining the direction of agricultural development. Ever since the early settlement period, when the land allotment system treated the prairie landscape as homogeneous, surveying it into uniform quarter-section blocks of 160 acres (64.75 ha) and, for the most part, requiring cultivation (Lambrecht 1991), there has been little consideration given to the long-term sustainability of land use in the prairie region.

This paper surveys the impact of government policy, culture, economics and physical science on the sustainability of prairie land use. It outlines historical factors that have contributed to the land mining characteristics of prairie agriculture and examines several recent or current policies and programs for their effects on land use. Some problems with scientific and economic measurement and methods of evaluation as they affect sustainable land management (SLM), especially how economists value stocks of resources and the future, are described. The implications of relying on these imperfect measurements of human interaction with the environment when planning SLM are discussed. Some suggestions are made for future policy development and for more comprehensive inclusion of environmental considerations in economic analysis.

## HISTORICAL BACKGROUND - CULTURAL VALUES, PAST POLICIES AND THE APPLICATION OF SCIENCE

The final decades of the nineteenth century and the first quarter of the twentieth century were a period of mass migration to the Canadian Prairies. The promise of rich, untouched, but accessible and cheap land—the *Last Best West*—was the primary impetus for the flow of hopeful settlers.

Early European and Canadian explorers of the region, most notably Captain John Palliser (1857-1860), had expressed grave reservations about the suitability of the southern portions for cultivated agriculture (Warkentin 1964).[5] However, in the late 1870's, the noted geologist and explorer John Macoun, a fervent "booster" of the prairie region, gave advocates of settlement the support they needed. He stated that "... he had never seen a bad crop in the Northwest regardless of the character of the soil, [and that there is] no such thing as the fertile belt at all—it [is] all equally good land." (Waiser 1989).

Large scale settlement began some years later in response to an increasing demand for wheat from an industrializing British Empire and Europe. Steam shipping, steel rolling mills, railway construction and early maturing Marquis wheat were technological innovations which quickened the pace of development. These advances, when linked with both the real and imagined natural endowments of the region, created an unbounded optimism among politicians, settlers and scientists about the potential for prairie agriculture.

However, from the beginning of Euro-Canadian settlement, this optimism was tested by droughts, early frosts and crop diseases. Hot dry winds and drifting soil frequently impaired the vision and buried the dreams of many pioneers. Prairie residents use the wry, yet hopeful term *Next Year Country* to describe the cycles of booms and busts. Natural calamities, environmental degradation, and prolonged periods of low wheat prices have been accepted as temporary setbacks or inconveniences in the drive toward the promised agricultural "bonanza" (Stegner 1962).

The dominant paradigms that framed the development of prairie agricultural society had European roots: land should be cultivated, land should be privately owned and divided in an orderly fashion, and man has dominion over land and beast. Aboriginal expertise in prairie living, reflected in the perhaps apocryphal observation of an aboriginal leader about ploughed land that "grass

[is] no good upside down" (Popper and Popper 1988), was swept aside as the new culture struggled to master nature.

Farming systems were imported from Europe and Eastern North America where conditions were more amenable to annual cropping than those of the semi-arid prairie. Even the agricultural vocabulary, which contrasts terms such as *improved* (cultivated) with *unimproved* and *waste* land (native prairie, forest and wetlands), indicates the gulf between the dominant cultural values and the development of a sustainable interaction between humans and prairie ecosystems.

The environmental damage caused by agricultural activity on the Canadian Prairies was not inevitable, although it follows the pattern of agricultural development in semi-arid lands throughout history. Prairie agriculture developed in response to the powerful forces of technological change, distant market demand, demographic upheavals abroad, and an imported cultural and economic system. Government policy could have sought to incorporate these factors into a system of sustainable land management suited to the unique natural characteristics of the prairies. Instead, policy has usually supported agricultural development that has mined resources through its dependence on land-extensive monoculture production of annual crops for export, and cultivated summerfallow.

In the last 75 years, a series of agronomic and environmental setbacks should have caused policy makers to pause and reflect on their promotion of the wheat economy. The depopulation of the inner core of the Palliser Triangle (Figure 1), which began prior to 1920 after only a decade of settlement, was a major indication of flaws in the blueprint for prairie settlement. The Government of Saskatchewan's *Royal Commission of Inquiry Into Farming Conditions* (1921) recognized the fragile nature of the soil and the variability of climate in this region. Many of the issues raised in that inquiry remain relevant today. In Alberta, the formation of the Special Areas in the Palliser core, which effectively made the depopulation of the 1920's and 1930's permanent, was a strong response to the economic and environmental consequences of misplaced settlement (Jones 1987).

The great drought and depression of the 1930's came the closest to focusing permanent attention on the environmentally precarious nature of prairie agriculture. The massive loss of farming population from the driest parts of the prairies, and the formation of the Prairie Farm Rehabilitation Administration (PFRA) with the task of returning the most unsuitable cultivated land to perennial pasture lands, seemed to indicate that the natural limitations of cultivated agriculture on the prairies had been identified. However, the resettlement of some *droughted out* prairie farmers in the muskeg and stony, Grey

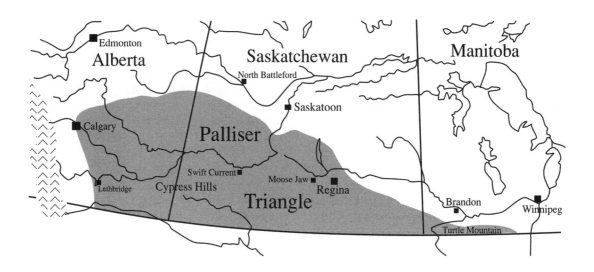

Figure 1. The Palliser Triangle (Adapted from Gray 1978).

Wooded soils of the northern forest "which condemned them to a life worse than what they had left" reveals that the *fertile belt* of Prairie agriculture still had an ill-defined geography (Polischuk *ca.* 1977). Mistakes have been made in the agricultural settlement of the wetter, forested portions of the prairie provinces as well as in the dry grassland region.

The great drought of the 1930's was soon seen as a temporary setback rather than a defeat. Much of the human misery associated with this period was forgotten with the outbreak of World War II, and the return of better weather and an improvement in grain prices. In the following years, government agricultural departments moved away from promoting resource conservation, and again devoted their efforts to increasing production and subduing nature. Environmental degradation was regarded as an inevitable side-effect of progress, or amenable to technological "fixes".

Debate over the suitability of parts of the prairies for annual cultivation and densely populated farming settlement was largely dormant until the mid-1980's, when agriculture entered a period of depressed returns, frequent droughts and increased environmental awareness. This debate now has been revived both in Canada and the United States. A striking example of the wide range of thought on the issue comes from two American authors who envision the return of much of the American Great Plains (and the most arid portion of the Canadian Prairies) to a *Buffalo Common* where low-level human impact is appropriately matched to the long-term soil and climatic capabilities of the region (Popper and Popper 1988). The Conservation Reserve Program in the United States and the Permanent Cover Program in Canada, under which land has been taken out of annual cultivation for significant periods of time, are examples of how this type of thinking has permeated even government policy. The interest of researchers and farmers in minimum and zero-till annual cropping, organic production, game farming, farm woodlots and native fruit production, among others, provide additional evidence of changing attitudes.

Today, even some strong supporters of conventional agriculture on the Canadian Prairies concede that agriculture has contributed to extensive environmental degradation. It has been responsible for loss of topsoil, declines in soil organic matter, soil salinization, disruption of water cycles, and loss of biological diversity (Environment Canada 1991). The rewards from the market place, which supposedly justified such use of the land, have proven to be erratic and disappointing. Much

of the impact of new technology has been spent offsetting losses in natural soil productivity. Even bright spots in production technology such as conservation tillage, fertilization, increased use of crop rotations and the introduction of canola and several other specialty crops have not alleviated the basic economic and environmental problems facing the region's agriculture. Despite increasing knowledge about the relative economic and environmental sustainability of various agricultural systems and practices, government policies and cultural attitudes, including those within the scientific community, continue to steer agriculture in an unsustainable direction.

## THE ENVIRONMENTAL IMPACTS OF CANADIAN AGRICULTURAL POLICIES AND PROGRAMS

Government policies have an important influence on the nature of human impact on the environment. Canada has never had a well-coordinated set of agricultural policies with a common vision and defined goals for prairie agriculture. However, among the various conflicting policies and *ad hoc* programs there has been a constant identifiable theme. Major agricultural policy initiatives have promoted and continue to promote annual cultivation on the prairies, especially for wheat production and export, with little regard for the environmental limitations of the region.[6]

In this section of the paper, a number of federal and provincial agricultural policies, programs and agencies, as well as some general regulations which affect agriculture, such as income taxes, are examined for their effect on SLM.[7] It is apparent that, although environmental concerns have rarely been addressed explicitly in them, these policies are a major determinant of the environmental impact of prairie agricultural production. Several programs and agencies are noted for their stated environmental objectives.

Questions arise as these policies and programs are examined. Do they reflect the broad goals which public policy should promote, or the narrow self interest of powerful groups? Can governments which face elections within five year intervals develop coordinated policies which adequately address issues of sustainability? Why have prairie residents, especially in Saskatchewan, strongly supported policies which include unsustainable elements?

7

Governments alone cannot be blamed for a lack of environmental understanding and vision. Indeed, in a democracy, society has the opportunity to express its preferences (we get the government we deserve), although some groups are more effective than others in doing so. Rausser (1990) has examined the political economy of agriculture in the United States in order to understand the motivation for government intervention:

*Are these massive governmental interventions the result of productive policies that correct for market imperfections, lower transaction costs, or effectively regulate externalities? In other words, is the U.S. government acting as a benign, perfect instrument that is presumed in conventional welfare economics? Or, are these programs the result of manipulation by powerful commodity or agricultural interest groups actively engaged in rent seeking or directing unproductive activities ...? In contrast to the tradition of Pigou and Mead, this perspective does not regard the state or public sector as a benevolent guardian of the public interest. Machiavelli and Hobbes are its inspiration. In effect, agricultural interest groups are presumed to behave much like the proverbial 800 pound gorilla—he walks where he wants, he stands where he wants, he sits where he wants, and he gets what he wants. In the case of U.S. agricultural policy, it will be argued that these two extremes only set the outside bounds on actual government behaviour. Accordingly, a resounding no must be the response to both of the questions posed.*

Determining the motives for, and effectiveness of, government intervention is significant for developing SLM strategies for the Canadian Prairies. Some see government's role as that of intervening to *fix* market failures, including unsustainable agricultural production. Others view government intervention as undesirable, and demand less government because of the influence of powerful interest groups on it. While governments cannot *create* sustainability, government policy will continue to be a major determinant of the sustainability of agricultural production in the Canadian context. Since this is the case, careful attention must be paid to the rationale, design, and implementation of policy.

## Major Agricultural Policies and Programs

(1) **The Canadian Wheat Board (CWB)** became an export monopoly for both Canadian wheat and barley by the late 1940's in order to market the grains to the long

term advantage of all producers. Unfortunate aspects of this regulation have been:

(a) Delivery quota regulations from 1954 to 1982, when the *Bonus Acres* provision was added (Wilson 1979)[8], were based only on cultivated acreage, with no recognition of varying land quality or cropping intensity. Low quality and fragile land could be brought into annual cultivation and receive the same delivery quota allotment as the most productive soils. The system also supported the practice of summerfallow. The Bonus Acres provision, which gave extra delivery opportunities to those farmers who cropped a higher percentage of their cultivated land (with traditional crops), only partially addressed this problem. For 1993-1994, new quota provisions use contracts with producers for fixed volumes of grain, and largely remove use of acreage quotas for barley and wheat. Open market grains such as flax and canola have been given open quotas. This recent change has removed the incentive to cultivate marginal land to obtain delivery quota.

(b) Production targets of the 1980's, which actively promoted export wheat production. This directly conflicted with the development of a more diversified and sustainable agriculture.

(2) **The Temporary Wheat Reserves Act**, which operated from the mid-1950's to 1970, paid the storage cost for a fixed volume of commercial wheat inventory. This supported wheat production for export relative to other crop and livestock production.

(3) **Crop Insurance (CI)** (1961- ) has provided federal and provincial government dollars to reduce production risk and offset financial losses when yield shortfalls occur. Large amounts of land in the soil classes that are, under the Canada Land Inventory Agriculture Capability classification, deemed to be unsuitable for annual cultivation remain eligible for CI.[9] CI reduces the cropping risk on low quality and fragile land, encouraging the continuation of annual crop production on these lands. Native prairie, forest, and wetlands also receive support if broken and converted to crop production. The Farm Income Protection Act of 1991, which governs both CI and the Gross Revenue Insurance Plan (GRIP; see number 8 below), does provide for the denial of payments to farmers who use poor agronomic practices. Both CI and GRIP are also in the process of undergoing federal environmental reviews. Reviews of other federal programs may follow.

(4) **Lower Inventories For Tomorrow (LIFT)** (1970-71) encouraged a reduction in wheat area planted and an increase in perennial forage and summerfallow in response to low wheat prices and large Canadian wheat stocks. The area in summerfallow on the prairies increased from an average of 11.1 million ha in 1967-69 to 14.9 million ha in 1970 (Dominion Bureau of Statistics, 1972) in response to financial incentives to reduce wheat acres and to restrictions on wheat delivery opportunities for producers who did not decrease wheat acreage (Wilson 1979). Some land was summerfallowed two years in a row (double summerfallowed) due to LIFT. Participation in the perennial forage option in the program, which was much more environmentally friendly than increased summerfallow acreage (especially double summerfallow), was relatively low. Very little land was more than temporarily removed from annual cultivation.

(5) **The Western Grain Stabilization Act (WGSA)** (1976-1990) was designed to stabilize net cash flow to the entire prairie region (Fulton *et al.*1989). Levies were deducted on eligible commercial grain sales, and payouts were triggered when net cash flow levels for the prairie grain sector declined. Only the seven historically important crops were included for most of the years the program operated.[10] Additional crops were included just before the termination of WGSA.

(6) **The Western Grain Transportation Act (WGTA)** (1983- ) replaced the former statutory rates for grain transportation by rail, known as the Crows Nest Pass Rates. Under WGTA, the federal government allowed freight rates to increase substantially for transportation of export grain to seaports, and for domestic grain to Thunder Bay. Initially, the federal government paid over two thirds of the formulated rail rate up to a maximum total amount. The producers' share of costs can increase annually as part of the agreement. This subsidy is for a selected list of grains and grain products and, although the list was expanded when WGTA replaced the statutory rates, potential new crops are added only through effective producer lobbying. While WGTA has allowed grain freight rates for producers to increase, it continues to favour grain production for export at the expense of diversified, environmentally positive land uses such as hay production or pasture, which are ineligible for freight rate subsidies. These land uses must compete with annual crops that are subsidized by WGTA. (Dehydrated alfalfa is eligible for the WGTA subsidy.)

(7) **The Special Canadian Grains Program (SCGP)** provided $1 billion in cash to Canadian grain and oilseed producers for the 1986-1987 crop year and $1.1 billion for the 1987-1988 crop year in response to the world grain trade war. In the first year, only traditional major crops were eligible for payments. In the second year, the list of eligible crops was broadened. Dehydrated alfalfa was included, but production from cultivated hayland or pasture remained ineligible. A positive aspect of SCGP was that the payments were related to the productive capacity of the soil.

(8) **The Gross Revenue Insurance Plan (GRIP)**, a federal-provincial program introduced in 1991, paid a guaranteed revenue per acre based on historical yield times a guaranteed indexed moving average price by crop. Traditional crops plus a few specialty crops were included. A result of GRIP 1991 was that additional acreage was planted. Any reduction of existing summerfallow acreage which can be attributed to the program was positive for soil conservation. If fragile land was brought into annual production because of GRIP, it worked against sustainability. A major weakness of GRIP was that forages harvested as hay or pasture were again excluded (Gray *et al.* 1991). Program revisions occurred in Saskatchewan in 1992 which reduced the support level and some of the cropping distortions fostered by GRIP, although forages and pasture land remain excluded.

The common feature of the above programs is that they largely have been production support programs which have encouraged, in many cases, inappropriate annual cultivation, specifically for the production and export of grain. They have not supported farmers in the adoption of sustainable farming practices.

## Taxation and Other Policies

Income taxes, which are a joint federal and provincial matter, have treated the clearing and breaking of land as an eligible cost for calculating income tax. Land assessment and taxation and some aspects of Crown Land management and development, among other provincial and municipal policies, have also tended to reflect the dominant extractive philosophy that has governed agricultural development on the prairies. Rosaasen et al. (1990) describe the property taxation system in Saskatchewan as follows:

*The Saskatchewan property taxation system does not punish the farmer when his farming practices contribute to soil degradation. Land is assessed*

9

*based on its productivity potential in Saskatchewan and a mill rate is established to determine the annual property taxes payable. Assume two farmers have adjoining quarter sections which were assessed at one point in time at $2,500 each. Assume that Farmer A was a good manager and maintained the quality of his land, but Farmer B employed management practices which resulted in serious erosion by both wind and water. Subsequent to a period of inflation, Farmer A's land is assessed at $5,400 and Farmer B's land is assessed at $4,800. Farmer A now pays a larger property tax as his contribution to roads and education in the municipality, based on his higher assessment.*

*If an entirely different perspective of the property tax system and good management practices were employed, land use might change radically. An organic matter index of the soil could be taken. If it increased between assessments, property taxes would decline. If organic matter decreased, then property taxes would increase. The incentive for the individual should be consistent with the societal view of the proper use and management of the land resource.*

The linear thinking that better land should pay more taxes seems equitable. However, it neglects resource management through time.

## Environmental Initiatives

**The Permanent Cover Program (PCP),** administered by the Prairie Farm Rehabilitation Administration (PFRA), signed farmers to ten or twenty-one year agreements to maintain low quality land in permanent cover such as forages or trees. Over the last several years, the program removed about 520,000 ha of fragile land from annual cultivation. At present, program funding has expired, but extension is being sought. Perlich and Gray (1992) estimated that the government saves $2.40 or more in other subsidies for every $1.00 allocated to PCP.

**Federal-Provincial Agreements on Soil Conservation** were recent environmental initiatives promoting the extension of soil conservation information and technology to Prairie farmers. They have recently been extended for several years, but with reduced funding.

**PFRA Community Pastures, Saskatchewan Provincial Community Pastures,** and other grazing land projects across the prairies are long-standing programs which maintain fragile land in grass and tree cover and encourage livestock production.[11] Provincial beef stabilization programs and the Tripartite stabilization program provide further examples of programs that have encouraged red meat production. Some wildlife programs (publicly and privately funded) financially support the conversion of fragile cultivated land back to grass and trees, especially for waterfowl nesting near wetland areas.

Funding for specific *environmental programs* is minute compared to funds for export grain programs. Major production and income support policies seem to conflict with some less extensive policies that encourage sustainable activity.

## LAND MANAGEMENT ON THE CANADIAN PRAIRIES - OUR FRAGMENTED APPROACH

### Cooperatively Defining Sustainability

How does a society develop a system and process of SLM that includes a productive agriculture? In particular, how can the "land mining" characteristics of present prairie agriculture be modified so that agriculture becomes an integral part of a sustainable management system for prairie resources? Politics, culture and science have all contributed to the current form of prairie agriculture. Together, they are also key to the development of SLM. Our approach thus far, however, has been largely fragmented. Barriers between spheres of influence and, in the scientific community, barriers between disciplines must be removed or at least crossed.

Applied scientists (including many agricultural economists), land owners or managers, and the general population tend to consider SLM from a purely practical perspective, where present economic necessity is paramount. Pure scientists, "environmentalists" and philosophers ponder what are considered to be the more esoteric and obscure scientific, ethical and philosophical points, divorced from the practical decisions being made. In both cases, there is little attempt to integrate the wide variety of thought on the issue. Thus, various groups define SLM based on the limited perspectives of their own disciplines.

Economists often conduct benefit-cost analyses to determine the types and timing of alternative land uses. The answers are a function of key assumptions about future events, the relative value placed on the present versus the future, and the substitutability of resources. The particular assumptions employed may not account for all of the relevant information from other disciplines or all of the concerns of society. In addition, some relevant information is simply unavailable.

Lawyers and bankers may concentrate their efforts on the potential for litigation and liability arising from pollution (Logsdon 1990). Physical scientists, sometimes in isolation and without a focus, measure changes in productivity, losses in organic matter, and rates of erosion and salinization. Ranchers often extol cattle ranching as fundamentally environmentally friendly, while ignoring soil degradation on improperly managed grazing lands. Many farmers claim that if current financial returns were better, they could and would incorporate soil-conserving practices into their operations. Historically, this claim has not been reflected by their activities during prosperous times.[12] Some environmentalists call for the restoration of the prairies to their natural state. Politicians have responded to these pressures by implementing policies that placate the most powerful interest groups. In the past, governments have offered subsidies and supported development strategies that have largely ignored environmental considerations. However, recent pressures have moved the environment higher on the government's agenda.[13]

A successful SLM system requires all of the identified groups to cooperatively answer some fundamental questions. Useful answers must incorporate the full range of human knowledge and expertise. How can stocks and flows of resources be appropriately accounted for? How can flows of resources be equitably distributed? Should soil and related resources be used now or saved and even improved for future generations? Do individual species and natural resources have intrinsic value even if they have no foreseeable economic benefits? What do market forces tell us about sustainability?

Quiggin (1991) provides a basis to initiate a discussion on SLM:

*Sustainability is in fashion, and, as with all fashionable terms, it is used in many ways and in support of many different policy agendas. At one extreme, "sustainable" has been treated as a synonym for "organic." At the other, the term has been used to give a veneer of environmental*

*respectability to policies which are, effectively, "business as usual." At its core, sustainability embodies two main concerns. The first is that the natural environment forms the basis of all human productive activity. This is most obviously true of agriculture, but it applies to all forms of industry. The concern is that pervasive environmental damage might gradually undermine the capacity of the environment to support productive activity.*

*The second main theme in the literature on sustainability is the concern that gradual environmental degradation may lead to a reduction in well-being, even if production of food and manufactured goods is maintained and increased. In economic terms, this concern may be related to those services of the environment which are consumed directly rather than being employed in production, and to benefits, for example those yielded by standing forests, which are best viewed in terms of stocks rather than flows.*

Tietenberg (1988) addresses the sustainability question as follows:

*The sustainability criterion suggests that, at a minimum, future generations should be left no worse off than current generations. Allocations that impoverish future generations, in order to enrich current generations, are, according to this criterion, patently unfair.*

## The Lack of an Interdisciplinary View— An Economist's Perspective

The division of scientists into rigid disciplines and the resulting compartmentalization of knowledge fosters narrowness of view. Broad problems are neglected as many scientists concentrate on smaller ones which can be solved, but may be of little consequence.

The story is told of a person who, upon leaving the bar, dropped his keys and lost them. Later, his friends found him crawling around looking for them. When asked where he'd lost them, he pointed to the other end of the parking lot. "Why are you looking here, then?" his friends asked. "Why, because the light is better over here!" was the indignant rejoinder (adapted from McCloskey, 1985). Perhaps academics are so enamoured with the technical "light" their particular disciplines are able to shed that they forget to shine this light on the appropriate problems.

It is easy to observe the narrowness of disciplines other than one's own. A personal experience illustrates the point:

*During the mid-1970's energy crisis, I [Rosaasen] reviewed a study which examined conventional production of wheat, canola, and beef and calculated the units of fuel, chemicals, fertilizer and other inputs required to produce each unit of output. Each output was expressed in kilocalories of energy per unit. There was no differentiation between the value of a unit of wheat or meat—only kilocalories of energy.*

*When invited to hear the presentation and join a group for lunch, my response was curt: "Sorry, I'm busy—but here is a dollar. Tell the author to buy a gallon of gasoline and have a good lunch!"*

Economists readily recognize that there is a difference in the level of utility received from a steak, pizza or salad that is not accounted for in a physical scientist's measure of kilocalories of energy. It is harder for an economist to look at the discipline of economics with the same critical eye.

Each discipline uses abstractions in developing theory. Sometimes there is a gap between the abstractions and the real world. Biologists observe the result of bacteria multiplying in a petri dish, and develop a predictable population growth curve through time. If this is extrapolated to humans, without consideration of human intellect and ability to foresee consequences and make adjustments, the application of science has been incomplete.

If gravity was assumed to be the only force involved in the movement of bodies, then physicists would predict that the earth and moon would come together. Discipline development and new discoveries have fostered the expansion of the theoretical framework used by physicists. It is recognized that there are other important forces which affect the movement of heavenly bodies.

Economists also develop theoretical frameworks and abstractions. Based on observation of human response to economic incentives, *individualism* and *rational behaviour* have become fundamental features of economic theory. Economists consider individual decisions to be rational responses to a pursuit of utility. While a model of utility theoretically includes human response mechanisms such as feelings of love and concern for

other individuals, community, and nature, these are difficult to measure. Economists, therefore, frequently measure utility in terms of money. *Homo economicus* (Daly and Cobb 1989), illustrated in Figure 2, is a caricature of an individual using money as the single decision variable.[14] Perhaps this is how some noneconomists view the *rational economic man* described by economists.

"**Homo economicus**"

Figure 2. *Homo economicus* (Nast St. Hill 1974; Daly and Cobb 1989).

The necessity of reducing real and complex problems to a manageable size for academic study requires abstractions and simplifying assumptions. The danger of oversimplification in this process has been defined as the fallacy of misplaced concreteness. Daly and Cobb (1989) describe this:

*Walter Bagehot, in his Economic Studies, wrote of Ricardo: "He thought he was considering actual human nature in its actual circumstances, when he was really considering a fictitious nature in fictitious circumstances."... Whitehead called this "the fallacy of misplaced concreteness." He defined it as "neglecting the degree of abstraction involved when an actual entity is considered merely so far as it exemplifies certain categories of thought."... More generally it is the fallacy involved whenever thinkers forget the degree of abstraction involved in thought and draw unwarranted conclusions about concrete actuality. Nicholas Georgescu-Roegen wrote: "It is beyond dispute that the sin of standard economics is the fallacy of misplaced concreteness."*

The use of common words that have different meanings in different professions inhibits clear communication between physical scientists and economists. To a physical scientist, *marginal land* is land that is fragile. It may be prone to drought or degradation, such as erosion by wind or water, or due to climate, soil quality, topography or other physical factors. For an economist, land can be a heavy clay loam, protected from erosion and with good moisture, and still be *marginal land*. It is marginal because it is unable to support profitable crop production at the current price level, perhaps because it is at too great a distance from the market, or because product prices are low relative to production costs. The land may have a high production potential, but it may simply be unprofitable to crop at current prices. This land is *at the margin* where the cost of producing another unit of output exceeds the value of that unit of output. The different terminologies of the various disciplines need to be recognized and clarified.

The broadening of disciplines, and more interdisciplinary cooperation in both research and education, will become increasingly important as the sustainability debate expands. Analytical frameworks will need to be restructured to ensure that more physical scientists include economics in their analysis, and that economists better incorporate biophysical realities in their work.

## SUSTAINABILITY—SOME ECONOMIC CONSIDERATIONS

### Imperfect Knowledge

Economic analysis often assumes that *Homo economicus* lives in a world of perfect information. This simplification sometimes does not deal adequately with the realities that aggregate information is incomplete and individual knowledge of all current alternatives and the future is finite. Hayek (1945) described this two pronged problem as follows:

*The peculiar character of a rational economic order is determined precisely by the fact that the knowledge of the circumstances of which we must make use never exists in concentrated or integrated form, but solely as the dispersed bits of incomplete and frequently contradictory knowledge which all the separate individuals possess. The economic problem of society is thus not merely a problem of how to allocate 'given' resources—if 'given' is taken to mean given to a single mind which deliberately solves the problem set by these "data".*

*It is rather a problem of how to secure the best use of resources known to any of the members of society for ends whose relative importance only these individuals know. Or, to put it briefly, it is the problem of the utilization of knowledge not given to anyone in its totality.*

Risk premiums are often used by economists to incorporate imperfect knowledge into economic models. A high risk premium lowers the value of future income flows; the value of the future is discounted relative to the present. This has negative implications for sustainability, if intergenerational equity is a fundamental aspect of sustainability. A risk premium can only be precisely quantified for events where probability can be objectively determined. Heady (1952) states:

*In summary, 'uncertainty' refers to future events where the parameters of the probability distribution cannot be determined empirically ... While subjective probabilities (either in an ordinal or cardinal sense) may be assigned to these anticipations, no method exists by which actual numerical values may be assigned these.*

The assignment of a risk premium to an uncertain future is subjective. Current economic thinking views virtually all probabilities as subjective.

### Valuation of the Future

*(a) Measurement Over Time*
The unknown future causes both physical scientists and economists immense problems as they strive to find and measure the truth. Measurement which incorporates time is a problem for economists since the value of currency (the usual measuring stick) is subject to change over time. Measures of economic growth, levels of economic activity and the benefits of specific projects are usually expressed in currency units such as dollars, yen

or marks. However, these currencies are like *rubber rulers* which will stretch or contract under certain circumstances.[15] For example, if inflation occurs, then what was measured as 100 dollars last year may be measured as 125 dollars this year.[16] Economists subtract the inflation rate (for example, 8 percent) from the nominal interest rate (for example, 12 percent) to determine the *real* rate of return on an investment (4 percent). Accurate forecasts of interest and inflation rates over a decade or more are difficult to achieve.

*(b) Discounting*

Humans tend to value the present more than the future. Their choices, whether implicit or explicit, of the relative values of the present and the future are influenced by cultural attitudes toward sustainability and available (not perfect) information.

Economics uses a formal process for comparing returns over time known as present value analysis, discounting, or capital budgeting.[17] The value of a future flow of benefits is discounted at an *appropriate rate* to arrive at a net present value (NPV). A private firm investing in a factory faces a capital cost in terms of the cost of borrowing or the return required on equity capital. When determining a discount rate for future flows of income, there is a need to adjust the interest rate to a *real* rate and to consider the risk of the investment since future returns are unknown and uncertain. A high discount rate places a large premium on current benefits. Future benefits are heavily discounted. Figure 3 indicates the contribution to present value of $10,000 annually over 50 years in *real* dollar terms at various dis-

count rates. The area under each curve gives the NPV of the total flow of income, cumulating the present values of the individual annual payments at the respective discount rate.

The stream of benefits to a society may be different than the stream of benefits for an individual or private firm because of the limited life span and limited capacity of an individual or firm to capture all of the benefits or incur all of the costs. If a society uses a high discount rate it will tend to use resources now rather than saving them for the future or utilizing them over a longer time span. Although a zero discount rate has sometimes been suggested by economists as a means to foster sustainability, it does not guarantee sustainability, and it creates problems in the allocation of capital.

How, then, should a discount rate be chosen? Should a common rate be applied to all projects? Daly and Cobb (1989) argue that it is not appropriate to evaluate a sustainable development project against an unsustainable project:

*For example, if a sustainably managed forest can yield 4% and is judged an uneconomic use of land on the basis of a 6% discount rate, which on closer inspection turns out to be based on unsustainable uses of resources, including perhaps the unsustainable clearing of that same forest, then clearly the decision simply boils down to sustainable versus unsustainable use. If we have already adopted a policy of sustainable development, then of course we choose the sustainable*

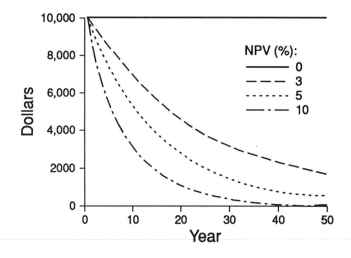

Figure 3. Net present value of an income flow.

*alternative, and the fact that it has a negative present value when calculated at a nonsustainable discount rate is simply irrelevant. The present value criterion itself is not irrelevant because we are still interested in efficiency—in choosing the best **sustainable** alternative. But the discount rate must then reflect only sustainable alternative uses of capital. The allocation rule for attaining a goal efficiently (maximize present value) cannot be allowed to subvert the very goal of sustainable development that it is supposed to be serving! Use of an unsustainable discount rate would do just that.*

How does society achieve an intergenerational balance in resource use? What is the value of a person living now relative to one born 30 years or 130 years from now? Should resource use be increased now to prevent current starvation, or is starvation a purely distributional problem? Rawls (1971) hypothesizes that people from all generations establishing the rules to govern society from behind a "veil of ignorance" where the rules are made before determining which generation each individual would live in. Future generations would not be impoverished by actions of the present generation if this decision framework could be employed.

If the current extraction rate for resources is high, this may impoverish future generations.[18] Some have suggested that money be placed in a trust account to earn interest to compensate future generations (Tietenberg 1988). This concept is questionable.[19] Money conveys to the holder a command over goods and services. Goods and services are created by combining resources. If no resources remain to create goods and services, what will "192 quizillion dollars (US)" command?

Some decisions are irreversible when dealing with resource depletion in benefit-cost analysis. What is the value of maintaining biodiversity for the future? Or, conversely, what is the cost of extinction of even a single species? The depletion of a resource such as coal or soil, or a species such as Whooping Cranes, entails significantly higher costs than are conventionally calculated due to the reduction of future alternatives. The risk of loss of alternatives for the future should be incorporated in present value analysis. Arrow and Fisher (1974) suggest that "the expected benefits of an irreversible decision should be adjusted to reflect the loss of options it entails."

A decision which expands future alternatives (options) has a positive value (a benefit) while a decision which reduces future alternatives has a negative value (a cost). Work by Gray (1991) indicates that investment decisions in machinery which incorporate a delay in purchase may be optimal since they expand alternatives. "The value of waiting" may be positive since new technology may become available. Investments in public goods such as research and education may expand future opportunities and, therefore, the positive option value created should be incorporated into any analysis. New uses for a resource may make it more valuable in the future. This positive option value because of uncertainty should result in the use of a lower discount rate rather than a higher one.

## Methods of Accounting and Measurement of Welfare

Economists have concentrated on measuring economic activities as flows of goods and services. Less attention has been paid to accounting for stocks and quality of natural resources. Economic growth has often been defined and measured as the rate of increase in Gross National Product (GNP).[20] The output approach to GNP accounts for the annual drawdown of human-made capital, but no widely-used measure of GNP includes changes in the quantity and quality of natural resource stocks. A simple analogy to illustrate the neglect of the environment in National Accounting has previously been used by Rosaasen *et al.* (1990).

*Perhaps the method of measuring Gross National Product (GNP) or the value of all the goods and services produced has contributed to an undervaluation of the natural environment and our stock of resources. Economists measure the cash flow in the economy in terms of goods and services and capital structures, but rarely look at the stock of resources that remain or their condition. An example which may clarify this is the story of the farmer who did very well on his rented Land Bank land, selling topsoil as garden soil in town! This misuse of resources may be obvious to most, but what about the general degradation of crop land throughout Saskatchewan?[21]*

## Externalities

An externality is an external economy or diseconomy in which a third party is benefited or damaged by economic activity without compensation. Water pollution by an industrial firm is an external diseconomy, or negative externality, to downstream users. An individual purchasing a scenic area provides a positive externality for all who pass (Tietenberg 1988). Externalities often have remained outside the focus of analysis for many economic problems. Recently, there is increased interest, both theoretical and empirical, in having them more fully incorporated. Neglecting externalities fails to account for the total impact of an activity. The application of legal "technology" to environmental issues through regulations provides one method to internalize the costs of externalities. Regulations which require firms polluting rivers to clean up the pollution or compensate downstream users are examples of the internalization of former externalities.

Pollution, such as from a smoke stack emitting a toxic chemical, has often been viewed in the past as a local problem of point source pollution. Building taller smoke stacks (a solution which did not incorporate much information) alleviated the local problem. Then, acid rain became a recognized regional and national problem. Similarly, depletion of the ozone layer, formerly an unknown externality, is now seen as a global problem tied to specific human activities. Errors in underestimating the level and duration of environmental impacts are now apparent. Some externalities have become widely recognized, although the development of an adequate data base for accurate quantification remains a challenge. For example, what is the long run impact of the use of toxic chemicals in agriculture? There is not yet an entire generation (70 years) which has been exposed to modern agricultural chemicals from birth, either as

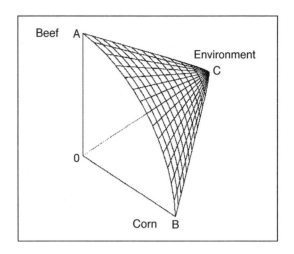

Figure 5. Production possibilities frontier, including environment.

applicators of the chemicals or as consumers of products which were grown with the assistance of chemicals.[22] Life expectancy statistics of farmers derived from current data may have limited validity in the chemical safety debate.

## Technological Change

Traditional economics accepts the predominant view in science that technological change will inevitably result in a more efficient combination of resources and increased output. An outward shifting production possibility frontier (PPF) is used to describe this (Heady 1952).

The PPF in Figure 4 indicates the various combinations of beef and corn that can be produced with a given set of resources. According to conventional theory, new technology in the form of a higher-yielding variety of corn will result in an outward shift from PPF to PPF. (A steer with a better feed conversion ratio would expand beef output.) However, if the environment is considered, this view may be incomplete. New technology may allow the measurement of ozone destruction and chemical pollution, the cost of dredging canals silted-in from soil erosion, or other traditionally unmeasured costs arising from production. There now is a need to consider the environment as a third good along with corn and beef (Figure 5). Environmental quality at point C is *undisturbed*, since there is zero output of beef and corn. At the plane surface, where line AB is joined, environment is not considered or valued in the output decision choice. Placing any value on the environment results in a movement along the production possibility surface to

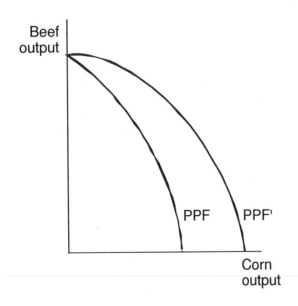

Figure 4. Production possibilities frontier.

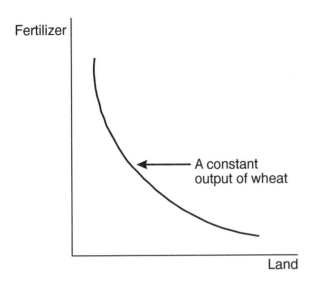

Figure 6. Combinations of land and fertilizer to produce wheat.

isoquant can be conceived where 15 billion people can be fed using three cups of soil and the appropriate amount of chemical fertilizer.[25] However, larger and larger amounts of fertilizer are required for each unit of soil withdrawn or used up. Resource-augmenting technological change must be relied upon to increase the range over which the substitute can be used. In their analyses, physical scientists and economists have often implicitly relied on the substitutability of future technology for depleted natural resources. The existence of substitutes does not guarantee sustainability, as it says nothing about the availability of any of the resources. A renewable resource which is depleted more rapidly than it can regenerate, or a low and declining stock of a non-renewable resource, becomes increasingly valuable as the available physical quantities are reduced.

Experiments have been conducted where topsoil is scalped (removed) to various depths and the subsequent crop yields of unamended scalped plots are compared to those amended with chemical fertilizer and manure (Larney 1991). The results indicate that manure is superior to chemical fertilizer in supplying plant growth requirements at greater depths of scalping. At some level of topsoil removal, the fertilizer does very little to restore fertility and yields are very low, because fertility is not the only factor limiting yield. At some greater level of soil loss, the ability of manure to substitute for topsoil also declines.

lower levels of beef and corn output.[23] Regulations that require farmers to clean up the now-measurable environmental damage will reduce the basket of resources available for production, since some of the resources will be used for prevention or cleanup. The result will be a decrease of the physical output (inward shift of the PPF for beef and corn if viewed in two dimensions) due to new legal technology being applied.

## Substitutability of Inputs

Economics recognizes the possibility of substitution of resource inputs in the production of an output. An isoquant[24] representing the various combinations of land and fertilizer which produce a given output of wheat becomes very steep or flat at low levels of land or fertilizer due to diminishing rates of substitution at these levels (Figure 6). Given conventional technology today, there can be some wheat output with land and no fertilizer, but virtually none with fertilizer and no land, assuming other inputs are held constant. Of course, if some new technology such as hydroponics is applied and the plant set afloat on the ocean, wheat could be produced with zero land and the application of fertilizer. Obviously, such technology is not cost effective.

The assumption of substitutability between inputs to produce an output is only relevant over a limited range of physical quantities and relative prices. Absurd conclusions can be drawn if resources are never viewed as a constraint or relative input prices are neglected. An

## Property Rights, Legal Issues and Liabilities

Well-defined property rights are required to produce efficient allocations in a market economy. The criteria for well-defined property rights include universality, exclusivity, transferability and enforceability (Tietenberg 1988). Property rights are normally less than *efficient*, contributing to unsustainable activity. The existence of common property resources such as air, fish, timber stocks or pasture increases the tendency toward an unsustainable allocation of resources (Tietenberg 1988).

There are some peculiar constraints in the Canadian land tenure system. Hunting rights, rights of passage and, for a time, mineral rights were given to the landowner at the time of agricultural settlement. In parts of Europe, these rights could be separate packages of ownership rights. However, land use regulations in the prairie region have usually supported agriculture as the highest and best use of land. Regulations evolved which permit landowners to market grain or domestic livestock but not to market wildlife hunting rights, limiting the land use choices available to a land owner.

Property rights issues extend beyond the land to areas such as patents for chemicals and genetic materials. Private firms now control the genetics of an increasing number of seed varieties. The control of genetic material may confer tremendous power and wealth in the future. There may well be legal challenges to the private ownership of banks of genetic material which were taken from countries where peasant farmers had selected stock over thousands of years (for example, new wheat varieties developed from such varieties as Red Fife and Hard Red Calcutta).

The increasing amount of research now taking place in the private sector is likely to be different than the type of research carried out in the public sector. For example, a publicly funded scientist might seek to develop a "growth additive" which breaks the dormancy of wild oats and causes all existing seeds to germinate at one time, to be killed by tillage or herbicides. A private firm may not pursue such a research path because of the lack of potential for ongoing sales of wild oat herbicide. Private firms will also avoid research which cannot be patented. Some governments are even encouraging their scientists to move towards patentable research.

There will be different distributions of the benefits achieved under these different conditions. If Charles Saunders, the Canadian government-employed researcher who developed early-maturing Marquis wheat, had been able to use legal technology to patent it, his wealth may have been much greater, while the income of the prairie farm sector and the whole prairie economy may have been reduced. Research programs by the public sector or the private sector do not inevitably lead to positive net benefits. In retrospect, research may have followed the wrong path. If research results are disseminated, repetition of the same error can be prevented.

Some environmental pollution conflicts can be resolved through a proper definition and enforcement of property rights. Regulations which set a level of pollution as a right can be allocated to the victims of pollution or the polluters. The Coase Theorem suggests that, under certain conditions, the entitlement can be made "to either party and an efficient allocation will result. The only effect of the court's decision is to change the distribution of costs and benefits among the affected parties" (Tietenberg 1988). However, the distributional effects of an *efficient* allocation which give the pollution rights to the polluter are important. Giving the entitle-

ment to current polluters would reward them relative to "past sins". More efficient firms, with lower levels of pollution per unit of output, perhaps using environmentally friendly technology, would eventually purchase their pollution rights. Current non-polluters (including less industrialized countries) would need to purchase the pollution entitlements from existing firms. The logic of "If you pay me, I'll quit pissing in your soup!" does not appear to be a good distributional criterion for the initial allocation! Neither should the payment for quitting be perpetual. Allocating rights to the current polluter beyond the life of the current fixed capital employed would create a windfall gain. The current polluters would also capture the gains of technological change if their right to pollute is institutionalized and made tradable.

The choice of institutions a society makes may be a major factor in determining the rate and type of development, the distribution of benefits of technology, the cost of litigation, and the ultimate sustainability of the system.

## SUSTAINABILITY — INCOMPLETE UNDERSTANDING IN SCIENCE

Physical scientists, like economists, sometimes have difficulties with accurate measurement and the inclusion of all important variables in their analyses. Even though physical scientists may use the best available data and best science to develop recommendations, new information often lessens the usefulness of, or sometimes even negates, these recommendations. In the late 1880's, the practice of leaving cultivated prairie land idle every two or three years, known as summerfallow, was adopted (Jones 1987). Cultivated summerfallow became the recommended practice for conserving moisture and controlling weeds in dryland farming systems for almost a century. Agricultural scientists preached its virtues for most of that period. Since the 1970's, most crop and soil scientists have completely reversed their original enthusiasm for the practice, citing its contribution to soil degradation and salinization, and its inefficiency as a method of water conservation.[26]

Agricultural chemicals have been licensed by government and promoted by agricultural specialists within the government and at universities. Over time, however, externalities have been discovered, including incidents of damage to adjacent crops or trees, ground and surface water pollution, applicators' health problems, and residues detected in food products. These discoveries suggest that a closer assessment of environmental and health risks is required. The cases of DDT, Agent Orange, and Thalidomide suggest that some potential dangers have been significantly underestimated or understated.

Science has not always been able to provide new production technology while simultaneously protecting society and the environment. Perhaps it has been the frame of reference, rather than the tools, which has been inadequate. Unfortunately, legal suits may be the mechanism where the off-site effects of some of these technologies will be incorporated into market transactions. The threat of liability may reduce or eliminate use of some chemicals. Many agricultural scientists and farmers view this development with consternation, but it seems that even the ability to measure chemical residues in parts per trillion does not restore public confidence in a system where the application of technology has failed before.

## CONCLUSION

Without an adequate and comprehensive definition, a fully developed philosophy, and an expressed intent by society, the practice of SLM on the prairies and elsewhere is likely to fail. Soil and related natural resources will continue to be "mined."

Commons (1934) argued that an understanding of law, culture, ethics and economics is needed to explain human behaviour. SLM requires a multidisciplinary and crossdisciplinary effort. Compartmentalization of knowledge and narrowing of disciplines do not foster a broad understanding of sustainability. Physical scientists must include the decision-making abilities of humans in their models. Economists need to ensure that their work is congruent with biophysical realities. All scientists must realize that the values or uses of many natural resources are unknown.

Economists must recognize the historical risk of using money as a measure and store of value, since its value is subject to fluctuations over time. An appropriate question when considering the use of natural resources over time is: "For how many years should the resource be sustainable?" If the answer is 250 years, a lower discount rate must be incorporated than if the answer is 20

years. A planning horizon that exceeds the life spans of people we know personally is not unreasonable.[27]

There is often a positive value in waiting to use resources (positive option value). Reduced social discount rates which reflect positive option values for activities which use high levels of natural resources seem appropriate for present value analysis. Both the stocks and flows of these resources must be considered.

Identification and incorporation of externalities is a necessary step in developing sustainable human activity. Humans and ecosystems are vulnerable if we blindly depend on yet-undeveloped technology as a counterweight to environmental degradation. Economists should clearly recognize that there are limits to the range over which inputs are substitutable, and that low levels of natural resource stocks force extremely high rates of substitution.

There is a need for a better understanding of institutions and an improved policy process, if SLM is to be developed on the prairies. Otherwise, shortcomings and inconsistencies such as those observed in present Canadian agricultural policies will distort attempts to encourage sustainable activity and protect the environment. The difficulty of developing policies which support SLM is not unique to Canada. Rausser (1990) outlines lessons learned from U.S. agricultural policy experience:

*(1) Political support can be generated for redistributive commodity policies when they are masked by the promotion of environmental quality and the protection of future generations.*

*(2) Combining commodity policy with resource policies would have been more difficult if institutional investments (such as soil conservation districts) had not been previously undertaken.*

*(3) Farmers require compensation if production is to be restrained and conservation practices encouraged, but such schemes are only acceptable when agricultural market conditions are depressed.*

*(4) The apparent contradictions in programs, where one supports conservation and another does not, may be due to the interest groups and the effective institutional arrangements that enable them to generate sufficient support for government action.*

Canada does not have the same history of cloaking agricultural commodity programs in environmental guise, since conservation has, unlike in the U.S., only recently become a major factor in policy discussions. However, it is possible that political pressure will move new programs in the direction described by Rausser.

The role of government should be to protect the long-term interest of its citizens. The expected longevity of a society is beyond that of an individual or a particular government. Regulations and institutions may modify individual behaviour over time. Therefore, policy changes and adjustments to the legal structure should seek to accurately reflect long-term societal goals by rewarding the individual for behaviour which is consistent with the desired evolution of the local or world environment. Soil erosion does not occur because we are unaware of its causes—rather, the expected value to the farmer of the benefits of current agronomic practices exceed the expected value of alternative practices that result in lower erosion levels. Based on current rules, current assumptions and prevailing cultural attitudes, farmers have made and are making rational choices: "land mining" has been profitable for many prairie farmers. Institutional change could alter farmers' behaviour. For example, increasing, rather than decreasing, property taxes if land is eroded would internalize more of the costs of erosion, influencing farmers' agronomic practices.

Society can take steps to reform institutions, adjust property rights, and implement safeguards against monopoly control of innovations if it so chooses. Unfortunately, policies implemented by governments may be reflecting the short-term view of voters. The need, then, is to improve education to ensure that the choices made are informed. Adjustments to incorporate a greater integration of knowledge may be required within educational institutions.

The requirements for human sustainability and environmental sustainability are rapidly and obviously converging. An informed society is more likely to make wise choices. Actions today that limit future choices entail a loss in option value and a high risk. The model of history suggests that Politicians bat first, Economic Forces bat second and Mother Nature bats last.[28]

# REFERENCES

Arrow, K.J. and Fisher, A.C. 1974. Environmental preservation, uncertainty and irreversibility. Quarterly Journal of Economics: 312-19.

Canadian Wheat Board. Seeded and quota acreage statistics. CWB. Winnipeg, Various years.

Commons, J.R. 1934. Institutional economics: its place in political economy. MacMillan. New York.

Coupland, R.T. 1981. A preliminary ecological analysis of land use in the Canadian agricultural system. Ottawa. Prepared at the request of Environment Canada.

Daly, H.E. and Cobb Jr., J.B. 1989. For the common good. Beacon Press. Boston.

Dominion Bureau of Statistics. Field crop reporting series. Catalogue #22-002. 1969-1972. Ottawa.

Environment Canada. 1991. A report on Canada's progress towards a national set of environmental indicators. SOE Report 91-1. Ottawa.

Fulton, M., Rosaasen, K.A. and Schmitz, A. 1989. Canadian agricultural policy and prairie agriculture. Canadian Government Publishing Centre. Ottawa.

Government of Saskatchewan. 1921. Report of the Royal Commission of Inquiry into Farming Conditions. J. Reid, King's Printer. Regina, Saskatchewan.

Gray, J. 1978. Men against the desert. Western Producer Books. Saskatoon, Saskatchewan.

Gray, R.S. 1991. An irreversible investment model of the western canadian farm machinery market. Dissertation. University of California. Berkeley, California.

Gray, R.S., W. Weisensel, K. Rosaasen, W. Furtan, and D. Kraft. 1991. A new safety net program for Canadian agriculture: GRIP. Choices. Third Quarter: 34-35.

Hayek, F.A. 1945. The use of knowledge in society. American Economic Review 35: 520.

Heady, E.O. 1952. Economics of agricultural production and resource use. Prentice-Hall, Inc. Englewood Cliffs, New Jersey.

Jones, D.C. 1987. Empire of dust: Settling and abandoning the prairie dry belt. The University of Alberta Press. Edmonton, Alberta.

Lambrecht, K.N. 1991. The administration of Dominion lands, 1870-1930. Canadian Plains Research Center. Regina, Saskatchewan.

Larney, F.J. 1991. The value of topsoil depth in soil productivity: Preliminary experimental results, June 1991. Agriculture Canada. Lethbridge, Alberta.

Logsdon, G. 1990. Ag bankers shun chemical risks. New Farm (Sept-Oct): 42-44.

McCloskey, D.N. 1985. The rhetoric of economics. University of Wisconsin Press. Madison, Wisconsin.

Morrison, H., D. Savitz, R. Semenciw, B. Hulka, Y. Mao, D. Morison, and D. Wigle. 1993. Farming and prostate cancer mortality. American Journal of Epidemiology 137: 270-280.

Nast St. Hill, T. 1974. Thomas Nast: Cartoons and illustrations. Dover Publications, Inc. New York.

Pearce, D.W., (Ed.) 1992. The MIT Dictionary of modern economics. 4th Ed. MIT Press. Cambridge, Massachusetts.

Perlich, K. and R. Gray. 1992. An economic analysis of the Permanent Cover Program in Saskatchewan. Paper presented at Erosions: Causes to Cures Conference. Regina, Saskatchewan. Nov. 4.

Polischuk, P. *ca.*1977. Former Executive Director, Farm Resources Development Division, Government of Saskatchewan. Personal Communication. Regina, Saskatchewan.

Popper, D.E. and F.J. Popper. 1989. The fate of the plains. Chapter 12 *In* Reopening the Western Frontier (E. Marston, ed.). Island Press.

Quiggin, J. 1991. Discount rates and sustainability. Dissertation. Australian National University. Canberra.

Rausser, G.C. 1990. The political economy of agriculture in the United States. Pp. 57-91 *In* The political economy of agricultural trade and policy (H.J. Michelman, J.C. Stabler and G.G. Storey, (eds.). Westview Press, Inc. Boulder, Colorado.

Rawls, J. 1971. A theory of justice. Bellknap Press. Cambridge, Massachusetts.

Rosaasen, K., R. Eley, and J. Lokken. 1990. Federal government relief programs for farmers: Rewards for the late adjusters? Paper presented at Soils and Crops Workshop. Saskatoon, Saskatchewan. Feb.

Samuelson, P.A. 1964. Economics: An introductory analysis. 6th ed. McGraw-Hill Book Co. New York.

Saskatchewan Agriculture Services Co-ordinating Committee. 1987. Guide to farm practice in Saskatchewan. University of Saskatchewan Division of Extension and Community Relations. Saskatoon, Saskatchewan.

Saskatchewan Conservation Data Centre. 1993. Personal Communication. Regina, Saskatchewan.

Senate of Canada, Standing Senate Committee on Agriculture, Fisheries and Forestry. 1984. Soil at risk: Canada's eroding future. Ottawa.

Shields, J.S., H.P.W. Rostad, and J.S. Clayton. 1970. Inventory of Saskatchewan soils and their capability for agricultural use. Saskatchewan Institute of Pedology, University of Saskatchewan. Saskatoon, Saskatchewan.

Smith, A. 1937. The wealth of nations. The Modern Library. New York.

Spry, I., (Ed.) 1968. The papers of the Palliser expedition, 1857-1860. The Champlain Society. Toronto.

Statistics Canada. Grain trade of Canada. Catalogue #22-201. Ottawa. Various years.

Stegner, W. 1962. Wolf willow: A history, a story and a memory of the last plains frontier. The Viking Press. New York.

Thompson, J.H. 1976. Permanently wasteful but immediately profitable: Prairie agriculture and the Great War. Pp. 193-206 *In* Canadian Historical Papers. The Canadian Historical Association. Toronto, Ontario.

Tietenberg, T. 1988. Environmental and natural resource economics. Scott, Foresman and Company. Boston.

Waiser, W.A. 1989. The field naturalist: John Macoun, the Geological Survey and Natural Science. University of Toronto Press. Toronto, Ontario.

Warkentin, J. 1964. The western interior of Canada: A record of geographical discovery, 1612-1917. McClelland and Stewart Ltd. Toronto.

Wilson, C.F. 1979. Grain marketing in Canada. Canadian International Grains Institute. Winnipeg, Manitoba.

## NOTES

1. Original title of the paper. Previously published as: Rosaasen, K.A. and J.S. Lokken. 1993. Canadian agricultural policies and other initiatives and their impacts on prairie agriculture. Pp. 343-368 *In* Proceedings on sustainable Land Management for the 21st Century (C. Wood and J. Dumanski, eds.). Vol. 2, Plenary Papers, Lethbridge. This paper examines the impacts of government policy, culture and scientific (especially economic) thought and practice on the sustainability of natural resource use in prairie agriculture. The authors have addressed a wide spectrum of issues. As a result, some topics are little more than surveyed. The purpose of this paper is to provoke discussion, rather than to provide definitive solutions to the numerous obstacles facing the sustainable management of prairie lands. The authors thank Julian Alston, Darwin Anderson, Ed Driver, Ron Eley, Richard Gray, John Henning, Edward Knopf, Ray Nicholson and C.M. (Red) Williams for helpful comments on various drafts of the paper; W.A. Waiser for providing historical references; Darren Eurich and Trina Rosaasen for assistance with research, referencing and typing; D. and T. Friggstad for computer assistance with Figure 5; Joan Garvie and Lynne Sargeant who typed final changes; Julian Dumanski, Claire Fairbairn and Craig Wood for editorial review. The usual caveats apply.

2. The prairie region includes the agricultural areas of the provinces of Alberta, Saskatchewan, Manitoba and the Peace River District of British Columbia.

3. The prairie region continues to rank among the world's top wheat exporting areas. Canadian wheat exports (including durum), almost entirely originating in the prairie region, were about 18 percent of total world exports from 1988-1992 (Statistics Canada, various years). Acres seeded to wheat (including durum) in the prairie region averaged 43% of total annually cultivated acres from 1988-1992, excluding seeded haylands and pasture (Canadian Wheat Board, various years).

4. *Intensive*, in this example, does not refer to high levels of input use per unit of land but, rather, to what is often referred to as the *extensive* cultivation of the prairies.

5. Palliser concluded that "this large belt of country [the prairie region] embraces districts, some of which are valuable for the purposes of agriculture, while others will forever be comparatively useless." (Spry 1968).

6. See Rosaasen *et al.* (1990) and Gray *et al.* (1991). The argument here is that the erosion and degradation of soils are not caused because people are unaware of the causes of erosion nor because they are uncaring about the land or the environment; nor is the technology for suitable crops or production practices incapable of attaining an environmentally friendly outcome. Rather, the economic incentive, which is a combination of market forces, regulatory forces and the benefits achievable by an individual farmer, does not reward practices which conserve the soil and the environment.

7. This section only examines the environmental impacts of the various government policies and programs, and makes no assessment of other aspects of the policies and programs which may have merit.

8. See Saskatchewan Agriculture Services Coordinating Committee (1984) for a description of the Bonus quota acreage system.

9. Less than 40 million acres of land in Saskatchewan are considered well-suited for annual cultivation (Canada Land Inventory Agriculture Capability Classes 1-3) (Shields *et al.* 1970). Over 47 million acres of land in Saskatchewan were cultivated in 1991 (Statistics Canada 1991).

10. WGSA crops included wheat (including durum) oats, barley, rye, flax, canola (rapeseed) and mustard.

11. Even PFRA has been criticized on several counts and from alternative perspectives: (1) some native grassland has been broken and seeded to monocultures of introduced grasses; (2) some high quality land which could be cultivated has been permanently placed in

grass; (3) grazing management may not have prevented overgrazing, and (4) irrigation projects have not achieved the benefits anticipated.

12. In the prairie region the number of acres which were broken up (new breaking) averaged about 400,000 acres annually during the prosperous 1980-1982 period, but declined to about 80,000 acres annually for the period of 1990-1992 when crop returns from wheat, barley and canola were very low (Canadian Wheat Board, selected years). Do farmers actually do a better job of farming and sustaining the environment when they receive high prices for their production, or do they just become more efficient and more aggressive in their "mining" practices (dig harder when the gold price is up!)?

13. Agriculture Canada is now reviewing several programs such as Crop Insurance and the Gross Revenue Insurance Program for their environmental impacts. Requiring environmental cross-compliance to participate in farm support programs is under discussion. Federal-Provincial agreements on soil and water conservation are being extended in several provinces.

14. The caricature of *Homo economicus* was created by combining a Thomas Nast cartoon from 1871 (Nast St. Hill 1974) with a phrase from Daly and Cobb (1989).

15. An interesting parallel to the problem of measuring with money is the legal survey system which was set up on the Prairies in the late 19th century. The survey was not perfectly accurate since the length of the survey chain changed with temperature changes. In fact, land titles list the acreage of parcels of land with the proviso *more or less*. How chaotic would it be to resurvey the region under different weather conditions each decade?

16. Two centuries ago, Adam Smith warned that coinage was subject to fluctuations. He believed a land owner should specify rent in products such as corn rather than specify it in currency. Smith described dishonest rulers who would reduce the size and the purity of a coin and diminish its value. This was called debasement of currency. Today we use the euphemism *inflation*.

17. Discounting can be described as an evaluation process for future income from which explicitly incorporates the time value of money. A dollar invested at 10 percent yields $1.10 in a year or, the present value of receiving $1.10 one year from now is $1.00. The present value of a one time benefit $B$ received $n$ years from now is calculated as where $r$ is the interest rate. The process

of calculating the present value of a single benefit or a flow of benefits is called discounting. $r$ is the discount rate (Tietenberg 1988).

18. The authors recognize that in oligopolistic markets, current resource owners may rationally seek to reduce rates of extraction using the cloak of sustainability since this may increase price and profitability (economic rent) in the short term due to reduced supply.

19. History is rife with examples where paper money is worthless. Samuelson (1964) commented: *"Economic history is, alas, a history of inflations."*

20. Numerous economists have questioned the measurement of GNP and its appropriateness as a measure of human welfare (Daly and Cobb 1989). See Pearce (1992) for a definition of GNP and Net National Income.

21. The Land Bank was an agricultural program in Saskatchewan in the 1970's and early 1980's through which the provincial government purchased land from farmers (often retirees) and leased it to young farmers at relatively low rental rates.

22. Studies such as the recent statistical linking of prostate cancer and acres sprayed with herbicides still appear (Morrison *et al.* 1993) despite the assurances of the chemical industry and government officials that chemicals are safe.

23. Beef and wheat production may be complementary to the environment as well as competitive. Only the competitive range is graphed in Figure 5.

24. An isoquant is a graphical conceptual tool used by economists to indicate how two substitutable inputs (for example, land and fertilizer) can be combined in different combinations to produce an equal volume of output (for example, bushels of wheat).

25. This example is obvious hyperbole, designed to make readers stop and think about assumptions of resource availability and the range over which they are relevant.

26. Many economists have had a harder time recommending against summerfallow. It has usually been assumed in farm budgeting that there is no difference in future soil productivity arising from alternative crop enterprises. Summerfallow often budgets out well with this assumption.

27. The senior author's grandfather was born in 1880 and lived to 1965. The author's children were born in the 1970's and early 1980's, so his grandchildren will probably be born between 1994 and 2020. It is not unrealistic to expect that those grandchildren, whom he hopes to know, could easily live beyond the year 2080. The life spans of people known to an individual will often cover a period of over 200 years!

28. In a baseball game, the last batter has a unique position, in that there is no opportunity to alter the outcome of the game after his or her performance.

# PRAIRIE ECOSYSTEM MANAGEMENT

# AN ALBERTA PERSPECTIVE

# PRAIRIE CONSERVATION FORUM

## PRAIRIE ECOSYSTEM MANAGEMENT
## AN ALBERTA PERSPECTIVE

A Draft Discussion Document

Individuals who participated in the preparation of this document are:

| | |
|---|---|
| Barry Adams | Alberta Agriculture, Food and Rural Development |
| Cheryl Bradley | Consultant (co-author) |
| Steve Brechtel | Alberta Fish and Wildlife |
| John Dormaar | Agriculture and Agri-Food Canada |
| Ian Dyson | Alberta Regional Co-ordination Services (chairman) |
| Lorne Fitch | Alberta Fish and Wildlife |
| Pat Herzog | Lethbridge Community College |
| Andy Hurly | University of Lethbridge |
| Peter Lee | Alberta Parks Service |
| Delinda Ryerson | Alberta Environmental Centre |
| Liz Savoy | Helen Schuler Coulee Centre, City of Lethbridge |
| Brad Stelfox | Alberta Environmental Centre |
| Kevin Van Tighem | Parks Canada |
| Cliff Wallis | Cottonwood Consultants (co-author) |
| Walter Willms | Agriculture and Agri-Food Canada |
| Craig Wood | Prairie Farm Rehabilitation Administration |

Cleve Wershler assisted with collection of information.

December, 1995
Lethbridge, Alberta

# PREFACE

On November 15, 1994, a group of individuals with a broad range of interest in prairie conservation met in Lethbridge, Alberta, for a brainstorming session about a rapidly evolving model for renewable resource management known as "ecosystem management." Most members of the group were helping to organize the 4th Prairie Conservation and Endangered Species (PCES) Workshop in Lethbridge scheduled for February 23-26, 1995. Ecosystem management had been named as one of four theme areas for the workshop; however, committee members had a fuzzy understanding, individually and collectively, of its meaning. There was a sense that it might provide a valuable framework for future decisions about prairie management. Upon the suggestion of the organizing committee chair, Ian Dyson, they agreed to meet to explore the current thinking regarding ecosystem management and to assess its usefulness for prairie management.

The November 15th session began with a presentation by Dr. Brad Stelfox on ecosystem management in the boreal forests (Stelfox 1994). This presentation had been developed for the Alberta Forest Conservation Strategy as an introduction to key concepts of ecosystem management and the implications of applying it to forest management. Considerable discussion followed about how these concepts might be applied to the prairie, and their potential usefulness. There was agreement to work together as a team on more fully developing the key concepts of **prairie** ecosystem management based on the literature and the team's collective experience, and to present the results to participants at the 4th Prairie Conservation and Endangered Species Workshop - "Sharing the Prairies: Sustainable Use of a Vulnerable Landscape", February 22 - 26, 1995 in Lethbridge, Alberta.

Over a three-month period, the multi-disciplinary group developed a computerized presentation and *Draft Discussion Document*. Cheryl Bradley and Cliff Wallis worked between meetings to put the committee's ideas into written and graphic form. Committee members reviewed and commented on draft materials, and reached consensus on the content of the presentation and discussion document.

The 45-minute presentation was given by Lorne Fitch and Barry Adams during a plenary session on the first day of the PCES workshop. Over 400 copies of the *Draft Discussion Document* were distributed in registration packages to workshop participants. A questionnaire regarding the contents of the document was attached. Following the plenary presentation, participants were asked to consider the concepts in the presentation, review the discussion document, and complete the questionnaire. Twenty-two questionnaires were completed and returned. These were summarized and several of the suggestions incorporated into the revised document. The *Summary of Responses to the Questionnaire* is included in the workshop proceedings.

The purpose of developing a proposed framework for prairie ecosystem management is to provoke thought and discussion about the concepts of ecosystem management and their application to the prairies. Informal conversations at the PCES workshop, a workshop session on ecosystem management, and participants' responses to the questionnaire suggest general endorsement of the framework for prairie ecosystem management as presented in this document. The next important step, however, must be review by a broader audience and consideration of practical application of the concepts. Individuals involved in this initiative are working at clarifying and testing the concepts in their work and encourage you, the reader, to do the same.

Copies of the presentation (slides and speaking notes) on Prairie Ecosystem Management, which is based on this document, are available at cost from Ian Dyson, Corporate Management Service, Alberta Environmental Protection, 530 - 8 St. S., Lethbridge, Alberta T1J 2J8.

# TABLE OF CONTENTS

# LIST OF TABLES

# LIST OF FIGURES

# 1.0 THE PRAIRIE ECOSYSTEM

For many Canadians and Americans, the prairie is home. We have a sense of place, of living within, and belonging within, the prairie environment. Each of us has a vision of prairie, of what it was and what it should be. Sharon Butala, a rancher and author who lives in southwestern Saskatchewan, expresses her vision in this way:

> *"The salvation and foundation of our nation lies in a renewed relationship with Nature as a people, and in a flourishing rural life . . . I see (people living in the country) aware of themselves as vital to the human community in providing the direct link to Nature our species must maintain. I see them as the preservers of a body of knowledge thousands of years old, as caretakers, stewards of the land, and maybe even, in a much better world than this one, as the wise men and women to whom others will turn for guidance and healing." (Butala 1994)*

## 1.1 Definition of Prairie Ecosystem

We all have different visions when we think of the word "prairie" and we have different views about what comprises the prairie ecosystem. For some, it includes fields of grain. For others, it is native grassland with grizzly bears, wolves and free-roaming herds of bison. For some, it includes modern man. For others, it includes only aboriginal people or no people at all.

Ecologists describe an ecosystem as soils, plants, animals, minerals, climate, water, topography and all the ecological processes that link them together. For the purposes of this document, the prairie ecosystem includes two major ecoregions, the grasslands and aspen parkland, and all their parts. We recognize distinctive parts of the prairie ecosystem, but the parts are all interconnected. Differences in climate and parent material across the prairie ecosystem have resulted in distinctive, recognizable units such as aspen parkland, fescue grassland, tall-grass prairie, and mixed-grass prairie. Native grasslands, shrublands and aspen groves, native wetlands (including lakes), river valleys, and sand dunes were key parts of the prairie ecosystem before settlement. According to Statistics Canada's 1991 census, native habitats now occupy about 25 percent of the prairie landscape with cultivated areas for crops occupying 68 percent, tame pastures 6 percent and cities and towns about 1 percent (Statistics Canada 1992).

The parts of the prairie ecosystem are interconnected with some of its elements moving among the parts. For example, nutrients, wildlife and people move freely among the parts. Manufactured products, like herbicides and fertilizers, and introduced species occasionally move from settled areas to other parts of the ecosystem.

## 1.2 Key Ecosystem Factors and Processes

Because one of our premises is to observe natural systems, understand functions and apply that knowledge, the first portion of our discussion deals with native prairie ecosystem dynamics. For millennia, the prairie ecosystem has been affected by dynamic physical forces of climate acting on geologic parent material and life forms through processes such as drought, flood, erosion and deposition (both by wind and water). Soil disturbance is another process—from massive gouging by glaciers before 10,000 years ago, and more recently from digging and trampling by prairie wildlife. Fire also frequently acted on the ecosystem, ignited either by lightning or humans. Energy and nutrients flow from plants that fix the sun's energy (photosynthesis) to the grazers (herbivory), the predators (predation), and the decomposers (decomposition). Table 1 lists some key factors and processes of the native prairie ecosystem which are referred to in this document. Other important processes are climatic or geomorphic such as mass wasting and salinization, and biological such as parasitism, commensalism, symbiosis, nitrogen fixation, and soil pedogenisis. All ecosystem processes have varied over time and vary across the prairies.

Table 1. List of Prairie Ecosystem Factors and Processes.

## Native Prairie Ecosystem Dynamics

| FACTOR | PROCESS |
|---|---|
| Climate Acting on: | • Drought |
| | • Flood |
| Parent Material & Life | • Erosion |
| | • Deposition |
| Landform | • Soil Disturbance |
| Fire | • Fire |
| | – Lightning |
| | – Human-induced |
| Life | • Photosynthesis |
| | • Grazing |
| | • Predation |
| | • Decomposition |

### 1.3 Range of Variation in Prairie Ecosystem Processes

Prairie ecosystem processes have always been dynamic and variable; however, there are limits to the variation, barring a major climatic shift and desertification or another ice age, for example. The glaciers destroyed or displaced most prairie life. Current biodiversity on the northern prairies reflects the adaptations of life forms to the variation in ecosystem processes since deglaciation.

The range of variation of processes or disturbance events over time can be measured. For example, data about the magnitude and timing of annual peak flood events are used to develop a flood frequency curve (Figure 1). The flood frequency curve indicates how often a flood of a certain magnitude has occurred over the period of record. The area under this curve can be considered the range of variation. Data show that when a dam is placed on a river, downstream annual floods below the one-in-two year return interval increase in magnitude, whereas those of longer return interval decrease in magnitude. There is less variability. The range of variation, shown as the area under the curve,

decreases. If flows were altered so that the peak flood is identical year after year, the curve would be a flat line with no range of variation.

Range of variation in the size, intensity and return interval of key prairie disturbance processes, such as fire, flood or grazing, could be represented on a three-dimensional graph as is shown in Figure 2. Where the axes intersect represents no variation in size, intensity or return interval. High variation would plot close to the end of the axes. Although little actual data are available on the size, intensity and return interval of disturbance events from before settlement, scientific and historical evidence suggests that natural variation was large. For example, sometimes a disturbance such as prairie fire, occurred over hundreds of square kilometres; sometimes it was very small. If the area burned by fires was always the same size, range of variation would be plotted at the zero point of the axis. Occasionally, disturbances were of very high intensity, such as a major flood, although more often they were small to medium events. In some areas, a disturbance such as grazing by large herds of bison may have occurred almost every year at the same time of year, whereas other areas may

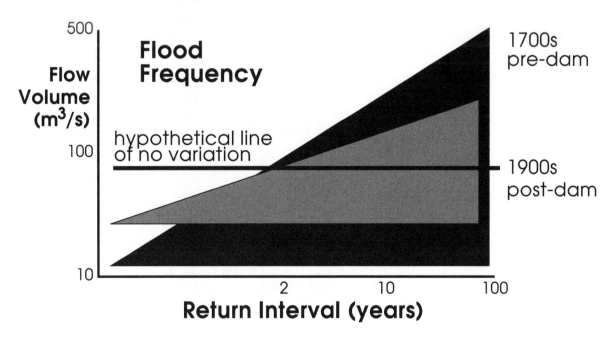

Figure 1. Range of variation: Flood frequency (from: Bradley and Smith 1984, Rood and Mahoney in press).

# Range of Variation
## -Prairie Disturbances

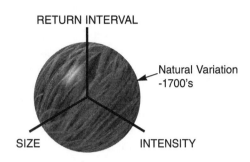

Figure 2 - Range of variation in disturbance size, intensity and return interval.

not have been exposed to bison for several decades. The movement of bison was affected by other disturbances, such as fire. Each ecosystem process affected, or was affected by other ecosystem processes.

The sphere in Figure 2 represents a hypothetical composite plot of variation for all prairie disturbances. It crosses the axes of variation in size, intensity and return interval far from the centre to indicate an overall large range in variation. Prairie species evolved with these disturbances and it appears many species adapted to disturbance or became dependent on it for regeneration or survival. Altering this sphere of variation dramatically, by either making it bigger or smaller, probably would result in the loss of many prairie species.

It is useful to examine what we know about various disturbances or ecosystem processes occurring naturally on the prairie and how these disturbances have changed since the early 1900's.

## 1.3.1 Erosion/Deposition: Riverine

River floodplains on the prairies support a diversity of vegetation communities, from cottonwood forests to tall shrublands to wetland. This diversity is due to flooding and the processes of erosion and deposition during floods, which result in channel migration. Rates of channel migration are linked to flood frequency. Several studies on the prairies have shown that plains cottonwood depend on floods to create conditions for seeding

establishment (Rood and Mahoney 1990; Hughes 1994). If the range of variation of flooding is reduced significantly, which often occurs with dams and diversions, cottonwood forests do not replace themselves and eventually disappear from the floodplain.

## 1.3.2 Erosion/Deposition: Sand Dunes

Some prairie species are adapted to active sand dune habitats and are found nowhere else. Examples are the kangaroo rat, western spiderwort and some species of grasshopper and tiger beetle. Ecosystem processes responsible for keeping sand dunes active are wind erosion and deposition, mainly in periods of drought. Fire and intense grazing also may have a role to play by reducing the stabilizing effect of vegetation. Comparison of air photos from the 1950's and the 1990's shows that dunes are rapidly stabilizing throughout the prairies (Wallis and Wershler 1988). Many species associated with active dunes are considered rare or threatened. We suspect, but are not sure, that our management of prairie ecosystem processes has resulted in the stabilization of dunes.

## 1.3.3 Soil Disturbance

By soil disturbance, we mean processes that directly disrupt top soil. Over millennia, primary agents for soil disturbance in native grasslands were probably bison, ground squirrels and badgers. Today, cultivation is by far the dominant agent. In the 1700's, for example, the pattern of wallows and mounds in the prairie ecosystem was small, irregular patches that were widely scattered. These disturbances were ephemeral as animals moved about the landscape. Since the late 1800's, the amount and pattern of surface disturbances have changed dramatically. Surface disturbance from cultivation, cities and roads consists of large rectangles or straight lines that are widespread.

This disturbance occurs year after year in the same place. Today, 95.0 million hectares, or 75 percent of prairie Canada has been cultivated—68 percent (31.6 million ha) of Alberta's prairie, 80 percent (50.0 million ha) of Saskatchewan's prairie and 78 percent (13.1 million ha) of Manitoba's prairie regions (Statistics Canada 1992). In prairie Alberta, there are about 109,600 oil and gas well sites that have been cleared along with associated access routes and pipelines (Kerr *et al*. 1993). Tourism Saskatchewan (1994) boasts of more road surface than any other province in Canada—a total of 250,000 km (about 150,000 mi.).

# Process: Soil Disturbances
## Impacts on Birds

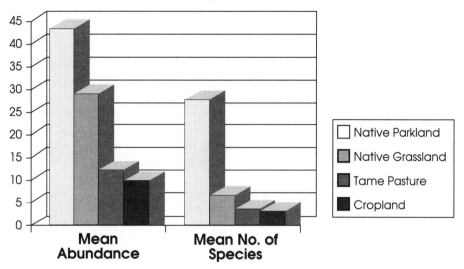

Figure 3 - Comparison of bird populations in native parkland, native grassland, tame pasture and cultivated land. (from: Prescott *et al.* 1994b)

Native prairie life for the most part, is not adapted to such a massive and frequent soil disturbance as cultivation. Studies have shown that the number of bird species and abundance decrease dramatically from native parkland and grassland to tame pasture and cultivation (Figure 3). Other effects of cultivation, roads and cities on the prairie ecosystem are fragmentation of habitats and introduction of nonnative species either deliberately for human use or by accident. For example, about 15 percent (275) of Alberta's 1,750 vascular plant species have been introduced, many of which outcompete native species for resources (Moss and Packer 1983). Attempts to control the spread of exotic species such as spotted knapweed, leafy spurge and timothy have proven expensive and largely ineffective.

## 1.3.4 Fire

Fire has occurred for thousands of years in the prairie ecosystem, some lightning-induced and others human-induced. Use of fire by North American aboriginal peoples is well documented, whether to aid in hunting by influencing movement of game, to control invasion of woody species, or to reduce invertebrate pests (Anderson 1976). Unlike forests, where stand age or fire scars give clues to fire size, intensity and frequency, evidence of past fires is lacking in the prairies. However, there is speculation that fire probably occurred more fre-

quently on the prairies than in forests, but that the distribution of fire sizes was similar—a lot of small fires, fewer medium ones and a very few large fires (Figure 4). Some sites were subject to infrequent high-intensity fires, and others characteristically experienced frequent,

# Process: Fire
## Native Prairie Fire Patch Size and Frequency

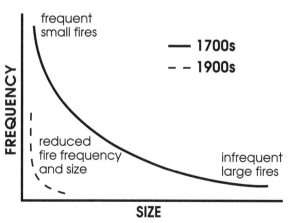

Figure 4 - Range of variation: Fire size and frequency. (from: Higgins *et al.* 1986)

low-intensity fires. For example, moister areas might have burned less frequently, but when they did there was more fuel to burn which increased the intensity of the fire. In the 1900's, suppression of fire by modern society has resulted in a significant decrease in the size and occurrence of burned patches on the prairie. The range of variation is considerably reduced.

Studies of controlled burns in the prairies have shown fire to have important ecological effects on vegetation composition and structure, insect populations and soil properties, including productivity (Appendix II in Kerr *et al.* 1993). However, we don't know the overall effects of fire suppression on prairie biodiversity. Furthermore, the question is complicated by the effects of grazing, which approximate some of the effects of fire, and by the interaction of fire and grazing. For example, grazing can reduce the intensity of fire by reducing litter build-up and fire can produce a flush of green vegetation which attracts grazers. Both fire and grazing can prevent the expansion of shrublands and woodlands into the grasslands.

### 1.3.5 Grazing

Much has been written about the demise of 30 to 50 million bison from the plains of North America, but little is known about the role of these huge herds of graz-ers in the prairie ecosystem. Surely they, and a suite of other large mammals, including elk, pronghorn, deer and bighorn sheep, had a considerable influence on the vegetation that they grazed, browsed and trampled. Historical accounts suggest bison moved in large herds, upwards of 10,000; their migrations were erratic; and where they did graze the pressure was intense (Roe 1951). Cattle, which evolved in other parts of the world, now graze native grasslands where once there were bison. However, intensive management, such as winter feeding, allows them to survive on the plains of North America. We have gone from an open system where grazing patterns were climatically defined to a closed system where management dictates pattern, timing and intensity of grazing.

Observation of bird and mammal species on the prairies indicates that they evolved and adapted to variation in grazing intensity and timing (Kantrud and Kologiski 1983; Prescott *et al.* 1994 a and b). Some species, such as mountain plover, McCown's longspur and Richardson's ground squirrel, are found primarily in more heavily grazed grasslands. Other species, such as Baird's sparrow, Sprague's pipit and meadow vole, frequent more lightly grazed grasslands. Most bird and mammal species on the prairies are adapted to moderate levels of grazing (Figure 5). The same is true for plants (Willoughby 1992).

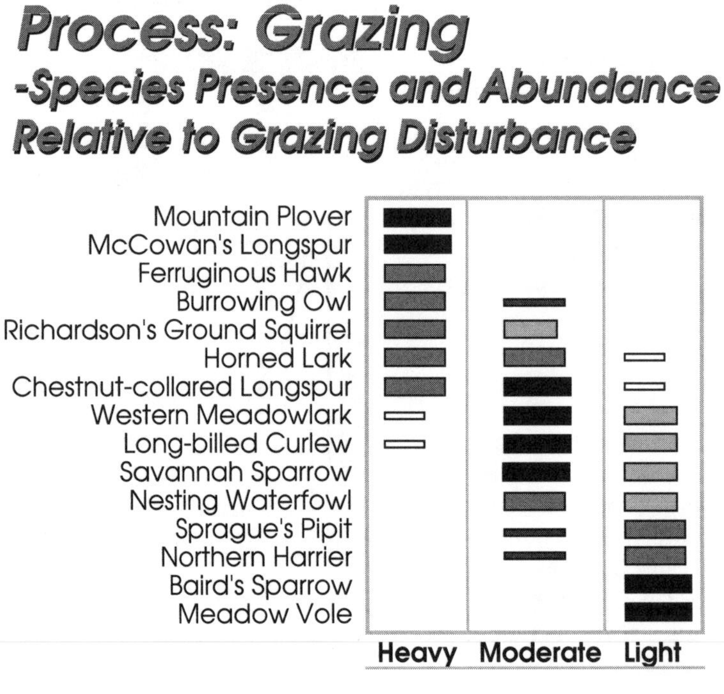

**Process: Grazing**
**-Species Presence and Abundance**
**Relative to Grazing Disturbance**

Figure 5 - Species under light, moderate and heavy grazing intensity. (adapted from: Prescott *et al.* 1994a)

# Process: Grazing
## Variation in Grazing Intensity of Native Prairie

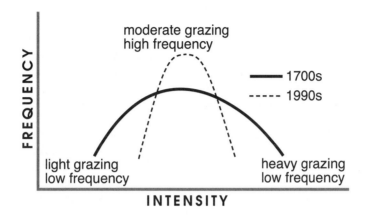

Figure 6. Range of variation: Grazing intensity and frequency.

This distribution of wildlife species suggests that variation in grazing intensity on the prairie before settlement was low frequency of lightly grazed areas, high frequency of moderately grazed areas and low frequency of heavily grazed areas (Figure 6). Current range management strives for moderate grazing pressure and uniform distribution of use. These objectives are implemented with the application of grazing systems that maintain the health of the prairie and avoid degradation of areas where livestock may concentrate, such as riparian habitats. Although certain grazing systems can increase the homogeneity of grassland architecture by concentrating livestock, in practice, most systems are applied with moderate grazing pressure that permit selective grazing, and the creation of overgrazed and undergrazed patches which contribute to landscape heterogeneity on a relatively small scale. Furthermore, the use of grazing systems will allow the creation of planned heterogeneity on a large scale by controlling the grazing pressure and the time of grazing within paddocks. Judicious grazing management can promote biodiversity while maintaining high productivity.

## 1.3.6 Predation

Historical accounts indicate there were nine species of mammalian carnivores, besides humans, in the prairie ecosystem before the 1900's. Carnivores are at the top of the food chain and are considered to reflect overall ecosystem integrity. During the 1900's, four of the largest carnivores have been extirpated from the Canadian prairies (grizzly bear, gray wolf, black-footed ferret and swift fox), three are considered at risk (bobcat, long-tailed weasel and badger), and two are considered not at risk (coyote, striped skunk) (Figure 7). *Homo sapiens* was and continues to be the predominant predator who tolerates few others and the only one whose population has increased dramatically since the turn of the century.

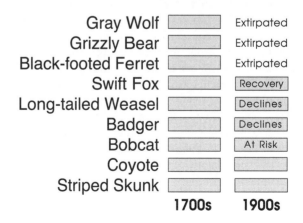

Figure 7 - Status of carnivorous mammals in the Alberta prairies. (from: Alberta Fish and Wildlife 1991)

Wildlife management in the 1900's has focused on large predator and prey species considered "game" or "pests." Population dynamics of these species are substantially changed reflecting significant changes in the flow of energy and nutrients through the prairie ecosystem food chain.

Our practice of managing for, or against, single species, without considering effects on other species and overall ecosystem function, has allowed several species to fall through the cracks. For example, persecution of ground squirrels as a pest species is believed to have contributed to the decline of burrowing owls and some raptors; and elimination of wolves is believed to have resulted in increases in coyotes, which in turn led to increased predation on swift foxes and contributed to that species' decline. Loss or disruption of habitat is given as the primary reason for decline in most prairie species (Alberta Fish and Wildlife 1991). This might suggest a re-examination of management philosophy.

## 1.4 Changes in Prairie Ecosystem Dynamics in the 1900's

The foregoing information suggests that many prairie ecosystem processes have changed substantially or are no longer allowed to function as a result of our society's uses and demands. Changes in one process can indirectly affect other ecosystem processes. The cumulative effects of these changes on the prairies have implications for biodiversity and natural resiliency and for sustainability of the system without high economic inputs.

Figure 8 presents a series of images depicting ecosystem processes for various parts of the 1990's prairie ecosystem that contrast with processes in the pre-1900's ecosystem. The processes considered are drought, erosion (wind and water), flood, grazing, decomposition, photosynthesis, soil disturbance, fire, and predation. Decomposition refers to the incorporation of organic matter into the soil by diverse soil micro-organisms. Not all processes are represented. For example, salinization was a pre-settlement process that has been greatly accelerated with changes in land use. Representation of these changes in Figure 8 is qualitative and based on what we now know, or understand about native prairie dynamics.

Key concepts depicted in Figure 8 are:

- The native prairie ecosystem is presumed to be in dynamic equilibrium, self-sustaining and resilient to natural variation in disturbances. This dynamic equilibrium is influenced in different ways in different parts of the ecosystem.

- Native grassland in the 1990's is experiencing reduced erosion, fire and predation. Cattle are the primary input and red meat, and other livestock by-products, the primary output. This ecosystem is the least altered from the native prairie of the scenarios being presented.

- Tame pasture in the 1990's is experiencing reduced erosion, soil disturbance (at least as an ongoing process), fire and predation. Grazing is increased. The primary output is red meat but more inputs—energy, fertilizer, and nonnative plant species are required than on native grassland.

- Cultivated cropland experiences decreased fire, predation and decomposition. Decreased decomposition refers to the decrease in diversity of soil microorganisms and in the decline in incorporation of organic matter into the soil. Erosion, soil disturbance and herbivory through cropping are greatly increased. Ecosystem processes are extremely altered from native prairie. Cultivated cropland in comparison to tame pasture requires more inputs: fertilizer, pesticides, fossil fuels, nonnative species and, in irrigated areas, water. Outputs are crops.

- Cities and towns experience greatly reduced drought (as a result of water management projects), erosion, flood, fire and predation. Soil disturbance is increased. Again, ecosystem processes are extremely altered from the native prairie. High inputs include fossil fuels, chemicals, water, minerals, lumber and nonnative species. Outputs are people and products.

What do these changes in ecosystem process signal?

## 2.0 INDICATORS REGARDING ECOLOGICAL AND ECONOMIC SUSTAINABILITY AND RESPONSES

Just as we have run up an economic debt nationally, we may be accumulating an ecological debt on the prairies. Once seriously disrupted, ecological processes may take many years to recover. There are ecological and economic indications that our current use of the prairies cannot be sustained. These indicators include the following:

- loss of prairie biodiversity,

- loss of soil and soil organic matter and increased salinity,

- increased chemical inputs on cultivated land,

- increased pollutants and salinity in prairie water bodies and groundwater,

- decline in net farm income (cost of inputs rising relative to price of outputs), and

- decline in rural population.

Growing concern about threats to ecological and economic sustainability on the prairies has prompted governments, industry and the not-for-profit sector to work on defining and addressing important issues in prairie management.

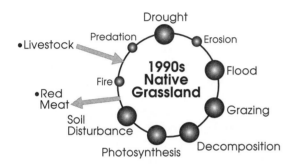

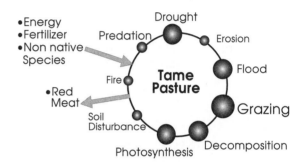

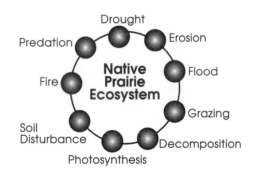

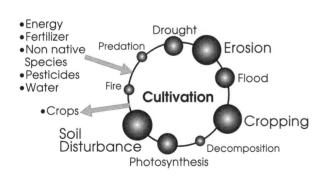

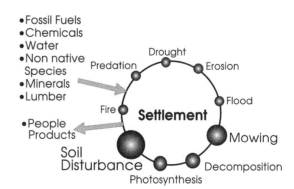

Figure 8 - Prairie Ecosystem Dynamics Under Various Land Uses.

## 2.1 Loss of Biodiversity

### Indicators

Relative to other ecoregions in Canada, the prairie ecoregion has a high proportion of the birds and terrestrial mammals that are threatened or endangered (Environment Canada 1991). The southern prairies, southern British Columbia and the Quebec City-Windsor corridor, all of which are characterized by intense development pressures, are the concentration sites of Canada's endangered species (Biodiversity Working Group 1994). In Alberta, 73 percent, or 16 of 22 wildlife species (amphibians, reptiles, birds, and mammals) that are now considered at serious risk rely on prairie habitats (Alberta Fish and Wildlife 1991); and about one-quarter of 324 vascular species considered rare are prairie species (Packer and Bradley 1984; Argus and Pryer 1990). Although detailed assessments of many species are lacking, habitat loss and degradation are the principal reasons given for those known to have declined.

An 11-year study of successional and native grasslands in Minnesota found that the productivity of more diverse plant communities is more resistant to, and recovers more fully from a major drought (Tilman and Downing 1994). Each additional species lost had a progressively greater impact on drought resistance. These authors suggested that these findings might extend to other perturbations such as grazing, late or early frosts, unusually wet or cool years, hail and fire. This study implies that long-term stability of primary production in the prairie ecosystem depends on biodiversity. Such findings raise concerns about resilience and maintenance of productivity on the three-quarters of the prairies that have been converted to species-poor cropland and tame pasture.

### Response

The Committee on the Status of Wildlife in Canada (COSEWIC), formed in 1978, has evaluated close to 300 species and efforts are underway to develop recovery plans for birds and mammals classified as endangered. The Prairie Conservation Action Plan was developed in the late 1980's to influence policy and attitudes so as to conserve the biological diversity found in the Canadian Prairies (World Wildlife Fund 1989). In 1994, a federal-provincial-territorial working group developed a biodiversity strategy for Canada, to address growing concern in Canada about preserving biodiversity and to meet Canada's obligations under the United Nations

Convention on Biological Diversity, ratified in 1992 (Biodiversity Working Group 1994).

Monoculture cropping systems will continue to be the predominant cropping system in the prairies in the foreseeable future (Statistics Canada 1994). Although inherently unstable, they give high annual yields, create their own economies of scale and use specialization to increase production levels. High inputs will be required to maintain the productivity of lands that are cropped annually.

## 2.2 Loss of Soil and Soil Organic Matter and Increased Salinity.

### Indicators

Soil erosion by wind and water is widespread in the cultivated portions of prairie Canada. Average annual soil loss in the prairie provinces up to 1983 was, by wind, 160 million tonnes and, by water, 117 million tonnes (Prairie Farm Rehabilitation Administration 1983). In 1991, estimates of soil erosion caused by water were highest in Saskatchewan, with soil erosion values estimated at more than 67 million tonnes; Alberta was next, with estimated gross soil erosion value of 22.9 million tonnes; and Manitoba lost 12.6 million tonnes (Statistics Canada 1994). As well, loss of 40 to 50 percent of original soil organic matter has occurred in the brown, dark brown and black soil zones of the prairies as a result of the export of nutrients by crops, tillage and erosion (Government of Canada 1991).

In addition, since settlement, 2.2 million hectares of cultivated dryland in the prairie provinces have experienced salinization as a result of elevated groundwater tables arising from decreased water use by crops as compared to native vegetation (Prairie Farm Rehabilitation Administration 1983). Continuation of these trends would pose a very real threat to long-term stability of agricultural production in the prairie ecosystem.

### Response

More than 70 percent of prairie farms are now using at least one erosion control practice, such as strip cropping and conservation tillage, to control the environmental stress imposed by traditional close-row monoculture systems (Statistics Canada 1994). Since 1989, the federal-provincial Permanent Cover Program has turned 517 165 hectares of environmentally sensitive farmland in the prairie provinces to tame pasture (Craig Wood, PFRA, pers. comm).

## 2.3 Increased Chemical Inputs on Agricultural Land

### Indicators

Although initially high, crop yields generally decrease within 20 to 30 years of converting native prairie to cropland because of progressive loss of soil fertility. Since the early 1950's, to counteract this decline, fertilizers have been widely applied to cultivated land. Between 1970 and 1985, application of nutrients, particularly nitrogen and phosphorous, in the form of fertilizer increased between 100 and 1000 percent for individual subbasins in prairie Canada. This increase was in response to both declining native soil fertility and increased yields from improved crop varieties (Government of Canada 1991). Not only does this trend pose questions about sustaining agricultural productivity (ecologically and economically), but also about effects on water quality.

Agricultural pesticides include herbicides, insecticides, fungicides and vertebrate toxicants used to prevent or control weeds, insects, diseases and vertebrate pests. They have been widely used since the 1950's. Between 1970 and 1985, the amount spent on agricultural pesticides increased between 500 and over 1000 percent for individual subbasins in prairie Canada (Government of Canada 1991). The highest concentration of insecticide spraying in Canada occurred in southern Saskatchewan and parts of prairie Alberta in 1985. Pesticides can reach water supplies through a variety of paths.

### Response

In the last 30 years, there has been a dramatic increase in the number of farmers who test the soil for plant-available nutrients, allowing them to match fertilizer use to crop needs and minimize the risk of over-applying fertilizer.

Organochlorine insecticides, such as DDT, and mercurial fungicides are no longer used because of their toxicity and residual accumulation. In the 1990's, synthetic pyrethroids, such as deltamethrin and permethrin, are commonly used for insect control. These products have lower acute and chronic toxicities and short lives as residues.

## 2.4 Increased Pollutants and Salinity in Prairie Water Bodies and Groundwater.

### Indicators

Because all life depends on water for survival, water quality is regarded as a good indicator of overall ecosystem health. Pollutants from municipal, industrial and agricultural activities are known to have increased in prairie rivers, lakes and groundwater in the 1900's. However, data to quantify the sources, the amounts and the trends are sparse and sporadic. Data that exist include the following:

- Since testing began in the late 1960's, herbicides, insecticides and fungicides have been detected in prairie rivers; however, usually not in concentrations exceeding the guideline value for protection of aquatic life. Prairie rivers most often were found to contain 2,4-D and lindane (Statistics Canada 1994).

- Some rivers and lakes in the prairies have high nutrient-loadings, but the relative contributions from municipalities, industry and agriculture, as well as trends and environmental implications have yet to be determined. Nutrients (especially phosphorous) released into rivers from municipal wastewater treatment facilities are known to result in eutrophication downstream. It has also been demonstrated in the South Saskatchewan River and in the Bow and Oldman rivers that water returning from irrigation systems has concentrations of total dissolved solids up to double what they were before irrigation (Statistics Canada 1994).

- Sampling of groundwater wells, in 1986, revealed 43 wells in Alberta, Saskatchewan and Manitoba to be contaminated, the majority of these from waste disposal or industrial operations (Statistics Canada 1994).

### Response

The Prairie Provinces Water Board has established a total phosphorus objective of 0.05 milligrams per litre and a total nitrogen objective of 0.5 milligrams per litre. The Bow River downstream of Calgary has shown improvement since 1982 (Environment Canada 1991).

Under the Canada-Alberta Environmentally Sustainable Agriculture Agreement (CAESA), there are currently studies of the potential impacts of nutrients, herbicides, sediments and livestock waste on surface and groundwater resources in Alberta (CAESA 1994).

## 2.5 Decline in Net Farm Income

### Indicators

In 1975, realized net farm income (income for outputs minus the cost of inputs) in Canada reached a high of about $2.5 billion. Fall in net farm income in the late 1970's prompted an increase in direct subsidies to farmers. Since 1985, without ongoing programs and special assistance, realized net farm income would have been at zero or negative. Even with these payments, many farmers require income from supplemental sources, usually achieved from off-farm employment. Rising costs of inputs such as pesticides and fertilizer, and demands to provide low-cost foods to consumers, in Canada and other parts of the world, are two factors contributing to a decline in economic stability of the agricultural industry on the prairies (Prairie Farm Rehabilitation Administration 1992).

### Response

Recently, governments and the agricultural communities in both Alberta and Saskatchewan have set new strategic directions for their agricultural and food industries. Promoting environmentally sustainable agriculture is an important component of both strategies (Alberta Agriculture 1993; Saskatchewan Agriculture and Food 1993). A joint federal-provincial initiative is underway to develop a National Environmental Strategy for Agriculture and Agri-food. The environmental issues being addressed relate not only to natural resources and environmental quality, but also to pesticide and biotechnology regulations, international trade and public perception about environmental performance.

## 2.6 Decline in Rural Population

### Indicators

The rural population of the prairie provinces declined from about 1.7 million in 1941 to 1.2 million in 1991, while the urban population increased from about 0.6 million to 3.4 million. Of the rural population, the on-farm portion has declined from about 1.1 million in 1946 to about 0.4 million in 1991. On-farm population on the prairies is projected to continue to decrease but at a slower rate than in the past. This trend threatens the economic and social stability of rural communities (Prairie Farm Rehabilitation Administration 1992).

### Response

Prairie residents are considering opportunities for diversification of the rural economy in order to maintain viable rural communities.

## 3.0 ECOSYSTEM MANAGEMENT PRINCIPLES

"Ecosystem Management" is the handle being put on the emerging view about how to address ecological problems. Contrary to how it sounds, ecosystem management does not presume to manage all components of the ecosystem, but rather to manage our activities so that overall ecosystem integrity is maintained, biodiversity is preserved and an ecologically sustainable flow of benefits is achieved. Ecosystem management is not entirely new, but rather it involves a shift in management focus from sustaining yields of competing resource outputs to sustaining ecosystems. Sound ecological management contributes to economic sustainability. For example, ecologically sound range management translates into a sustainable livelihood for ranchers.

## 3.1 Suggested Principles

The Ecosystem Management Team that developed this presentation and the draft discussion document suggests four key principles of ecosystem management. These principles, which follow below, could be used to assess how well current policies and programs contribute to sustaining ecosystems.

**First Principle: Ecosystem management maintains and restores native prairie so society can derive and sustain all the benefits that flow from it (ecological, economic and social).**

This principle requires blocks of native prairie representative of the full range of native prairie habitats and biodiversity as well as large enough and intact enough to maintain ecological integrity. In some areas of the prairie ecosystem, such as the aspen parkland, fescue grassland and tall-grass prairie, options for maintaining native prairie are extremely limited. Restoration of significant tracts of native prairie may be warranted.

Where industrial incursions occur into native prairie, reclamation objectives under ecosystem management

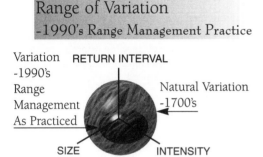

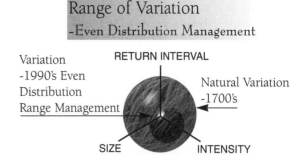

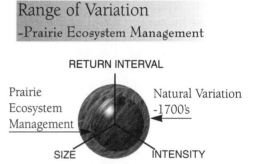

Figure 9 - Hypothetical range of variation under various management practices.

would be to restore to native condition and to avoid or reduce impact as much as possible in the first place.

**Second Principle: Ecosystem management attempts to perpetuate and approximate natural factors and processes.**

Rather than focusing on individual species and their needs, ecosystem management focuses on landscapes and the dynamic forces such as erosion/deposition, drought, flood, fire, photosynthesis, herbivory, predation and decomposition. By allowing these processes to operate naturally or approximating them through management, it is assumed there will be a better chance of preserving biodiversity (that is, the full range of life forms evolved under and adapted to these processes) and of sustaining the flow of benefits to society.

Cultivation of annual crops, by its very nature, is a dramatic alteration of the natural range of variation in ecosystem processes (Figure 9). However, crop production is an important part of our economy and there will always be cropland on the prairie, provided society is willing to sustain the required inputs. Moving toward ecosystem management on cropland means trying to reduce inputs of fertilizers, pesticides, fossil fuels and water as well as reducing soil disturbance and erosion and enhancing the soil's organic matter. Indeed, examples like crop residue management, the permanent cover program and biological control strategies for weeds and insects are evidence of thinking in terms of ecosystem processes.

Range management, after dealing with the immediate conservation issues of riparian management and broad landscapes that are heavily grazed, needs to manage animal distribution to enhance the range of natural variation (Figure 9). Patchy grazing, with lightly, moderately and heavily used areas is desirable. Use patterns, previously viewed as inefficient, may precisely match the needs of a variety of plant and wildlife species. Range management that overintensifies or homogenizes grazing will reduce the range of natural variation.

**Third Principle: Ecosystem management applies ecological knowledge to prairie management, monitors the results and adapts as required.**

Adaptive management is the catchword for this concept. For example, important components of prairie ecosystem management would be monitoring soil condition, water quality, vegetation composition and structure and biodiversity, as well as altering management practices if there are threats to overall ecosystem health or integrity. This principle requires that we have widely agreed-upon measures of ecological health or integrity. Adaptive management can occur on many scales: over the entire prairies, including cultivated areas as well as native grasslands, wetlands, rivers and lakes; and, just as importantly, on the individual ranch or farm.

**Fourth Principle: Ecosystem management is multidisciplinary and interjurisdictional.**

Ecological boundaries are respected rather than only political ones. Management decisions are made by individuals and teams with a breadth of knowledge, especially about ecology (how natural systems work), but also about the economy and society. For example, biologists would become more aware of agricultural economics and rural life, and landholders would become more aware of prairie ecology, and the two groups would spend more time communicating with each other about common issues. Adopting this principle would help form a common purpose for prairie management.

Adopting the principles of ecosystem management could have far-reaching implications for how we manage and live in the prairie; indeed, it could affect how we think about and understand our place in the prairie ecosystem. It will reflect a shift in values away from controlling or living separate from our natural environment to respecting and living within it. We do not yet completely know or understand all the implications of this approach.

## 3.2 Conclusion

We are becoming increasingly aware as a society that economic and social sustainability is linked to ecological sustainability. In 1952, David Costello, a range scientist and author of *The Prairie World*, summed it up thus:

> *"People are the greatest of the biological factors. Through their increasing knowledge of ecology, they have within themselves the power to act on their environment for their own greatest good. They will have to apply that knowledge, not through edict, arbitrary decision, or economic or political force, but within the limits of natural law, if they are to succeed." (Costello 1952)*

In the prairie, our decisions as individuals and communities will determine how successful we are at managing our activities so that overall ecosystem integrity is maintained, biodiversity is preserved and an ecologically sustainable flow of benefits is achieved. A visible example of such benefits are ranching operations where generations have learned to read the native grasslands, and to manage them through an ecological approach, resulting in stable, profitable operations that have survived for three or more generations. It is examples such as these we must encourage and follow, if Sharon Butala's vision of a renewed relationship with Nature and a flourishing rural life is to be realized.

## BIBLIOGRAPHY

Alberta Fish and Wildlife. 1991. The status of Alberta wildlife. Alberta Forestry, Lands and Wildlife Pub. No I/413. Edmonton.

Anderson, R.C. 1976. Role of fire in grassland management. Environmental Management 3: 51-57.

Argus, G.W., and K.M. Pryer. 1990. Rare vascular plants in Canada: Our Natural Heritage. Canadian Museum of Nature.

Biodiversity Working Group, Federal-Provincial-Territorial. 1994. Draft Canadian Biodiversity Strategy. Draft for Discussion Purposes.

Bradley, C., and D.G. Smith. 1984. Meandering channel response to altered flow regime: Milk River, Alberta and Montana. Water Resources Research 20: 1913-1920.

Butala S. 1994. The perfection of the morning: An apprenticeship in nature. Harper Collins Publishers Ltd., Toronto.

Canada Alberta Environmentally Sustainable Agriculture Agreement. 1994. Impacts of agriculture on surface waters in Alberta study design.

Costello, David. 1952. Ecology and range management. Journal of Range Management 5: 2.

Environment Canada. 1991. A report on Canada's progress towards a national set of environmental indicators. State of the Environment Report No. 91-1.

Alberta Agriculture. 1993. Creating tomorrow: A direction for Alberta's agriculture and food industry. Edmonton.

Government of Canada. 1991. The state of Canada's environment. Ottawa.

Higgins, K.F., A.D. Kruse and J.L. Piehl. 1986. Effects of fire in the Northern Great Plains. U.S. Fish and Wildlife Service, Cooperative Extension Service, South Dakota University, and U.S. Department of Agriculture. Report EC761.

Hughes, F.M.R. 1994. Environmental change, disturbance and regeneration in semi-arid floodplain forests. Pp. 321-345 *In* Environmental change in drylands: Biogeographical and Geomorphological Perspective (A.C. Millington and K. Pye, eds.). John Wiley & Sons Ltd., England.

Kantrud, H.A., and R.L. Kologiski. 1993. Avian associations of the Northern Great Plains grasslands. Journal of Biogeography 10: 331-350.

Kerr, D.S., L.J. Morrison and K.E. Wilkinson. 1993. Reclamation of native grasslands in Alberta: A review of the literature. Alberta Land Conservation and Reclamation Council Report No. RRTAC 93-1. Edmonton.

Moss, E.H., and J.G. Packer. 1983. Flora of Alberta. 2nd Edition. Universtiy of Toronto Press, Toronto.

Packer, J.G., and C.E. Bradley. 1984. A checklist of the rare vascular plants in Alberta. Provincial Museum of Alberta Natural History Occasional Paper No. 5.

Prairie Farm Rehabilitation Administration. 1983. Land degradation and soil conservation issues on the Canadian prairies. Regina.

Prairie Farm Rehabilitation Administration. 1992. Rural prairies sustainabilty background Paper.

Prescott, D.R.C., R. Arbuckle, B. Goddard and A. Murphy. 1994a. Methods for the monitoring and assessment of avian communities on NAWMP landscapes in Alberta, and 1993 results. Alberta North American Waterfowl Management Plan Centre. Edmonton, Alberta.

Prescott, D.R.C., A.J. Murphy and E. Ewaschuk. 1994b. An avian community approach to determining biodiversity values of NAWMP habitats in the aspen parkland of Alberta. Alberta North American Waterfowl Management Plan Centre. Edmonton, Alberta.

Roe, F.G. 1951. The North American buffalo: A critical study of the species in its wild state. University of Toronto Press. Toronto, Ontario.

Rood, S.B., and J.M. Mahoney. 1990. Collapse of river valley forests downstream from dams in western Prairies: probable causes and prospects for mitigation. Environmental Management 14: 451-464.

Rood, S.B., and J.M. Mahoney (in press). River damming and riparian cottonwoods along the Marias River, Montana.

Saskatchewan Agriculture and Food. 1993. Agriculture 2000: A strategic direction for the future of Saskatchewan's agriculture and food industry. Regina.

Statistics Canada. 1992. 1991 census of agriculture. Ottawa.

Statistics Canada. 1994. Human activity and the environment 1994. Ministry of Industry, Science and Technology. Ottawa, Ontario.

Stelfox, B. 1994. Presentation for the Ecosystem Management Strategic Issue Working Group, Alberta Forests Conservation Strategy. Alberta Environmental Centre, Vegreville, Alberta.

Tilman, D., and J.A. Downing. 1994. Biodiversity and stability in grasslands. Nature 367: 363-365.

Tourism Saskatchewan. 1994. The Great Saskatchewan Vacation Book. Saskatchewan Economic Development, Regina, Saskatchewan.

Wallis, C., and C. Wershler. 1988. Rare wildlife and plant conservation studies in sandhill and sand plain habitats of southern Alberta. Alberta Forestry, Lands and Wildlife; Alberta Recreation and Parks and World Wildlife Fund Canada. Edmonton, Alberta.

Willoughby, M. 1992. Species diversity and how it is affected by livestock grazing in Alberta. Alberta Public Lands Range Notes 13.

World Wildlife Fund. 1989. Prairie Conservation Action Plan: 1989-1994.

# 4th Prairie Conservation and Endangered Species Workshop

## Questionnaire on "PRAIRIE ECOSYSTEM MANAGEMENT: AN ALBERTA PERSPECTIVE.,

Thank you for taking the time to read the draft discussion document on prairie ecosystem management in your registration package. Please take a few minutes to answer the following questions regarding the information contained in the plenary presentation and the draft document. Responses will be summarized and included in the workshop proceedings.

Do you agree with the description of the prairie ecosystem and processes presented in Section 2 of the Discussion Draft?

☐ Strongly Agree     ☐ Agree     ☐ Don't Know     ☐ Disagree     ☐ Strongly Disagree

If you disagree, which aspect(s) do you consider has (have) been mischaracterized and why?

**The Discussion Draft proposes four key principles of ecosystem management (Section 4.0). In your view should these principles be applied to prairie management?**

1) Prairie management should strive to maintain and restore native prairie so society can derive and sustain all the benefits that flow from it (ecological, economic and social).

☐ Strongly Agree     ☐ Agree     ☐ Don't Know     ☐ Disagree     ☐ Strongly Disagree

2) Prairie management should attempt to perpetuate and approximate natural factors and processes.

☐ Strongly Agree     ☐ Agree     ☐ Don't Know     ☐ Disagree     ☐ Strongly Disagree

3) Prairie management should apply ecological knowledge to prairie management, monitor the results and adapt as required.

☐ Strongly Agree     ☐ Agree     ☐ Don't Know     ☐ Disagree     ☐ Strongly Disagree

4) Prairie management should strive to be multi-disciplinary and inter-jurisdictional.

☐ Strongly Agree     ☐ Agree     ☐ Don't Know     ☐ Disagree     ☐ Strongly Disagree

**What are the potential benefits of moving in this direction?**

**What are your concerns?**

Are there other principles which in your view should be applied to prairie management?

☐ No    ☐ Yes    If yes, what principles would you suggest?

Have you found the presentation and discussion draft on ecosystem management informative or useful?

☐ No    ☐ Yes    If useful, how would you use it?

Would you like a copy of the slide presentation on ecosystem management at cost (approx. $50)?

☐ No    ☐ yes    If yes, please provide your name and address.

Other Comments:

**What is your interest in prairie management?  Check as many as apply.**

☐ Farmer
☐ Rancher
☐ Range Consultant
☐ Range Scientist
☐ Agriculture Industry Representative
☐ Oil and Gas Industry Representative
☐ Environmental Consultant
☐ Environmental Educator
☐ Environmental Activist
☐ Environmental/Conservation Organization Representative

☐ Biologist
☐ Naturalist
☐ Elected Government Official
☐ Government Land Manager
☐ Government Fish and Wildlife manager
☐ Government Water Manager
☐ Government Planner
☐ Student
☐ Other (please specify): _____

*Please put this form in the box provided at the registration desk or mail to Institute for Renewable Resources management, Lethbridge Community College, Lethbridge AB T1K 1L6.   Thank you*

# SUMMARY OF RESPONSES TO QUESTIONNAIRE

## Cheryl Bradley

## DISTRIBUTION AND RESPONSE RATE

A presentation on ecosystem management was given and about 400 copies of the draft discussion document on which the presentation was based were distributed in registration packages at the workshop. The objective was to provoke thought and discussion among participants about the concepts of ecosystem management and application to the prairies. This objective was accomplished as evidenced by numerous informal discussions among participants, as well as a well-attended, formal group discussion on ecosystem management on Sunday morning, the results of which are provided elsewhere in the proceedings.

A questionnaire regarding the contents of the document was attached to each discussion draft in the registration packages. During the Friday afternoon plenary presentation on ecosystem management, workshop participants were asked to consider the concepts in the presentation, review the related draft document and then complete the questionnaire. Completed questionnaires could be returned to a box at the registration desk or by mail. Twenty-two questionnaires were completed, a six percent response. A summary of these responses follows.

## COMMENTS ON THE DRAFT DISCUSSION DOCUMENT

### Description of the Prairie Ecosystem and Processes

Seventeen respondents (77%) strongly agree (5) or agree (12) with the description of the prairie ecosystem and processes presented in Section 2.0 of the draft discussion document. Three (14%) disagree.

Suggestions for improving the description are:

- Include reference to climate and geologic/geomorphic processes (e.g. mass wasting) as important elements in the prairie ecosystem;

- Recognize the various ecoregions (mixed grass, fescue, tall grass, aspen parkland) in the prairie

ecosystem and that they are determined largely by climate; include aspen grovelands and shrublands as key constituents of a prairie ecosystem;

- State clearly that frequency curves for fire size (Figure 4) and grazing intensity (Figure 6) and some of statements regarding predation are assumptions and are not based on actual data;

- Recognize that processes, such as fire, may differ in timing and scale among various systems in the prairies; recognize the interaction between fire and grazing and the effects of temporal influence on grazing impacts;

- Consider including a diagram depicting nutrient cycling and energy flows in a prairie ecosystem;

- Recognize that riparian and sand dune areas are more dynamic (less stable) than other prairie landscape units with respect to erosion and/or flood and have their own type and rate of natural processes; and

- Re: Figure 8, recognize outputs such as livestock by-products and food from crops; 1990's native grassland and tame pastures probably experience higher erosion than 1700's native prairie due to high intensity/high frequency grazing; In the cultivated system, decomposition is increased, not decreased; herbivory is increased, but is also exported from the system.

Many of these suggestions have been incorporated into the revised document.

### 2.2 Principles of Ecosystem Management

More than 18 (82%) respondents agree or strongly agree with each of the four key principles of ecosystem management which had been proposed in Section 4.0 of the draft discussion document. One respondent disagrees with Principle 1 (maintaining and restoring native prairie) and one each were uncertain about their agreement with Principles 1 and 2 (perpetuating and approximating natural factors) largely because the implications were not clear.

Three (14%) respondents could not suggest other principles that should be applied to prairie management, however fourteen (67%) respondents believe there are additional principles. There is not a strong concurrence among the various suggestions. Suggestions provided for additional principles follow the comments regarding the four proposed principles.

## *Proposed principles and comments on them:*

Principle 1: Ecosystem management maintains and restores native prairie so society can derive and sustain all the benefits that flow from it (ecological, economic and social).

Comments:

- It can be done for its own sake, or for benefits to other species or ecosystems, not just to benefit society;

- Focus on conserving large portions of native prairie both in wilderness areas, where there is no permanent human occupation, and in biosphere reserve areas, where human activities are compatible with the pre-industrial prairie ecosystem; and

- How can this be implemented on croplands?

**Principle 2:** Ecosystem management attempts to perpetuate and approximate natural factors and processes.

Comments:

- Some components of the system may be irreversibly altered and require compensation;

- May not have enough area of native prairie for natural disturbance regimes to apply;

- Disturbance and ecological processes are now operating on a much changed biota;

- Change to "...perpetuate the full spectrum of ecosystem processes";

- Grain cropping cannot approximate natural disturbance patterns; can croplands or settlements be part of ecosystem management? and

- Man is part of nature.

**Principle 3:** Ecosystem management applies ecological knowledge to prairie management, monitors the results and adapts as required.

Comments:

- Change to "...applies eco-centric knowledge...";

- Adaptive management should be based on honouring current knowledge and not assumptions about natural processes; and

- Also apply agronomic knowledge.

**Principle 4:** Ecosystem management is multi-disciplinary and inter-jurisdictional.

Comments:

- Change "multi" to "trans" or "supra";

- Need ecosystemic framework unconstrained by borders or agencies; and

- How can we apply this to private land, especially private cropland?

## *Suggestions for Additional Principles:*

- Ecosystem management includes humans (economics, taxation, land policy, "natural" behaviour of man);

- Ecosystem management is on-the-ground action;

- Lack of information should not prevent action;

- Prairie management should contribute to global environmental quality;

- Preserve options;

- Mother Nature is full of surprises;

- Without waste there is no ecosystem;

- Ecosystem management is directed and constrained by eco-centric values; and

- The spiritual aspect/connection is important.

## 2.3 Benefits of Moving Towards Prairie Ecosystem Management

Fourteen (64%) respondents commented on the potential benefits of moving in the direction of proposed ecosystem management principles. Benefits identified are:

- Sustaining a healthy prairie ecosystem; maintenance of biological diversity; reduction of fragmentation of habitat; maintaining native range;

- Sustaining benefits to people; benefits are economic as well as less tangible ones such as quality of life, mental and physical health, survival and conserving prairie culture/heritage;

- A stronger connection between humans and their environment; social, environmental and economic benefits are interlinked;

- Acquiring a better understanding of how prairie ecosystems function and maintain themselves and applying this understanding to management;

- Shared and informed decision-making; gaining agreement on management principles across different interest groups; recognizing and understanding tradeoffs and linkages; more integrative approach to management; recognizing that both "sides" (agriculturalists and ecologists) have valid points and can help each other; only through cooperation do we have any chance of accomplishing progress that is both meaningful and ongoing; new, innovative approaches could result;

- Greater efficiency and reduced costs; the only practical direction to take; and

- Provides focus to prairie management.

## 2.4 Concerns about Moving towards Prairie Ecosystem Management

Thirteen (59%) respondents expressed concerns about, or barriers to, moving in the direction of the proposed ecosystem management principles. These concerns are:

- Some areas of native prairie are so small or fragmented that it may be difficult to allow natural processes to operate or there may be a need to compensate; is there enough native prairie for nat-

ural disturbances to operate on the pre-1700 scale? does the reduced area affect how we should "manage" these disturbances?

- Dramatically changed large mammal and carnivore populations may affect our ability to approximate predation processes; disturbance and ecological processes are now operating on a much changed biota;

- What are our benchmarks and assumptions? how valid/proven are they? what spatial and temporal scales/frameworks do we use to determine structural and functional representativeness?

- Ecological knowledge always will be increasing therefore we will need to continually adapt management; this could be problematical;

- There may be loss of economic development opportunities that may be sustainable, due to lack of knowledge; there is a need for balancing resource needs, and for conflict management;

- There will be public resistance; lack of public knowledge and understanding about ecosystems will make it difficult to implement ecosystem management; far too many of us are afraid of change, afraid to risk; there will be economic and safety concerns with respect to fire or patch overgrazing; problem with semantics; why not "prairie conservation" rather than "ecosystem management"?

- How do the principles translate into action? these are pie-in-the-sky, theoretical concepts if they cannot be implemented; what are the concrete goals and actions required? if practical management solutions are not identified it will be business-as-usual; can we go beyond the rhetoric and get the job done? and

- This will not work without a multi-disciplinary, prairie-wide strategic planning process; provincial plans must conform to the prairie-wide plan; do not depend on government legislation and public policy for implementing; how can we accomplish this?

## 2.5 Usefulness of the Presentation and Discussion Draft

Eighteen (82%) respondents found the presentation and discussion draft to be informative or useful. Comments about its usefulness were:

- A clear, concise, well-considered, and logical presentation of key concepts in prairie management;

- Useful as a starting point to develop meaningful solutions and implementation;

- Useful to stimulate interdisciplinary discussion on prairie planning and management;

- Useful for staff development in the short-term and for clients in the long-term;

- Useful as an educational tool at many levels;

- Provides motivation and support for moving towards action; and

- Supports the argument for gathering, analyzing and using spatial and temporal ecological data in management; there is an opportunity with prairie ecosystems to attain a deeper understanding of landscape patterns (biotic and abiotic characteristics) than has traditionally been seen in landscape approaches in forested areas.

## 2.6 Other Comments

Ten (45%) respondents provided other comments. They were:

- I like the ideas presented and can envisage how they could be implemented on range lands and protected areas, but not on croplands;

- This work fits nicely with, and would benefit from World Wildlife Fund Canada's work on gap analysis and ecological integrity;

- Concern that agriculture is being singled out to challenge its assumptions; all interests need to reexamine their assumptions;

- Superb report and presentation; excellent presentation; provocative and informative presentation;

- Wonderful explanation of the concepts; very broad scope, well covered and delivered; and

- Recommend producing a video of the presentation, with some modifications, and incorporating as a lecture module in post-secondary courses.

Three individuals offered to participate in the further development of the concepts/document/approach.

## 3.0 INTEREST OF RESPONDENTS

Respondents were asked to indicate their interest in prairie management. More than one category could be checked.

| | |
|---|---|
| Farmer | 2 |
| Rancher | 1 |
| Agriculture Industry Representative | 1 |
| Soil Scientist | 1 |
| Environmental Consultant | 7 |
| Environmental Educator | 4 |
| Environmental Activist | 3 |
| ENGO Representative | 4 |
| Biologist | 8 |
| Naturalist | 7 |
| Government Land Manager | 4 |
| Government Fish Wildlife Manager | 1 |
| Government Water Manager | 2 |
| Government Planner | 1 |
| Student | 2 |

# 3.0 PRAIRIE CONSERVATION ACTION PLAN

# IMPLEMENTING THE PRAIRIE CONSERVATION ACTION PLAN IN ALBERTA, 1989 - 1994: TAKING STOCK AND MOVING ON

## Ian W. Dyson

*Regional Environmental Coordinator, Prairie Region, Alberta Environmental Protection,
Lethbridge T1J 2J8*

## INTRODUCTION

Although five years is so fleeting, a great deal of water has passed under the Alberta prairie conservation bridge in that time. Currently a transitional period is underway between taking stock of the approaches and accomplishments associated with the old plan and fashioning a new plan and a means of realizing its intentions that will take us up to the millennium.

Over the course of the past year in Alberta, a perspective shift from looking back to looking forward has occurred. I would like to walk you through the highlights of that process, focusing on:

- The assessment of the 1989 to 1994 PCAP;

- June 1994 Lethbridge Prairie Conservation Workshop;

- Draft outline of a new Alberta PCAP; and

- Transition from Prairie Conservation Coordinating Committee to Prairie Conservation Forum.

## PCAP ASSESSMENT

A 'measuring stick' stocktaking assessment of accomplishments under the old PCAP was something each of the three prairie provinces agreed to undertake as an initial step in the process of moving toward a revised prairie-wide PCAP.

In Alberta's case this task was facilitated by the fact that one of the key roles of the Prairie Conservation Coordinating Committee (PCCC) was to encourage effective implementation of the PCAP. In discharging this task, a reasonable documented record of progress has been kept—initially in the form of a detailed implementation tracking record and more recently in the form of highlighted accomplishments recorded in the committee's annual reports for each of the ten goals of the PCAP. This material was all compiled and summarized during the period February through April 1994 and is recorded in the document, "Assessment of the PCAP 1989 to 1994, What has been Accomplished in Alberta?" (PCCC September 1994). That document actually only covers the 1989 to 1993 period and is currently being revised to include agency accomplishments in the final year.

Table 1. Report card summary of PCAP implementation in Alberta ('0' denotes no progress has been made whatsoever, while a '10' denotes full and complete implementation of the PCAP's recommendation; the ratings reflect a rounded average from the scores of an eight member evaluatory panel consisting of both government and nongovernment members with a wide variety of professional specializations).

| GOAL | .1 | .2 | .3 | .4 | .5 | .6 | .7 | .8 | .9 | .10 |
|------|----|----|----|----|----|----|----|----|----|-----|
| 1 | 7 | 6 | 7 | | | | | | | |
| 2 | 6 | 3 | 2 | 8 | 3 | 4 | | | | |
| 3 | 2 | 6 | 6 | 6 | 8 | 8 | 3 | 3 | 10 | |
| 4 | 6 | 6 | 6 | | | | | | | |
| 5 | 10 | 6 | ? | 4 | 6 | 10 | 4 | | | |
| 6 | 10 | 2 | 1 | 7 | 6 | ? | | | | |
| 7 | 2 | 7 | 4 | 4 | 5 | 5 | | | | |
| 8 | 3 | 4 | 4 | | | | | | | |
| 9 | 7 | 7 | 7 | 5 | 7 | 3 | 8 | 6 | 7 | 5 |
| 10 | 1 | 0 | 3 | | | | | | | |

The assessment identifies, in point form, specific accomplishments that relate directly to each action recommendation in the original PCAP. Gaps, where additional action is required to complete the recommendation, are also identified. A qualitative assessment of how well each action recommendation has been carried out was also produced by the PCCC Steering Committee to provide a quick 'report card' summary (Table 1). The report card shows that generally solid progress has been made in inventorying prairie and raising public awareness, poor progress has been made in terms of research, promoting private land stewardship and government conservation programs, and highly variable progress has been made in remaining areas of the plan dealing with protecting sites and endangered species management.

Because of the large number of action recommendations and follow-up activities, reference should be made to the detailed report for accurate information. The following, however, provides a highlight accomplishment summary for each of the key themes of the old PCAP.

### Theme 1: Identifying Remaining Prairie and Parkland (Goal 1)

The vast majority of inventory work specified by the first PCAP has been undertaken with Environmentally Significant Area (ESA) inventories, NAWMP and Ducks Unlimited Canada projects, and a reconnaissance inventory of native grass prairie in southern Alberta. Gaps remain for ESA's in some parkland municipalities and the Special Areas. A reconnaissance level inventory of native prairie and parkland in central Alberta remains to be undertaken. Maximum applied use is likely not being made of the information that is available.

### Theme 2: Protecting Remaining Prairie and Parkland Ecosystems (Goals 2, 3 and 4)

Alberta is only part of the way towards achievement of this objective. A large number of activities have occurred over the last five years in identifying areas that might be candidates for protection. This culminated in the report of the Special Places 2000 Advisory Committee. Protective action is being considered or has been implemented for some areas. Each ecoregion has at least one reasonably large area that is either being protected or is a candidate for protection. Limited progress has been made in creating the broader network of protected areas and the interconnecting corridors. Discussion continues about how large the major sample

areas should be, how much of each ecosystem needs to be protected, what degree of protection is necessary and how to achieve a balance between creating protected areas and developing a conservation approach across all remaining native prairie and parkland.

### Theme 3: Protecting Threatened and Endangered Species (Goals 5 and 6)

Significant progress has been made in developing and implementing recovery plans for a number of threatened and endangered species. To this point there is little data on how successful most of these plans have been. We now have in place mechanisms for identifying species that are or could be of concern. No new Endangered Species legislation has been enacted at the federal or provincial level, although a number of discussion papers have been developed.

### Theme 4: Creating An Appropriate Policy and Regulatory Environment (Goal 7)

Governments at all levels have expressed strong support for conservation objectives, but little progress had been made in converting intent into action. While a number of agricultural policies that were detrimental to prairie conservation have been amended, these amendments have not been driven by conservation concerns but by government fiscal restraint and economic factors. Regional and local planning authorities have been slow to build conservation objectives into their planning procedures and priorities. The proposed amendments to the Alberta Planning Act could be detrimental to prairie conservation.

### Theme 5: Integrating Conservation Into Land Use Decisions Across the Whole Prairie Landscape (Goal 8)

Too little emphasis was put on this whole area in the PCAP. Some specific activities and programs have been initiated with individual producers and a small number of extension and education programs have been initiated for producers, especially on range management. However the general farm community has not become actively involved in the PCAP program and has not bought into its overall objectives. This is a major shortcoming in the whole prairie conservation program and unless it is addressed will hamper the achievement of this goal as well as progress towards other goals that involve land use and management.

**Theme 6: Promoting Public Awareness About the Importance of Protecting Prairie Ecosystems (Goal 9)**

Significant progress has been made in building public awareness about the importance of wildlife and wildlife habitat. A number of school programs are in place. Interpretative programs and similar activities have been initiated through government agencies and special interest groups. A number of municipalities have become actively involved in promoting conservation and in providing wildlife viewing opportunities in urban settings. The important thing now is to convert public interest into governmental and societal action.

**Theme 7: Promoting Research Into Prairie Conservation (Goal 10)**

There has been discussion but little or no action on these proposals. No prairie research committee has yet been struck. The concept of a centre for research in Alberta has been considered but no action has been taken. While range research is going on in a number of centres, this research continues to be oriented primarily towards forage production rather than ecosystem protection.

# PRAIRIE CONSERVATION WORKSHOP

A two day multi-party workshop was held in Lethbridge in June 1994 to expose a range of stakeholders to the results of the assessment and to generate ideas for a revised plan. Participants included PCCC member organizations as well as additional invitees from agricultural, environmental, industry, fish and game, local government, consulting and academic sectors.

The first workshop session focused on the assessment. Participants expressed a high comfort level with the assessment and few errors and omissions were identified. Participants then reviewed each theme area of the old PCAP, identifying where enough has been done and where additional efforts are needed. The results (Table 2) provided the Steering Committee with some clear pointers as to where emphasis needed to be placed in the revised PCAP.

The second workshop session addressed the theme of an Alberta prairie conservation vision for 2000 A.D. There was a high level of consistency in workshop participants' vision, with two key elements repeatedly emphasized:

1. A healthy, sustaining prairie ecosystem where biological diversity is maintained and is secure for the future; and

2. A mainstream societal conservation ethic that is applied in practice to all activities and decisions on the prairies.

Discussing constraints and barriers to achieving the vision generated the following listing:

- Dollars;

- Time (major commitment of time required, time people have to give is limited, time is of the essence, effecting change is a slow process and takes a long time);

- Peoples' will (lack of commitment/trust, conflicting values and interests, us versus them, mentality, frontier mentality);

- Lack of appropriate incentives (government policies, e.g., agricultural subsidies, lack of economic incentives encouraging conservation, costs of conservation are borne unequally);

- Lack of experience/expertise;

- Apathy, not all parties prepared to participate; and

- Poor marketing of conservation/lack of media interest.

Participants then address 'enablers'—assets and strengths that will held in achieving the vision. The following list was generated:

- Still have a representative native landscape and landbase to work from;

- Positive attitudes (society's attitudes becoming more progressive over time, interest and willingness in people working together, commitment within government, industry receptive, long established tradition of stewardship on native rangelands);

Table 2. Prairie Conservation Workshop: where has enough been done and where does more need to be done?

**Theme 1: Identifying remaining prairie and parkland (Goal 1).**
-Need improved accessibility to data.
-Need inventories to be kept current, be appropriately synthesized/analyzed and be available in automated form (CDC/data bases).
-Need to make better use of information that is available.
-Need to fill inventory gaps i.e., ESAs in Central Alberta/more detailed inventories.

**Theme 2: Protecting remaining prairie and parkland ecosystems (Goals 2,3 and 4).**
-Need more emphasis on the broader, holistic ecosystem, i.e., landscape management—avoid island biogeography problem.
-Need more emphasis on private lands. What's the status of habitat on private lands? Availability of tools for land-holders to use.
-Definitional clarity 'protection', 'conservation'.
-Doing reasonably well on public land, importance of native rangelands.

**Theme 3: Protecting threatened and endangered species (Goals 5 and 6).**
-Too much focus on the visible, high profile, 'mega fauna' species. Need balance.
-Need to adopt 'coarse filter' (biodiversity)/habitat/ecosystem) approaches as opposed to 'fine filter' (species specific) management and recovery plans.
-Significant progress made on number of recovery plans.
-Endangered species legislation controversial.
-Uncertainty that we have a good 'handle' on all species.

**Theme 4: Creating an appropriate policy and regulatory environment (Goal 7).**
-Overall, progress have been limited and slow, except in the wetlands area.
-Increased future emphasis needs to be placed on individuals and less on governments (personal ethical decision making, education and stewardship as opposed to legislation, policy and regulation).
-Need mechanisms to effectively address private land.
-Need to resolve outstanding policy conflicts e.g., access.

**Theme 5: Integrating conservation into land use decisions across the whole prairie landscape (Goal 8).**
-New approaches need to be non-threatening to landholders.
-Much more needs to be done in this area.
-Keys are awareness, education, compensation and mitigation.
-Government adoption of integrated resource management is positive.

**Theme 6: Promoting public awareness about the importance of protecting prairie ecosystems (Goal 9).**
-Made significant progress, but this area needs even more emphasis.
-Key are school studies in ecosystems, industry partnerships and extension activities with people on the land (applied focus).
-Need more effective communication with critical audiences (e.g., Special Places 2000).

**Theme 7: Promoting research into prairie conservation (Goal 10).**
-Need to be innovative—seek new possibilities, options and mechanisms to make progress.
-Create the need and research will follow, good decisions are based on good research/information.
-Progress to date limited, research tends to be first victim in times of restraint.
-Opportunities in areas such as integration and consideration, information management and extension (local landholders).

- Concept of conservation widely accepted (sustainable development, appreciation of and desire for native prairie, common goals);

- Commitment to working cooperatively (networks, PCCC, volunteers); and

- Improved decision-making processes (fair, open, public involvement, conservation and protection issues considered).

In the final session of the workshop, participants discussed what the key themes of a revised prairie conservation agenda should be. In terms of content for a new plan, emphasis was placed on:

- Consolidation/integration/availability of information;

- Ecosystem management/biodiversity—focus on protecting the ecosystem as opposed to species;

- Enhancing conservation mechanisms available to landholders e.g., economic incentives, private conservancy;

- Ensuring plan objectives are measurable; and

- Effective communications, extension, awareness, education strategies.

In terms of planning process issues, participants stressed the importance of:

- Buy-in by landholders and industry;

- Involvement of all stakeholders; and

- Local empowerment, especially in implementation.

## OUTLINE ALBERTA PCAP

Armed with the results of both the assessment and the workshop, PCCC Steering Committee members met several times over the summer and early fall to draft the outline of a revised PCAP for Alberta. Members agreed to:

1. Keep verbiage to a minimum; produce a 'bare bones' outline;

2. 'Carry over' significant items of uncompleted business from the first PCAP even where such recommendations are controversial in Alberta e.g., designated protection/endangered species legislation; and

3. Build in the constructive recommendations for revised content arising from the Lethbridge workshop.

The Steering Committee identified several enduring characteristics from the old plan which it felt important to continue, including:

- Focus on the conservation of native prairie species, communities and habitats;

- Commitment to a prairie-wide vision; and

- Encouragement of multi-party partnerships, networking and cooperative approaches.

Several new emphasis were also identified, reflecting changes since the original PCAP was published in 1988 as follows:

- An attempt to broaden the base of support beyond which the original plan received, especially in the agricultural community;

- Community empowerment and local involvement (more 'bottom up' as opposed to "top down" initiatives);

- Shift towards ecosystem management and sustainable development approaches;

- Focus on holistic and landscape approaches, rather than just a narrow species by species approach;

- New awareness of the importance of microfauna;

- Emergence of new information technologies;

- Changing role of government (downsizing, deregulation and privatization); and

- Need to reflect the distinctive requirements of each province.

The vision, principles and goals of the draft Alberta PCAP outline are listed in Table 3. The complete document was reviewed by the PCCC at its October 1994

Table 3. Alberta PCAP: vision, principles and goals.

| | |
|---|---|
| **PCAP 1989-1994 Vision:** | Canadians need to ensure that native prairie, with its wild plants and animals, survives in the west and is conserved for its intrinsic values, from which this and future generations can benefit. |
| **Alberta Vision 1996-2000:** | The biological diversity of native prairie ecosystems in Alberta is conserved for the benefit of current and future generations. |
| **Guiding Principles:** | The main focus of effort over the period 1995-2000 will be directed towards con serving Alberta's prairie ecosystems. |
| | A conservation ethic will be applied to all activities and management decisions on the prairies. |
| | All stakeholders will be involved in the process of achieving the prairie conser vation vision. Stakeholders will work cooperatively and form partnerships to achieve prairie conservation objectives. |
| | Stakeholders will be empowered at a local community level to work towards prairie conservation initiatives, using local knowledge and expertise. |

**Alberta Goals 1996-2000:**

Goal 1    Advance the identification, understanding and use of information about Alberta's prairie ecosystems.

Goal 2    Ensure governments at all levels have in place policies, programs and regulations that favour the con servation of Alberta's native prairie ecosystems.

Goal 3    Adopt land use and management practices across the whole prairie landscape that sustain diverse ecosystems.

Goal 4    Increase awareness of the values and importance of Alberta's native prairie ecosystem.

---

Edmonton meeting following which a formal review by all PCCC member organizations took place. Additional revisions were made and the revised outline tabled for peer review at the 'Sharing the Prairies Workshop'. Current plans call for a more general public review in the spring of 1995 followed by integrating the Alberta PCAP with the initiatives also underway in Saskatchewan and Manitoba to produce a revised prairie wide PCAP, 1996-2000 by December 1995. A chronological summary of the process used in Alberta to draft a revised PCAP is presented in Table 4.

## NEW PLAN, NEW COMMITTEE

Among the three prairie provinces, Alberta had a unique jurisdictional response to the challenge posed by the first PCAP—creation of the large, multi-party PCCC to oversee its implementation.

The PCCC has met about three times annually in rotating centres in prairie and parkland Alberta. Sometimes it holds field trips in association with its business meeting. It publishes an annual report and annually recommends up to three recipients for the government's Alberta Prairie Conservation Awards. Over the years, the PCCC has excelled as a contacts/networking forum and has also had some conspicuous successes in moving the prairie conservation agenda forward. It has also become somewhat institutionalized, has struggled with the time and resourcing commitments that its members can contribute and has generally been eclipsed by more high profile and better resourced strategic initiatives.

Table 4. Process for revising the PCAP in Alberta.

| | | |
|---|---|---|
| **1994** | | |
| JANUARY | | |
| FEBRUARY | | |
| MARCH | | |
| APRIL | Draft assessment of PCAP (PCCC Steering Committee) | |
| MAY | | |
| JUNE | Lethbridge Workshop. Review assessment. Discuss directions for new PCAP | |
| JULY | | |
| AUGUST | PCCC Steering Committee draft outline PCAP based on Assessment and Workshop | |
| SEPTEMBER | | |
| OCTOBER | Review outline at PCCC/PCF meeting (Edmonton) | |
| NOVEMBER | | |
| DECEMBER | Review and feedback by PCF member organizations | |
| | | |
| **1995** | | |
| JANUARY | Revise draft PCAP Outline | |
| FEBRUARY | Review of draft outline at `Sharing the Prairies' workshop | |
| MARCH | Summarize `Sharing the Prairies' feedback | |
| APRIL | | |
| MAY | Public Review | |
| JUNE | | |
| JULY | | |
| AUGUST | | |
| SEPTEMBER | Final revisions/Integration with Manitoba and Saskatchewan | |
| OCTOBER | | |
| NOVEMBER | | |
| DECEMBER | Publish PCAPII | |

In January 1994, members agreed some fine tuning was in order and identified the following strengths and weaknesses of the committee:

Strengths:

- Excellent forum for information exchange and networking;

- Opportunity to build trust, relationships, education, shared experiences, partnerships, etc.;

- Field trips help to ensure the committee stays in touch with real, on the ground issues;

- Provides a focus on subjects and activities relating to prairie conservation;

- Allows for open discussion in a noncontroversial environment;

- Unique in its wide range of representation;

- Members have a breadth of training and expertise; and

- Ability to deal with issues in a flexible way.

Weaknesses:

- Time and resources of all members to devote to PCCC initiatives is limited and becoming more so. Not effective as an implementation committee;

- Lacks clear procedures in dealing with issues. Consensual nature of PCCC's modus operandi makes it difficult for the PCCC to address any controversial issues;

- Persistent uncertainty about the appropriate role and authority of the committee;

- Effective participation on the committee is difficult for members who have not bought into the PCAP;

Table 5. Prairie conservation forum.

| | |
|---|---|
| **DURATION:** | Encourage effective implementation of the PCAP in Alberta and provide an ongoing profile for prairie and parkland conservation initiative. Role has three key elements:<br>1. Networking and Information Exchange<br>2. Steering PCAP Implementation<br>3. Public Awareness and Education |
| **MEMBERSHIP:** | Open door policy. Meetings public. |
| **OPERATIONS:** | Chair elected annually<br>Permanent secretary<br>Steering Committee elected annually<br>Prairie Conservation Issues<br>Sub-Committees |

• Large and varied membership makes committee unwieldy;

• Members operate under various constraints imposed by their professional or agency/organizational affiliation; and

• Lack of frank discussion and information exchange on major policies and initiatives.

It was agreed that a 'new face' should be put on the committee for the new plan. The new, improved Prairie Conservation Forum (PCF) was formally constituted in October 1994. The new committee represents less a fundamental reworking than a fine tuning and revamping of the committee to focus its strengths (Table 5). A 'wide open' membership policy, together with a more conscious focusing on sharing experiences and seeking advice are two key changes.

## CONCLUSION

As a species we are concept junkies and our conspicuous consumerism assures that in the natural resource management field, as in the supermarket, we have an ongoing propensity to sample new products. Integrated resource management replaces multiple use, only to be swept aside by sustainable development, which is replaced by landscape ecology, buried in turn by ecosystem management. Old plans, of course, beget new plans and shining, fresh, and vibrant committees replace the ennui of the chloroform committees of the past. To the extent that such gyrations are mechanical, automatic responses, they are, of course, A BAD THING, but to the extent that they reflect genuine attempts to retain currency and relevancy in a rapidly changing world, they are very much A GOOD THING. At the same time, because change occurs so quickly, the need for common, enduring threads is strong.

Alberta's prairie conservation agenda for the future, and the institutional means of delivering it, builds on our applied experiences, successes and failures over the past five years. The old plan and the old committee required some fine tuning to ensure their continued relevance. In the final analysis, however, enabling institutions, committed individuals and teamwork will be the key to any successes we achieve in the future, as they have been in the past.

# ALBERTA DRAFT PRAIRIE CONSERVATION ACTION PLAN 2

## Lynda Patterson (Session Chair, summarizing reports from Dug Major, Bill Dolan, and Miles Scott-Brown)

*Oldman River Regional Planning Commission, 905 - 4th Ave. S., Lethbridge, Alberta T1J 0P4*

Dug Major, the first of three speakers, provided an outline of the process used to prepare the draft Prairie Conservation Action Plan No. 2. He identified four major events/circumstances that led to the closure of the first Prairie Conservation Action Plan (PCAP), and the initiative toward the second version:

1. The need to extend the 1989-1994 time frame given to PCAP No. 1.;

2. Gaps in PCAP No. 1 were identified by the Prairie Conservation Coordinating Committee (PCCC);

3. Many of the actions resulting from PCAP No. 1 had been completed and needed to be inventoried; and

4. The PCCC had completed an evaluation of the achievement of PCAP No. 1 goals and had identified some issues that required more attention.

To help provide direction on the preparation of PCAP No. 2, the PCCC sponsored a workshop for approximately 50 people representing a wide spectrum of interests. Essentially the purpose of the workshop was to review PCAP No. 1 and to determine "where we are" and "where we are going" with this planning process. Highlights of the input provided by the workshop participants included:

1. The plan needs to be more innovative and requires more research;

2. There should be more emphasis on the whole enviroscape; and

3. There should be more emphasis on private lands, i.e. target more on individual effort as opposed to government.

Preparation of the Prairie Conservation Action Plan is recognized as an evolving process.

The second speaker, Bill Dolan, gave an overview of the contents of PCAP No. 2. He recognized a key guiding principle of PCAP No. 2—that conservation of prairie ecosystems will be accomplished through the cooperation of all stakeholders; "we must work together".

Within the goals and objectives of PCAP No. 2 substantial effort has been made to recognize:

1. The impact of policy and politics;

2. That what is done on the ground is the most important;

3. That public review is essential; and

4. That the full potential of PCAP No. 2 will only be realized through the concerted effort of Alberta, Saskatchewan and Manitoba.

In a very interesting slide presentation Miles Scott-Brown reviewed the changes between PCAP No. 1 and draft PCAP No. 2 and why these changes were made. Some of the key limitations recognized in PCAP No. 1 were its generality and the lack of input from the interest groups representing farming and ranching. Major changes between PCAP No. 1 and PCAP No. 2 include:

1. Recognition of prairie diversity; and

2. An increased emphasis on restoration and conservation.

In presenting PCAP No. 2 it will be essential to:

1. Change people's perspective on what constitutes "prairie";

2. Formulate goals and objectives based on the input of a wide variety of stakeholders and interest groups; and

3. Increase public awareness of the contents of PCAP No. 2.

In the second part of the session, delegates were given the opportunity to discuss:

1. Gaps they may have observed in PCAP No. 2;

2. Opportunities for prairie conservation provided by PCAP No. 2;

3. Building ownership of and support for PCAP No. 2; and

4. The opportunity for PCAP No. 2 to serve as a template for other prairie provinces.

Some of the observations made by delegates included:

1. Government endorsement of and support for PCAP No. 2 will be critical to its success;

2. Implementation of the Plan will be necessary at all levels of agencies and government;

3. More "marketing" of the Plan is required;

4. More presentation of the Plan through the media is essential; and

5. Should priorities be set on the goals of PCAP No. 2?

Session 32 of the "Sharing the Prairies Workshop" gave delegates in attendance a comprehensive introduction to the Alberta Draft Prairie Conservation Action Plan. My thanks to the speakers, Dug Major, Bill Dolan and Miles Scott-Brown and to the participants for their input.

# SASKATCHEWAN EVALUATION OF THE PRAIRIE CONSERVATION ACTION PLAN

## Syd Barber[1] and Greg Riemer[2]

[1]Saskatchewan Environment and Resource Management, 3211 Albert St., Regina, Saskatchewan S4S 5W6
[2]Agricultural Services, Saskatchewan Wetland Conservation Corporation, Rm. 110, 2151 Scarth St., Regina, Saskatchewan S4P 3Z3

The Prairie Conservation Action Plan (PCAP) is a five year (1990-94) blueprint with ten goals to conserve native grassland and maintain the health of the entire prairie ecosystem in the Prairie Provinces. This paper is a brief overview of the Saskatchewan evaluation of the PCAP which was prepared by a committee of government and non-government people representing both the agriculture and environment communities. Committee members who authored reviews of the various goals are:

- Joyce Belcher, Sask. Conservation Data Centre - Goals 1 and 10.

- Laura Lawton and Syd Barber, Saskatchewan Environment and Resource Management (SERM), Policy and Public Involvement and Sustainable Land Management - Goals 2 and 3.

- John Vandall, SERM, Parks and Facilities - Goal 4.

- Dale Hjertaas, SERM, Wildlife - Goals 5 and 6.

- Greg Riemer, Agricultural Services, Saskatchewan Wetland Conservation Corporation (SWCC) - Goals 7 and 8.

- Doug McKell, Saskatchewan Soil Conservation Association - Goal 9.

Final editing was undertaken by Syd Barber and Marlene Robins, SERM Sustainable Land Management and Greg Riemer, SWCC, following an early February, evaluation committee meeting which identified much new information to include in the report. Brenda Oates, also with SERM Sustainable Land Management, assisted extensively with the editing process. The end result is a product that reflects a large measure of consensus among the participants, but not necessarily the view of any one individual, agency or organization.

The following is a generalized assessment of Saskatchewan's progress towards achieving the 10 basic goals in the PCAP:

- Goal 1. Inventory - **little**;

- Goal 2. Protected areas - represent major ecoregions - **moderate**

- Goal 3. Protected areas - represent habitat subregions - **moderate**

- Goal 4. Habitat management and restoration - **moderate**

- Goal 5. Endangered species - protect and enhance - **moderate**

- Goal 6. Endangered species - keep from adding to list - **little**

- Goal 7. Policy & planning - recognize conservation objective - **moderate**

- Goal 8. Private stewardship - encourage - **moderate**

- Goal 9. Education and extension - **moderate**

- Goal 10. Research - **little**

Progress on the actions within these Goals ranged from completed to no meaningful action undertaken. The results of this evaluation have been elaborated on in the main body of the complete report and just highlighted in this paper.

Native prairie habitat inventory and ecological research (Goals 1 and 10) are related and have received a similar low priority during the first half of the decade. There are some notable accomplishments and initiatives, however, including:

a) production of an authoritative, provincial ecological land classification system as depicted by the Ecoregions of Saskatchewan;

b) the establishment of the Conservation Data Centre to act as a clearing house for biological information on native flora and fauna, with particular emphasis on threatened and endangered species;

c) some ecological research sponsored by the Canada-Saskatchewan Agriculture Green Plan Agreement; and

d) the fledgling Prairie Ecosystem Sustainability Study (PECOS) centred around Swift Current, which will conduct an integrated investigation of the ecological, economic and social aspects of sustainable use of that prairie landscape.

More substantial progress has been made establishing and managing "protected areas" to represent, and ensure the conservation of, the full variety of native prairie plants, animals and the natural communities they form (Goals 2, 3 and 4). Among the major accomplishments, Grassland National Park has been established through the acquisition by Parks Canada of approximately 42,000 ha of land, roughly half the area intended for inclusion in the park.

The provincial Wildlife Habitat Protection Act was amended to include an additional 610,000 ha of provincial Crown land within the Mixed Grassland ecoregion. A Land Use Plan was prepared with public consultation for the approximately 100,000 ha Great Sand Hills. Ducks

Unlimited Canada and SWCC have also secured upland and wetland habitat totalling 118,000 ha since 1986, mostly during the 1990's as the primary delivery agent for the North American Waterfowl Management Plan. In addition, vegetation management plans have been prepared and are being implemented in most Provincial Parks within the Prairie Ecozone.

The Protected Area Study conducted by Saskatchewan Environment and Resource Management reveals that only 5% of the Aspen Parkland and Moist Mixed Grassland ecoregions are included in some form of a protected area. The other two Prairie ecoregions - the Mixed Grassland and the Cypress Upland - are represented by 15% and 19% protected area, respectively.

Much energy has been expended on direct work with endangered, threatened and vulnerable species, with significant results (Goals 5 and 6). Recovery plans have been prepared, and are being implemented, for all prairie animal species listed as threatened or endangered by the Committee on the Status of Endangered Wildlife in Canada (COSEWIC). The Swift Fox is being introduced with promising results. Unfortunately, wild plant and animal species continue to be added to the COSEWIC list, and there is grave concern for the deteriorating status of the burrowing owl. There is increasing recognition that the key to keeping wild species off this endangered species list is conservation of their habitat.

Government policy and planning (Goals 7 and 8) is increasingly sympathetic to natural resource conservation objectives, although this is often incidental to economic policy change. Policy reform is being strongly influenced by international events such as the General Agreement on Tariff and Trade (GATT) and the Biodiversity Convention signed at Rio. National and provincial Round Tables on the Environment and the Economy, established in the wake of the United Nations Bruntland Commission, have also been influential. Further policy refinement is required. One example of the significant change taking place, however, is the abolition of the long standing Canadian Wheat Board Quota system, long thought to be a negative influence on the conservation of native habitats.

The private stewardship of natural areas advocated by Goal 8 continues to be advanced primarily by non-government organizations, but with significant effect. The Saskatchewan Wildlife Federation reports they have 149,000 ha of private land enrolled in their voluntary Wildlife Tomorrow program, including 60,000 ha recruited since 1989. Good management of native rangelands is the centrepiece of the Grazing and Pasture Technology Program run by the Saskatchewan Stock Growers, with financial assistance from the Canada - Saskatchewan Agriculture Green Plan Agreement. Ducks Unlimited Canada, Nature Saskatchewan, and the Saskatchewan Soil Conservation Association all actively promote conservation of wildlife and their habitats by private land owners and managers.

Moderate progress has also been made during the last five years with respect to education (Goal 9), but many people in the conservation community feel this and the private stewardship area (Goal 8) have the greatest need and potential for expansion. A major accomplishment during the last decade has been the integration of Project WILD into the Saskatchewan school curriculum. Some 9,000 teachers have now been trained in the use of this supplementary, but officially recognized, material on nature. A Project SOILS module has recently been developed in the province and added to the Project WILD package.

**The PCAP Evaluation Committee has concluded the plan has had a positive but small effect on Saskatchewan conservation events during its tenure.** Little of the considerable progress relative to the plan's goals, can be attributed to the existence of the plan. This is partly due to lack of broad involvement in the preparation of the document, especially from the agriculture community. Other contributing factors were the lack of appropriated resources and assigned responsibilities. The PCAP has the potential to be a more effective catalytic and coordinating mechanism in future, if the historic shortcomings are recognized and corrected. However, there are many closely related initiatives, such as the Canadian Biodiversity Strategy, that must be taken into consideration when deciding the future of the Prairie Conservation Action Plan.

# MANITOBA SUMMARY OF THE PRAIRIE CONSERVATION ACTION PLAN

## Barry Neil Verbiwski

*Manitoba Department of Natural Resources, Box 24, 1495 St. James St., Winnipeg, Manitoba R3H 0W9*

This Plan did not have the profile of the North American Waterfowl Management Plan (NAWMP). Yet, this plan was more critical than the NAWMP particularly as it related to tall grass prairie. Imagine, historically there was some 600,000 hectares in Manitoba. It is now estimated that there is perhaps only 1% (6,000 hectares) remaining. How much more critical a habitat issue could there be in Manitoba?

The assessment was undertaken by a committee consisting of Manitoba Natural Resources (DNR), Conservation Data Centre (CDC), Manitoba Habitat Heritage Corporation, Environment Canada (CWS), Ducks Unlimited (DU) and Delta Waterfowl and Wetland Research Station. The Manitoba Naturalists' Society (MNS) also provided comments on an early draft of the assessment.

**GOAL 1** - Identify, inventory tall-grass prairie, aspen parkland and mixed grass prairie eco-regions, make this inventory information available for distribution and conduct seminars about these eco-regions.

The MNS began to focus on tall-grass prairie in 1987 by conducting the first systematic survey to identify remnant sites of prairie within its' historical range. Between 1987 and 1994 over 720,000 hectares of land was surveyed and one hundred and twenty individual sites totalling 4,800 hectares of tall-grass prairie were located. Some of this was loacted outside the historic range as identified in the Prairie Conservation Action Plan (PCAP). Systematic inventories were also completed on 53 of the sites. Most of the sites are located in southeast Manitoba, nine others in Winnipeg and four other sites within two Wildlife Management Areas (WMAs) and a Prairie Farm Rehabilitation Administration (PFRA) pasture.

Surveys for mixed-grass prairie have also been completed on seven townships of land. Approximately 4,500 hectares of mixed-grass prairie were located in three areas.

The aspen parkland eco-region was not surveyed. Using the natural lands classification, there is an estimated 46,472 square kilometres (464,720 hectares) within the Aspen-Oak, Western Upland and Pembina-Tiger Hills natural land regions.

**GOAL 2** - Protect at least one large representative area in each of the four major eco-regions.

There are 38 wildlife management areas in the aspen parkland eco-region encompassing 616 square kilometres or 61,606 hectares of land. These are secured areas but not entirely protected from developments like mineral extraction.

In addition to the WMAs, there are several PFRA pastures, twelve Provincial Parks, a Military base and two Provincial Forests. All these are Crown lands, secured for various purposes but not protected from developments or unusual habitat restoration techniques, like military training exercises.

The historic range and areas immediately adjacent the historic range of tall grass prairie were surveyed and approximately 4,500 hectares was identified. Of this total, 1,953 hectares have been purchased and leased and a tall grass prairie preserve established. Overall, 49% of the total tall grass prairie area known in Manitoba has been secured.

Most of the sites of fescue prairie known are located within the Riding Mountain National Park and are protected against mineral and oil and gas exploration and development.

Seven townships (161,280 hectares) were surveyed in the mixed grass eco-region of southwestern Manitboa. Approximately 4,500 hectares were inventoried and of this 192 hectares purchased and 65 hectares leased.

**GOAL 3** - Establish a system of protected native prairie ecosystems and where possible connecting corridors. This system should include representative samples of each habitat subregion.

The foundation to allow this to happen is now mostly in place through such key documents as Provincial Land Use Policies, bio-physical descriptions of Natural Land Regions, Provincial Parks Act, Systems Plans for WMAs, PFRA pastures, and the Sustainable Development Strategy for Natural Lands and Special Places. All these are required to support the concept of connecting corridors and the development of working plans of action.

Over 42,000 hectares of aspen parkland has been secured through WMAs and Provincial Parks. Aspen parkland is also found within other natural land regions but the amount of aspen parkland remaining is not known. Not included are areas of aspen parkland that have been secured through the NAWMP, Habitat Enhancement Land Use Program, DU and PFRA pastures.

The tax assessment notices now identify "conservation lands" from the improved (agriculture) lands. Landowners now know which lands are taxed at varying rates and the amount of conservation land that has been classified.

**GOAL 4** - Protect threatened ecosystems and habitats by preparing and implementing habitat management and restoration plans.

There has been a concerted effort towards tall grass prairie. Unfortunately little is known about mixed grass and fescue prairie with the exception of three or four areas.

In many instances various agencies are rehabilitating areas of prairie. As well, management plans have been implemented at Oak Hammock Marsh and Lake Francis WMAs, Beaudry Provincial Park and one PFRA pasture. Management by controlled burns is ongoing within the Tall Grass Prairie Preserve.

Rehabilitation of native prairie is an extremely expensive process. In one instance, the Department of Highways has rehabilitated a site between the median of a major provincial highway but with limited success to this point. However the important thing is not that Highways undertook the rehabilitation project but more importantly it acknowledged the significance of native prairie. In most instances, proponents of development are requested to avoid sites of native prairie first, if this is not possible then they are required to mitigate for the loss. Developers themselves are soliciting ways to maintain, improve and mitigate for losses. Manitoba is also attempting to incorporate the concept of "zero net loss" of prairie into development plans.

**GOAL 5** - protect and enhance the population of prairie species designated nationally or provincially as vulnerable, threatened, endangered or extirpated, by implementing recovery and management plans.

A "Species at Risk" Policy and Guidelines have been developed. As well, through participation at COSEWIC and RENEW, Manitoba established an "Endangered Species Advisory Board" with representatives from the department, non government interests including aboriginal people and the academic community. The Board advises the Minister of Natural Resources but it has no authority to designate funding towards any particular study or requirement.

Manitoba proclaimed an "Endangered Species Act" and has also developed recovery plans for some species like the peregrine falcon. In other instances there isn't enough contiguous blocks of prairie remaining to support a recovery program for plains bison and antelope. Consequently the focus is towards threatened or endangered species rather than extirpated species.

**GOAL 6** - Ensure that no additional species becomes threatened, endangered or extirpated.

Participation at forums, workshops and membership on national and international committees greatly improves the chances that species will not become threatened and/or extirpated. As well, the CDC will increase our capability to monitor faunal and flora species.

Inventories are being conducted to evaluate staging areas for shorebirds. One area, the Shoal Lakes, is being designated as a "Western Hemisphere Shorebird Reserve.

**GOAL 7** - Encourage governments to more explicitly incorporate conservation of native prairie in their programs.

Several changes have taken place which would now make the goals more attainable. Some other changes like those influenced by the General Agreement on Tariffs and Trade (GATT) will also have positive influences towards attaining a higher degree of accomplishment.

Through the Round Table Discussions on the Environment and Economy, several documents were developed through public consultation which have been used to revise and develop policy. In particular, the revised Provincial Land Use Policies recognizes tall-grass prairie and areas with unique features. As well, the description of the natural land regions will provide a base to work and revise the map of the eco-regions.

The CDC will incorporate information on endangered, threatened and vulnerable species and habitats. At the local/regional level, through the integrated resource management process, all resource disciplines are represented. A "Sustainable Development Act" has also been proposed to cover all sectors of society. Through Manitoba's involvement in the development of the "Biodiversity Strategy for Canada" ecosystem management and management for biodiversity have become the common words. As well, the draft Species at Risk Policy addresses implementation of species recovery programs and land management as it relates to endangered species.

Local committees, like the Conservation Districts and the Soil and Water Conservation Associations are getting the message to local government councils and landowners at the farm gate about endangered wildlife and habitats.

**GOAL 8** - Encourage balanced use of private lands that allows sustained use of the land while maintaining and enhancing the native biological diversity of the prairies.

Through GATT, changes in agriculture policy will remove or reduce export subsidies and there will be less incentive to convert native prairie and other natural areas to agriculture. This has the potential to profoundly affect native prairie and natural areas. Should conservation incentives be available they would substitute for some of the lost subsidies making landowners more receptive to easements to protect natural habitats.

There is a great deal of pressure internationally for environmental sustainability and biodiversity. This is being reflected in some programs like agriculture. A series of agriculture use guidelines have been recently developed while promoting agriculture developments now slso must consider the environmental consequences.

**GOAL 9** - Promote awareness for the values and importance of prairie wildlife and wild places.

Interpretive programs are a major component of provincial parks, Oak Hammock Marsh Conservation Centre, Fort Whyte and the Living Prairie Museum. These programs encourage conservation, restoration, management and enhancement of prairie habitats and wild places.

There are a few schools, mostly aboriginal that have wildlife or natural life components in their education programs. These are supported through the Native Education Branch of the Department of Education and the Manitoba Indian Cultural Education Centre. One "Regional Composite School" at Swan River, has a full course in environmental studies. Some other materials have been approved as curriculum for middle years science and social studies modules titled "The Living Soil." Other resource material have also been produced and made available for distribution like "The Tall-Grass Prairie Handbook and Curriculum Guide."

**GOAL 10** - Promote research relevant to prairie conservation.

The centre did not materialize however CWS is attempting to form a prairie based management group for specific species that will include government and non government agencies.

## PCAP SUMMARY

Manitoba has achieved much success in some areas of the plan particularly where it relates to tall grass prairie. While we have fallen short in achieving some actions and goals there now is a solid foundation to allow the work to continue regardless if there is a second PCAP.

Government sought the advise of the people about the environment and economy through a questionnaire and town hall type workshops and discussions known as the Manitoba Round Table on the Environment and Economy. From this process emanated several core documents on the land, water, forests, special places etc. It has been through these documents, that policy and programs have been refocused. Integrated resource management decision making became the standard operating procedure for DNR. This concept of involving people is largely what PCAP is about, bringing people and views together. This has certainly been the case in Manitoba. For example, the Tall Grass Prairie Preserve would not be, if there had not been a common goal and vision shared to work towards this common goal by the many non-government and government agencies including the Local Government District of Staurtburn.

While PCAP itself did not change policy it did bring a focus to the status of the prairie which has become reflected in policy. The revised Provincial Land Use Policies, Manitoba Regulation 184/94 intended to promote sustainable development, recognize this. The policy states that habitats and lands "..in danger of becoming scarce.. like the tall-grass prairie are significant natural features". The policies embody critical elements of PCAP and will have tremendous benefit to the future of the tall grass prairie eco-region and the other natural regions.

Much work still needs to be undertaken: surveys, inventories of sites, developing new partnerships and relationships, communicating and extension of services through workshops and demonstrations, securing critical areas, identifying research requirements, influencing policy and guidelines and the list goes continues. These seem to be staggering objectives. But there needs to be some order to the work ahead.

Since the inception of PCAP many things have changed, most importantly the attitude of people. Seemingly people, regardless of their agendas are more receptive to working together towards common goals. It takes a great deal of energy to be negative and critical. A solid foundation is in place through public consultation by the round Table discussions, revised Provincial Land Use Policies, the description of Natural Places, the Biodiversity Strategy for Canada and the network of agencies and an ever vigilant public, all committed towards working together. All these will be necessary for the next five years.

The principles upon which PCAP was founded, biodiversity gives support to the continuation of the work to achieve the actions of PCAP in our everyday work activities as managers, researchers, students, policy makers and landowners.

## GAPS IN MANITOBA PCAP 1988 to 1994

1. Surveys are required to identify other sites of tallgrass prairie, mixed grass prairie and aspen parkland on private land but also WMAs, PFRA Pastures, Provincial Parks and federal Crown lands. As well inventories are required in other areas of the province like the Swan River Valley for fescue prairie.

2. Management plans need to be developed for WMAs, Provincial Parks and completed for the Shilo Military Base.

3. Steps are required to secure other lands when they become available.

4. The shortage of native grass seed to supply the demand needs to be addressed.

5. Status reports are required for culivers' root and great plains ladies tresses. As well, additional shorebird inventories are required.

6. A system is also required to bridge the Nature Conservancy's CDC ranking system for rare plants and animals with COSEWIC.

7. Communication needs to be strengthened between environmental agencies and non environmental agencies like industry including agriculture.

8. Municipal governments still remain outside a formal process for review of activities unless under extreme circumstances where a substantial amount of Crown land is involved whcih is likely to be impacted by a development.

9. The Regional Planning Commissions were not established. This commission would have provide the opportunity for landowners and local government representatives to be more involved in developing recommendations through an integrated decision making process.

10. Incentives need to be developed for landowners and Rural Municipal governments who retain native lands.

11. Landowners must become a fundamental component of any committee and management team involving private and Crown land.

12. First Nations people must also become partners as they can bring a new perspective to programs aimed at maintaining and enhancing the natural biological diversity of the prairies.

13. There are a number of agencies delivering a variety of programs which may be confusing to landowners. It has become extremely difficult to keep pace with the many initiatives. These programs need to be guided by an overall strategy.

14. There still remains a great deal of work to be done to develop a university and college course in prairie conservation and wildlife and wildland interpretation..

15. A prairie-wide interprovincial committee is required to direct and encourage applied research on native prairie.

# PRAIRIE CONSERVATION ACTION PLAN: CONCLUDING SUMMARY

## Syd Barber,
*Theme Reporter*

*(Note: The following is not a verbatim transcript of the presentation made, simply an approximation of it, based on the overheads presented at that time.)*

I am going to summarize the Prairie Conservation Action Plan (PCAP) discussions at this Workshop in the context of the past, present and future.

I have prepared a one page summary of the three provincial PCAP evaluations that have been done (see below). This is my own attempt to capture all this work on one page, and to bridge the somewhat different evaluation approaches taken by the different provinces. It is intended to show some general patterns, and should not be interpreted too narrowly. The numerical ratings shown for Alberta are an average of those which appear in their "report card" on the PCAP.

Table 1 suggests that significant progress has been made towards the goals and objectives outlined in the PCAP, but that a lot remains to be done. The predominant progress rating is Moderate (M). Saskatchewan and Manitoba have concluded that much of its progress has been incidental to the existence of the PCAP. It is important progress nonetheless, and the Plan has provided some stimulation and an important "yardstick" of measure.

Looking more closely at the evaluation summary reveals both some common trends and significant differences among the three provinces. Alberta and Manitoba have made more progress on inventory (Goal 1) than has Saskatchewan, but all three provinces believe there has been little advance on the research front (Goal 10). The three provinces also uniformly rate progress on protected area establishment (Goals 2-5) and policy reform (Goal 7) as moderate. There is wide variation in perceived progress on the other two themes, endangered species conservation (Goals 5 and 6), and education and extension (Goals 8 and 9).

The evaluations encompass the past five years and tell us, generally, where we are at present. Now, what about the future? Is there a niche for the Prairie Conservation Action Plan?

The PCAP wrap-up workshop this morning concluded that, yes, there is a continued niche for this plan. One of its greatest strengths is that it can provide an action oriented, ecosystem framework for implementation of initiatives such as the Biodiversity Strategy. It is complementary to the forest ecosystem management plans developing on the Prairies and can serve to elevate the profile of grassland conservation, something that tends to get overlooked relative to other conservation issues.

There were mixed views expressed here this week on how actively any future PCAP should attempt to coordinate prairie conservation work within a province. This uncertainty spills over into the question of what level of generalization or specificity a new plan should be written at. One view holds that any new plan should be at a high level of generalization (i.e., principles), consistent with a general guide for loose coordination of related activity. Another view is that the Plan should have quantitative goals, identified priorities and possibly even assigned responsibilities.

The level of specificity issue extends to what kind of a Prairie-wide Plan could be constructed, and how that would be done. There was a consensus that each province would have to build their plan "from the ground up", through a lot of public and government consultation in each jurisdiction. The provincial components could then be bridged with a meaningful Prairie document, analogous to how the North American Waterfowl Management Plan evolved here.

Prairie Environment Ministers have agreed to work towards preparation of a new PCAP by the end of calender 1995, subject to the just-completed evaluation. Alberta is in the vanguard, having tentatively decided to go ahead with a new PCAP for the province, at least, and having produced a draft of that document. Manitoba and Saskatchewan have yet to fully reflect on the evaluation findings and decide on the cost-effectiveness of participating in a new PCAP. Discussions at this Workshop will assist deliberations in those provinces.

The three provincial evaluations combined with the draft, new, Alberta version of PCAP, serve to illustrate the future priorities in prairie conservation, whether a new Plan is devised or not. The first of three, broadly defined, priority area is information acquisition and extension. This is roughly equivalent to Goals 1, 8, 9 and 10 of the old Plan. The draft Alberta document takes definition of this area one step further, presenting a new Goal 1 revolving around inventory, research and data management. Their new Goal 4 is concerned with information extension, including the promotion of private stewardship with private land owners and managers, and work within the formal education system.

There is consensus that policy reform remains vital to the advance of prairie conservation, as reflected by the fact it is Goal 2 in the draft, new PCAP for Alberta. There is significant positive change in the policy arena now as some long standing, conservation negative, agricultural policies are being changed or discontinued. More remains to be done in reforming existing policy, and new policy is needed to address some conservation issues.

Finally, "protected areas" remain relevant to prairie conservation, although the traditional concept is changing. Alberta recognizes the continued relevance of this approach to conservation, by defining Goal 3 of the draft Alberta PCAP in these terms. They have encompassed the old PCAP goals 2, 3 and 4 in this one new theme.

The prevailing view seems to be that "protected areas" should, in future, be approached from a broader viewpoint in terms of ecological, economic and social criteria. Privately owned and managed lands should be eligible for recognition as protected areas, depending on the

Table 1. PCAP - 3 provincial evaluation.

| Goal | Alberta | Saskatchewan | Manitoba |
|------|---------|--------------|----------|
| 1 | 6.7 (H) | L | M |
| Protected Areas | | | |
| 2 | 4.3 (M) | M | M |
| 3 | 5.8 (M) | M | L |
| 4 | 6.0 (M) | M | M |
| Endangered species | | | |
| 5 | 6.6 (H) | M | H |
| 6 | 5.2 (M) | L | H |
| Policy | | | |
| 7 | 4.5 (M) | M | M |
| Ed. + Ext. | | | |
| 8 | 3.7 (L) | M | M |
| Ed.+ Ext. | | | |
| 9 | 6.2 (H) | M | M |
| Research | | | |
| 10 | 1.3 (L) | L | L |

nature of that management. Also, economic use of the land for other purposes (eg. cattle grazing) should not automatically disqualify the area as a protected area. We have to start looking beyond land uses to the ecology of the landscape and making judgements based on those more fundamental criteria. Gap analyses should be conducted to determine the bio-geographic priorities for augmenting a network of secure natural areas.

# 4.0  ECOSYSTEM MANAGEMENT

# SUSTAINABLE AGRICULTURE AND ECOSYSTEM MANAGEMENT

## Rod K. Heitschmidt

*Fort Keogh Livestock and Range Research Laboratory, USDA-ARS, Miles City, Montana 59301*

## INTRODUCTION

Sustainable agriculture and ecosystem management are subjects of great interest and lively debate in many segments of the world's society. These debates stem largely from differing viewpoints as to what is sustainable agriculture (USDA 1980; Lowrance *et al.* 1986; Dover and Talbot 1987; Keeney 1989; Science Council of Canada 1992; Crews *et al.* 1991; Lehman *et al.* 1993) and what is ecosystem management (Grumbine 1994; Glenn 1995). As such, no concise universally acceptable definitions of either sustainable agriculture or ecosystem management have yet emerged. This is in part because both of these terms are more often viewed as management philosophies rather than methods of operation (MacRae *et al.* 1993) and as such, acceptance or rejection of their definition are linked closely to human value systems (Clark and Weise 1993; Stone 1993). But regardless of their precise definitions, most agriculturalists agree that the concepts of sustainable agriculture and ecosystem management are of paramount importance to the sustainability of our biosphere and its ever increasing human population.

The broad objective of this paper is to merge the concepts of sustainable agriculture and ecosystem management in such a way so as to expedite the development of sustainable agriculture systems. I believe the ecosystem concept is fundamental to understanding what agriculture generally and sustainable agriculture specifically are all about. Thus, I shall sequentially: 1) review the fundamentals of the ecosystem concept; 2) relate these to the sustainability of currently accepted agricultural practices; and then 3) close by presenting a challenge to all "ecosystem managers."

## THE ECOSYSTEM CONCEPT

An ecosystem can be defined as simply an assemblage of organisms and their associated chemical and physical environment (Briske and Heitschmidt 1991). As such, an ecosystem can be anything from a test tube of bacteria to our entire biosphere. But regardless of the ecosystem of interest, the structural organization of all ecosystems can be described as consisting of four components; one non-living and three living. Basically, the abiotic (i.e., non-living) component defines the chemical and physical environment of the biotic (i.e., living) component which is composed of producers, consumers, and decomposers. Producers are organisms that capture solar energy (i.e., green plants), consumers are organisms that obtain their energy by consuming other organisms (i.e., animals), and decomposers are the final or last consumers of organic matter (i.e., primarily bacteria and fungi).

The integrity of an ecosystem is dependent on: 1) the efficient capture of solar energy and its subsequent flow through the system; and 2) the efficient cycling of the raw materials required to capture and process solar energy. Food chains are energy processing pathways that determine the pattern of energy flow through an ecosystem. Food chains impact ecological efficiencies in accordance with the first two laws of thermodynamics. In their simplest form, these laws state that although energy can be transformed from one form to another, it can never be created nor destroyed nor can any transformation be 100% efficient. The impact of these laws on energy flow through an ecosystem is that they dictate that the amount of energy that will flow through an ecosystem is set by the primary producers, and that a portion of this energy, usually greater than 90%, will be lost each time the energy is transferred from one trophic level to another.

The second indispensable function performed by ecosystems is the cycling of nutrients. Nutrients are the abiotic raw materials required by organisms to capture and process solar energy. The cycle revolves around the assimilation of nutrients by the primary producers followed by the sequential reduction of complex organic compounds by consumers to simpler, less complex forms.

### The Ecosystem Concept and Sustainable Agriculture

Agriculture is traditionally defined as the business of producing food and fiber. But a basic understanding of the structure and function of ecosystems reveals that agriculture can be defined also as the business of managing ecosystems to capture solar energy and transfer it to people for their use. It can be reasoned then that success in agriculture is closely linked to the employment of ecosystem management tactics that either enhance: 1) the efficiency that solar energy is captured; and/or 2) the efficiency that captured solar energy is harvested; and/or 3) the efficiency that harvested solar energy is assimilated.

Examples of management practices attempting to improve the efficiency that solar energy is captured, harvested, and assimilated are numerous. For example, irrigation, fertilization, and the planting of hybrid seeds are common tactics utilized to enhance efficiency of solar energy capture. Two examples of tactics used to improve the efficiency whereby captured solar energy is harvested are the use of insecticides and livestock grazing of post-harvest residue. The most common factor affecting assimilation efficiencies is quality of foodstuff. In fact, food quality can be defined relative to its effect on assimilation efficiencies in that high and low quality foods are those that result in high and low net energy gains to consuming organisms.

An understanding of how ecosystems function also provides a means for defining sustainable agriculture. For example, based upon the ecosystem concept, sustainable agriculture might be broadly defined as ecologically sound agriculture or narrowly defined as eternal agriculture, that is, agriculture that can be practiced continually for eternity.

## Ecological and Economic Risks

Current agricultural technology carries with it some ecological and economic risks. These risks are revealed in the data presented in Table 1 which show that although use of fertilizers, etc. (i.e., fossil fuels) will increase crop yields, the "cost" for this yield increase is a reduction in ecological efficiencies. Thus, risks in agriculture can be attributed in part to a historical perspective that agriculture's continued success (i.e., sustainability) is tied to developing the technology needed to "control" nature as opposed to "living with" nature. Because the integrity of natural ecosystems is dependent on the efficient capture and processing of solar energy, ecosystem control strategies that alter natural flows of energy necessarily require large inputs of exogenous energy. Risks accompany these control strategies because of future uncertainties about: 1) the availability of cheap sources of exogenous energy (e.g., fossil fuels); and 2) the potential disruption of critical life

supporting ecological systems due to the continued generation of control strategy by-products (i.e., pollutants).

Central to the sustainability debate are the omnipotent technology and ecological constraint hypotheses. The omnipotent technology hypothesis embraces the fundamental concept that resource depletion (e.g., fossil fuels) automatically sets into motion a series of economic forces that alleviate the effects of depletion on society as a whole (Cleveland 1987). On the other hand, the omnipotent ecological constraint hypothesis (Heitschmidt 1991) is the underlying hypothesis supporting biophysical economic theory. Biophysical economics differ from standard economics in that they attempt to more fully factor the role of natural resources into the economic process (Pearce 1987). The focus is on merging ecology and economics so as to ensure that what is economically sound on the short-term is ecologically sound on the long-term. In this sense, it is important we recognize that economics is simply a measure of the intensity of society's beliefs rather than a measure of the merits of those beliefs (Sagoff 1981). As such, some argue that "Economics can no longer afford to ignore, downplay or misrepresent the role of natural resources in the economic process. In the final analysis, natural resource quality sets broad but distinct limits on what is and what is not economically possible. Ignoring such limits leads to the euphoric delusion that the only limits to economic expansion exists in our own minds" (Cleveland 1987).

## Forms of Sustainable Agriculture

These economic-ecological debates are central to the development of agricultural management strategies that are both ecologically and economically sustainable. Surely the results of the study presented in Table 1 provides some motivating interest for society to examine the general direction of agriculture research. Our industry's heavy reliance on cheap fossil fuels is obvious and currently quite profitable. But is it the way of the future, and if not, what technology are we developing to meet this challenge? If we accept the premise that sustainable agriculture is eternal agriculture, i.e., agriculture that can be practiced forever, then what forms of agriculture might we consider sustainable?

Currently, there are three forms of agriculture that can be considered sustainable: 1) organic gardening; 2) non-mechanized silvaculture; and 3) grazing of indigenous rangelands. This is so because none of these forms are dependent on fossil fuels. Of particular interest is the much maligned idea that grazing of indigenous rangelands is a form of sustainable agriculture. The fundamental characteristic of sustainable animal agriculture systems must be that animals act as "energy brokers", that is, they convert low quality human feedstuff (e.g., corn stalks, spoiled grains, waste products, etc.) into high quality human feedstuff (e.g., meat, milk, eggs, etc.). Thus, livestock grazing of indigenous grasslands is fully sustainable in many regions of the world where no cultural energy inputs are required to maintain a productive herd of animals. Rangeland agriculture is grazing, and when properly managed, rangeland agriculture is fully sustainable, having gone on long before the discovery of fossil fuels and will, without doubt, go on long after the depletion of fossil fuels.

## THE CHALLENGE

Any discussion concerning the sustainability of animal agriculture would be shallow and incomplete without some consideration given to the sustainability of the human race. From an ecological perspective, humans are omnivorous animals that most often occupy either the second (herbivorous) or third (carnivorous) trophic level of food chains. Occupation of trophic levels greater than the second is in many instances a luxury afforded to only a privileged few, that being those living in an environment where human food demand is well below supply. However, when human food demand begins to exceed supply, the Laws of Thermodynamics dictate that humans occupy the second trophic level to the maximum extent possible. In such instances, the role

of animal agriculture is relegated to that of "energy broker" as discussed above. But, if human populations do not voluntarily come into equilibrium with their food supply, mass starvation will occur in accordance with the Laws of Thermodynamics. Thus, the long-term health of agriculture is dependent first and foremost on the long-term health of our human population. The ecological ills of our biosphere are largely the result of one animal's activities, that being human beings.

But in the end, the issue of sustainable agriculture must go beyond the idea that it is eternal agriculture because without the use of fossil fuels, it is not possible for agriculturalists to feed and clothe the world's human population. As shown in Table 1, fossil fuel technology is a major reason that agriculturalists can produce an abundance of food and fiber. So what is the issue of sustainable agriculture all about? It is about the issue of how we can maintain high yields of agricultural products while maintaining high levels of ecological efficiencies. The challenge to ecosystem managers, agricultural scientists, etc. is to develop the technology that will allow us to maintain and/or increase product yields while increasing ecological efficiencies.

## ACKNOWLEDGMENTS

This research was conducted under a cooperative agreement between USDA-ARS and the Montana Agric. Exp. Sta. and is published as contribution J-3009 from the Montana Agric. Exp. Sta. Mention of a proprietary

Table 1. Energy output/cultural energy input ratios for corn production systems in Mexico (manpower only) and the United States (conventional)[a]

| Item | Management system | |
| --- | --- | --- |
| | Mexico | United States |
| | ——————(kcal/ha)—————— | |
| A. Cultural energy inputs | 553,678 | 8,390,750 |
| | ——————(kg/ha)—————— | |
| B. Grain yield | | |
|   1. Weight | 1,944 | 7,000 |
| | ——————(kcal/ha)—————— | |
|   2. Energy | 6,901,200 | 24,500,000 |
| C. Energy output:input | 12.5 | 2.9 |

[a]Pimentel 1984..

product does not constitute a guarantee or warranty of the product by USDA, Montana Agric. Exp. Sta., or the author and does not imply its approval to the exclusion of other products that may also be suitable. USDA-Agricultural Research Service, Northern Plains Area, is an equal opportunity/affirmative action employer and all agency services are available without discrimination.

## LITERATURE CITED

Briske, D.D., and R.K. Heitschmidt. 1991. An ecological perspective. Pp. 11-26 *In* Grazing management an ecological perspective (R.K. Heitschmidt and J.W. Stuth, eds.). Timber Press, Inc., Portland, Oregon.

Clark, E.A., and S.F. Weise. 1993. A forage-based vision of sustainable agriculture. Pp. 95-110 *In* Agriculture research in the Northeastern United States: Critical review and future perspectives. Agrononomy Society of America, Madison, Wisconsin.

Cleveland, C.J. 1987. Biophysical economics: historical perspective and current research trends. Ecological Modelling 38: 47-73.

Crews, T., C. Mohler, and A. Power. 1991. Energetics and ecosystem integrity: The defining principles of sustainable agriculture. American Journal of Alternative Agriculture 6(3): 146-149.

Dover, M., and L. Talbot. 1987. To feed the earth: Agroecology for sustainable development. World Resources Institute.

Glenn, D. 1995. Viewpoint: Ecosystem management: Voices of reason and common sense. Rangelands 17: 20-22.

Grumbine, R.E. 1994. "What is ecosystem management?" Conservation of Biology Journal 8: 27-38.

Heitschmidt, R.K. 1991. Ecology, economics and ethics in range management. Proceedings Fourth International Rangeland Congress 2: 927-932.

Keeney, D.R. 1989. Toward a sustainable agriculture: need for clarification of concepts and terminology. American Journal of Alternative Agriculture 4: 101-105.

Lehman, H., E.A. Clark, and S.F. Weise. 1993. Clarifying the definition of sustainable agriculture. Journal of Agricultural and Environmental Ethics 6: 127-143.

Lowrance, R., P.F. Hendrix, and E.P. Odum. 1986. A hierarchical approach to sustainable agriculture. American Journal Alternative Agriculture 1: 169-173.

MacRae, R.J., J. Henning, and S.B. Hill. 1993. Strategies to overcome barriers to the development of sustainable agriculture in Canada: The role of agribusiness. Journal of Agricultural and Environmental Ethics 6: 21-81.

Pearce, D. 1987. Economic values and the natural environment. Discussion paper in economics No. 87-08. Department of Economics, University College, London.

Pimentel, D. 1984. Energy flow in agroecosystem. Pp. 121-132 *In* Agricultural ecosystems unifying concepts (R. Lowrance, B. Stinner and G. House, eds.). John Wiley and Sons, New York, New York.

Sagoff, M. 1981. Economic theory and environmental law. Michigan Law Review 79: 1393-1419.

Science Council of Canada. 1992. Sustainable agriculture: The research challenge. Report 43, July, Science Council of Canada, Ottawa, Ontario.

Stone, C. 1993. "The gnat is older than man." Princeton University Press, Princeton, New Jersey.

United States Department of Agriculture. 1980. Report and Recommendations on Organic Farming. U.S. Government Printing Office, Washington, DC.

# ECOSYSTEMS THEN AND NOW: A HISTORICAL-ECOLOGICAL APPROACH TO ECOSYSTEM MANAGEMENT

## Charles E. Kay

*Department of Political Science, Utah State University, Logan, UT 84322-0705.*

## INTRODUCTION

Before ecosystem management can be implemented or ecological integrity preserved, long-term ecosystem states and processes must first be quantified. For as Aldo Leopold noted over 40 years ago, "if we are serious about restoring (or maintaining) ecosystem health and ecological integrity, then we must first know what the land was like to begin with" (Covington and Moore 1994). Unless we know what factors structured ecosystems in historic and pre-Columbian times, we can not predict how those systems will respond to modern management. Moreover, we also have to answer the age-old question of whether food (resources) or predation structured pre-Columbian ecosystems. Without a window to the past as a guide to where we might be going, it is impossible to institute meaningful ecosystem management. Historical journal observations, archaeological evidence, repeat photographs, and data on current ecosystem states and processes can be used to determine what factors structured ecosystems in earlier times.

## HISTORICAL OBSERVATIONS

Some researchers have used selected quotes from historical journals as evidence that certain species, primarily ungulates and large predators, were or were not abundant during the late 1700's and early 1800's (e.g. Nelson 1967, 1969a, 1969b, 1970, 1972, 1973; Byrne 1968; Spalding 1990, 1992). With selective quotations, however, there is always a question of whether or not the author included only those passages that supported his or her preconceived hypothesis. To overcome any problems of bias, wildlife observations left by early explorers should be systematically recorded on a continuous time basis. Those data should then be tabulated in three ways; game killed, game seen, and animal sign seen or referenced (Kay 1990, Kay et al. 1994, Kay and White 1995).

In addition, only first-person journals penned at the time of the event or edited versions of the same written soon afterwards should be used, because later narrative accounts are less accurate (White 1991). Even "the humblest narrative is always more than a chronological series of events" (McCullagh 1987). The ideological implications of most narrative historical accounts are "no different from those of the narrative form in fiction" (Galloway 1991), because narratives are always influenced by prevailing cultural myths, such as the idea that the West was a Garden of Eden teeming with wildlife but filled with hostile savages (White 1991). Moreover, standard analytical techniques should be used to judge the accuracy of all historical source materials (Forman and Russell 1983).

## HISTORICAL AND REPEAT PHOTOGRAPHS

To compile repeat photosets, the scenes depicted in historical photographs are rephotographed as they appear today (Rogers *et al.* 1984). Those paired images are then compared to document long-term vegetation changes, as well as changes that may have occurred in fire frequency or other disturbance regimes. Repeat photographic studies are common in the western United States, but are rare in Canada (Kay 1990, Kay *et al.* 1994).

Historical photographs can also be used to judge the number of ungulates that occupied areas in the past. If elk (*Cervus elaphus*), for example, were as abundant in the 1800's as they are today in various national parks (Kay 1990, Hess 1993, Kay *et al.* 1994), then favored forage species, like aspen (*Populus tremuloides*) and willows (*Salix* sp.), should show the effects of elk browsing similar to plants today. In other words, historical photographs of aspen and willows should show that those communities were as heavily browsed in the 1800's as they are at present (Kay 1990, Kay *et al.* 1994, Kay and White 1995). If aspen and willows depicted in historical images do not show evidence of repeated browsing, that would not only indicate that fewer ungulates used the range in the past, but it would also indicate that factors other than food limited those ungulate populations. Thus, historical photographs are not just snapshots in time, but they also are important indicators of long-term ecosystem states and processes, especially when combined with present vegetation measurements (Kay 1990, Kay *et al.* 1994).

## ARCHAEOLOGICAL EVIDENCE

Similarly, faunal remains recovered from archaeological sites can be used to determine the relative abundance of ungulate species in pre-Columbian times. If a particular ungulate species dominates the present ungulate community and if today's conditions are thought to represent the "pristine" or "natural" state of the ecosystem, then it is logical to assume that the same ungulate species should predominate archaeologically recovered faunal remains. If that is not true, then it would indicate present conditions are not representative of earlier times (Kay 1990, 1994a; Kay *et al.* 1994; Kay and White 1995).

To be used effectively, though, archaeological data for entire ecosystems must be systematically compiled and synthesized. Consideration must also be given to site formation processes, as well as to any biases that may have been caused by differential preservation or differential transportation. Archaeological faunal remains should be tabulated and reported as both MNI (minimum number of individuals) and NISP (number of identified specimens) (see Kay 1990, 1994a; Kay *et al.* 1994 for details).

## EXAMPLES FROM THE YELLOW-STONE ECOSYSTEM

There are currently an estimated 100,000 elk in the Yellowstone Ecosystem and over 4,000 bison (*Bison bison*) in Yellowstone National Park itself (Harting and Glick 1994). According to the National Park Service, these large ungulate populations are assumed to be "natural" and to represent the "pristine" state of the ecosystem (Houston 1982, Despain *et al.* 1986). If that were true, then early explorers should have reported an abundance of game. Between 1835 and 1876, 20 different expeditions spent a total of 765 days in the Yellowstone Ecosystem, yet they reported seeing elk only once every 18 days and bison were seen on only three occasions, none of which were in Yellowstone Park itself (Kay

1990). In addition, no one reported seeing or killing even a single wolf (*Canis lupus*), another indication that game was scarce (Kay in press a). Moreover, while the explorers were in Yellowstone, their journals contain 45 references to a lack of game or a shortage of food (Kay 1990). Thus, historical records provide no evidence that thousands of resource-limited elk inhabited Yellowstone during the 1800's (Kay 1990, in press a).

Again according to the National Park Service (Houston 1982, Despain *et al.* 1986), thousands of elk and other ungulates have always inhabited Yellowstone and those animals have always heavily impacted the vegetation. That is to say, the agency claims that high-lining of conifers and heavily browsed aspen and willows are natural and not signs of overgrazing. If this were true, then woody vegetation depicted in historical (ca. 1870 to 1890) photographs should reflect that fact. Historical photographs, however, show no evidence of any ungulate browsing (Kay and Wagner in press). Moreover, repeat photographs of tall willows (n=44) and aspen (n=81) show that aspen and willows have declined by more than 95% since Yellowstone was established as the world's first national park in 1872 due to repeated ungulate browsing, not other factors (Kay 1990, Chadde and Kay 1991). So, ungulate high-lining of conifers and repeated browsing of other woody vegetation are not "natural," but instead represent a departure from conditions that existed prior to the establishment of Yellowstone National Park. Moreover, since conifers and other woody species depicted in early images were approximately 70 to 100 years old or older when they were photographed and since they show no evidence of ungulate use, this would indicate that few, if any, elk wintered in Yellowstone from the late 1700's through the 1870's (Kay and Wagner in press).

Archaeological data indicate that elk and other ungulates were also rare in pre-Columbian times. Elk now comprise over 80% of total ungulate numbers in Yellowstone but elk bones are rarely unearthed from archaeological sites - averaging 3% or less of the total (Kay 1990, 1992). This is not due to the fact that Native Americans either could not, or chose not to, kill elk, nor is it due to differential preservation or differential transportation (Kay 1990, 1994a; Kay *et al.* 1994). Instead elk are rarely recovered from intermountain archaeological sites because elk and other ungulates were not abundant in western mountains during pre-Columbian times (Kay 1990, 1994a). Evidence suggests that this was also true in the Canadian Rockies.

## CANADIAN ROCKIES

Elk are now the most abundant ungulate in Banff National Park's Bow Valley and other parts of the Canadian Rockies, but are those populations indicative of past conditions? In addition, is the park's present vegetation reflective of earlier times, or has it changed due to modern management that has excluded fire for over 100 years? Like Yellowstone, aspen is also declining in Banff's Bow Valley, but is this "natural" or an artifact of park management (Kay *et al.* 1994, Kay and White 1995)?

Based on repeat photographs, aspen in Banff's Bow Valley has declined precipitously since that national park was established. Immediately outside the park where elk numbers are lower, however, aspen still continues to flourish. Aspen has also successfully regenerated inside Banff's exclosures while it has declined on adjacent outside plots suggesting that repeated elk browsing, not climatic change, is responsible. Aspen has also declined with advancing forest succession, but even when burned, aspen has failed to successfully regenerate due to repeated elk browsing. While aspen is often thought to be a "seral" species, successional replacement of aspen by conifers is not normal because aspen does not commonly reproduce from seed. Although aspen has maintained its presence in Banff's vegetation mosaic for thousands of years via root suckering, it is now disappearing from the park. Clearly, something is different today than in earlier times. Moreover, the very persistence of aspen in the central Canadian Rockies over the millennium, indicates that ungulate use, and especially elk browsing, was not as intense in the past as it is now (Kay *et al.* 1994, Kay and White 1995).

The ecology of aspen also suggests that aboriginal burning may have been more important than lightning fires in structuring pre-Columbian vegetation communities. Historical photographs and fire frequency studies indicate that aspen burned at frequent intervals in Banff's Bow Valley prior to park establishment. Aspen, however, will carry fire only when it is leafless and when understory fuels are dry, conditions that occur only in early spring or late fall (Fechner and Barrows 1976, DeByle *et al.* 1987). During both those periods, though, there are few lightning strikes and virtually no lightning fires in the Canadian Rockies (White 1985, Johnson and Larsen 1991), something that is true throughout the range of aspen in western North America. Thus, if aspen burned frequently in the past as historical data suggest it did, then the vast majority of those fires were likely set by native peoples (Kay 1995).

Repeat photographs, historical observations, and fire ecology data all indicate that frequent, low-intensity, fires were once the norm in Banff's Bow Valley and in other montane regions of the Canadian Rockies. Grasslands, open forests, aspen, and shrubfields were once common, but have now largely been replaced by conifers under 100 years of fire exclusion and suppression. Forests have both grown-up and thickened-up since Banff National Park was established setting the stage for high-intensity crown fires, something that seldom occurred in the past (Kay *et al.* 1994, Kay and White 1995).

Repeat photographs, aspen ecology, historical observations, and archaeological data, all indicate that elk are more abundant in Banff's Bow Valley today than at any point in the past. There is no evidence that current elk densities are reflective of conditions at park establishment or in pre-Columbian times. Between 1792 and 1872, for instance, 26 different expeditions spent 369 days traveling through the Canadian Rockies on foot or horseback yet reported seeing elk on only 12 occasions or once every 31 party-days (Kay and White 1995). Similarly, few elk bones have been recovered from archaeological sites in the Canadian Rockies (Kay *et al.* 1994), a pattern that is true throughout western North America (Kay 1990, 1992). Moreover, archaeological data suggest that all ungulate species were relatively rare in the Canadian Rockies during pre-Columbian times.

## CANADIAN PRAIRIES

Historical journals and archaeological faunal evidence do indicate that bison and other ungulates were more common on the Canadian prairies, but other data suggests that even those populations were being limited by factors other than food. First, ethnohistoric and archaeological studies reveal that Native Americans in the mountains and on the plains commonly consumed large quantities of berries, such as serviceberries (*Amelanchier alnifolia*) and chokecherries (*Prunus virginiana*). Palliser (1969), Thompson (Tyrrell 1916, Coues 1965), Kane (1971), Hind (1971), Henry (Coues 1965), and others, for instance, reported that berries were abundant during the early 1800's in wooded draws on the Canadian prairies. In September 1869, the Cook-Folsom-Peterson Expedition encountered Native Americans who were gathering and drying large quantities of chokecherries at the mouth of Tom Miner Creek a few kilometers north of Yellowstone Park. "Here we found a wickiup inhabited by two old squaws who were engaged in gathering and drying choke-cherries ... they had two or three bushels drying in the sun" (Haines 1965). The Washburn Expedition of 1870 reported that near Yellowstone Park "we crossed a small stream bordered with black cherry trees (chokecherries), many of the smaller ones broken down by bears, of which animal we found many signs" (Langford 1972). Since shrubs have to be at least 2 m tall before branches are commonly broken down by feeding bears, chokecherry plants in 1870 not only produced abundant berries but were also very large.

Conditions today are very different. Serviceberry and chokecherry plants in Yellowstone are now less than 50 cm tall and they produce virtually no berries because the plants are repeatedly browsed by large numbers of resource-limited elk and other ungulates (Kay in press b). Resource-limited ungulate populations and large quantities of berries are mutually exclusive on western ranges. Even moderate numbers of ungulates curtail berry production because those plants provide highly preferred forage, especially in winter. The fact that Native Americans throughout the West, including the plains, consumed large quantities of berries both historically and prehistorically means that ungulate numbers were low and that those populations were not limited by food (Kay 1994a).

A second line of evidence that ungulate numbers were low is aboriginal buffer zones. Mech (1977, 1994) reported that wolf packs used the edges of their territories less frequently than the central part of their ranges in order to avoid encounters with neighboring wolves. This reduced predation pressure along the territorial edges, which permitted more white-tailed deer (*Odocoileus virginianus*) to survive in those areas. Mech (1977) could find only one other instance of this buffer zone phenomena in the literature, a paper by Hickerson (1965) entitled "The Virginia Deer and Intertribal Buffer Zones in the Upper Mississippi Valley." Hickerson (1965) noted that

*Warfare between members of the two tribes had the effect of preventing hunters from occupying the best game region intensively enough to deplete the (deer) supply .... In the one instance in which a lengthy truce was maintained between certain Chippewas and Sioux, the buffer, in effect a protective zone for the deer, was destroyed and famine ensued.*

My research, however, has uncovered frequent references to buffer zones created by Native American hunting (Kay 1994a). Lewis and Clark (1893), for instance, noted that "With regard to game in general, we observe that the greatest quantities of wild animals are usually found in the country lying between two nations at war." In 1859, General Raynolds, who led an expedition across the Dakota and Montana prairies, found an abundance of grass but no game east of the Powder River. Along the Powder River, though, he reported an abundance of game and little grass, whereas to the west he again encountered an abundance of grass and no game. Raynolds (1868) noted that

*The presence of these animals (bison) in such large numbers in this barren region (Powder River) is explained by the fact that this valley is a species of neutral ground between the Sioux and the Crows and other bands nearer the mountains, or, more correctly speaking, the common war ground visited only by war parties, who never disturb the game, as they would thereby give notice to their enemies of their presence. For this reason the buffalo remain here undisturbed and indeed would seem to make the valley a place of refuge.*

Similarly, Palliser (1969) reported that game on the Canadian prairies was more abundant in aboriginal buffer zones.

*... I must admit, we ran some risk of being surprised by an Indian war-party .... As a general rule, the more dangerous the country the greater the probability of finding (an) abundance of game, showing in more ways than one the truth of the old sportsman's adage, "the more danger the more the sport." This part of the country is so evidently the line of direction (demarcation) between the three hostile tribes, that none of them dare venture into it for hunting, except when driven to desperation by hunger ... Much therefore as I enjoyed the (present) locality for a hunting camp, seeing buffalo on all sides, elk feeding in the distance, and fresh deer tracks in every direction ... Boucharville (my guide) did not relish it at all, and began already to calculate how soon we were to go away.*

Hind (1971) too noted that game on the Canadian prairies was "most abundant" in aboriginal buffer zones.

So, historical sources indicate that aboriginal hunting tended to extirpate or to drive out game animals, and resource depletion around camps and villages has frequently been reported in studies of modern hunter-gatherers (Kay 1994a, in prep). This pattern would be expected if people pursued an optimal-foraging strategy with no effective conservation practices (see below). Tribal territory boundary zones also explain how early explorers could encounter an abundance of game in a few locations and a lack of game elsewhere. Many aboriginal buffer zones were up to 200 km or more wide.

Third, beaver (*Castor canadensis*) also provide evidence that historical ungulate populations were not limited by resources. There is little question that millions of beaver inhabited western North America prior to the fur trade (Johnson and Chance 1974, Kay 1994b). While beaver commonly inhabited mountain streams, large numbers were also found along water courses on the Canadian and U.S. prairies, and especially in Canada's aspen parklands. The number of beaver on untrapped streams was phenomenal. One Hudson Bay Company fur brigade, for instance, caught 511 beaver from one small northern Utah drainage in just 5 days (Kay 1994b). To support these large numbers of beaver, woody vegetation that beaver need for food and dam building materials, like aspen, willows, and cottonwoods (*Populus* sp.), must have been plentiful. Moreover, those plants could not have been subjected to repeated browsing by large numbers of resource-limited ungulates, because those species are among the first to be eliminated by high levels of herbivory.

Yellowstone provides an excellent example of the impact resource-limited ungulates have on beaver populations. During the early 1800's, Osborne Russell (1965) spent weeks trapping beaver on what is now the park's northern range. Even after Yellowstone was established as the world's first national park in 1872, there were still hundreds, if not thousands, of beaver on the northern range (Kay 1990). Today, however, beaver are ecologically extinct on Yellowstone's northern range because the park's resource-limited ungulates, through repeated browsing, have eliminated the tall willows and aspen beaver need for food (Chadde and Kay 1988, 1991; Kay and Chadde 1992). Thus, if large numbers of beaver were once common, as we know they were, then that implies ungulates had to be limited by factors other than food.

Fourth, the widespread burning of the prairies in historical and pre-Columbian times provides another line of evidence that large numbers of resource-limited bison

did not inhabit the plains. Early historical observations provide ample evidence that during the late 1700's and early 1800's, prairie fires often burned for days and single fires covered huge areas, often running for 100 to 200 km or more (Nelson and England 1971, Thomas 1977, Higgins 1986). Large numbers of ungulates and large prairie fires, however, are mutually exclusive, because heavy grazing reduces standing plant biomass, prevents the accumulation of plant litter, and creates discontinuous fuel patterns, all of which prevent the growth and spread of fire (Norton-Griffiths 1979). So, if there were large fires on the Canadian prairies, as we know there were (Fidler 1990), that means bison and other ungulates could not have been food limited.

Carnivore predation and native hunting are two factors that could once have limited ungulate numbers throughout western North America. Recent research in Alaska and Canada indicates that wolves and other carnivores, primarily bears - both grizzly (*Ursus arctos*) and black (*U. americanus*), more often than not, limit ungulate populations (e.g. Gasaway *et al.* 1992; Messier 1991, 1994; Seip 1991, 1992). Today, across much of Canada and Alaska, carnivore predation limits ungulate populations to only 10% or so of what the available habitat could support. In Canada's Wood Buffalo National Park, for instance, bison have declined from around 12,000 animals during the late 1970's when wolf control was terminated, to only 3,500 today, and wolf predation has been identified as the primary factor responsible for that decline (Carbyn *et al.* 1993).

As I have discussed elsewhere, however, wolves are less efficient predators than Native Americans (Kay 1994a, 1995, in prep). The presence of aboriginal buffer zones, for instance, indicates that predation by wolves and other carnivores was not the primary factor limiting pre-Columbian ungulate populations. Moreover, contrary to prevailing beliefs, Native Americans were not conservationists, but instead harvested ungulates the exact opposite of any predicted conservation strategy. By prey-switching to alternative foods like small mammals, fish, and vegetal species, which made up 80% to 90% of most aboriginal diets, Native Americans could have taken their preferred ungulate prey to low levels or extinction without adversely effecting human populations. Furthermore, carnivore predation and native hunting were synergistic and together they decimated ungulate populations that did not have refugia in time or space (Kay 1994a, in prep).

Ungulates in the Rocky Mountains had few effective refugia, so in those areas, ungulate populations were exceedingly low or nonexistent. This explains why there were few moose (*Alces alces*) in western North America at historical contact, and why bison and other ungulates failed to prosper in the grasslands of the Columbia Basin (Kay in prep.). On the plains, however, bison and other ungulates had a refugia in time; i.e., they undertook long-distance migrations (Moodie and Ray 1976, Morgan 1980). Bergerud (1990, 1992) concluded that the sole reason barren ground caribou (*Rangifer tarandus*) migrate is to avoid wolf predation, not to secure food. Even migratory populations, however, are not able to elude all their predators. Caribou populations that migrate still have densities seven times less than food-limited caribou on predator-free islands (Seip 1992). Thus, widely quoted estimates that 50 to 70 million bison inhabited western North America prior to European contact are too high. Instead, five to 10 million bison is a more realistic estimate. This, in turn, suggests that fire was much more important in structuring the Canadian prairies than was grazing.

## CONCLUSIONS

Historical data, old photographs, archaeological evidence, and information on current ecosystem states and processes can be used to determine how ecosystems functioned at various points in the past (then) and now. Those data show that, contrary to prevailing beliefs, Native Americans were the ultimate keystone species that once structured ecosystems throughout the West. Moreover, the idea that North America was a "wilderness" untouched by the hand of man prior to 1492 is a myth created, in part, to justify appropriation of aboriginal lands and the genocide that befell native peoples (Denevan 1992, Gomez-Pompa and Kaus 1992, Simms 1992, Stannard 1992). The Americas as first seen by Europeans were not as they had been crafted by God, but as they had been created by native peoples (Kay 1995). Unless the importance of aboriginal land management is recognized and modern management practices changed accordingly, our ecosystems will continue to lose the biological diversity and ecological integrity they once had, even in national parks and other protected areas (Wagner and Kay 1993, Kay and White 1995).

It must be remembered, through, that Native Americans had little immunological resistance to European introduced diseases such as smallpox, and that epidemics substantially reduced native populations throughout western North America up to 200 years before actual face-to-face contact with Europeans (Dobyns 1983, Ramenofsky 1987, Campbell 1990). So even the earliest explorers, such as Peter Fidler (1990) in Canada or Lewis and Clark (1893) in the United States, did not see western North America as it was in pre-Columbian times. Instead, there were fewer native people, probably less burning, and certainly more ungulates (Kay 1994a, 1995, in prep).

## ACKNOWLEDGEMENTS

I wish to thank Cliff White, Walter Willms, Randy Simmons, Fred Wagner, the Welder Wildlife Foundation, and Parks Canada for their support.

## LITERATURE CITED

Bergerud, A.T. 1990. Rareness as an anti-predator strategy to reduce predation risk. Transactions of 19th International Union of Game Biologists Congress. Proceedings held September 1989, Trondheim, Norway. Vol. 1. Population dynamics: 15-25.

Bergerud, A.T. 1992. Rareness as an antipredator strategy to reduce predation risk for moose and caribou. Pp. 1008-1021 *In* Wildlife 2001: Populations (D.M. McCullough and R. Barrett, eds.). Elsevier Applied Science, New York, New York

Byrne, A.R. 1968. Man and landscape change in the Banff National Park area before 1911. *In* Studies in land use history and landscape change. National Park Series No. 1, University of Calgary, Calgary.

Campbell, S.K. 1990. Post Columbian cultural history in northern Columbia Plateau A.D. 1500-1900. Garland Publishing Inc., New York, New York.

Carbyn, L.N., S.M. Oosenbrug, and D.W. Anions. 1993. Wolves, bison, and the dynamics related to the Peace-Athabasca Delta in Canada's Wood Buffalo National Park. Circumpolar Research Series 4. University of Alberta, Edmonton, Alberta

Chadde, S., and C.E. Kay. 1988. Willows and moose: A study of grazing pressure, Slough Creek exclosure, Montana, 1961-1986. University of Montana, Montana Forest and Conservation Experiment Station Research Note 24.

Chadde, S.W., and C.E. Kay. 1991. Tall willow communities on Yellowstone's northern range: A test of the "natural regulation" paradigm. Pp. 231-264 *In* The Greater Yellowstone Ecosystem: Redefining American's wilderness heritage (R.R. Keiter and M.S. Boyce, eds.). Yale University Press, New Haven, Connecticut.

Coues, E., ed. 1965. New light on the early history of the greater northwest: The manuscript journals of Alexander Henry and David Thompson 1799-1814. Reprinted by Ross and Haines, Minneapolis, Minnesota. Originally published by Francis P. Harper, New York, New York. 1897.

Covington, W.W., and M.M. Moore. 1994. Southwestern ponderosa forest structure: Changes since Euro-American settlement. Journal of Forestry 92: 39-47.

DeByle, N.V., C.D. Bevins, and W.C. Fisher. 1987. Wildfire occurrence in aspen in the interior western United States. Western Journal of Applied Forestry 2: 73-76.

Denevan, W. 1992. The pristine myth: The landscape of the Americas in 1492. Association of American Geographers Annals 82: 369-385.

Despain, D.G., D. Houston, M. Meagher, and P. Schullery. 1986. Wildlife in transition: Man and nature on Yellowstone's northern range. Roberts Rinehart Inc., Boulder, Colorado.

Dobyns, H.F. 1983. Their numbers become thinned: Native American population dynamics in eastern North America. University of Tennessee Press, Knoxville, Tennessee.

Fechner, G.H., and J.S. Barrows. 1976. Aspen stands as wildfire fuel breaks. Eisenhower Consortium Bulletin 4: 1-26. U.S. Forest Service Rocky Mountain Forest and Range Experiment Station, Ft. Collins, Colorado.

Fidler, P. 1990. A look at Peter Fidler's journal: Journal of a journey over land from Buckingham House to the Rocky Mountains in 1792 & 3. B. Haig, ed. Historical Research Centre, Lethbridge, Alberta.

Forman, R.T., and E.W. Russell. 1983. Evaluation of historical data. Ecological Society Bulletin 64: 5-7.

Galloway, P. 1991. The archaeology of ethnohistorical narrative. Pp. 453-469 *In* Columbian Consequences (D.H. Thomas, ed.). Smithsonian Institution Press, Washington, D.C. Vol. 3.

Gasaway, W.C., R.D. Boertje, D.V. Grangaard, D.G. Kellyhouse, R.O. Stephenson, and D.G. Larsen. 1992. The role of predation in limiting moose at low densities in Alaska and Yukon and implications for conservation. Wildlife Monograph 120.

Gomez-Pompa, A., and A. Kaus. 1992. Taming the wilderness myth. Bioscience 42: 271-279.

Haines, A.L. 1965. Valley of the upper Yellowstone. University of Oklahoma Press, Norman.

Harper, J.R., ed. 1971. Paul Kane's frontier: Including wanderings of an artist among the Indians of North America. University of Texas Press, Austin, Texas.

Harting, A., and D. Glick. 1994. Sustaining greater Yellowstone, a blueprint for the future. Greater Yellowstone Coalition, Bozeman, Montana.

Hess, K., JR. 1993. Rocky times in Rocky Mountain National Park: An unnatural history. University Press of Colorado, Niwot, Colorado.

Hickerson, H. 1965. The Virginia deer and intertribal buffer zones in the upper Mississippi Valley. Pp. 43-65 *In* Man, culture and animals: The role of animals in human ecological adjustments (A. Leeds and A.P. Vayda, eds.). American Association for the Advancement of Science Publication 78.

Higgins, K.F. 1986. Interpretation and compendium of historical fire accounts in the Northern Great Plains. U.S. Fish and Wildlife Service Resource Publication 161.

Hind, H.Y. 1971. Narrative of the Canadian Red River exploring expedition of 1857 and of the Assinniboine and Saskatchewan exploring expedition of 1858. Charles E. Tuttle Company, Rutland, Vermont.

Houston, D.B. 1982. The northern Yellowstone elk: Ecology and management. MacMillan Pub., New York, New York.

Johnson, D.R., and P.H. Chance. 1974. Presettlement over harvest of upper Columbia River beaver populations. Canadian Journal of Zoology 52: 1519-1521.

Johnson, E.A., and C.P.S. Larson. 1991. Climatically induced change in fire frequency in the southern Canadian Rockies. Ecology 72: 194-201.

Kay, C.E. 1990. Yellowstone's northern elk herd: A critical evaluation of the "natural regulation" paradigm. Ph.D. Dissertation, Utah State University, Logan, Utah.

Kay, C.E. 1992. Book review — The Jackson Hole elk herd: Intensive wildlife management in North America. Journal of Range Management 45: 315-316.

Kay, C.E. 1994a. Aboriginal overkill: The role of Native Americans in structuring western ecosystems. Human Nature 5: 359-398.

Kay, C.E. 1994b. The impact of ungulates and beaver on riparian communities in the Intermountain West. Natural Resources and Environmental Issues 1: 23-44.

Kay, C.E. 1995. Aboriginal overkill and native burning: Implications for modern ecosystem management. Eighth George Wright Society Conference on Research and Resource Management on Public Lands, Portland, Oregon. April 17-21, 1995 (in press).

Kay, C.E. In press a. An alternative interpretation of the historical evidence relating to the abundance of wolves in the Yellowstone Ecosystem. Paper presented at the Second North American symposium on wolves: Their status, biology, and management. University of Alberta, Edmonton, Alberta. August 25-27, 1992.

Kay, C.E. In press b. Effects of browsing by native ungulates on shrub growth and seed production in the Greater Yellowstone ecosystem: Implications for revegetation, restoration, and "natural regulation" management. Paper presented at the Symposium on Wildland Shrub and Arid Land Restoration, Las Vegas, Nevada. October 19-21, 1993.

Kay, C.E. In prep. Aboriginal Overkill: The role of native Americans in structuring western ecosystems. Oxford University Press, New York, New York.

Kay, C.E., B. Patton, and C. White. 1994. Assessment of long-term terrestrial ecosystem states and processes in Banff National Park and the central Canadian Rockies. Resource Conservation, Parks Canada, Banff National Park, Banff, Alberta.

Kay, C.E., and C.W. White. 1995. Long-term ecosystem states and processes in the central Canadian Rockies: A new perspective on ecological integrity and ecosystem management. Eighth George Wright Society Conference on Research and Resource Management on Public Lands, Portland, Oregon. April 17-21, 1995. (in press).

Kay, C.E., and F.H. Wagner. In press. Historic condition of woody vegetation on Yellowstone's northern range: A critical test of the "natural regulation" paradigm. Paper presented at: Plants and their environments — First biennial scientific conference on the Greater Yellowstone Ecosystem. Yellowstone National Park, Mammoth, Wyoming. Sept. 16-17, 1991.

Kay, C.E., and S.W. Chadde. 1992. Reduction of willow seed production by ungulate browsing in Yellowstone National Park. Pp. 92-99 In Proceedings, Symposium on Ecology and Management of Riparian Shrub Communities (W.P. Clary, E.D. McArthur, D. Bedunah, and C.L. Wambolt, eds.). U.S. Forest Service General Technical Report INT-289.

Langford, N.P. 1972. The discovery of Yellowstone Park. University of Nebraska Press, Lincoln, Nebraska.

Lewis, M., and W. Clark. 1893. The history of the Lewis and Clark expedition. Edited by E. Coues, originally published by Francis P. Harper, New York. Republished in 1964 by Dover Publications, New York. Vol. I: 1-352, Vol. II: 353-820, Vol III: 821-1364.

McCullagh, C.B. 1987. The truth of historical narratives. History and Theory (Beiheft) 26: 30-45.

Mech, L.D. 1977. Wolf-pack buffer zones as prey reservoirs. Science 198: 320-321.

Mech, L.D. 1994. Buffer zones of territories of gray wolves as regions of intraspecific strife. Journal of Mammalogy 75: 199-202.

Messier, F. 1991. The significance of limiting and regulating factors on the demography of moose and white-tailed deer. Journal of Animal Ecology 60: 377-393.

Messier, F. 1994. Ungulate population models with predation: A case study with the North American moose. Ecology 75: 478-488.

Moodie, D.W., and A.J. RAY. 1976. Buffalo migrations in the Canadian plains. Plains Anthropologist 21: 45-52.

Morgan, R.G. 1980. Bison movement patterns on the Canadian plains: An ecological analysis. Plains Anthropologist 25(88 part 1): 143-160.

Nelson, J.G. 1967. Man and landscape in the western plains of Canada. Canadian Geographer 11: 251-264.

Nelson, J.G. 1969a. Some observations on animals, landscape, and man, in the Bow Valley Area: c. 1750-1885. Pp. 219-237 *In* Vegetation, soils, and wildlife (J.G. Nelson and M.J. Chambers, eds.). Methuen, Toronto, Ontario.

Nelson, J.G. 1969b. Land use history, landscape change and planning problems in Banff National Park. International Union for the Conservation of Nature Bulletin 2: 80-82.

Nelson, J.G. 1970. Man and landscape change in Banff National Park: A national park problem in perspective. Pp. 63-96 *In* The Canadian parks in perspective (J.G. Nelson, ed.). Harvest House, Montreal, Quebec.

Nelson, J.G. 1972. Some reflections on man's impact on the landscape of the Canadian prairies and nearby areas. Pp. 33-50 *In* The Canadian prairies (P.J. Smith, ed.). University of Toronto, Toronto, Ontario.

Nelson, J.G. 1973. Animals, fire and landscape in the northwestern plains of North America in pre and early European days. Pp. 63-79 *In* Prairie perspectives (A.W. Rasporich and H.C. Klassen, eds.). Holt, Rinehart, and Winston, Toronto, Ontario.

Nelson, J.G., and R.E. England. 1971. Some comments on the causes and effects of fire in the northern grasslands area of Canada and the nearby United States, 1750-1900. Canadian Geographer 15: 295-306.

Norton-Griffiths, M. 1979. The influence of grazing, browsing, and fire on the vegetation dynamics of the Serengeti. Pp. 310-352 *In* Serengeti: Dynamics of an ecosystem (A.R.E. Sinclair and M. Norton-Griffiths, eds.). University of Chicago Press, Chicago, Illinois.

Palliser, J. 1969. Solitary rambles and adventures of a hunter in the prairies. Charles E. Tuttle Company, Rutland, Vermont.

Ramenofsky, A.F. 1987. Vectors of death: The archaeology of European contact. University of New Mexico Press, Albuquerque, New Mexico.

Raynolds, F.W. 1868. Report on the exploration of the Yellowstone River in 1859-60. U.S. Senate Executive Document 77, 40th Congress, 2nd Session.

Rogers, G.F., H.E. Malde, and R.M. Turner. 1984. Bibliography of repeat photography for evaluating landscape change. University of Utah Press, Salt Lake City, Utah.

Russell, O. 1965. Journal of a trapper, 1834-43. (A.L. Haines, ed.). University of Nebraska Press, Lincoln, Nebraska.

Seip, D.R. 1991. Predation and caribou populations. Rangifer (Special Issue) 7: 46-52.

Seip, D.R. 1992. Wolf control and the management of ungulate populations. Pp. 331-340 *In* Wildlife 2001: Populations (D.M. McCullough and R. Barrett, eds.). Elsevier Applied Science, New York, New York.

Simms, S.R. 1992. Wilderness as a human landscape. Pp. 183-201 *In* Wilderness tapestry (S.I. Zeveloff, L.M. Vause, and W.H. McVaugh, eds.). University of Nevada Press, Reno, Nevada.

Spalding, D.J. 1990. The early history of moose (*Alces alces*): Distribution and relative abundance in British Columbia. Royal British Columbia Museum Contributions to Natural Science 11: 1-12.

Spalding, D.J. 1992. The history of elk (*Cervus elaphus*) in British Columbia. Royal British Columbia Museum Contributions to Natural Science 18: 1-27.

Stannard, D.E. 1992. American holocaust. Oxford University Press, New York, New York.

Thomas, G. 1977. Fire and fur trade: The Saskatchewan District: 1790-1840. The Beaver (Autumn): 32-39.

Tyrrell, J.B., ed. 1916. David Thompson's narrative of his exploration in western America 1784-1812. The Champlain Society, Toronto, Ontario.

Wagner, F.H., and C.E. Kay. 1993. "Natural" or "healthy" ecosystems: Are U.S. National Parks providing them? Pp. 257-270 *In* Humans as components of ecosystems (M.J. McDonnell and S.T. Pickett, eds.). Springer-Verlag, New York, New York.

White, C.A. 1985. Wildland fires in Banff National Park 1880-1980. Occasional Paper 3. National Parks Branch, Parks Canada, Environment Canada, Ottawa, Ontario.

White, R. 1991. It's your misfortune and none of my own: A history of the American West. University of Oklahoma Press, Norman, Oklahoma.

# RESTORATION OF GRASSLAND ECOSYSTEMS -
# AGRONOMY OR ECOLOGY?

## R.E. Redmann

*Department of Crop Science and Plant Ecology, University of Saskatchewan, Saskatoon,
Saskatchewan S7N 0W0*

## ABSTRACT

Native climax grassland ecosystems developed over centuries, building up nutrient capital, complex niche structure, and networks of interactions among large numbers of species. Restoration of native grassland on disturbed sites is a major challenge. Forage crop agronomists have developed techniques for establishment of monocultures or simple mixes of exotic species, but have had no experience with restoring and managing diverse grassland communities of native plant species. Active ecological restoration attempts to facilitate successional processes producing ecosystems which resemble natural climax grasslands. Agronomy contributes to active restoration by providing useful techniques for seed harvesting and processing, tillage and weed control practices, and planting methods. Restoration is limited by the lack of appropriate seed supplies and by the complex germination and establishment requirements of native species. The ability to restore ecosystems is hindered by inadequate knowledge about mutualistic and competitive interactions among plants, animals and microbes. Allowing natural succession to proceed without human involvement (passive restoration) is an option in special circumstances.

## INTRODUCTION

### Background

The concept of ecosystem restoration has become widely accepted by agencies and individuals interested in recreating native ecosystems on disturbed sites. Restoration apparently had its origins in the tallgrass prairie region of the USA, where the original grassland vegetation was almost completely obliterated after European settlement. It was necessary to reconstruct these prairie ecosystems if they were to be studied at all. Prairie restoration was pioneered at the University of Wisconsin Arboretum, beginning in 1936, and at the University of Illinois (Burton *et al.* 1988, Jordan *et al.* 1987). Grassland restoration continues to develop in the tallgrass prairie region, and progress in the field is documented in the thirteen published proceedings of the biennial North American prairie conferences.

Restoration is both art and science, perhaps with emphasis on the former. Some sixty years of restoration efforts in the tallgrass prairie have produced a number of practical recommendations and formulas for success. Burton *et al.* (1988) point out that restoration has not always been guided by controlled experimentation and systematic application of ecological theory. On the other hand, Schramm (1992) argues that "the cautious, experimental and scholarly approach [of scientists] is of little help in guiding the practical process of establishing a prairie planting".

The history of restoration in the mixed grassland region of Canada is short and nearly non-existent. In fact, official policy promoting the breaking of native grassland for cultivation or pasture "improvement" was still going on relatively recently. For example, several hundred hectares of native *Agropyron-Koeleria* grassland in the Matador Community Pasture in Saskatchewan were broken in the 1970's.

The recent interest in revegetation using native species represents a search for a self-sustaining vegetation cover requiring minimal inputs for purposes of wildlife habitat development, grazing or reclamation of mined land and other disturbed sites (Joyce 1993). This is linked to the view that native species might be superior to introduced exotics for establishment of permanent vegetation (Redmann *et al.* 1993a). Seeding native grasses on rangeland has been common in the western USA for decades (Vallentine 1989). Restoration goes beyond revegetation - the goal is to reestablish a total ecosystem resembling that which would occur naturally at a particular site.

My objective in this paper is to describe and discuss how ecological theory applies to the restoration of grassland ecosystems, and how lack of ecological knowledge is an impediment to restoration of natural grassland ecosystems. I want to distinguish restoration from revegetation, and argue that simply seeding native grass stands is not restoration in the strict sense of the term.

## Definitions

Grassland *restoration* is the facilitation of natural successional processes leading to the development of ecosystems which resemble those of native climax grassland. Restoration is usually an **active** process involving techniques to speed up succession, e.g. seeding climax plant species mixtures. The use of restoration as a technique for raising basic scientific questions, and testing hypotheses, in turn leading to improved restoration practices, is called **restoration ecology** (Jordan *et al.* 1987). In some cases **passive** restoration is possible, for example in areas where natural succession is allowed to proceed without human input. The establishment of relatively simple perennial plant communities, composed of exotic species or even artificially selected natives, using conventional agronomic practices, is **revegetation**, not restoration.

Succession is the basic ecosystem process underlying restoration. Classical (or Clementsian) succession predicts the existence of a single stable climatic climax community in a region. Pristine climax grassland communities are the target toward which grassland restoration is aimed. Sites with pristine vegetation are widely used as standards for comparative evaluation of rangeland condition.

## TRENDS IN ECOLOGICAL SUCCESSION

Native climax grassland ecosystems have persisted for centuries, building up nutrient capital, e.g. nitrogen, and providing niches for species evolution, producing a large reservoir of species diversity along with an intricate network of species interactions. Climax communities are structurally complex, with large numbers of species that have narrow niches and complex life cycles (Table 1).

Cultivated agro-ecosystems, which have replaced natural grasslands throughout most of the prairies, are kept at the early stages of succession, and are inherently unstable and subject to degradation owing to their low species and structural diversity, simple linear food chains, and leaky nutrient cycles with poor nutrient conservation. Agronomy is that branch of agriculture devoted largely to the management of these early successional ecosystems. There are ways to overcome the inherent instability of cultivated agroecosystems: planting forages in rotation or as permanent cover, combined with ruminant animal agriculture. Forage agronomists in the prairies usually have emphasized establishment of high-yielding monocultures or simple mixes of exotic species for this purpose. Agronomy has had a strong influence on reclamation practices on disturbed land such as areas strip-mined for coal. However, agronomists have no experience with restoring and managing diverse grassland communities made up of native plant species.

Table 1. Trends in ecosystem development (modified from Odum 1969).

| Early Stages | | Mature Stages |
|---|---|---|
| Low species diversity | <————————> | High species diversity |
| Low equitability | <————————> | High equitability |
| Simple structure | <————————> | Complex structure |
| Broad niches | <————————> | Narrow niches |
| Simple life cycles | <————————> | Complex life cycles |
| Linear food chains | <————————> | Web-like food chains |
| AGRONOMY<———————————————————————————> ECOLOGY | | |
| TILLAGE  ————> REVEGETATION  ————> RESTORATION | | |

Agronomic knowledge contributes to active restoration efforts by providing useful information on seed threshing and processing, tillage and weed control practices, seed drilling and other planting methods, including use of cover crops and mulches, herbicide application to reduce competition, and in certain cases even fertilization and irrigation techniques. There are four important elements for successful restoration using this active approach: (1) availability of acceptable native seed or other plant material for propagation, (2) site and seedbed preparation, (3) seeding, and (4) monitoring and management of the established community.

Some agronomic approaches to species selection and seed supplies may be inappropriate for ecosystem restoration. The lack of native seed, and high seed prices, have been barriers to restoration of native grassland in the Canadian prairies. A solution proposed by agronomists is to develop cultivars of native species, and to move toward incorporation of native species into the commercial seed trade. Artificial selection can eliminate characteristics which are adaptive in natural plant populations. For example, artificial selection has reduced seed dormancy in green needlegrass (Schaaf and Rogler 1970). Schramm (1992) draws attention to the "monocultural switch grass syndrome" in which easily-established stands of switch grass cultivars are proclaimed to be tallgrass prairie restorations.

The ecological approach to restoration requires the use of local seed sources and aims for natural levels of genetic variation in plant communities. Schramm (1992) argues that by working within similar climatic regions, over distances of about 200 miles, local genes can be preserved, while limited mixing can recreate the gene transfers that must have occurred in the original prairie. *Ex situ* collections from widespread, genetically diverse species better reflect the diversity present in geographically disjunct native stands; collections should be maintained separately to provide appropriate genetic stock for introduction into different geographic areas (Walters *et al.* 1994). Even self-fertile grasses with wide distribution have been shown to be made up of genetically distinct races (Wang and Redmann 1995).

## ECOSYSTEM PROCESSES

### Climate and Fire

Our cousins from the tallgrass prairie region deserve credit for developing the basic concept of restoration,

and many techniques for successful establishment of prairie ecosystems. Restoration in the mixed grassland region faces distinct problems which can be traced to differences in the relative importance of two major driving forces, climate and fire, in the two regions.

In the drier climate of the mixed grassland region water is the primary limiting factor for grassland establishment. Drought during the year of seeding can cause a complete failure of stand establishment, and substantial economic loss, considering the high cost of native plant seed. Hot dry conditions near the soil surface reduce seed germination and the emergence and survival of seedlings. Low water potential delays initiation of seed germination, slows the rate of germination and decreases final germination percentage (literature in Qi and Redmann 1993). Depth of seeding is critical: shallow seeding can produce inadequate root development and desiccation injury; seeding too deep reduces emergence success. The seedling morphology of species like *Bouteloua gracilis* make the young plant particularly vulnerable to desiccation injury (Redmann and Qi 1992). Seedlings of *B. gracilis* do not germinate unless surface soil layers are moist for a minimum time period (Bokhari *et al.* 1975).

After stand establishment, drought remains the dominant driving force controlling the functioning of mixed grassland ecosystems. Vegetative and reproductive growth in native mixed grassland are strongly controlled by water supply. Our recent work in Grasslands National Park showed low percentages of seed fill in *Koeleria gracilis*, *B. gracilis* and *Agropyron smithii*, which apparently is related to late season drought. *Koeleria* plants growing on slope positions receiving run off had greater seed fill than those on upland topographic positions (Table 2).

Fire is a powerful management tool in establishing and maintaining more mesic grasslands such as the tallgrass prairie and fescue prairie. Schramm (1992) concludes that tallgrass prairie restoration develop and improve more quickly if burned every year for at least five years, including the spring after the first year growth. Fire is unlikely to play an important role in establishment of mixed prairie, and even in established stands it can have adverse effects on water relations and productivity (Redmann *et al.* 1993b).

Table 2. Percentage seed fill in *Koeleria gracilis* growing in Grasslands National Park (G. T. Clark and R. E. Redmann, unpublished)

| Sampling Date | Plant Community | |
|---|---|---|
| | Upland | Slope |
| July 21, 1994 | 0.6 a[1] | 8.1 a |
| August 7 | 2.1 a | 19.9 b |
| August 24 | 2.5 a | 5.2 a |
| September 10 | 0.2 a | 4.3 a |

[1]Means having the same letter do not differ significantly

## Species Diversity and Community Organization

A serious limitation to our ability to restore ecosystems is inadequate knowledge of ecological processes in communities, including mutualistic relationships (e.g. plant-plant, plant-animal and plant-micro-organism). The large numbers of species required to restore natural grassland presents establishment and management problems of a complexity never faced by agronomists dealing with monocultures or simple mixes. This complexity is traceable in part to problems of scaling in ecology, e.g. the tendency to combine small entities from a low level of organization with large entities from higher levels (Allen and Hoekstra 1987). My intention here is to give some examples of the degrees of complexity that probably need to be considered in efforts to restore entire ecosystems.

Mixed grassland plant communities in Grasslands National Park have as many as 23 vascular plant species, most of which share the community resources in a relatively equitable fashion (Fig. 1). Bazzaz and Parrish (1982) propose that the co-existence of large numbers of plant species in grasslands results from : (1) niche separation among habitats in the landscape, (2) niche differentiation within individual communities, and (3) regeneration characteristics that allow species to become established on disturbed sites. Plants species divide up the basic resources available to them but have different optima of resource acquisition in space or time

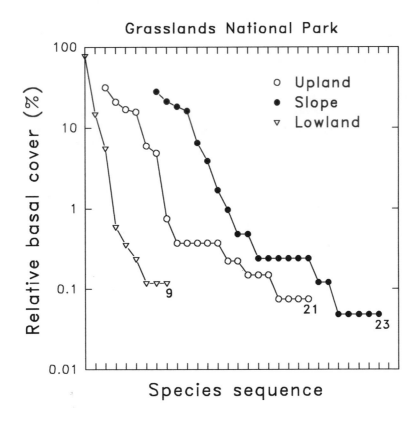

Figure 1. Dominance-diversity curves for three plant communities in Grasslands National Park, Saskatchewan (sampled in 1994).

(Burton *et al.* 1988). A clear example of this is the separation in time of warm (C4) and cool (C3) season grasses when they occur together in the same community. Other organisms such as mycorrhizal fungi, insect pollinators and insect seed dispersers also can be "resources" for some plant species.

Parrish and Bazzaz (1979) found that plant species of a mature tallgrass prairie showed more pollination niche specialization and separation than those in early successional communities. Greater niche differentiation in late successional communities results from natural selection to reduce competition for pollinators. Viable plant populations in a community are dependent on adequate pollination. For example, seed germination in the prairie species *Silene regia* is lower in small populations, as a result of inbreeding depression associated with reduced pollinator activity (Menges 1991). In purple prairie clover (*Petalostemon purpureum*), the number of flower stems in a population is significantly related to the percentage of flowers fertilized, and to the number of seeds attacked by seed predators (Hendrix 1994). Small populations are less likely to attract pollinators or support seed predators.

Disturbance and random factors also contribute to the species diversity of natural communities. Some prairie species are able to colonize small-scale disturbances such as the mounds created by ants and rodents, or the mineral soil exposed in dust wallows (see literature in Burton *et al.* 1988). Unfortunately the native ruderal ("weedy") species that once filled these niches are often replaced by exotic weeds which are able to invade native prairie by colonizing disturbed sites. Some of the aggressiveness of weedy exotics may be attributed to their allelopathic properties.

The degree of subtlety in plant-animal interaction in natural communities is illustrated by the role played by ants. Even after 50 years, ants have not spread from an unploughed natural prairie to restored tallgrass prairie in Wisconsin (Kline and Howell, 1987). The way that soil and vegetation might change after introduction of ants in this restored area remains unknown. Ants also play an important role as seed predators. The flush of seed production by *Artemisia frigida* in late season may be a mechanism to saturate seed predation by ants (J.T. Romo, personal communication). The pattern of plant species distribution on restored prairies can be different from natural prairie remnants (Powers 1987), but the factors determined these patterns are scarcely understood.

Mycorrhizal fungi make a beneficial contribution to the nutrient and water relations of plant communities ranging from dry grasslands to tropical forests. Mycorrhizae can increase plant diversity in early successional communities, and, in general, diversity of arbuscular mycorrhizal (AM) fungi is correlated with plant species diversity (literature cited in Dhillion and Friese 1994). Many late seral species establish only when appropriate AM fungi are present, therefore introduction of AM fungi may facilitate succession and hasten restoration. Dhillion and Friese (1994) report that 96% of prairie plants are mycorrhizal. Coarse-rooted plants tend to be more strongly mycorrhizal than fine-rooted. The grama grasses have low levels of infection. During restoration efforts in Wyoming it was found that a particular sequence of colonization events led to a diverse community rich in native species (Miller 1987). In this case the shrubs acted as nurse plants, improving the microenvironment, and permitting establishment of mycorrhizal grasses and other species.

## NATURAL SUCCESSION AS A RESTORATION OPTION

Allowing natural succession to proceed with little human interference (***passive restoration***) is an option that can be considered for restoration in some grassland regions. Parts of Grasslands National Park are "go-back" lands (abandoned cultivated fields) which have undergone natural succession to something approaching climax. The time scale for grassland succession in this region is about 40 years (Coupland 1950). Natural succession may be the best option for restoration of disturbed areas which have some or all of the following characteristics: (1) already at an advanced seral stage, (2) small size, (3) close to a productive natural seed source, and (4) a large edge:area ratio. Native seed dispersal into smaller disturbed areas is more effective because many grassland species tend not to disperse seed very far from parent plants. Supplemental seeding which does not disturb the soil, and/or other management practices which introduce later seral stage species may help speed succession. Although natural succession is a viable option for restoration of some previously disturbed grasslands, active strategies must continue to be developed for restoration of formerly cultivated land without native grassland nearby, and for areas to be converted from exotic perennial forages to native grassland.

# LITERATURE CITED

Allen, T.F.H. and T.W. Hoekstra. 1987. Problems of scaling in restoration ecology: a practical approach. Pp. 289-299 *In* Restoration ecology - A synthetic approach to ecological research (W. R. Jordan, M.E. Gilpin and J.D. Aber, eds.). Cambridge University Press, Cambridge.

Bazzaz, F. A., and J. A. D. Parrish. 1982. Organization of grassland communities. Pp. 233-254 *In* Grasses and grasslands: systematics and ecology (J.R. Estes, R.J. Tyrl and J.N. Brunken, eds.). University of Oklahoma Press, Norman, Oklahoma.

Bokhari, U.G., J.S. Singh and F.M. Smith. 1975. Influence of temperature regimes and water stress on germination of three range grasses and its possible ecological significance to a shortgrass prairie. Journal of Applied Ecology 12: 153-163.

Burton, P.J., K.R. Robertson, L.R. Iverson, and P.G. Risser. 1988. Use of resource partitioning and disturbance regimes in the design and management of restored prairies. Pp. 46-88 *In* The reconstruction of disturbed arid lands - An ecological approach (E.B. Allen, ed.). Westview Press, Boulder, Colorado.

Coupland, R.T. 1950. Ecology of mixed prairie in Canada. Ecological Monographs 20: 271-315.

Dhillion, S.S., and C.F. Friese. 1994. The occurrence of mycorrhizas in prairies: application to ecological studies. Pp. 103-114 *In* Proceedings of the Thirteenth North American Prairie Conference (R.G. Wickett, P.D. Lewis, A. Woodliffe and P. Pratt, eds.). Department of Parks and Recreation, Windsor, Ontario.

Hendrix, S.D. 1994. Effects of population size on fertilization, seed production and seed predation in two prairie legumes. Pp. 115-121 *In* Proceedings of the Thirteenth North American Prairie Conference (R.G. Wickett, P.D. Lewis, A. Woodliffe and P. Pratt, eds.). Department of Parks and Recreation, Windsor, Ontario.

Jordan, W.R., M.E. Gilpin, and J.D. Aber. 1987. Restoration ecology: ecological restoration as a technique for basic research Pp. 3-21 *In* Restoration ecology - A synthetic approach to ecological research (W.R. Jordan, M.E. Gilpin and J.D. Aber, eds.). Cambridge University Press, Cambridge.

Joyce, J. 1993. Native plants: exploring grass seed production and markets. Agriculture Canada- PFRA, Regina, Saskatchewan.

Kline, V.M., and E.A. Howell. 1987. Prairies. Pp. 75-83 *In* Restoration ecology - A synthetic approach to ecological research (W.R. Jordan, M.E. Gilpin and J.D. Aber, eds.). Cambridge University Press, Cambridge.

Menges, E.S. 1991. Seed germination percentage increases with population size in a fragmented prairie species. Conservation Biology 5: 158-164.

Miller, R.M. 1987. Mycorrhizae and succession. Pp. 205-219 *In* Restoration ecology - A synthetic approach to ecological research (W.R. Jordan, M.E. Gilpin and J.D. Aber, eds.). Cambridge University Press, Cambridge.

Odum, E.P. 1969. The strategy of ecosystem development. Science 164: 262-270.

Parrish, J.A., and F.A. Bazzaz. 1979. Differences in pollination niche relationships in early and late successional plant communities. Ecology 60: 597-610.

Powers, J. 1987. Restoration practice raises questions. Pp. 85-87 *In* Restoration ecology - A synthetic approach to ecological research. (W.R. Jordan, M.E. Gilpin and J.D. Aber, eds.). Cambridge University Press, Cambridge.

Qi, M.Q., and R.E. Redmann. 1993. Seed germination and seedling survival of C3 and C4 grasses under water stress. Journal of Arid Environments 24: 277-285.

Redmann, R.E., and M.Q. Qi. 1992. Impacts of seeding depth of emergence and seedling structure in eight perennial grasses. Canadian Journal of Botany 70: 133-139.

Redmann, R.E., B. Pylypec and Z.M. Abouguendia. 1993a. Comparative herbage yields of eight seeded grasses at Saskatoon, Saskatchewan. Pp. 106-114 *In* Managing Canadian rangeland for sustainability and profitability (F. Taha, Z. Abouguendia, and R. Horton, eds.). Proceedings of the First Interprovincial Range Conference, Saskatoon.

Redmann, R.E., J.T. Romo, B. Pylypec, and E.A. Driver. 1993b. Impacts of burning on primary productivity of *Festuca* and *Stipa-Agropyron* grasslands in central Saskatchewan. American Midland Naturalist 130: 262-273.

Schaaf, H.M. and G.A. Rogler. 1970. Registration of Lodorm green needlegrass. Crop Science 10: 726-727.

Schramm, P. 1992. Prairie restoration: a twenty-five year perspective on establishment and management. Pp. 169-177 *In* Proceedings of the twelfth North American Prairie Conference (D. D. Smith and C.A. Jacobs, eds.). University of Northern Iowa, Cedar Falls, Iowa.

Vallentine, J.F. 1989. Range developments and improvements. Academic Press, New York.

Walters, T.W., D.S. Decker-Walters, and D.R. Gordon. 1994. Restoration considerations for wiregrass (*Aristida stricta*): Allozymic diversity of populations. Conservation Biology 8:581-585.

Wang, X.Y. and R.E. Redmann. 1995. Adaptation to salinity in *Hordeum jubatum* L. populations studied using reciprocal transplants. Vegetatio (in press).

# RESTORATION OR RECLAMATION: WHAT'S THE DIFFERENCE IN DOLLARS AND SENSE?

## Stephen J. McCanny

*Cultural and Natural Ecology, Professional and Technical Service Center, Department of Canadian Heritage, 457 Main St. Winnipeg, Manitoba R3B 3E8*

Restoration ecology is a science dedicated to imposing rapid change on landscapes, usually in a manner that enhances the long-term productivity of the land as well as its adaptation to the local climate. Bradshaw (1980) describes restoration as "those activities which seek to upgrade damaged land that has been destroyed and to bring it back into beneficial use, in a form in which the biological potential is restored." He goes on to distinguish between a more precise definition of <u>restoration</u>, where land is to be returned to its former use and <u>reclamation</u>, where some new use of the land is involved. This is a good starting point for trying to disentangle the usage of these two terms, which have come to represent different philosophies of land management. Even though they offer different and sometimes emotionally charged perspectives on the revegetation of a piece of land, these concepts are actually quite difficult to distinguish in practice.

There are two basic differences between restoration and reclamation projects:

1) a difference in the point of reference used to judge the success of the project,

2) a difference in ethical perspectives.

Reclamation projects are judged by how quickly and inexpensively the land can be changed from a given starting point. The point of reference is the community composition of the vegetation at the beginning of the project. The greater the difference between the current composition of the vegetation and its initial composition, the more successful the project becomes. Of course, reclamation projects have target vegetation compositions and success also will be judged by how close the current composition comes to those targets. However, the emphasis is placed on rapid change from the starting point, provided it is in the right general direction.

Restoration projects place much more emphasis on attaining the target species composition. This composition is the point of reference for judging the success of

the restoration. Generally, the target of a restoration project is the community composition of the land before contact with western civilization. This composition may be documented or else inferred from local undisturbed vegetation. The speed and cost of the restoration project are less critical to its success.

A more profound difference between restoration and reclamation is their ethical basis. Reclamation takes an <u>anthropocentric</u> perspective. Any and all forms of land use can be justified as targets for a reclamation project, provided they contribute to the economic support or general well being of humans. Restoration, on the other hand, takes a <u>biocentric</u> viewpoint, supporting the stability and enhanced function of the entire biotic community. While the distinction between benefits to a single species and benefits to an entire community of organisms would seem clear, it is difficult , if not impossible to draw that distinction in practice. Human needs and desires can be determined by market forces and political processes but there is no process for determining the needs and rights of a clone of blue grama grass or a nitrogen fixing bacterium. We must rely on scientific research and environmental advocacy to get a sense of " what is good for the land". Ultimately, human decision making is anthropocentric—the greatest good for the greatest number of people. A biocentric viewpoint may profoundly affect the development of a revegetation plan but the plan must be attractive from an anthropocentric viewpoint or else it will not be implemented.

## THE REVEGETATION OF ABANDONED LAND

The agricultural history of the Great Plains has been dominated by the competing interests of ranchers and farmers. The battleground for this conflict has been marginal farmland. This land is either too dry or its soil is too thin or rocky to sustain long-term cultivation. The dividing line between acceptable and marginal crop land is sensitive to climate, economics and politics. Several times during that history it became expedient to return cropland to perennial grassland. I will examine these episodes of revegetation for their underlying ethical approach and for the means by which they were evaluated. In particular, I will focus on the period between 1935-1945, when abandoned homesteads were being reseeded to grasslands, and the period between 1985 and the present, which was affected by the Conservation Reserve Program in the United States. I will use these examples to place the current revegetation efforts at Grasslands National Park in perspective.

## Crested Wheatgrass and the "Dirty Thirties"

The determination of Europeans to colonize and thrive on the Great Plains was well expressed by the "Dry Farming" movement, led by H. W. Campbell in the United States and W. R. Motherwell in Canada (Hargreaves 1957, Gauthier *et al.* 1993). This mixture of science and railway-sponsored regional promotion was critical for the settlement of the Great Plains. One component of the research undertaken in this cause would prove to be important for conservationists. A series of botanical investigations by the United States Department of Agriculture between 1898 and 1912 led to the introduction of 34,000 species and varieties of Eurasian plants to the Great Plains (Hargreaves 1957). Among the forage crops introduced during that period, there were few successes. By 1922, the USDA was recommending renewed exploration for exotic forage grasses, since all attempts at breeding commercial varieties of native grasses had failed (Hargreaves 1957).

Smooth brome (*Bromus inermis*) was introduced around 1880 and by the turn of the century was being promoted by scientists as a forage crop. However, the difficulty in eradicating brome from fields under crop rotation was already apparent, as was its preference for moister soils (Hargreaves 1957).

Crested wheatgrass (*Agropyron pectiniforme*) was first introduced from Siberia in 1898. However, its value as a drought-resistant, early-season forage was not recognized until the Dry Farming Movement came up against the climatic extremes of 1917 to 1920 and 1930 to 1939. In 1915 the Northern Great Plains Field Station in Mandan, ND seeded a stand of crested wheatgrass. Within a year, it yielded 3,550 pounds per acre (3,975 kg/ ha) of hay. The stand continued to be productive for 30 years, averaging 1,675 pounds per acre (1,878 kg/ ha) over a period that included several severe droughts. Two publications in 1934 promoted the use of crested wheatgrass on both sides of the international boundary (Westover and Rogler 1934, Kirk *et al.* 1934). Their excitement over the discovery of a high yielding, drought-resistant forage that also had good seed production and handling properties is clear. It was touted as the ideal species for reseeding abandoned crop land and depleted rangeland. It also had potential as a drought-resistant lawn species. However, the claim by Kirk *et al.* (1934) that "crested wheatgrass is relished by all classes of livestock" was perhaps a little too enthusiastic.

The demand for crested wheatgrass seed exceeded the supply throughout the 1930's (Kirk *et al.* 1934, Joyce 1993). The native seed industry was still in its formative stages. Though some wild seed was harvested and planted, the methods were only then being worked out (Hijar 1988). Native seed contributed very little to the stabilization of drought-stricken farmland and deteriorated rangeland in the 1930's and 1940's.

The ethic behind this revegetation project was clearly anthropocentric. The land was losing value as a result of wind erosion. The point of reference was clearly the initial condition of weed infested or barren soil. For the northern Great Plains, crested wheatgrass was a cost-effective solution to the problem. In providing forage for feeding cattle and root mass for binding soil, the reclamation effort was a success. Subsequent research has shown that crested wheatgrass stands have lower biodiversity than native prairie (Wilson and Belcher 1989) and that, because of its early seasonal development, there is now a shortage of late season forage on many parts of the range (Waddington pers. comm.). However, let us consider the consequences if crested wheatgrass had not been developed. Soil is without doubt the most important ecological resource on the Great Plains. The annual loss of millions of tons of soil from the land would have been catastrophic for both its agricultural potential and for the insect fauna and microflora that the soil contains.

## The Conservation Reserve Program

Another major attempt at revegetating the Great Plains is currently coming to a close in the United States. Established by the Food Security Act of 1985, the Conservation Reserve Program (CRP) was designed to remove surplus crop acreages from production. At the same time, both soil and wildlife conservation were promoted. Seventeen million hectares of cropland were enrolled in the program, most of it being highly erodible and not recommended for cropping. Of the five classes of land use sponsored by CRP, perennial native grass cover was the most common in several states

(McGinnies and Hassell 1988). This was a great boon for the native grass seed industry. The program reduced soil erosion in the northern Great Plains by 40 metric tons per hectare (Kruse 1994a) and within five years returned almost a quarter of the soil organic carbon lost over decades of cultivation (Gebhart *et al.* 1994). The program also benefitted wetland conservation (Kruse 1994a).

Several pieces had fallen into place for the native grass seed industry during the fifty years between the Dust Bowl and the Conservation Reserve Program. A forerunner of the CRP, the Soil Bank program (1957-1961), saw the beginnings of extensive harvesting of wild seed (Hijar 1988). At the same time the techniques for cropping native grass cultivars were developed. Unfortunately, these techniques were not in place until the end of the Soil Bank program. Without subsidies, the demand for native grass seed declined and seed companies turned to more profitable products (Hijar 1988). Research continued through the 60's and 70's and many new native cultivars were released (McGinnies and Hassell 1988). When the Conservation Reserve Program started in 1985, the productive capacity to grow thousands of tons of native seed was in place.

Let us consider whether the Conservation Reserve Program is a reclamation or a restoration project. The 10 year time frame implicit in every CRP agreement and the emphasis on native biodiversity shows a biocentric approach that is unprecedented in government sponsored revegetation programs on the Great Plains. However, it seems clear that the program his being judged from the point of reference of the initial cropland rather than that of the original prairie as a target. Critics have pointed out that the CRP land was the same land that was revegetated during the Soil Bank program (Hijar 1988). In fact, despite efforts to enhance biodiversity, the great majority of native grass seeds sown under CRP belong to the same list of six species used during the earlier program. The use of cultivars is also suspect for a restoration program, since it restricts the genetic variation of each species used. As the first of the ten year contracts end this autumn, there is little prospect for a renewed Conservation Reserve Program (Kruse 1994b). Depending on the market for grain, much of the land is likely to come under cultivation again. This kind of land use change will not be confused with restoration.

# REVEGETATION AT GRASSLANDS NATIONAL PARK

The Park Conservation Plan at Grasslands National Park commits us to explore options for restoring as much as possible of the prairie ecosystem that predated the arrival of Europeans on the Great Plains. Revegetation will be a major component of those efforts, especially in light of the 2,000 ha of land within the current park boundaries that has been profoundly disturbed by human activity in the past 80 years. I will focus on the recently cultivated land within the park. This land has a high priority for revegetation because of the combined threats of soil erosion and noxious weed invasion. The park is engaged in an ongoing program of land acquisition. Approximately half of the proposed 900 square kilometres within the proposed park boundaries have been purchased. Apart from the 540 ha of cultivated land within the current boundaries, there are approximately 200 ha of land within the remainder of the proposed park area that are being actively cultivated. The major plant associations are a *Stipa comata - Bouteloua gracilis* grouping on uplands and an *Artemisia - Agropyron smithii* grouping in the Frenchman River Valley.

## How Much Does It Cost?

The preliminary assumptions for calculating the cost of revegetating the recently cultivated land in the park are given in Table 1. I have included the cultivated land beyond the current park boundaries in the calculations since much of this will be acquired during the next few decades. The seeding rate is based on the work of Launchbaugh and Owensby (1970). It is exactly twice the seeding rate used for drilling seed in semi-arid grassland by Ducks Unlimited (Kilfoyle 1995). Ducks Unlimited reduce seeding rates in dry environments to avoid competition for moisture. We will be performing seeding trials to examine the efficiency of this approach. If adopted, a seeding rate of 10 kg of pure live seed (PLS) would virtually cut all cost estimates in half. The non-seed costs were estimated as one third of the total cost per area for Ducks Unlimited plantings. This includes salaries, equipment, herbicide and fuel for seeding and managing a stand during its first year.

Four methods were compared. The first involved the purchase of commercial seed, usually cultivars, from within the ecoregion. The aim of this approach is to establish stands of perennial grass species that are native to the park. The mix of seeds chosen will be driven by the cost of the seed as much as their adaptation to the

Table 1. Assumptions for revegetation program at Grasslands National Park

| | | |
|---|---|---|
| Area to be revegetated: | 750 ha | Michalsky & Ellis 1994 |
| Seeding rate: | 20 kg PLS[1]/ ha | Kilfoyle 1995 |
| Commercial seed purity: | 70% PLS | Joyce 1993 |
| Seed costs: | $9/kg PLS - $280/kg PLS | Joyce 1993 |
| Non-seed costs: | $75/ha | |

[1]Pure live seed.

microsites in the land to be revegetated. The second approach involves the collection and cleaning of seed produced in native prairie within the park's boundaries. Kilfoyle (1995) surveyed the availability of seed sources in the park for this purpose. Though locally collected, the species mix of prolific seed producers will not always reflect the dominant vegetation in a region. The third approach also involves the collection of local plant material, in this case native hay. Because the spreading of native hay does not ensure good soil contact for the seeds, it is not usually considered as a sole seed source for revegetation (Vallentine 1989). Here, I introduce it as a means of speeding up natural succession. The fourth approach is doing nothing at all. Figures 1 and 2 demonstrate the course of natural succession on a chronosequence of cultivated fields within the park (data from Michalsky and Ellis 1994). Except for fields that experienced very little disturbance, we cannot be sure of the time until the vegetation reaches a stable species composition. I will assume a period of

100 years for natural succession and a period of 50 years for succession enhanced by native hay.

The four options will be evaluated on :

i) their cost;

ii) the number of species that can be reintroduced; and

iii) the susceptibility of the method to soil erosion.

The latter will be judged by the time required to establish a complete cover of perennial species.

Table 2 compares the cost of single and multi-species collections of both seed and hay. Kilfoyle (1995) estimated that 550 kg PLS can be collected during a field season through the operation of a single pull type seed stripper (Argyle Machine Co.). Here, I estimate the

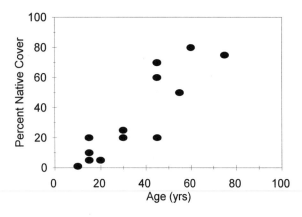

Figure 1. The decrease in the percentage of bare ground with increasing time since cultivation.

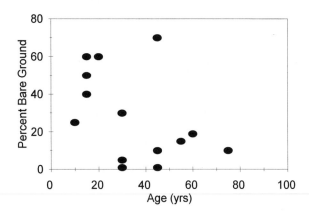

Figure 2. The increase in native plant cover with increasing time since cultivation.

Table 2. Expenses for local seed and hay collection.

| | Seed | | Hay | |
|---|---|---|---|---|
| | 1 species | 10 species | 1 species | 10 species |
| Salaries | | | | |
|    1 person @ $100/ day | $ 2,000 | $ 8,000 | $ 2,000 | $ 8,000 |
|    2 people @   $80/ day | $ 2,800 | $ 9,600 | $ 2,800 | $ 9,600 |
| Seed Strippers | | | | |
|    26K over 15 years | $ 1,733 | $ 1,733 | | |
| Equipment rental & Fuel | $ 1,500 | $ 6,000 | $ 1,500 | $ 6,000 |
| Seed Cleaning | $ 6,000 | $8,000 | | |
| Total per year | $14,033 | $33,333 | $ 6,300 | $23,600 |
| Total for 750 ha<br>   incl. non seed costs | $266,745 | $551,910 | $150,750 | $410,250 |

costs for collecting a metric ton (1,000 kg) of pure live seed, requiring the operation of two machines to maximize efforts during the short harvest periods of specific species (e.g. *Stipa comata*). It will require 15 productive years to produce the 15 metric tons of seed required for revegetating 750 ha of land. I assumed that both machines will require replacement during that period. The total investment of $26,000 is amortized over the 15-year period. Estimates for hay harvests differ only in the absence of seed cleaning and seed stripping costs. Harvests would be conducted with locally rented forage harvesters.

The relationship between species richness and revegetation cost is given in Figure 3. For the commercial seed option the result for one species is based on *Agropyron trachycaulum* at $9.45 per kg of pure live seed. The ten species commercial option is based on a 1:2:1 mix of three price classes of seed; $9.45, $37.80, and $250 per kg PLS. Commercial seed costs clearly increase more rapidly with increased diversity than those of the locally collected material.

Table 3 shows the expected time to completion for each of the four revegetation options. Notice that three extra years are added to the local seed project to account for drought years (Kilfoyle 1995). The cumulative area exposed to soil erosion is the sum of the bare soil sur-

face areas in each year of the revegetation project. The relative erosion risk is much reduced in the commercial seed scenario, because of the potential for a large seed supply. Natural succession after a disturbance of this magnitude clearly presents the highest erosion risk.

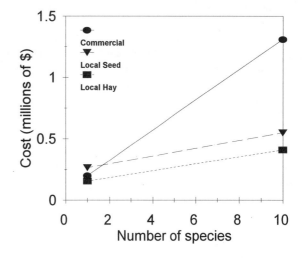

Figure 3. The relationship between species richness and revegetation cost for three scenarios.

Table 3. Soil loss considerations.

| | Time until completion (years) | Cumulative area exposed to soil erosion (ha) | Relative erosion risk |
|---|---|---|---|
| Commercial | 6 | 2,625 | 1 |
| Local Seed | 18 | 7,125 | 2.7 |
| Native Hay | 50 | 19,125 | 7.3 |
| Succession | 100 | 37,875 | 14.4 |

## Does It Make Sense?

The revegetation of a national park would appear to be a prime example of a restoration project. The target species composition and level of ecosystem function are important references in judging the success of the project. At Grasslands National Park, we have thousands of hectares of native prairie with which to compare the results of our revegetation project. In addition, the mandate of Parks Canada to promote ecological integrity, though difficult to define, comes close to a biocentric perspective. On the other hand, one could view this exercise as a touristic reclamation. We are converting the land to a new and essentially anthropocentric use, the viewing and appreciation of natural spaces. In practical terms, the initial abandoned state of the land will also be an important reference point for judging the success of the project. The sooner we can stabilize the soil surface and the vegetative cover, the fewer management problems we will have with this land.

Given the increased cost for a comparable level of species richness, there seems to be little advantage in planting commercial cultivars in Grasslands National Park. I recommend the use of locally collected seed in an aggressive program to reseed this cultivated land within the next two decades. The use of native cultivars to stabilize land until sufficient seed is available for proper revegetation is an expensive option that could be explored if the severity of soil erosion on these lands is identified as a major threat.

## LITERATURE CITED

Bradshaw, A.D.1980. The restoration of land: The ecology and reclamation of derelict and degraded land. University of California Press, Berkeley.

Gauthier, D., R. Widdis, and M. Lewry. 1993. An historical ecological review of agricultural activities in Grasslands National Park and region, 1870-1930. Report for Parks Canada, Prairie and Northern Region.

Gebhart, D.L., H.B. Johnson, H.S. Mayeux, and H.W. Polley. 1994. The conservation reserve program and soil organic carbon content. Abstracts, Society for Range Management, Colorado Springs, Colorado.

Hargreaves, M.W.M. 1957. Dry farming in the northern Great Plains, 1900-1925. Harvard University Press, Cambridge.

Hijar, D. 1988. CRP symposium: History of the native plant seed industry, September 17,1987. General Technical Report, Rocky Mountain Forest Range Experiment Station, U.S. Department of Agriculture No. 158.

Joyce, J. 1993. Native plants: Exploring grass seed production and markets. Report for Agriculture Canada, Prairie Farm Rehabilitation Administration and Ducks Unlimited Canada.

Kilfoyle, D. 1995. Native grass seed collection within Grasslands National Park, Saskatchewan. Report for Parks Canada.

Kirk, L.E., T.M. Stevenson, and S.E. Clarke. 1934. Crested wheat grass. Dominion of Canada, Department of Agriculture, Pamphlet No. 157.

Kruse, A.D. 1994a. CRP and its long range potential for wetland reserve, environmental, and conservation easements in the Northern Great Plains. Abstracts, Society for Range Management, Colorado Springs, Colorado.

Kruse, A.D. 1994b. CRP in the northern great plains, a cost or a benefit to the American taxpayer? Abstracts, Society for Range Management, Colorado Springs, Colorado.

Launchbaugh, J.L. and C.E. Owensby. 1970. Seeding rate and first year stand relationships for six native grasses. Journal of Range Management 23: 414-417.

McGinnies, W.J. and W.G. Hassell. 1988. Establishment of native and introduced range plants in the Central Great Plains. General Techmical Report, Rocky Mountain Forest Range Experiment Station, U.S. Department of Agriculture No. 158.

Michalsky, S.J. and R.A. Ellis. 1994. Vegetation of Grasslands National Park. D.A. Westworth and Assoc. Ltd., Calgary, Alberta.

Westover, H.L. and G.A. Rogler. 1934. Crested wheatgrass. U.S. Department of Agriculture Leaflet No. 104.

Wilson, S.D. and J.W. Belcher. 1989. Plant and bird communities of native prairie and introduced Eurasian vegetation in Manitoba, Canada. Conservation Biology 3: 39-44.

Vallentine, J.F. 1989. Range developments and improvements. 3rd ed. Academic Press, New York.

# RESEARCH ON PEST CONTROL METHODS THAT MINIMIZE ENVIRONMENTAL IMPACT

## Dan Johnson

*Agriculture and Agri-food Canada, Lethbridge Research Station, Lethbridge, Alberta T1J 4B1*

Pests such as foliage-eating insects cause significant damage in most crop systems, and their control often involves environmentally harsh measures. Environmental impacts include direct toxicity of pesticides to non-target species, reduction of food supplies, disruption of ecological processes determining the results of competition and predation, effects of the accumulation of residues in trophic systems, physiological impacts on reproduction, and a range of other direct and indirect impacts. The conflict of the economic and environmental risks has long been recognized, and pest managers have been challenged to find alternatives that minimize both. Pesticides may even have negative impacts on pest control, in some cases resulting in the creation and maintenance of worse pests through elimination of natural enemies and the development of pest resistance. With these balances and problems in mind, entomologists in Canada (initially in Nova Scotia apple orchards, and presently in many other crops) championed a system of integration of pest control practices, based on monitoring and rational spray decisions. Calendar spraying was rejected in favor of rational management based on detailed monitoring, and the value of the activities of natural enemies of pests were recognized and conserved when possible.

Some entomologists were already working to reduce the use of harsh, long-lived products, when they were challenged and supported in these efforts by public interest generated by Rachel Carson's *Silent Spring* in 1962. The search for safer pest control continues based on the obvious need for safety to people and the environment. The "Code of Ethics for Registered Professional Entomologists" begins with "1.1 The Professional Entomologist's knowledge and skills will be used for the betterment of human welfare". Lehman (1993) points out that "If we destroy ourselves along with the insects, weeds, fungi, etc., we have hardly bettered human welfare." I would add that we have not bettered our welfare if we greatly reduce biodiversity and destabilize our ecological environment.

Most modern research on pest control is based on an integrated approach. Integrated pest management (IPM) rejects the old concept of reducing the cost of food as low as possible. This older focus had resulted in management that sought eradication of pests, an impossible task when a pest is entrenched and adapted to its niche. IPM is usually based on several things: an understanding of the ecology of the pest-crop interaction and the ecosystem in which it is embedded; a realistic assessment of the abundance and activity of the pest, based on appropriate and accurate monitoring; the economic injury level concept (essentially, that you do not take action to "control" a pest unless you are confident that you need to); recognizing and protecting the population controls that result from the activities of natural enemies of the pest, notably predators, parasites and disease; methods of growing plants (e.g., crop rotation) that interfere with the activities or life cycles of the pests; choosing of crops or varieties that are less susceptible to damage; setting of standards of acceptable damage; and judicious use of minimized rates of chemical insecticides only where no alternative is available to do the job. IPM is not applied easily to all systems (for example, extensive monitoring is difficult on the prairies), but IPM systems have been so successful in some landmark crop protection systems to control such diverse pests as scale insects, boll weevil, orchard mites and weeds (Pimentel 1981; see also chapters on each crop in Burn *et al.* 1987) that research on new methods of controlling pests is often considered from the IPM perspective from the beginning of the research program.

IPM naturally offers some possibility of reducing environmental impacts, because it is based on an ecological approach that avoids serious economic loss while also minimizing adverse side effects. In some cases, reduction of adverse side effects provides benefits in the way of reduced pest activity, through complexities that are best understood through a systems approach. In a sense, routine control decisions gave rise to rational control decisions, and the approach has been developed to the point that pest control is approaching a holistic level. In a reductionist system, the pest problems are the main driving force behind decisions regarding crop protection, whereas in a holistic system, pest control by natural factors is the main controlling influence on decision-making (Tait 1987).

Within the concept (and often the yet-to-be-achieved objective) of IPM, research has been directed towards particular methods of pest management that reduce environmental impact, either by replacing chemical insecticides, or by changing the way that they are used.

In the remainder of this report, I review some examples of alternative methods of pest control being researched for use on the Canadian Prairies, drawing on a range of recent research and personal experience.

## PLANT RESISTANCE

One good way to avoid environmental impacts of pest control actions is to make the actions unnecessary. Modern breeding and biotechnology research offer opportunities for identification or development of crop varieties that are resistant to pest attack. For example, Hinks and Olfert (1992) review the considerable differences among cereal cultivars in their susceptibility to grasshopper damage. In some cases, new cultivars for the Prairies have been tested for susceptibility to damage and preference by a number of pest species before the cultivars are released (Muendel and Johnson 1987) and to determine which might actually increase growth and survival of the pest insects (Johnson and Muendel 1987). The potential of developing resistant crops is another reason for preserving naturally occurring genetic and ecological diversity.

## BIOLOGICAL CONTROL OF WEEDS

It is 200 years since insects were first used against a plant pest (prickly pear cactus in India; biocontrol of weeds is reviewed by Harris 1991). The principle is based on locating and releasing the natural enemies of weeds, usually insects or agents of plant disease, that kill the weed or reduce its vigor. Biological control of weeds using foliage-eating beetles has been successful in Australia, Canada and the U.S. The result has not only been considerable savings to livestock producers, but the environmental side effects are often positive, in that nearly pure stands of weeds have been replaced by diverse plant communities (Harris 1988). The trick is to find an insect that will attack the weed, reduce the success of the weed, reproduce to maintain the pressure, and not attack other plant species.

## BIOLOGICAL CONTROL OF INSECTS

Most insect populations are limited either by natural enemies (predators, parasites or pathogens), weather, or both. If a pest has natural enemies in its region of origin, then classical biological control, in which the natural enemy is imported and released, is a possible pest control method that is usually environmentally harmless. If the pest is native and especially susceptible to attack, the possibility for control via mass releases of parasites (inundative control) exists. An example of the potential for more widespread use of this technology is indicated in recent tests of mass releases of the microscope wasp *Trichogramma brassicae*. Yu and Byers (1994) found that the wasp reduced European corn borer near Taber, Alberta, by 85 to 87% in 1991 and 45 to 95% in 1992, without the use of chemical pesticides.

## MONITORING WITH SEX-ATTRACTANTS

Some insects use semiochemicals to signal each other on their locations and reproductive status. The presence of sex-attractants that will attract male moths has provided a valuable IPM tool, in that changes in populations can be tracked and even predicted. For example, Byers and Struble (1987) used specific attractants to simultaneously monitor 5 species of cutworm (red-backed, darksided, pale western, clover and army) in southern Alberta from 1978 to 1983. Advance warning of the geography of pest problems is the first step in avoiding inefficient panic spraying. In some cases, insect surveys have be used in conjunction with geographic information systems to track the pest and limit spraying to the worst infestations (Johnson 1989b).

The use of volatile sex-attractants to disrupt mating is related possibility being researched in several systems, to prevent the pest build-up rather than attempt to suppress it when it is too late to do so without an environmental impact.

## MICROBIAL CONTROL OF INSECTS

Insects may succumb to disease under certain conditions, and considerable research has been directed towards discovery and development of naturally occurring microbes that could be used in place of chemical insecticides (reviewed in Burges 1981; and Fuxa and

Tanada 1987). There has been a great amount of interest in the bacterium "Bt", but this is primarily a microbe used against forest caterpillars. On the Prairies, fungi and protozoa have been tested to control grasshoppers, a major pest that causes considerable environmental concern because of the sudden upsurge in insecticide application that follows an outbreak. If even 10% of the insecticide used against grasshoppers during a year of heavy infestation (Table 1) could be replaced with a biological or microbial control method, it would mean tens of thousands of hectares that would not receive insecticides. Tests using the fungus *Beauveria bassiana* have indicated a potential for reductions in grasshopper populations of 60% (Johnson and Goettel 1993), but this method has failed under conditions of prolonged heat and dryness. A more useful role for microbes may lie in sublethal effects. The purpose of insect control is to reduce crop losses caused by insects to plant tissue. Most control measures are designed to kill sufficient numbers of insects so that the total amount of feeding is reduced to an acceptable level. Consequently, routine tests of the efficacy of insecticides, both chemical and microbial, tend to be based on assessment of insect mortality. This approach is so common that in the field of crop protection, efficacy is treated as a synonym of mortality. However, insecticides can be effective in protecting crops for a number of other reasons, including effects on food consumption, development, reproduction and activity. This is particularly true of microbial agents applied to debilitate pest insects while remaining endemic. This approach was used by Johnson and Pavlikova (1986), who found that although the protozoan *Nosema locustae* does not provide quick, dramatic mortality of grasshoppers (Johnson 1989a), it is able to

Table 1. Summary of purchases of insecticide for grasshopper control in Alberta[1] during peak outbreak years

**1985**

| Product | Purchases | Percent | Total lires | Total hectares | Perc. of ha |
|---|---|---|---|---|---|
| Furadan | 2,305 | 34.79 | 119,764 | 440,618 | 56.61 |
| Decis EC | 1,395 | 21.06 | 24,910 | 168,013 | 21.59 |
| Lorsban | 560 | 8.45 | 73,775 | 74,641 | 9.59 |
| Sevin XLR | 1,642 | 24.78 | 149,606 | 60,545 | 7.78 |
| Cygon[2] | 365 | 5.51 | 22,994 | 26,587 | 3.42 |
| Hopper-Stopper | 174 | 2.63 | 11,001 | 4,452 | 0.57 |
| Malathion | 184 | 2.78 | 5,982 | 3,458 | 0.44 |
| Total | 6,625 | 100.0 | 408,032 | 778,314 | 100.0 |

**1986**

| Product | Purchases | Percent litres | Total hectares | Total of ha | Perc. |
|---|---|---|---|---|---|
| Furadan | 2,388 | 41.78 | 127,403 | 468,722 | 65.15 |
| Decis EC | 920 | 16.10 | 15,440 | 104,138 | 14.48 |
| Lorsban | 479 | 8.38 | 60,031 | 60,735 | 8.44 |
| Sevin XLR | 1,027 | 17.97 | 69,129 | 27,976 | 3.89 |
| Cygon[2] | 512 | 8.96 | 41,960 | 48,517 | 6.74 |
| Hopper-Stopper | 201 | 3.52 | 15,456 | 6,255 | 0.87 |
| Malathion | 188 | 3.29 | 5,335 | 3,084 | 0.43 |
| Total | 5,715 | 100.0 | 334,754 | 719,427 | 100.0 |

[1] Source: Alberta Agriculture Insecticide Rebate Program
(Dolinski and Johnson 1991)

[2] Liquid spray dimethoate products, primarily the product Cygon.

reduce feeding by grasshoppers to half that of healthy grasshoppers. This microbe does not effect any living things other than the grasshopper family and would therefore be an environmentally rational alternative.

## RATES AND TARGETING

One of the main methods of reducing insecticide use is via improved dose-targeting. This may include reductions in the rates of spray application, improving the timing of application so that pesticide is not wasted on resistant stages of the pest, or altering the insecticide carrier. An example is carbaryl on wheat bran as a bait for grasshopper control. This pesticide was ranked, by the Canadian Wildlife Service, as being least damaging to waterfowl, burrowing owl, and pheasants (Forsyth 1989, Fox *et al.* 1989), but the recommended rates for spray application are high at 550 to 1,125 g active ingredient per hectare. Field tests in Alberta (Johnson and Henry 1987) resulted in registration of a dry bait formulation that provides acceptable grasshopper control with approximately one-fourth as much insecticide, and with the added attraction of no spray drift. Not all insecticides are appropriate to this methodology, however. Another possible grasshopper bait, containing chlorpyrifos, was rejected by researchers as too environmentally harsh on small mammals (Gregory *et al.* 1993).

## NEW AND OLD PESTICIDES

The history of pesticide impacts has been briefly summarized elsewhere in this symposium (P. Martin). The long-lived organochlorines commonly used on the Prairies were replaced in the 1970's, often with products that lacked the long residue life and bioaccumulation problems of the OC's, but made up for it by being more toxic (for example, carbofuran). A new generation of pyrethroid insecticides was introduced for use on grassland (grass residues were measured by Hill and Johnson 1987). This new family of insecticides offered some environmental solutions because of much lower toxicity to wildlife, but they soon required restrictions to avoid serious impacts on the aquatic invertebrates that serve as food for waterfowl. Novel possibilities are being researched, such as photo-activated dyes that are toxic only to insects in sunlight, or derivatives from plants that are naturally toxic to insect pests, but these will also require consideration and testing before their full impacts and environmental side effects are understood.

## CROPPING PATTERN AND INTER-CROPPING

It has long been recognized that some pests are benefitted by continuous monoculture, and that crop rotations will put these pests at a disadvantage, or even preclude their existence for a generation. This is the cultural side of integrated control, by which changes in cropping patterns and choices can dramatically reduce the use of chemical pesticides. Organic gardeners often attest to reduced insect problems in mixed plantings, and similar methods of intercropping, strip cropping and undersowing have been studied in larger field situations as pest management methods. Edwards *et al.* (1992) found that predators known to be natural enemies of pest insects were 4 to 10 times more abundant in intercropped areas than in monocultures. Therefore, increasing crop diversity favors populations of natural enemies that in turn reduce the need for chemical insecticides. The subsequent reductions in chemical use can result in greater diversity, with direct benefits to wildlife. In a long-term study in the U.K., reduced use of chemical insecticides on the edges of cereal crops also allowed an increase in food for gray partridge and pheasants (Sotherton *et al.* 1993).

## LITERATURE CITED

Burges, H.D. 1981. Microbial control of pests and plant diseases 1970-1980. Academic Press, London.

Burn, A.J., T.H. Coaker, and P.C. Jepson, eds. Integrated Pest Management. Academic Press, London.

Byers, J.R. and D.L. Struble. 1987. Monitoring population levels of eight species of noctuids with sex-attractant traps in southern Alberta, 1978-83: Specificity of attractants and effect of traget species on abundance. The Canadian Entomologist 119: 541-556.

Carson, R. 1962. Silent spring. Riverside Press, Cambridge.

Dolinski, M.G. and D.L. Johnson. 1991. Feasibility of long-term grasshopper management. Farming for the Future Final Report. Project #88-0328.

Edwards, C.A., G.E. Brust, B.R. Stinner and D.A. McCartney. 1992. Work in the United States on the use of cropping patterns to promote natural enemies of pests. Aspects of Applied Biology 31: 139-148.

Forsyth, D.J. 1989. Potential effects of pesticide on wildlife in wetlands. Pp. 199-210 *In* Proceedings of the Symposium on Water Management Affecting the Wet-to-Dry Transition: Planning at the Margins (W. Nicholaichuk and H. Steppuhn, eds.). November 8 and 9, 1988, University of Regina, Water Studies Institute, Saskatoon, Saskatchewan.

Fox, G.A., P. Mineau, B. Collins, and P.C. James. 1989. The impact of the insecticide carbofuran (Furadan 480F) on the burrowing owl in Canada. Technical Report Series No. 72, Canadian Wildlife Service, Ottawa, Ontario.

Fuxa, J.R. and Y. Tanada. 1987. Epizootiology of insect diseases. John Wiley & Sons, New York.

Gregory, D.A., D.L. Johnson and B.H. Thompson. 1992. The impact of bran baits treated with the insecticides carbaryl, chlorpyrifos, and dimethoate on the survivorship and reproductive success of non-target mouse populations. Agriculture, Ecosystems and Environment 45: 95-103.

Harris, P. 1988. Environmental impacts of weed-control insects. BioScience 38: 542-548.

Harris, P. 1991. Classical biocontrol of weeds: its definition, selection of effective agents, and administrative-political problems. The Canadian Entomologist 123: 827-849.

Hill, B.D. and D.L. Johnson. 1987. Persistence of delta methrin and its isomers on pasture forage and litter. Journal of Agricultural and Food Chemistry 35: 373-378.

Hinks, C. and O. Olfert. 1992. Cultivar resistance to grasshoppers in temperate cereal crops and grasses: A review. Journal of Orthoptera Research 1: 1-8.

Johnson, D.L. 1989a. The effects of timing and frequency of application of *Nosema locustae* (Microspora: Microsporida) on the infection rate and activity of grasshoppers (Orthoptera: Acrididae). Journal of Invertebrate Pathology 54: 353-362.

Johnson, D.L. 1989b. Spatial analysis of the relationship of grasshopper outbreaks to soil classification. Pp. 347-359 *In* Estimation and analysis of insect populations. Lecture Notes in Statistics vol. 55.

Johnson, D.L. and M.S. Goettel. 1993. Reduction of grasshopper populations following field application of the fungus *Beauveria bassiana*. Biocontrol Science and Technology 3: 165-175.

Johnson, D.L. and J.E. Henry. 1987. Low rates of insecticides and *Nosema locustae* (Microsporidia: Nosematidae) on baits applied to roadsides for grasshopper (Orthoptera: Acrididae) control. Journal of Economic Entomology 80: 685-689.

Johnson, D.L. and E. Pavlikova. 1986. Reduction of consumption by grasshoppers (Orthoptera: Acrididae) infected with *Nosema locustae* Canning (Microsporidia: Nosematidae). Journal of Invertebrate Pathology 48: 232-238.

Johnson, D.L. and H.-H. Muendel. 1987. Grasshopper feeding rates, preferences and growth on safflower. Annals of Applied Biology 111: 43-52.

Lehman, H. 1993. New directions for pesticide use. Pp. 3-9 *In* The Pesticide question (D. Pimental and H. Lehman, eds.). Chapman & Hall, New York.

Muendel, H.-H. and D.L. Johnson. 1987. Safflower susceptibility and response to feeding by grasshoppers. Annals of Applied Biology 111: 203-212.

Pimentel, D. 1981. CRC handbook of pest management in Agriculture, Vol III. CRC Series in Agriculture, Boca Rouge, Florida.

Sotherton, N.W., P.A. Robertson, and S.D. Dowell. 1993. Manipulating pesticide use to increase the production of wild game birds in Britain. Pp. 92-101 *In* Quail III: National Quail Symposium (K.E. Church and T.V. Dailey, eds.). Kansas Department of Wildlife and Parks, Pratt, Kansas.

Tait, E.J. 1987. Planning an integrated pest management system. Pp. 189-208 *In* Integrated pest management (A.J. Burn, T.H. Coaker, and P.C. Jepson, eds.). Academic Press, London.

Yu, D.S. and J.R. Byers. 1994. Inundative release of *Trichogramma brassicae* Bezdenko (Hymenoptera: Trichogrammatidae) for control of European corn borer in sweet corn. The Canadian Entomologist 126: 291-301.

# POTENTIAL EFFECTS OF HERBICIDES ON WILDLIFE IN PRAIRIE CANADA

## Douglas J. Forsyth

*Canadian Wildlife Service, 115 Perimeter Road, Saskatoon, Saskatchewan S7N 0X4*

## INTRODUCTION

Agricultural weed control in the three Prairie Provinces requires the application of about 19 million kilograms of herbicide per year, divided almost equally between broadleaf weed and wild oat herbicides (Lewis 1991). There is thus considerable potential for wildlife and habitat to be exposed annually to a multitude of these chemicals, due to the close association between cropland and areas of native vegetation (Sheehan *et al.* 1987). These chemicals may be adversely affecting terrestrial and aquatic fauna either through direct toxicity or indirectly through effects on plant life. Most of the wildlife habitat that remains in prairie cropland consists of islands of upland habitat associated with wetlands or aspen groves. Trees, shrubs and forbs in these areas provide nesting cover or food for dabbling ducks (Clark, 1989), songbirds (Semenchuk 1992, Johns 1993) and various wild mammals. The Canadian Wildlife Service evaluated in detail the potential indirect effects of pesticides, including herbicides, on prairie waterfowl through their effects on vegetation and aquatic organisms (Sheehan *et al.* 1987). Guidelines for protecting nontarget plants from the effects of herbicides (Boutin *et al.* 1993) have been submitted to the newly established Pest Management Regulatory Agency to be adopted as a regulatory proposal in 1995, with the ultimate goal of acceptance as the official Canadian guidelines for testing effects of pesticides on nontarget plants. The environmental concerns and approach taken in developing regulatory guidelines for Canada have been summarized elsewhere (Freemark and Boutin 1994, 1995, Boutin *et al.* 1995). Although herbicides are applied annually to about 80% of the prairie wheat crop and 91% of the canola crop (Sheehan *et al.* 1987, Forsyth 1989), their off-field effects on upland vegetation and aquatic food webs are not well documented. Drifting phenoxy herbicides have caused severe damage to shelterbelt trees, but no data exist to document their effects on native shrubs or forbs. Thus we do not know if the plant communities near cropland have been altered through decades of exposure to drift and runoff of an increasing number of herbicides. Aerial application, which accounts for approximately 5 to 10% of the annual herbicide treatment of prairie crops, greatly increases the amount of drift, compared with ground application, and introduces the risk of direct spraying of ponds and upland habitat (Sheehan *et al.* 1987).

## TOXICITY OF HERBICIDES TO WILDLIFE

Most of the herbicides currently used by prairie farmers are of very low acute oral toxicity to birds and mammals, with a few exceptions (Freemark and Boutin 1995). Bromoxynil (Pardner®) and paraquat (Gramoxone®), both classified as moderately toxic to birds and mammals (Table 1), have the same LD50 (the dose that is lethal to 50% of a test population) value of 200 mg per kg of body mass for the mallard (*Anas platyrhynchos*). Laboratory mice (*Mus musculus*) are slightly more sensitive than are rats (*Rattus norvegicus*) to bromoxynil and paraquat, whereas the LD50 of difenzoquat (Avenge®) for rats is 470 mg/kg (moderately toxic) compared to 31 to 44 mg/kg (highly toxic) for mice (Hartley and Kidd 1987). Cyanazine (Bladex®) also ranks as moderately toxic to birds or mammals (Table 1), with LD50 values of 182 mg/kg for the laboratory rat (Hartley and Kidd 1987) and 445 mg/kg for bobwhite (*Colinus virginianus*, Hudson *et al.* 1984); the LD50 of 2-4,D for the rat is 370 to 700 mg/kg. It is unlikely, however, that lethal quantities of any of these herbicides are available to wild birds or mammals exposed in the agricultural environment through inhalation of spray, absorption through the skin and consumption of contaminated vegetation. For example, bromoxynil sprayed at the maximum rate of 336 g of active ingredient (ai) per ha would result in about 32 mg/kg of herbicide in grass (Hoerger and Kenaga 1972), which would result in a total of 1 mg in the 25 g of grass a meadow vole (*Microtus pennsylvanicus*) could consume in one day (Golley 1960). The other routes of exposure might increase the total daily intake of chemical to 2 mg. Assuming that the LD50 of bromoxynil is similar between the vole and laboratory mouse (110 mg/kg: Hartley and Kidd 1987), a lethal dose for a 27 g vole

Table 1. Toxicities of selected herbicides commonly used in the Prairie Provinces. Classes of toxicity, modified from Freemark and Boutin (1995), are based upon acute oral LD50 values for the Mallard, Bobwhite, laboratory rat, and laboratory mouse: low (L) = >500; moderate (M) = 51-500; high (H) = 10-50. Toxicity data are from Hartley and Kidd (1987) and Hudson et al. (1984).

| Herbicide | Trade Name[a] | Toxicity Class | |
| | | Birds | Mammals |
|---|---|---|---|
| bromoxynil | Pardner® | M | M |
| cyanazine | Bladex® | L - M | M |
| 2,4-D | 2,4-D | L | L - M |
| dicamba | Banvel® | L | L |
| diclofop-methyl | Hoe-Grass® | L | L |
| difenzoquat | Avenge® | L | M - H |
| ethalfluralin | Edge® | —— | L |
| glyphosate | Roundup® | L | L |
| MCPA | MCPA | —— | L |
| metsulfuron-methyl | Ally® | L | L |
| paraquat | Gramoxone® | M | M |
| sethoxydim | Poast® | —— | L |
| triallate | Avadex BW® | L | L |
| trifluralin | Treflan® | L | L |

[a] Trade names are for products containing the active ingredient alone; many mixtures of herbicides are also marketed.

(Golley 1960) would be about 3 mg. This quantity is unlikely to be taken in by a vole. The deposits encountered by voles would probably be less than 32 mg/kg because they feed below the plant canopy, which would intercept much of the spray. In addition, herbicides are largely eliminated from the body through metabolism within 24 to 48 hours of entry and at least half of the initial deposit disappears from vegetation within about 3 to 15 days by volatilization, plant metabolism, sunlight, and rainfall (Kearney and Kaufman 1969, National Research Council of Canada 1978, Willis and McDowell 1987, Kent et al. 1992 a and b, Caux et al. 1993). In the case of difenzoquat applied at 850 g/ha, voles may be exposed to 82 mg/kg in grass, or 2 mg during one day of feeding, twice the lethal dose of 1 mg, based upon the LD50 for laboratory mice. The sensitivities of wild mammals to any herbicide may, of course, differ significantly from that of laboratory rats or mice. Although there is little or no published documentation of adverse physiological effects of herbicides on wild mammals or birds (Freemark and Boutin 1995), the foregoing examples of relatively toxic herbicides suggest that there may be potential for at least sublethal effects on some mammals. In general, however, the brief persistence of these chemicals both in the environment and within warm-blooded vertebrates would be expected to minimize adverse effects.

Avian embryos are more sensitive to chemicals than are adults or juveniles, as indicated by mortality of Mallard embryos exposed to herbicides applied as aqueous solutions to incubating eggs. Paraquat at three times the rate registered for application in Canada and trifluralin at 1.5 times its registered rate caused 50% mortality; another 12 common herbicides tested were much less toxic (Hoffman and Albers 1984). Paraquat applied to mallard eggs at the rate sprayed for chemical summerfallow resulted in 23% mortality (Hoffman and Eastin 1982). No data are available for the sensitivity of songbirds to herbicides, although the eggs of Ring Doves (*Streptopelia risoria*) were found to be more sensitive than were those of Mallards. Thus, the spraying of paraquat, and possibly trifluralin, may represent hazards as yet unquantified. The potential for direct toxic effects of herbicides on wildlife cannot be ignored, but since these chemicals are designed to kill plants, this review considers primarily the potential for indirect effects on wildlfe communities through phytotoxicity and effects on aquatic animals.

## Terrestrial Ecosystems

Observations made by biologists (V.L. Harms, plant taxonomist, University of Saskatchewan; E.A. Driver, ecologist, Canadian Wildlife Service; and R.C. Godwin, ecologist, Saskatchewan Research Council) who have been visiting islands of native vegetation in Saskatchewan over the past 25 years provide some indications of changes that appear to be occurring in communities of native plants. Pond margins have been invaded by field dock (*Rumex fennicus*) or stinging nettle (*Urtica gracilis*), a sign of disturbance. Similarly, the understory of aspen groves in cropland is frequently invaded by thistles (*Cirsium arvense* and *Sonchus arvensis*) where no disturbance by cattle exists, suggesting that herbicides may be involved. Yellow lady's slipper (*Cypripedium calceolus*) and blue-eyed grass (*Sisyrinchium montanum*) are becoming less common in pond margins. Field experiments would be required to determine whether these changes in floral composition are the result of herbicides depositing on foliage or entering root systems from runoff. At least three other possible causal agents must also be considered: (i) drought, (ii) fertilizers or (iii) silt from erosion. Nitrogen fertilizer is known to very significantly alter plant communities when applied continuously to pasture because the species best able to utilize it become dominant (O'Connor and Shrubb 1986).

The sulfonylureas and imidazolinones constitute a group of relatively new herbicides that are highly toxic to plants in very small doses. The products currently registered for use in the Canadian prairies include the sulfonylureas, Ally®, Amber®, Express®, Muster®, and Refine® and the imidazolinone, Assert®. Despite the extreme phytotoxicity of these products, no published data exist to document their effects on native prairie flora, either terrestrial or aquatic. A study of the sulfonylurea, chlorsulfuron (Glean®), showed that exposure of commercial cherry trees to very small amounts of the herbicide, simulating drift from sprayed wheat fields, significantly reduced fruit production (Bhatti *et al.* 1995). The sulfonylurea, metsulfuron-methyl (Ally®), is effective at controlling western snowberry (*Symphoricarpos occidentalis*) when sprayed at the rate of 5 g ai/ha (Bowes 1987). Therefore, its application (by ground sprayer only) to cereal fields at 4.5 g ai/ha (Ali 1992) could result in drift causing significant adverse effects on nontarget upland vegetation.

Extensive studies in the United Kingdom have shown that herbicides sprayed on cereal crops indirectly impaired the survival of young grey partridge (*Perdix perdix*) chicks by removing the host plants of their insect prey (Potts 1986, Sotherton 1991). When a 6-metre band of crop was left unsprayed around the edges of fields, densities of larval beetles, sawflies and plant bugs increased along with those of their broadleafed weed host plants. Survival of partridge chicks significantly improved as a result of the unsprayed bands known as "conservation headlands". Consequently, this management technique, which requires farmer cooperation and compensation for some reduced productivity, is gaining acceptance in the United Kingdom, Denmark, Sweden, Finland, the Netherlands and Germany (Sotherton 1991, Helenius 1994).

The declines occurring in some species of prairie songbirds (Peterjohn 1994, Knopf 1994) such as the western meadowlark (*Sturnella neglecta*) and grasshopper sparrow (*Ammodramus savannarum*) may be due to effects of agricultural herbicides on non-target plants. For example, some species of native plants that are important for nesting cover, or as food for insects used by very young nestlings, may be adversely affected by some herbicide recently introduced to prairie agriculture. Herbicides in the United Kingdom are believed to be responsible for population declines in two species of farmland bird: the linnet (*Carduelis cannabina*), due to loss of weeds that provide seeds for food; and the reed bunting (*Emberiza schoeniclus*), due to loss of weeds providing vegetative heterogeneity for nesting in clover fields (O'Connor and Shrubb 1986).

On the other hand, declines recently documented (Hlady 1994) in sharp-tailed grouse (*Pedioecetes phasianellus*) populations seem not likely to be linked to herbicide use because numbers of this species are declining in areas of pasture large enough that herbicides drifting from cropland should not affect food supply or nesting cover. This assumption is based on the observations from Europe that indicate lethal herbicide effects do not occur in vegetation beyond 2-6 m from field edges (Marrs *et al.* 1989). There remains the possibility, however, that annual exposure to sublethal amounts of highly phytotoxic chemicals (such as sulfonylureas) drifting several kilometres from sites of application (Bhatti *et al.* 1995) could adversely affect food plants important to adult grouse [eg., wild rose (*Rosa woodsii*) and snowberry (*Symphoricarpos occidentalis*), Pepper 1972). Experiments carried out in Denmark with the herbicide, isoproturon, showed that 50% of the label rate caused a 50% reduction of seed production in the wild plant, *Thlaspi arvense*, whereas 12.5 % of label rate caused a 17% reduction, relative to controls (Hald 1993).

Conservation headlands have also been shown to benefit butterflies, as increased densities of several species have been found on farms where the technique is used (Dover *et al.* 1990). No direct link has been demonstrated thus far, however, between herbicide use and butterfly populations (Dover 1994). Lepidopterists in Saskatchewan (R.R. Hooper, pers. comm.) and Alberta (J. Acorn, pers. comm.) have not noticed any species of butterfly becoming less abundant during the past 20 years, with the exception of the monarch butterfly (*Danaus plexippus*) in southern Saskatchewan. Although monarchs may have declined in numbers in the past several years because of an effect of herbicides on the milkweed host plant, problems in the Mexican wintering grounds of this migratory species may be affecting populations in Saskatchewan.

## Wetland Ecosystems

The amounts of herbicide that enter wetlands in the Prairie Provinces are not well documented. Available data for herbicides in rivers and lakes in agricultural areas provide an indication of the chemicals that may be entering wetlands; however, older reports do not include information on products more recently introduced to the market. The most commonly detected herbicide in waters of prairie rivers or lakes has been 2,4-D, found at maximum concentrations of 0.1-0.4 micrograms per litre ($\mu$g/L or parts per billion); also detected, in concentrations of 0.02-0.5 $\mu$g/L, were bromoxynil, dicamba, dichlorprop, diclofop-methyl, triallate and trifluralin (Gummer 1980, Williamson 1984, Muir and Grift 1987, Donald and Syrgiannis 1995). The main routes of entry of herbicides into surface waters are runoff from snow melt (Nicholaichuk and Grover 1983) or rainfall (Muir and Grift 1987), spray drift (Maybank *et al.* 1978, Grover *et al.* 1985), direct deposit from aircraft application (Sheehan *et al.* 1987, Grue *et al.* 1989) and long-distance atmospheric transport (Grover 1991). Wetlands and lakes, as relatively static bodies of water, have greater potential than rivers to accumulate chemicals to concentrations that could be toxic to aquatic organisms. The only published account of herbicide input to prairie ponds documented the presence of 2,4-D, dicamba, bromoxynil, diclofop-methyl and triallate at concentrations less than 5$\mu$g/L of water in two small ponds in an agricultural watershed during 1985-1987 when spring snowmelt and summer rainfall were below normal (Waite *et al.* 1992).

The toxicity of herbicides to aquatic organisms was reviewed in detail by Sheehan *et al.* (1987). Environmental fate and effects of herbicides on prairie aquatic organisms have more recently been investigated in laboratory microcosms (Lintott 1993) and field enclosures (Muir *et al.* 1991, Désy 1996). Drift of herbicide from ground spray equipment into pond waters is not likely to result in concentrations lethal to submerged macrophytes or aquatic invertebrates, since only about 1% of the applied dosage deposits within 10 m beyond the field edge (Freemark and Boutin 1995). Direct deposit of herbicide, through aerial application, to the surface of a small pond could result in concentrations known to be lethal to some aquatic plants. For example, 2,4-D amine applied at 880 g/ha, the maximum rate registered for use on cereals in Canada (Ali 1992), would result in 0.2 mg/L in pond water, assuming that 100% of the amount applied enters the water of a pond 15 cm deep, as the worst case scenario (the "expected environmental concentration" defined by Environment Canada: Peterson *et al.* 1994). This concentration is twice the value found to be lethal to the submerged macrophyte, *Myriophyllum sibiricum* (Forsyth 1989). Data from the manufacturers of the sulfonylurea, metsulfuron-methyl, showed that growth in shoot length of the submerged macrophyte, *Potamogeton pectinatus*, was inhibited by 77 to 90% relative to untreated controls by exposure to a concentration of 1 $\mu$g/L in the water (Chang 1987). Sulfonylureas are highly soluble in water and relatively stable under alkaline conditions. For example, the 50% decline time (DT50) of metsulfuron-methyl in water in the laboratory at 25°C increased from 5 weeks at pH 5.8 to 25 to 30 weeks at pH 6.9; thus, it could be expected to persist for more than 30 weeks in the predominantly alkaline water (pH up to 9.7) of prairie ponds (Chang 1987). Nonetheless, the DT50 of metsulfuron-methyl in the water of Ontario lake enclosures was only 29 days at pH 6.7 to 7.3 (Thompson *et al.* 1992). Field data are needed to demonstrate how readily these herbicides are transported to prairie ponds in runoff and if they remain available to aquatic plants for relatively extended periods of time.

Loss of submerged macrophytes in a pond would be detrimental to aquatic invertebrates that depend upon plants for food or substrates; these animals are important prey for waterfowl, shorebirds and amphibians. The effects on aquatic macrophytes of most of the herbicides used in large quantities in the Prairie Provinces are unknown. Observations of biologists working in prairie wetlands suggest that some ponds show signs of possible chemical effects: reduced complexity of associated upland vegetation, as noted above, as well as reduced diversity in communities of submerged macrophytes and aquatic insects (D.W. Parker, Aquatax Consulting, and E.A. Driver, Canadian Wildlife Service, Saskatoon, pers. comm.). Peterson *et al.* (1994), in testing 20 herbicides on 10 species of freshwater algae and one species of duckweed (*Lemna minor*), reported that triazine herbicides were highly toxic to algae and duckweed, that sulfonylureas were not toxic to algae but were highly toxic to duckweed and that 2,4-D, MCPA and bromoxynil were not highly toxic to algae or duckweed.

Very little information is available on the annual amounts of herbicide that may be entering prairie ponds in runoff from fields sprayed with the most commonly used herbicides. The majority of products, including 2,4-D, MCPA, difenzoquat, diclofop-methyl (Hoegrass®) and the sulfonylureas, are highly soluble in water. Bromoxynil and flamprop-methyl (Mataven®) are of moderate solubility; triallate (Avadex BW®) and trifluralin (Treflan®) are extremely low in solubility (Hartley and Kidd 1987). Thus, rainfall occurring in sufficient amounts to cause runoff (a heavy rainfall event of at least 25 mm, Woo and Rowsell 1993) could transport soluble herbicides in solution or insoluble herbicides adsorbed to soil particles. Runoff resulting from 25 mm of rain could result in 0.2 mg of 2,4-D amine per litre of water in a pond 15 cm deep, assuming a rate of application of 880 g/ha and a drainage area 10 times the surface area of the pond (Shjeflo 1968). These calculations also assume that runoff from heavy rainfall constitutes 4% of the rate of application, similar to spring snowmelt (Nicholaichuk and Grover 1983), that an average of 11.7% of heavy rainfall leaves the soil surface as runoff (reports of runoff following severe rainfall events by G.T. Miller, Prairie Farm Rehabilitation Administration, Regina, SK), and that runoff precedes significant losses from the soil due to photodegradation, microbial degradation or volatilization. A sulfonylurea such as metsulfuron-methyl under the same circumstances could be transported in runoff to result in 1.7 µg/litre in the pond water, sufficient to cause inhibition of growth among submerged macrophytes. Unlike 2,4-D, sulfonylureas may persist in ponds from one summer to the next so that accumulation of chemical in the water may result from annual applications. There are no data to document whether or not such buildup occurs. Similarly, there are no data on concentrations of herbicides in ponds adjacent to fields treated with major-use herbicides under conditions of normal rainfall.

The majority of herbicides are very low in acute toxicity to aquatic invertebrates, fish and amphibians (Johnson and Finley 1980, Sheehan et al. 1987, Harfenist et al. 1989). Four exceptions are bromoxynil, diclofop-methyl, triallate and trifluralin. Bromoxynil and diclofop-methyl are very rapidly degraded in pond water, however, so that mortality would probably be minimized (Muir et al. 1991, Lintott 1993). Little is known about potential sublethal effects on hormonal systems that could result in impairment of reproduction or survival of wetland fauna. Egg production by

*Daphnia pulex* was reduced in pond enclosures treated with triallate, compared to untreated enclosures (Désy 1996). Responses of fish to sublethal concentrations of toxic substances have included reductions in (i) resistance to pathogens (Malins et al. 1988), (ii) steroid hormone levels and (iii) gonad development (Gagnon et al. 1994). Triallate and trifluralin could persist in sediments where they may be available to aquatic invertebrates or amphibians for prolonged periods (Kent et al. 1992a and b). Information is lacking on the effects of prolonged exposure to herbicides combined with other herbicides or with low levels of lindane, found frequently in prairie rivers and lakes (Gummer 1980, Donald and Syrgiannis 1995).

The total disappearance of the leopard frog (*Rana pipiens*) from most of its range in the Prairie Provinces occurred in Manitoba during 1975 (Koonz 1993) and in Alberta during 1979-1980 (Roberts 1981, 1992). Populations of the spotted frog (*Rana pretiosa*) and Canadian toad (*Bufo hemiophrys*) are also known to be declining in Alberta (Roberts 1992). It seems possible that a widely used herbicide, such as triallate, that is relatively toxic to aquatic invertebrates and fish (Kent et al. 1992a) and persistent in sediments (Donald and Syrgiannis 1995), could affect leopard frogs during hibernation by absorption through the skin. Other relatively toxic (Harfenist et al. 1989), widely used pesticides possibly encountered by amphibians in the water and sediments of prairie ponds (eg., thiram and lindane from the seed coating product, Vitavax ®) might exert a synergistic effect in combination with triallate or other chemicals. The possibility of agricultural pesticides affecting leopard frogs seems relatively unlikely, however, because populations of this species disappeared from lakes in the foothills drainage area of the Red Deer River, where there is no farming activity (Roberts 1992, personal communication). In addition, some recovery in populations of leopard frogs has been reported in Manitoba (Koonz 1993) and Saskatchewan (Seburn 1992) since the declines were noticed, which would not be expected if annual exposure to pesticides were the cause.

## CONCLUSIONS

This summary of the properties of herbicides and some of the ways wildlife and natural habitat have been affected underscores the need for data from field studies to demonstrate whether or not the enormous quantities and constantly increasing variety of new herbicides used annually in the prairies are adversely affecting food webs. The following information is needed: (1) comparison of the diversity of terrestrial plants, insects and wildlife between organic and conventional farms; (2) input of herbicides and fertilizers into ponds, relative to amounts applied to surrounding cropland; (3) drift of sulfonylurea herbicides into, and effects on, upland habitat; (4) potential for herbicides to affect songbird populations through subtle effects on nesting cover or the seeds and insects they eat; (5) potential for herbicides and other toxic chemicals to influence amphibian populations; (6) effective means of communicating to farmers how they can manage pesticides to minimize effects on wildlife and habitat.

## LITERATURE CITED

Ali, S. 1992. Herbicides. Pp. 27-153 *In* Crop protection with chemicals (S. Ali ed.). Alberta Agriculture, Edmonton, Alberta.

Bhatti, M.A., K. Al-Khatib, A.S. Felsot, R. Parker and S. Kadir. 1995. Effects of simulated chlorsulfuron drift on fruit yield and quality of sweet cherries (*Prunus avium* L.). Environmental Toxicology and Chemistry 14: 537-544.

Boutin, C., K.E. Freemark and C.J. Keddy. 1993. Proposed guidelines for registration of chemical pesticides: nontarget plant testing and evaluation. Technical Report Series No. 145. Canadian Wildlife Service, Ottawa, Ontario.

Boutin, C., K.E. Freemark and C.J. Keddy. 1995. Overview and rationale for developing regulatory guidelines for nontarget plant testing with chemical pesticides. Environmental Toxicology and Chemistry 14: 1465-1475.

Bowes, G.G. 1987. Control of weeds in forage crops: rangeland and native pastures. Pp. 44-62 *In* Expert Committee on Weeds, Western Canada Section, Research Report, Volume 3.

Caux, P.-Y., R.A. Kent, M. Taché, C. Grande, G.T. Fan and D.D. MacDonald. 1993. Environmental fate and effects of dicamba: A Canadian perspective. Reviews of Environmental Contamination and Toxicology 133: 1-58.

Chang, F.Y. 1987. Metsulfuron-methyl. Discussion Document No. 87-04, Agriculture Canada, Pesticides Directorate, Ottawa, Ontario.

Clark, R.G. 1989. Use of prairie wetlands by breeding waterfowl. Pp. 233-242 *In* Proceedings of the Symposium on Water Management Affecting the Wet-To-Dry Transition: Planning at the Margins (W. Nicholaichuk and H. Steppuhn, eds.). Water Studies Institute, University of Regina.

Désy, J. 1996. Fate and effects of triallate in a prairie wetland. M.Sc. Thesis, University of Saskatchewan, Saskatoon, Saskatchewan.

Donald, D.B. and J. Syrgiannis. 1995. Occurrence of pesticides in prairie lakes in Saskatchewan in relation to drought and salinity. Journal of Environmental Quality 24: 266-270.

Dover, J.W. 1994. Arable field margins: factors affecting butterfly distribution and abundance. Pp. 59-66 *In* Field margins: integrating agriculture and conservation (N. Boatman, ed.), BCPC Monograph No. 58, British Crop Protection Council, Farnham, Surrey, United Kingdom.

Dover, J. N. Sotherton and K. Gobbett. 1990. Reduced pesticide inputs on cereal field margins: the effects on butterfly abundance. Ecological Entomology 15: 17-24.

Forsyth, D.J. 1989. Agricultural chemicals and prairie pothole wetlands: meeting the needs of the resource and the farmer - Canadian perspective. Transactions of the North American Wildlife and Natural Resources Conference 54: 59-66.

Freemark, K. and C. Boutin. 1994. Nontarget-plant risk assessment for pesticide registration. Environmental Management 18: 841-854.

Freemark, K. and C. Boutin. 1995. Impacts of agricultural herbicide use on terrestrial wildlife in temperate landscapes: a review with special reference to North America. Agriculture, Ecosystems & Environment 52: 67-91.

Gagnon, M.M, J.J. Dodson, P.V. Hodson, G. Van der Kraak and J.H. Carey. 1994. Seasonal effects of bleached kraft mill effluent on reproductive parameters in white suckers (*Catostomus commersoni*) population of the St. Maurice River, Quebec, Canada. Canadian Journal of Fisheries and Aquatic Science 51: 337-347.

Golley, F.B. 1960. Energy dynamics of a food chain of an old-field community. Ecological Monographs 30: 187-206.

Grover, R. 1991. Nature, transport, and fate of airborne residues. Pp. 89-117 *In* Environmental chemistry of herbicides, Volume II (R. Grover and A.J. Cessna, eds.). CRC Press, Boca Raton, Florida.

Grover, R., S.R. Shewchuk, A.J. Cessna, A.E. Smith and J.H. Hunter. 1985. Fate of 2,4-D iso-octyl ester after application to a wheat field. Journal of Environmental Quality 14: 203-210.

Grue, C.E., M.W. Tome, T.A. Messmer, D.B. Henry, G.A. Swanson and L.R. DeWeese. 1989. Agricultural chemicals and prairie pothole wetlands: meeting the needs of the farmer - U.S. perspective. Transactions of the North American Wildlife and Natural Resources Conference 54: 47-58.

Gummer, W.D. 1980. Pesticide monitoring in the prairies of western Canada. Pp. 345-372 *In* Hydrocarbons and halogenated hydrocarbons in the aquatic environment (B.K. Afghan and D. Mackay, eds.) Plenum Press, New York.

Hald, A. B. 1993. Seed setting of a non-target wild plant species at sublethal herbicide doses. Pp. 631-638 *In* Quantitative approaches in weed and herbicide research and their practical applications. Proceedings of the 8th European Weed Research Society Symposium, Braunschweig, Germany, 14-16 July, 1993.

Harfenist, A., T. Power, K.L. Clark and D.B. Peakall. 1989. A review and evaluation of the amphibian toxicological literature. Technical Report Series No. 61. Canadian Wildlife Service, Ottawa, Ontario.

Hartley, D. and H. Kidd. 1987. The agrochemicals handbook, 2nd edition. The Royal Society of Chemistry, The University, Nottingham, England.

Helenius, J. 1994. Adoption of conservation headlands to Finnish farming. Pp. 191-196 *In* Field margins: integrating agriculture and conservation (N. Boatman, ed.). BCPC Monograph No. 58, British Crop Protection Council, Farnham, Surrey, United Kingdom.

Hlady, M. 1994. Sharp-tailed grouse. Pp. 139-150 *In* Saskatchewan game management 1993-1994. Saskatchewan Environment and Resource Management, Wildlife Branch, Regina.

Hoerger, F. and E.E. Kenaga. 1972. Pesticide residues on plants: correlation of representative data as a basis for estimation of their magnitude in the environment. Environmental Quality and Safety 1: 9-28.

Hoffman, D.J. and P.H. Albers. 1984. Evaluation of potential embryotoxicity and teratogenicity of 42 herbicides, insecticides, and petroleum contaminants to mallard eggs. Archives of Environmental Contamination and Toxicology 13: 15-27.

Hoffman, D.J. and W.C. Eastin, Jr. 1982. Effects of lindane, paraquat, toxaphene and 2,4,5-trichlorophenoxyacetic acid on mallard embryo development. Archives of Environmental Contamination and Toxicology 11: 79-86.

Hudson, R.H., R.K. Tucker and M.A. Haegele. 1984. Handbook of toxicity of pesticides to wildlife. Resource Publication 153, United States Department of the Interior, Fish and Wildlife Service, Washington, D.C.

Johns, B.W. 1993. The influence of grove size on bird species richness in aspen parklands. Wilson Bulletin 105: 256-264.

Johnson, W.W. and M.T. Finley. 1980. Handbook of acute toxicity of chemicals to fish and aquatic invertebrates. Resource Publication 137, U.S. Department of the Interior, Fish and Wildlife Service, Washington, D.C.

Kearney, P.C. and D.D. Kaufman. 1969. Degradation of herbicides. Marcel Dekker, Inc., New York, New York.

Kent, R.A., M. Taché, P.-Y. Caux, S. De Silva and K. Lemky. 1992a. Canadian water quality guidelines for triallate. Scientific Series No. 195. Eco-Health Branch, Environment Canada, Ottawa, Ontario.

Kent, R.A., M. Taché, P.-Y. Caux and B.D. Pauli. 1992b. Canadian Water Quality Guidelines for trifluralin. Scientific Series No. 190. Eco-Health Branch, Environment Canada, Ottawa, Ontario.

Knopf, F.L. 1994. Avian assemblages on altered grasslands. Pp. 247-257 *In* A century of avifaunal change in western North America (J.R, Jehl, Jr. and N.K. Johnson, eds.). Studies in Avian Biology No. 15, Cooper Ornithological Society.

Koonz, W.H. 1993. Amphibians in Manitoba. Pp. 273-275 *In* Proceedings of the Third Prairie Conservation and Endangered Species Workshop (G.L. Holroyd, H.L. Dickson, M. Regnier and H.C. Smith, eds.). Provincial Museum of Alberta, Natural History Occasional Paper No. 19.

Lewis, E.T. 1991. Herbicides used for agricultural weed control in western Canada, 1987 - 1989. Economics Branch, Manitoba Agriculture, Winnipeg, Manitoba.

Lintott, D.R. 1993. Evaluation of the fate and toxicity of the herbicide diclofop-methyl using an aquatic model ecosystem. M.Sc. Thesis, Department of Biology, University of Saskatchewan, Saskatoon, Saskatchewan.

Malins, D.C., B.B. McCain, J.T. Landahl, M.S. Myers, M.M. Krahn, D.W. Brown, S.L. Chan and W.T. Roubal. 1988. Neoplastic and other diseases in fish in relation to toxic chemicals: an overview. Aquatic Toxicology 11: 43-67.

Marrs, R.H., C.T. Williams, A.J. Frost and R.A. Plant. 1989. Assessment of the effects of herbicide spray drift on a range of plant species of conservation interest. Environmental Pollution 59: 71-86.

Maybank, J., K. Yoshida and R. Grover. 1978. Spray drift from agricultural pesticide applications. Journal of the Air Pollution Control Association 28: 1009-1014.

Muir, D.C.G. and N.P. Grift. 1987. Herbicide levels in rivers draining two prairie agricultural watersheds (1984). Journal of Environmental Science and Health Part B 22: 259-284.

Muir, D.C.G., D.F. Kenny, N.P. Grift, R.D. Robinson, R.D. Titman and H.R. Murkin. 1991. Fate and acute toxicity of bromoxynil esters in an experimental prairie wetland. Environmental Chemistry and Toxicology 10: 395-406.

National Research Council of Canada. 1978. Phenoxy herbicides - their effects on environmental quality with accompanying scientific criteria for 2,3,7,8-tetrachlorodibenzo-*p*-dioxin (TCDD). Environmental Secretariat, NRCC No. 16075, Ottawa, Ontario.

Nicholaichuk, W. and R. Grover. 1983. Loss of fall-applied 2,4-D in spring runoff from a small agricultural watershed. Journal of Environmental Quality 12: 412-414.

O'Connor, R.J. and M. Shrubb. 1986. Farming and birds. Cambridge University Press, Cambridge.

Pepper, G.W. 1972. The ecology of sharp-tailed grouse during spring and summer in the aspen parklands of Saskatchewan. Wildlife Report No. 1, Saskatchewan Department of Natural Resources, Regina, Saskatchewan.

Peterson, H.G., C. Boutin, P.A. Martin, K.E. Freemark, N.J. Ruecker and M.J. Moody. 1994. Aquatic phytotoxicity of 23 pesticides applied at expected environmental concentrations. Aquatic Toxicology 28: 275-292.

Peterjohn, B.G. 1994. The North American breeding bird survey. Birding 26: 386-398.

Potts, G.R. 1986. The partridge: pesticides, predation and conservation. Collins, London.

Roberts, W.E. 1981. What happened to the leopard frogs? Alberta Naturalist 11: 1-4.

Roberts, W. 1992. Declines in amphibian populations in Alberta. Pp. 14-16 *In* Declines in Canadian amphibian populations: designing a national monitoring strategy (C.A. Bishop and K.E. Pettit, eds.). Occasional Paper No. 76. Canadian Wildlife Service, Ottawa, Ontario.

Seburn, C.N.L. 1992. The status of amphibian populations in Saskatchewan. Pp. 17-18 *In* Declines in Canadian amphibian populations: designing a national monitoring strategy (C.A. Bishop and K.E. Pettit, eds.). Occasional Paper No. 76. Canadian Wildlife Service, Ottawa.

Semenchuk, G.P. 1992. The atlas of breeding birds of Alberta. Federation of Alberta Naturalists, Edmonton, Alberta.

Sheehan, P.K., A. Baril, P. Mineau, D.K. Smith, A. Harfenist and W.K. Marshall. 1987. The impact of pesticides on the ecology of prairie-nesting ducks. Technical Report Series No. 19. Canadian Wildlife Service, Ottawa, Ontario.

Shjeflo, J.B. 1968. Evapotranspiration and the water budget of prairie potholes in North Dakota. Geological Survey Professional Paper 585-B, U.S. Department of the Interior, Washington, D.C.

Sotherton, N.W. 1991. Conservation headlands: a practical combination of intensive cereal farming and conservation . Pp. 373-397 *In* The ecology of temperate cereal fields (L.G. Firbank, N. Carter, J.F. Darbyshire and G.R. Potts, eds.). Blackwell Scientific Publications, Oxford.

Thompson, D.G., L.M. MacDonald and B. Staznik. 1992. Persistence of hexazinone and metsulfuron-methyl in a mixed-wood boreal forest lake. Journal of Agricultural and Food Chemistry 40: 1444-1449.

Waite, D.T., R. Grover, N.D. Westcott, H. Sommerstad and L. Kerr. 1992. Pesticides in ground water, surface water and spring runoff in a small Saskatchewan watershed. Environmental Toxicology and Chemistry 11: 741-748.

Williamson, D.A. 1984. A preliminary investigation into the presence of agricultural pesticides in the LaSalle and Assiniboine Rivers, Manitoba, Canada. Manitoba Department of Environment, Water Standards and Studies Report No. 84-5.

Willis, G.H. and L.L. McDowell. 1987. Pesticide persistence on foliage. Reviews of Environmental Contamination and Toxicology 100: 23-73.

Woo, M.-K. and R.D. Rowsell. 1993. Hydrology of a prairie slough. Journal of Hydrology 146: 175-207.

# INDIRECT EFFECTS OF INSECTICIDES ON WILDLIFE

## Pamela A. Martin[1], Daniel L. Johnson[2], Douglas J. Forsyth[3] and Bernard D. Hill[2]

[1]RR8 - 40 - 9, Lethbridge, Alberta T1J 4P4;
[2]Agriculture and Agri-food Canada, Lethbridge Research Station, Lethbridge, Alberta;
[3]Canadian Wildlife Service, 115 Perimeter Road, Saskatoon, Saskatchewan S7N 0X4

## HISTORICAL BACKGROUND

Insecticides have caused concern to avian wildlife conservationists since the realization of the devastating effects of persistent organochlorine and mercurial compounds on bird populations during the 1960's. Well-documented declines in populations of North American raptor and fish-eating waterbird species has been attributed to DDT effects on breeding success (Hickey and Anderson 1968, Risebrough 1986). The acute toxicity of dieldrin was considered responsible for the precipitous decreases in accipiter and falcon numbers in Great Britain (Ratcliff 1980, Nisbet 1988, Newton *et al.* 1986, Newton *et al.* 1992). Recovery of populations following the banning of these compounds in the early 1970's attests to their role in the declines (Anderson *et al.* 1975, Spitzer *et al.* 1978, Grier 1982).

During the two decades following their removal from market, persistent organochlorine insecticides were largely replaced by a new generation of insecticides that are still widely used. The organophosphorus and carbamate insecticides are considerably less persistent in the environment and do not bioaccumulate in animal tissues. Nevertheless, the high acute avian toxicity of many of these insecticides has resulted in further problems for birds. Many large die-offs, particularly of waterfowl, have been attributed to the agricultural use of specific carbamate or organophosphorus compounds (Hill *et al.* 1984, Environmental Protection Agency 1989). Of further concern are resulting incidents of secondary poisoning of raptorial species that feed on poisoned ducks in the field.

## INDIRECT VERSUS DIRECT EFFECTS

The documented effects of organochlorine, organophosphorus and carbamate insecticides on wild bird populations have typically been direct. Direct effects include acute or chronic toxicity influencing in the survival of affected individuals or impairing their reproductive success. In contrast, indirect effects of insecticides typically include the reduction of habitat quality through alteration of food resources. This may be particularly important during the brood-rearing season of birds. Juveniles of many bird species rely on arthropods and other invertebrates to provide the protein they require for rapid growth. The nestling diet of several grassland songbirds are composed entirely of terrestrial arthropods, with only horned lark (*Eremophilis alpestris*) nestlings consuming any appreciable quantity of seeds (Maher 1979, Knapton 1980, Petersen and Best 1986). Juvenile sharp-tailed grouse (*Tympanuchus phasianellus*), gray partridge (*Perdix perdix*) and ring-necked pheasants (*Phasianus colchicus*) consume large quantities of arthropods during their first 3 to 4 weeks of life (Southwood and Cross 1969, Pepper 1972, Whitmore *et al.* 1986). Ducklings also depend almost entirely on aquatic invertebrates for nutrition early in life (Chura 1961; Bartonek and Hickey 1969; Sugden 1973). Therefore reductions in invertebrate populations in brood-rearing habitat could reduce growth and survival of developing juvenile birds.

All insecticides have the potential to cause indirect effects through the removal of food resources. However, much concern has focused on a newer class of insecticides, the synthetic pyrethroids. These insecticides are considered to be a safer alternative method of insect pest control in comparison to the organophoshorus and carbamate compounds, as their avian and mammalian toxicity is very low (e.g., the dose which causes 50% mortality (LD50) in mallard ducks for carbofuran [carbamate] and deltamethrin [pyrethroid] are 0.48 versus 4,640 mg/kg body weight: Hudson *et al.* 1984, Elliot *et al.* 1978). While the direct toxicity of pyrethroids to birds is not a concern, they are known to have high broad-spectrum toxicity to aquatic and terrestrial invertebrates and recommended application rates are very low for this reason.

## INVERTEBRATE REDUCTIONS IN WETLANDS - IMPLICATIONS FOR WATERFOWL PRODUCTIVITY

The issue of wetland contamination with insecticides resulting in depletion of pond invertebrates has raised considerable concern among waterfowl biologists as aquatic invertebrates are the primary food resource of ducklings (Mineau *et al.* 1987, Forsyth 1989). Hunter *et al.* (1984) showed that carbaryl, a carbamate insecticide used in control of lepidopteran forest pests, applied at recommended rates over small forest wetlands, caused high invertebrate mortality resulting in reductions in growth rates of resident ducklings of about 40% compared to control birds. Research on prairie wetlands by Morrill and Neal (1990) indicated that aerial applications of deltamethrin caused close to 100% mortality of chironimid (family: Chironomidae) larvae (a major component of the aquatic invertebrate community, and important duckling food source) during the weeks following spray, and mallard (*Anas platyrhynchos*) ducklings kept on those ponds ceased gaining weight, relative to ducklings on control ponds. A further study (Martin and Forsyth, unpublished data) assessing impacts on invertebrate populations following a late season application of deltamethrin typical of those used in the control of diamond-backed moths in canola, showed severe reductions in chironomids and other invertebrates that persisted through the remainder of the summer. These studies indicated that ponds oversprayed with the pyrethroid insecticide would make poor brood-rearing habitat for waterfowl, supporting either reduced duckling growth rates, or being avoided entirely by broods. Given the substantial decline in prairie wetlands due to agricultural drainage, further reductions in quality of remaining suitable brood-rearing ponds is undesirable.

## FORESTRY SPRAYING - IMPACTS OF FOOD REMOVAL ON FOREST SONG-BIRDS

Extensive spraying for the control of lepidopteran pests occurs in forests of commercial value worldwide, and reductions in forest arthropods may have consequences for breeding songbirds. The pyrethroid insecticide, cypermethrin, applied for the control of the green moth in oak forests in Spain, caused 100% mortality of all lepidopteran larvae and reductions in most other arboreal arthropods (Pascual and Peris 1992). This reduction in food resources had substantial consequences for the reproductive output of resident popula-

tions of blue tit (*Parus caeruleus*) which forage in the oak forest canopy: nestling mortality was 81% and nest success 35% in the treated forest, compared to 6% nestling mortality and 100% nest success in untreated plots (Pascual and Peris 1992). As well, chick weight at fledging was lower in sprayed plots. In West Virginian forests, the lepidopteran strain of bacterial insecticide, *Bacillus thuringiensis* (Bt), and the growth regulator insecticide diflubenzuron (DBF), both of which are specific to lepidopteran larvae, were applied for Gypsy moth control (Sample *et al.* 1993). In plots where Bt was applied, forest canopy songbirds made fewer nesting attempts and there was a marked reduction in lepidopteran larvae, typically the predominant food item, in the diets of these birds. DBF did not appear to cause reductions in reproductive output, but territory size and foraging time of parent birds was increased, and body fat reserves decreased, relative to birds in unsprayed plots suggesting higher energetic demands on brood-rearing adults, with possible detriment to their future survival.

## INSECTICIDE APPLICATIONS IN AGRICULTURE - INDIRECT EFFECTS

Little research has focused on indirect effects of insecticides used for control of agricultural pests. One notable study involved widespread declines of the gray partridge in agricultural areas of England, which prompted investigations into the role of pesticides (Southwood and Cross 1969, Rands 1985). Chick survival was found to be low in sprayed fields and it was determined that there were severe reductions in the availability of the preferred arthropod food resource, caused by a combination of the use of herbicides and insecticides in crops (Southwood and Cross 1969). The implementation of unsprayed swaths adjacent to field margins resulted in increased arthropod numbers adequate to result in improvements in partridge chick survival rates and overall population growth (Rands 1985).

In North Dakota prairie rangeland, George *et al.* (1992) found no change in grassland bird abundance in an area to which carbaryl-treated bran bait had been applied for control of grasshoppers, compared to an untreated area. However, bran baits are targeted specifically towards grasshoppers and have less impact on non-target arthropods, therefore availability of overall arthropod potential food resources were essentially unchanged between the two sites (George *et al.* 1992).

Songbirds may be particularly sensitive to depletions in arthropods caused by insect control operations as their territories are small (frequently less than 1 ha) and their young are immobile. Unlike the precocial broods of waterfowl or galliform species, that may be led to areas of higher food abundance, the altricial young of songbirds are confined to the nest and nest area for at least the first two weeks of life. Johnson *et al.* (1993) assessed the impacts of food removal on grassland songbirds resulting from aerial grasshopper control applications of deltamethrin in large replicated plots of rangeland in southern Alberta. Despite 95% reductions in grasshopper numbers that persisted late into the summer, as well as decreases in non-target arthropod species, parameters of reproductive success of chestnut-collared longspurs (*Calcarius ornatus*) were unaffected. Growth rates and final fledging weights of nestlings were similar between nests in sprayed and unsprayed plots. Information gained through collection of esophageal ligature samples of longspur chicks indicated that although the grasshopper component of the diet of nestlings decreased from 80 to 90% in prespray and unsprayed plots, to <20% after spraying, total arthropod biomass fed to nestlings did not differ between sprayed and unsprayed plots. As well, rate of food delivery and distance flown by parent longspurs did not differ according to spray regime. These results indicate that these birds were able to efficiently switch away from such preferred food items as grasshoppers to arthropods that are unaffected by the insecticide, with no detectable reproductive consequences. Nevertheless, the ability of inexperienced post-fledging juvenile songbirds to feed themselves under conditions of low prey abundance is unknown, and this stage may be that most sensitive to food resource depletions in breeding habitat.

## CONCLUSION

The indirect consequences of insecticide application on wildlife are inevitably more subtle than those resulting from direct chemical toxicity, and as such are difficult to assess. Nevertheless, seasonal depletions in arthropod food resources in brood-rearing habitat in wetlands, forests and agricultural landscapes may constitute serious reductions in habitat quality having the potential to decrease reproductive output of resident bird populations. The measurement of indirect effects must be incorporated into the environmental impact assessment of the broadscale use of pesticides in agriculture and forestry.

## LITERATURE CITED

Anderson, D.W., Jehl, J.R. Jr., Risebrough, R.W., Woods, L.A. Jr., Deweese, L.R. and Edgecomb, W.G. 1975. Brown pelicans: Improved reproduction off the southern California coast. Science 190: 806-808.

Bartonek, J.C. and J.J. Hickey. 1969. Food habits of canvasbacks, redheads, and lesser scaup in Manitoba. Condor 71: 280-290.

Chura, N.J. 1961. Food availability and preferences of juvenile mallards. Transactions of the North American Wildlife and Natural Resources Conference 26: 121-133.

Elliot, M., N.F. Janes and C. Potter. 1978. The future of pyrethroids in insect control. Annual Review of Entomology 23: 443-469.

Environmental Protection Agency. 1989. Carbofuran. U.S. Environmental Protection Agency, Special Review Technical Support Document, Washington, DC.

Forsyth, D.J. 1989. Agricultural chemicals and prairie pothole wetlands: Meeting the needs of the resource and the farmer - Canadian perspective. Transactions of the North American Wildlife and Natural Resources Conference 54: 59-66.

George, T.L., L.C. McEwen and A. Fowler. 1992. Effects of carbaryl bait treatment on nontarget wildlife. Environmental Entomology 21: 1239-1247.

Grier, J.W. 1982. Ban of DDT and subsequent recovery of reproduction in bald eagles. Science 218: 1232-1235.

Hickey, J.J. and D.W. Anderson 1968. Chlorinated hydrocarbons and eggshell changes in raptorial and fish-eating birds. Science 162: 271-273.

Hill, E.F. and W.J. Fleming. 1982. Anticholinesterase poisoning of birds: Field monitoring and diagnosis of acute poisoning. Environmental Toxicology and Chemistry 1: 27-38.

Hudson, R.H., R.K. Tucker and M.A. Haegele. 1984. Handbook of toxicity of pesticides to wildlife, 2nd ed. Publication No. 153. U.S. Fish and Wildlife Service, Washington, DC.

Hunter, M.L. Jr., J.W. Witham and H. Dow. 1984. Effects of carbaryl-induced depression in invertebrate abundance on the growth and behavior of American black duck and mallard ducklings. Canadian Journal of Zoology 62: 452-456.

Johnson, D.L., P.A. Martin, D.J. Forsyth and B. Hill. 1992. Effects of the pyrethroid, deltamethrin, for grasshopper control on the food resources and reproductive success of grassland songbirds: Balancing crop protection with wildlife habitat requirements. Progress Report to Wildlife Toxicology Fund, World Wildlife Fund, Canada, Toronto.

Knapton, R.W. 1980. Nestling foods and foraging patterns in the clay-colored sparrow.to wildlife, 2nd ed. Publication No. 153. U.S. Fish and Wildlife Service, Washington, DC.

Maher, W.J. 1979. Nestling diets of prairie passerine birds at Matador, Saskatchewan, Canada. Ibis 121: 437-452.

Mineau, P., P.J. Sheehan and A. Baril. 1987. Pesticides and waterfowl on the Canadian prairies: A pressing need for research and monitoring. Pp. 133-147 *In* The value of birds (A.W. Diamond and F.L Filion, eds.). ICBP Technical Publication No. 6.

Morill, P.K. and B.R. Neal. 1990. Impact of deltamethrin insecticide on Chironomidae (Diptera) of prairie ponds. Canadian Journal of Zoology 68: 289-296.

Newton, I., I Wyllie and A. Asher 1991. Mortality causes in British barn owls (*Tyto alba*), with a discussion of aldrin-dieldrin poisoning. Ibis 133: 162-169.

Newton, I., I. Wyllie, and A. Asher. 1992. Mortality from the pseticides aldrin and dieldrin in British Sparrowhawks and Kestrels. Ecotoxicology 1: 31-44.

Nisbet, I.C.T. 1988. Relative importance of DDE and dieldrin in the decline of peregrine falcon populations. Pp. 351-376 *In* Peregrine falcon populations: their management and recovery (T.J.

Cade, J.H. Enderson, C.G. Thelander, and C.M. White, eds). The Peregrine Fund Inc., Boise, Idaho.

Pascual, J.A. and S.J Peris. 1992. Effects of forest spraying with two application rates of cypermethrin on food supply and on breeding success of the blue tit (*Parus caeruleus*). Environmental Toxicology and Chemistry 11: 1271-1280.

Pepper, G.W. 1972. The ecology of sharp-tailed grouse during spring and summer in the aspen parklands of Saskatchewan. Saskatchewan Department of Natural Resources Wildlife Report No. 1.

Petersen, K.L. and L.B. Best. 1985. Brewer's sparrow nest-site characteristics in a sagebrush community. Journal of Field Ornithology 56: 23-27.

Petersen, K.L. and L.B. Best. 1986. Diets of nestling sage sparrows and Brewer's sparrows in an Idaho sagebrush community. Journal of Field Ornithology 57: 283-294.

Rands, M.R. W. 1985. Pesticide use on cereals and the survival of grey partridge chicks: a field experiment. Journal of Applied Ecology 22: 49-54.

Ratcliffe, D.A. 1980. The peregrine falcon. Buteo Books, Vermillion, South Dakota.

Risebrough, R.W. 1986. Pesticides and bird populations. Current Ornithology 3: 397-427.

Sample, B.E., R.C. Whitmore and L. Butler. 1993. Indirect effects of two insecticides applied for gypsy moth control. Abstract I01, 14th Annual Meeting of the Society of Environmental Toxicology and Chemistry, Houston, Texas.

Spitzer, P.R., R.W. Risebrough, W II Walker, R. Hernandeq, A. Poole, D. Puleston and I.C.T. Nisbet. 1978. Productivity of ospreys in Connecticut-Long Island increases as DDE residues decline. Science 202: 333-335.

Southwood, T.R.E. and D.J. Cross. 1969. The ecology of the partridge. III. Breeding success and the abundance of insects in natural habitats. Journal of Animal Ecology 38: 497-509.

Sugden, L.G. 1973. Feeding ecology of pintail, gadwall, American widgeon, and lesser scaup ducklings. Canadian Wildlife Service Report No. 24.

Whitmore, R.W., K.P. Pruess and R.E. Gold. 1986. Insect food selection by 2-week-old ring-necked pheasant chicks. Journal of Wildlife Management 50: 223-228.

# LIVESTOCK AND WILDLIFE: A BROADSIDE

## Don Gayton

723 Robson St., Nelson, British Columbia V1L 5A9

As a society, we are free to choose land management options that range from "protected" to "dedicated," that is, from ecological reserves and wilderness areas at one extreme, to tree farms and feedlots on the other. Although these protected and dedicated options are both honourable and important, the truly interesting options lie in between, where environmental and resource extraction interests must work together.

Creating ecosystem management systems that respect the biological constraints of the landscape, that maintain a substantial component of native wildlife and vegetation, and that produce sustainable economic gain is a tremendous challenge, but also one that will give us intellectual, moral and spiritual satisfaction. Rather than our traditional going-forth-to-conquer-and-multiply, we must now learn how to go forth to collaborate and sustain.

I believe there is one economic activity that has a good chance of succeeding with this challenge, one that has good potential, if managed correctly, for permanent sustainability. That single activity is dispersed, managed livestock grazing on native rangelands.

The science of this activity, range management, has a lot to offer to ecosystem management. We were the ones, after all, who developed the fundamental concept of carrying capacity, and who pioneered land management that employs and mimics the natural processes of grazing and fire. However, the ranching and range management community should guard against becoming smug and complacent, because there are plenty of examples of bad range management still to be seen on the prairies.

If we respond honestly to Charles Kay's assertion (see article in these proceedings) that the numbers of pre-European contact elk, deer and bison were much smaller than we commonly assume, then we cannot make such a strong claim to be replacing the lost native ungulate component with our cows. Kay's theory is a double-edged sword: it argues for reductions in native ungulate populations at the same time that it removes some of the rationale for widespread livestock grazing. More thoughtful research and analysis is required in this area.

Ours is a dynamic and imperfect world, and we don't always have the luxury of analyzing problems for decades on end. We may look back, twenty years from now, and wonder why we devoted so much time and energy to interactions of livestock with wild ungulates and livestock with waterfowl, when the really critical, unsolved interactions were between livestock with the plains spadefoot toad, livestock with the spotted newt, and livestock with the badger. The bushtit and the canyon wren could easily rise up and make fools of all of us.

In our conference questionnaire, I was interested to see that a majority of respondents agreed with the statement that some wildlife populations are "managed populations," in the sense that humans exercise substantial control over their habitat, food sources and population sizes. In other words, certain species—and I would offer as examples elk, deer and game waterfowl—are managed very much like cows are. In the future, we may have to clarify our various occupations by hyphenating them to cow-rancher, duck-rancher, or elk-rancher! The point is though, that ranchers and wildlifers may have more in common than they currently realize.

I can cite another example of this newfound commonality of interest. The high desert country of Eastern Oregon has had its share of classic battles between the large ranchers and local wildlife advocates. These traditional opponents fought tooth and nail over deer, coyotes, antelope, ducks and so on. Then a great social change occurred: wealthy individuals from Portland discovered the scenic beauty of the high desert country, and began buying up the long-established ranches. Soon the dreaded "ranchette," the "subdivision" and the "recreational acreage" made their appearance on the landscape, along with overgrazing (by people who had no idea there was anything wrong with 5 horses on 4 acres), more fences, more dogs, more roads, and more ATV's. The environmental and wildlife community soon woke up to the fact that, as bad as they thought those crusty old ranchers might have been, this new alternative was an awful lot worse for their interests. The communities pulled together and found ways of keeping the big ranches intact, in some cases to the point that an environmental/wildlife funding agency would purchase an entire ranch from an individual wanting to retire, but continue to operate it as a ranch, so that subdivision would not occur.

We should be careful to not let traditional, partisan positions stand in the way of useful collaborations like in the Oregon example.

The livestock and wildlife communities stand at a crossroads: either they rise up to the challenge, adapt, use the best parts of their own unique traditions, and build on successful collaborations, or they stonewall, lobby, slip into recrimination, paranoia and ultimate defeat. The challenge, as I said before, is to devise workable ecosystem management schemes that provide equity to environmental, wildlife and resource interests.

The key elements of ecosystem management are the development of local coalitions of environmental and resource interest groups, backed by educated constituencies, collecting appropriate, arms-length biological monitoring data, and from that data making informed, consensus-based and independent land management recommendations. If this prescription sounds a bit overwhelming, just think of it as rehearsing for the future.

# LIVESTOCK-WILDLIFE INTERACTIONS

## Garry C. Trottier

*Canadian Wildlife Service, 4999-98 Ave. Edmonton, Alberta T6B 2X3*

We are considering the compatibility of livestock grazing and ecosystem management on prairie rangelands. Like all jargon, the term Ecosystem Management leaves you scratching your head wondering what it means. So in the following presentation I ask some practical questions regarding the application of this new direction that ecologists dream of following.

Don Gayton describes key elements in sustainable ecosystem management as the development of local coalitions of environmental and resource interest groups, backed by educated constituencies, collecting appropriate, arms-length biological monitoring data, and from that data making informed, consensus-based and independent land management recommendations. These are very close to a working definition recently presented by Edward Grumbine of the Sierra Institute.

"Ecosystem management integrates scientific knowledge within a complex socio-political and values framework, toward the general goal of protecting native ecosystem integrity over the long term" (Grumbine 1994).

Grumbine (1994) endorses 5 specific goals, or principles, central to ecosystem management.

1. Viable populations of native species are maintained in situ (Grumbine 1994). In general most people would agree that the dedication of prairie rangelands to livestock grazing meets this principle. We fully understand that the present states and functions of our rangelands are largely the direct result of some 140 years of livestock grazing. The results are acceptable are they not? Well, perhaps some conditions need improving, but many pastures vibrate with prairie wildlife at a level we have accepted as a lot better than the alternatives— namely cultivation or overgrazing.

2. All native ecosystem types are represented across their natural range of variability (Grumbine 1994). I anticipate future challenges in meeting this principle. Livestock production systems are structured in one direction; economically sustainable with efficient forage utilization. The status quo in these systems is annual grazing. So in my view this leaves few options to manage for variable effects. Therefore, in a landscape context we will need protected natural areas just to achieve certain other grassland states and functions.

3. Evolutionary and ecological processes are maintained; namely disturbance regimes including fire, nutrient cycles, and hydrological processes (Grumbine 1994). If we adhere to the spirit of maintaining the natural range of variability, can livestock production systems be modified to meet this challenge?

4. Management is extended over sufficient time periods to maintain the evolutionary potential of species and ecosystems (Grumbine 1994). This implies long-term commitments that cannot be compromised by changing economic pressures or government policies. Once the course is set it must be maintained.

5. We accommodate human use and occupancy within the above constraints (Grumbine 1994). My view on this is that recreational uses should be on an equal footing with economic uses, particularly on Crown Lands.

A key element in successful consensus building is modification of the way people think. With respect to livestock grazing on prairie rangelands, there are five entrenched ideas which I feel will have to be challenged as we move toward ecosystem management.

1. Grasslands will not survive if large herbivore grazing (livestock) is removed. This statement has to be put in perspective because it is an argument that is misused purposely to justify livestock grazing anywhere and everywhere. We have millions of acres of prairie rangeland that demonstrate what annual grazing does to grasslands. How and where do we allow for other regimes? Consider this statement by Dr. Jim Romo commenting on the push to have livestock grazing in Grasslands National Park. "Just as we need grazing on the landscape, we also need examples that are not grazed - with domestic livestock in traditional ways" (Romo 1992).

2. The natural range of variability is achievable regardless of scale and under traditional production oriented systems. There are many people who will want to

operate from this perspective. My concern is that this will put undue pressure on landowners, pasture managers, and natural area managers to pursue the range of variability goal in the grazing plan when it is physically impossible given the land unit in question and producer constraints.

Consider that in the primeval prairie there were opportunities for plants to escape from large herbivores for extended periods of time because the natural grazing system operated over a large scale disturbance mosaic. Patchy, unpredictable rainfall, wildfire, and insect infestations caused localized forage depletions which stimulated movement. Wildlife distributions were also limited by localized water deficiencies, minerals, navigable terrain, and native peoples.

Therefore, the dream of a natural range of variability must be considered in the context of a large landscape. In the landscape sense we will have to consider what are the gaps in disturbance effects that are not being attained solely under livestock grazing systems? The challenge will be how and where to fill those gaps.

3. Livestock grazing is analogous to primeval large herbivore grazing systems. As the saying goes, livestock grazing is the best option we have so lets make the best of it without question. This implies that we can expect livestock grazing to produce equivalent states and functions that grasslands developed under. But should we accept this so readily?

Consider the following example for comparison. The Acacia Savannas of Masailand, Kenya annually sustained 70-100 thousand pounds of wild ungulates per square mile as a natural grazing system but only 11 thousand pounds of cattle, sheep and goats (Talbot and Swift 1965, Talbot 1972). This begs the question, do we really understand the scope of innovations that will be required to manage rangelands for sustained ecosystem management?

4. Natural ecosystem functions will be maintained under livestock grazing in the absence of fire. Whether or not we want to admit it, the fact is, there is little or no room in production oriented grazing systems for fire, except perhaps as a range improvement tool to control woody encroachment. Without fire, can we still purport to be achieving the natural range of variability?

5. All this considered, I also wonder about the impact of economic pressures. A 50% increase in annual steer and heifer production between 1990 and the year 2000 in Alberta is likely to be realized.

How does the prairie land base support the increased forage requirements? Pasture and native range capacity, already at 110% is projected to be 160% by the year 2000 (Alberta Agriculture Market Analysis Branch, pers. comm.). Does this mean greater pressure on native prairie grasslands in the south? Will new grazing technologies be developed, and if so, will there still be room for the dream of maintaining natural ecosystem integrity?

Hopefully my questions will stimulate some thought and debate.

## LITERATURE CITED

Grumbine, R.E. 1994. What is ecosystem management? Conservation Biology 8:27-38.

Romo, J. 1992. Grazing in Grasslands National Park. The Grazing Gazette 1:7, Saskatchewan Stock Growers Association.

Talbot, L.M., and L.W. Swift. 1965. Production of wildlife in support of human populations in Africa. Proceedings International Grassland Congress 9:1355-1359.

Talbot, L.M. 1972. Ecological consequences of rangeland development in Masailand, East Africa. Pp. 694-711 *In* The careless technology (M. Taghi Farvar and J.P. Milton, eds.). Natural History Press, Garden City, New York.

# BIODIVERSITY ON THE FARM

## Gaylen Armstrong

*Consultant/Biologist, Alberta Agriculture, Food and Rural Development, Conservation and
Development Branch, Lethbridge, Alberta T1J 4C7*

The following definitions used by Alberta Agriculture, Food, and Rural Development are provided to clarify the terms used in this article:

- Sustainable land management, sustainable agricultural production, and sustainable development, means ensuring that our agri-food systems are economically viable and provide for basic human food and fibre needs, while conserving or enhancing the resource base and the quality of the environment for future generations.

- Soil and water conservation practices are actions carried out in order to maintain the quality of the environment and the agricultural productivity of the land.

- Biodiversity means the variety of life, which includes all our ecosystems, the species within, and their genetic make up. It is the environment in which we live. The agricultural landscape is, therefore, a significant part of biodiversity with its open fields, woodlots, wetlands, native and tame pasture, croplands, livestock, and wildlife.

In the context of farm management, biodiversity is maintained or enhanced through management of native and non-native habitat within the confines of sustainable agricultural production. For example, within the same agricultural landscape, farm A, with a mixture of bush, pasture, and cropland would receive a higher biodiversity value than nearby farm B with its cropland habitat only. Both of these farms are considered economically viable; in fact, farm B would be given strong approval in farm management circles for its tidy fields and clean borders.

## BIODIVERSITY VALUES

Do the farmer and the public lose out if we continue to reduce biodiversity by simplifying our landscapes through intensive agricultural practices?

The answer was a resounding "yes" by the majority of the world's countries at the Earth Summit in Rio de Janeiro in June, 1992. From an agricultural perspective, a continued reduction in biodiversity means, for example: fewer plant species (domestic and wild) which would threaten the capability to produce new disease resistant varieties of crops; reduced opportunity in applying biotechnology for advancement of crop production; job loss from industries relying on the existence of a biodiverse landscape that provides food, wood, recreation, tourism, medicines, water, and as yet unknown products.

## BIODIVERSITY ON THE FARM

If we are convinced that our existing agricultural landscapes should be managed for retention and enhancement of biodiversity, then why are we still losing it at an alarming rate? Several reasons for this loss are provided from experiences in integrated farm conservation planning (IFCP) with over 70 producers from across Alberta since 1986. IFCP is an initiative supported directly and indirectly by producers and several agencies such as Alberta Agriculture, Food and Rural Development; Alberta North American Waterfowl Management Plan; Alberta Conservation Tillage Society (ACTS); Wildlife Habitat Canada; Agriculture Service Boards; Ducks Unlimited; Prairie Farm Rehabilitation Administration (PFRA), etc.

Completing an IFCP with a farmer is simply sitting at the kitchen table with aerial photos of the farm, after three or four trips to the field with agricultural field staff and the farmer, and discussing the farm operation as to where improvements (soil and water conservation practices) could be made to make the farm more economically viable. In most cases the farmer usually identifies many of the improvements required.

The completed IFCP contains a list of recommended soil and water conservation practices with corresponding economic and other benefits as shown in Table 1.

Table 1. Example of recommended practices and benefits.

| Soil/Water Conservation Practices | Economic Benefits | Other Benefits |
|---|---|---|
| • establish permanent cover for tame pasture where cultivation exists in NE ¼. Manure heavily on exposed knolls prior to seeding. Graze in early spring and fall, to allow deferment of grazing on native range until June 15. | • erosion control on steep slopes for sustainable pasture production. Early spring pasture reduces supplementary feeding costs. Deferment of native range improves range condition resulting in improved livestock performance. | • improved water quality of runoff and improved soil conditions in pastures. Productivity during droughts. Wildlife habitat improved. |
| • cross fence and develop tank stock water system outside dugout in section 2. | • allows for rotational grazing system for more efficient use of forage. Water system improves water quality. Both the above improves livestock performance. | • as above |
| • control brush invasion of rangeland in S½. Consider burning as an economical alternative to mowing and spraying. Stock at 0.4 aum's/acre. | • increases forage production for improved livestock performance. | • as above |
| • retain existing native habitats (wetlands/poplar stands)in NE¼ & S½ of section 1. | • moisture retained by trapping snow, storing runoff, and recharging groundwater table. Confines salinity(wetlands). Controls floods, thereby controlling erosion. Wetlands provide forage, especially during droughts. These benefits result in sustainable crop production. | • results in potable water supplies on and off farm. Improved wildlife habitat including species that control agricultural pests. |
| • grassing drainage channels along right-of-ways. | • reduces soil erosion, especially along field edges, resulting in sustained crop production. | • results in potable water in runoff. Provides wildlife habitat. |

Most farmers agree that the practices are ecologically sound, sustainable, and contribute to biodiversity; but most farmers were reluctant to apply those practices that appear shaded in the following table, for one or more reasons. To illustrate their reasons for this reluctance, I refer you to the practice of retaining existing native habitats.

There have been several studies in the prairie provinces on the economics of wetland retention and drainage. Authors of these studies concluded that it is not cost beneficial to drain wetlands. For example, a recent study done in Saskatchewan determined a deficit of $1600 in converting 5 wetlands, at 1 acre each, to grain crops over a 10 year period. Given this fact and the direct economic and other farm benefits of retaining wetland and bush retention, why are farmers reluctant to retain these native habitats? Reasons for this reluctance are as follows:

a) Questionable cost benefits. Not enough convincing information is available that relates to local situations.

b) The conservation practice is perceived to be more of a societal benefit and, therefore, incentives are required.

c) Reluctant to apply unfamiliar conservation practices.

d) The economic benefits are longterm, not immediate.

e) Not convinced that a problem exists.

f) Not convinced of the benefits to the farm operation.

## REQUIREMENTS FOR RETENTION AND ENHANCEMENT OF BIODIVERSITY

What is needed to insure that producers automatically apply soil and water conservation practices and include considerations for biodiversity?

Some big changes are needed as follows:

a) We need policies and legislation that clearly define how our agricultural landscapes should be managed on a sustained basis. At the International Workshop On Sustainable Land Management For The 21st Century, Lethbridge, June, 1993, Caza and Neave (1994) states that "...we have failed to recognize the need to encourage and support private and corporate landowners to accept greater responsibility for managing land in a sustainable way." We, as public and producers should converge our ideas as to what we perceive the agricultural landscape should look like. At the moment, the perception varies from clean square neat fields of cropland to productive croplands interspersed with interconnected areas of native habitats.

According to Rosaasen and Lokken (1994), Canadian agricultural policies lack a supportive link to sustainable land management (SLM), and they suggest a major overhaul in policies to reflect consideration for all resources in the agricultural landscape.

b) We need supportive programs, accessible to all farmers, that promote sustainable agriculture and biodiversity. While there are several programs that support SLM initiatives, some are ill-funded, others are only applicable for certain areas, and some are short term. One of the most successful programs, the Permanent Cover Program, ran out of money! In a study done for ACTS by Haig and Haig (1992), adopters of conservation tillage practices suggested that they should pay lower crop insurance premiums, and non-adopters suggested increased funding for demonstration projects.

c) Interagency cooperation at the field level to provide advice on integrated farm conservation management is needed to demonstrate to farmers that agencies are not acting on conservation issues in a piece meal fashion. As stated by Rosaasen and Lokken (1994), the meaning of SLM varies according to limited perspectives of each agency. On receiving a completed IFCP, a farmer in the Camrose area, he stated that "...it was refreshing to see interagency cooperation rather than be attacked from several different fronts by scattered personnel all doing their specific job!"

d) We need a continuation and expansion of projects that promote sustainable agriculture with biodiversity. Jensen (1988) stated in an Alberta conservation tillage survey, that to better facilitate the adoption of conservation practices, demonstration projects should be adapted to local conditions and be economically feasible.

e) There is a proliferation of extension material on the market that fails to reflect integrated farm conservation planning that is clear, concise, and endorsed by the producer. There is a proposal underway to develop a producer-endorsed set of evaluation guidelines that provide information on the sustainability of a farm operation. This voluntary self-evaluation of the farm operation would provide the following advantages to the producer:

- Identifying alternative sustainable practices, resulting in increased farm income.

- Practices associated with on-farm environmental liability are identified. According to lending institutions, the less environmental risks of liability, the stronger your credit rating.

- Practices that negatively impact natural resources used by the producer and the public are identified for possible solutions.

- Practices that ensure the agricultural sustainability of the land for future producers are identified.

- Helps the producer to avoid future costs of inaction.

f) An all-encompassing producer lobby group is needed to encourage programs that support sustainable practices and biodiversity commensurate with the socioeconomic well being of the farm unit, and lobby for a restructuring of policies that are in conflict with SLM.

The above recommendations are a few things that need to be done if SLM, including biodiversity, is going to be part of the farm operation. Many of you in the audience today have made the same recommendations recently and in the past.

## CONCLUSIONS

Is it practical for farmers and ranchers to retain and enhance native habitats and thereby contribute to biodiversity and sustainable agriculture? Can the retention of native habitats be part of any producer's management mandate? The answers depend on two major points:

1) The producer must endorse the concept of SLM with biodiversity; and

2) There must be a support network to make the retention and enhancement of native habitats eco-

nomically expedient and ecologically sound. Producer endorsement comes from well-planned awareness programs that use all suitable information sources to the fullest (Jensen 1988), and the support network should include province-wide programs and policies that complements SLM and biodiversity initiatives on the farm.

Until these things happen, existing pilot projects and programs will continue to support whatever landowner, program, and project budgets will allow. With farmers such as members of ACTS and other conservation organizations, I'm optimistic that the agricultural landscape can reflect consideration for all resources, including biodiversity.

## LITERATURE CITED

Caza, C. and D. Neave. 1994. Philosophy and practicality - pillars to support sustainable development. Pp. 149-156 *In* Proceedings of the International Workshop on Sustainable Land Management for the 21st Century. Volume 2: Plenary Papers (R.C. Wood and J. Dumanski, eds.). The Organizing Committee. International Workshop on Sustainable Land Management. Agriculture Institute of Canada, Ottawa, Ontario.

Haig, R.J. and Catherine M. Haig. 1992. Conservation tillage in Alberta agriculture: a follow up study of adoption trends. Dept. of Rural Economy. Faculty of Agriculture and Forestry. Univ. of Alberta. Edmonton, Alberta.

Jensen, T. 1988. Conservation tillage survey. Report prepared by the Conservation and Development Branch, Alberta Agriculture, Edmonton, Alberta.

Rosaasen, K.A. and J.J. Lokken. 1994. Canadian agricultural policies and other initiatives and their impacts on prairie agriculture. Pp. 343-368 *In* Proceedings of the International Workshop on Sustainable Land Management for the 21st Century. Volume 2: Plenary Papers (R.C. Wood and J. Dumanski, eds.). The Organizing Committee. International Workshop on Sustainable Land Management. Agriculture Institute of Canada, Ottawa.

# IMPACTS OF AGRICULTURAL MANAGEMENT PRACTICES ON WILDLIFE HABITAT

## Graham Dorn

*Saskatchewan Wetland Conservation Corporation, Regina, Saskatchewan*

Settlement of Prairie Canada brought the European belief in man's dominance over land and beast. The combined effects of industrialization and settlement converted the buffalo commons of central North America to a wheat field, forever altering the landscape. In the process many species of flora and fauna were driven near, or to, extinction.

Government policies and programs have been very influential in directing land management and use. In the late 1850's John Palliser explored the prairie's agricultural potential and identified a large area as unsuitable for cultivated agriculture. Anxious to settle the west to keep it out of American hands, the Canadian government sent John Macoun out in the 1870's to report the Northwest was all equally good land, and that "he had never seen a bad crop." The Dominion Land Act promised settlers free land in return for building a dwelling and breaking the sod. Experimental Farms were established to develop and demonstrate farming practices. Conscription of the Indian Head, Saskatchewan Experimental Farm horses in support of the resistance of the Riel rebellion prevented seeding some of the crop that year, resulting in some of the cropland being summerfallowed to control weeds. The crop seeded on this summerfallow the following year outproduced the stubble seeded crop, and the benefit of summerfallow was born.

The productive capability of the rich, virgin prairie soils seemed limitless. The only constraint to crop production was seeded acres. Steam replaced horses as the prairie went under the plough. Records of government promoting wetland drainage date to 1915. Improvements in farm equipment and crop varieties allowed farmers to take advantage of climate and soil productive capacity, and during the 1920's Canada was the world's largest exporter of wheat. The drought of the 1930's was devastating. The hot, dry weather caused farmers and wetlands to disappear from the southern prairies. Farmers moved north to the forest fringe, to literally carve a living out of the bush. The Prairie Farm Rehabilitation Administration (PFRA) was born, with the task of returning the most marginal cultivated soils back to permanent cover and productivity. Shelterbelts were planted to help stabilize the soils, and wildlife habitat was returned to portions of the prairie. During this era wood was important for heating and cooking fuel, and aspen woodlots were often planted to provide some of this fuel.

Following World War II a new generation of farmers returned to the land. The rebuilding of Europe created a demand for grains, and the technologies developed during the war provided the tools. Grain production soared. The Canadian Wheat Board was given the monopoly to export prairie grains, and the quota system was used to evenly distribute farmer opportunities to deliver grain into this burgeoning export market. Quota was based on cultivated acreage, without regard for land quality or cropping intensity. Every cultivated acre was used to establish quota, which encouraged breaking marginal land and bush to increase grain delivery opportunities.

In Saskatchewan, the Conservation and Development (C&D) Branch of Saskatchewan Agriculture was established in 1949 as the provincial counterpart of the PFRA. The C&D projects included erosion control, water stabilization and development, pasture land reclamation, planting and maintaining shelterbelts, eradicating weeds and developing "underdeveloped" areas. Much of their early activity focused on the driest areas of the Brown Soil zone. Wildlife habitat was restored as abandoned agricultural lands were seeded to grass and trees. With abundant rains during the 1950's, the C & D evolved to include drainage of wet or flooded lands. Farming was profitable, and farm size grew as modern equipment developed. Discers replaced pony drills, self propelled combines became common, and wider tillage tools became available. Farmers could get closer to sloughs without getting stuck, and could break the old horse pasture. Wildlife habitat suffered. Grain prices remained firm during the 1960's allowing farmers continue to improve their equipment and expand farm size. Crop Insurance programs were introduced with the goal of stabilizing farm income. Sometimes crop insurance simply guaranteed marginal lands would be profitable to crop, thereby reducing risk and encouraging breaking of additional land. The 1960's were profitable, and improvements in machinery enabled farmers to increase farm size and bring additional land into annual cultivation. Crop protection products effectively controlled a variety of weeds, fertilization became common, and yields increased. But in a couple of years, world supplies of grain became burdensome and grain prices decreased.

In 1970, the Lower Inventories For Tomorrow (LIFT) program encouraged a reduction of crop acres and an increase in perennial forage and summerfallow in return for "quota," or opportunities to deliver grain for sale. Some land was summerfallowed twice and very little land was enroled in the perennial forage option, so LIFT was of little benefit to wildlife habitat. By 1973 world events caused wheat prices to double from their 1970 levels, and the rush was on to bring every acre into production. Crop protection products became important tools to help increase yields, and these products were often applied over wetlands and other marginal lands in an effort to eradicate all pests. Marginal lands, wetlands and bush were broken in an effort to maximize farm income, and the Income Tax Act provided a deduction for the costs to bring this additional land into production. Wildlife habitat suffered as a result, and late 1970's surveys indicated waterfowl and other wildlife populations were falling.

By the 1980's the boom was over, as high interest rates and drought caused many producers, and their bankers, to reevaluate the prairie agricultural production system. Scientists, too, examined the "system," as the first chinks appeared in the armour. Scientific studies confirmed what many had presumed. Waterfowl and other wildlife populations were declining, soil erosion was on the rise, soil salinity was everywhere, water quality was declining, dugouts and wells were going dry. In short, the "agricultural production system" had broken.

Senator Herb Sparrow documented the degredation of prairie soils in his book *Soils At Risk*, and became a crusader for soil conservation in Canada. In response, the governments of Canada and the provinces entered into soil conservation agreements which provided technical and financial assistance for soil conservation, shelterbelts, research and public awareness. The PFRA's Permanent Cover Program (PCP) seeded some 1.3 million acres to perennial forage and trees for contract periods of 10 and 21 years, creating vast areas of wildlife habitat.

Global production of grains, especially in the US and Europe, increased. The Americans and Europeans depressed world grain prices with an export subsidy trade war. To limit grain production, the US provided financial incentives to farmers to reduce the acres seeded to selected grains. To protect marginal soils, the Conservation Reserve Program (CRP) provided and annual payment to farmers in return for seeding crop land to perennial forage, creating some 37 million acres of wildlife habitat.

In 1985 the North American Waterfowl Management Plan (NAWMP) was signed by Canada and the US (Mexico signed later) to address the drop in continental waterfowl populations. As a partnership among agricultural, environmental and wildlife interests, the NAWMP encourages land management practices which conserve soil, water and wetlands for the benefit of agriculture, wildlife and all society.

Low grain prices were encouraging farmers to explore ways to lower production costs. Reducing tillage was beneficial to soil conservation, and also reduced production costs. Non-selective herbicide costs were dropping, and equipment capable of seeding directly into standing stubble was becoming commercially available. Direct seeding caught fire as soil conservation associations promoted the benefits of minimal disturbance seeding. Standing stubble is good for crop production, and good for wildlife habitat.

People continue to migrate from the country to the city in search of jobs. This urbanization results in the general population loosing touch with the natural world and current farming practices. They remember the "good old days" and are prepared to provide financial support to organizations which promise to restore the world to the "way it was." As well, this urban population places an increased interest in watching wildlife and supporting wildlife related organizations.

What effect will these changes to agricultural practices have on wildlife habitat conservation? I believe we have recognized the link between economically sustainable farming systems and a sustainable environment. Changes to our agricultural production systems benefit both agriculture and wildlife habitat. World trade rules have been changed to enable countries to use environmental payments as income support for landowners to conserve marginal lands and wildlife habitat. Agriculture and wildlife are both parts of the puzzle.

The looming world financial crisis encouraged governments to lower trade barriers and tariffs in an effort to reduce export subsidies. The North American Free Trade Agreement (NAFTA) and the General Agreement On Tariffs and Trade (GATT) promise a reduction in export subsidies in return for internal income support programs which are "green." Government payments for environmental protection are considered "green" and therefore acceptable.

Zero tillage and direct seeding will continue to grow, providing benefits to both wildlife and agriculture. Governments have recognized the economic and environmental costs of maintaining annual crop production on marginal lands. In response, incentives to crop marginal lands are being modified or removed. Water is recognized as important to the health of the land. Governments are developing policies to protect wetlands for the benefits they provide agriculture, wildlife and society. Many of these wetland areas are marginal for annual crop production, and were cultivated in response to government incentives.

Governments and farmers are recognizing the importance of farming the land, not the system. Lands will revert to their highest and best agricultural use. The most productive and economic lands will remain in crop production, while more marginal or non-economic lands will be converted to perennial forage and trees. This conversion to permanent cover will benefit agriculture, wildlife and society.

# BEING RURAL ON THE PRAIRIES: THE PAST AND THE FUTURE

## Jerome Martin

*Associate Director, Applied Sciences, Faculty of Extension, University of Alberta, Edmonton, Alberta*

European settlers came to the prairies because of free or inexpensive land. They brought with them European approaches to farming and rural living, knowing little if anything about the land to which they came. Since then our farming population has declined while agricultural productivity continues to be high (in traditional economic terms). Declining prices, increasing costs and continuing globalization have led to declining populations. The rural way of life has changed dramatically: many villages and small towns have vanished and even large towns are competing for survival. Agriculture was the economic rationale for settling the prairies and continues to be the primary industry, but, increasingly, urban people from Canada and other countries are becoming rural residents of our prairies. They are attracted by low housing costs and a relaxed life style. Some of these people are retirees, while others are young families who make their living in the arts or small business, often using high-tech information technology. They bring with them expectations of services similar to those in the city (good roads, access to information technology, and excellent medical care). Some towns have used intensive advertising and promotion campaigns to encourage retirees and electronic-agers' to relocate to their areas.

Farmers are also changing. The vast majority (80 to 90%) of farmers and their partners have and probably require some off-farm income. Also, many farmers and ranchers are looking for alternative on-farm enterprises, including eco-tourism, bed and breakfasts, alternative livestock production, consulting, and farm machinery production. Internet and the fax allow rural people to access the world, just as their city cousins do, although Internet access for rural people is often expensive and limited in the type of service it provides.

We need to revitalize and renew the prairies—the soils, the small towns, the habitats, the government policies that conflict with each other, the people. We as a society still know little about the prairie as an ecosystem. Grasslands are more threatened than rain forests, yet we take them for granted or, worse yet, consider them to be simply wheat fields-in-waiting. Science and scientists (whatever their bent) will not convince us to renew our prairies: a new generation of rural people, in conjunction with our poets, painters and concerned people from urban centres will do that, providing that we give them the support they need. Adopting the word 'sustainable' to justify each and every intensive agricultural practice is clearly not the answer—nor is depleting non-renewable resources throughout the world to produce cheaper and cheaper food ('globalization'). Rather we should focus on quality of life, diversity, and true sustainability as our goals for our precious prairie.

# SHARING THE PRAIRIES: BY WHOSE WORLDVIEW?

## Johan F. Dormaar[1], Evelyn Kelman[2], and Stanley Knowlton[3]

[1]*Research Scientist, Agriculture and Agri-Food Canada, Research Centre, Lethbridge, Alberta T1J 4B1*
[2]*President and* [3]*Culture Coordinator/Researcher, Sik-ooh-kotoki Friendship Society, Suite 200, 505-7th Street South, Lethbridge, Alberta T1J 2G8*

## FORMATION OF THE PRAIRIE

Students in soil science learn that there are five soil forming factors: parent material, climate, organisms, relief, and time. Prairie forming factors could be similar: parent material, climate, organisms, relief, and time. Both systems seem to be at a steady state. That is, they are contemporary expressions of historical events and processes. However, steady states change as pressures from the various soil/prairie forming factors change.

For the Canadian Prairies, parent material was supplied by the retreating glaciers. Climate/microclimate were supplied by their continental/microlandscape positions. Of course, it takes time for the various factors to assert their influence. Bison and other herbivores represent some of the organism factor. They contributed to the erosion and 'pollution' potential of the prairies. The vast herds of bison trampled the ground until it was impervious to water; "terrifying flashfloods then led to abrupt rises of streams and inundation of the lowlands fertilizing with their fecal loads the land." (Connell 1984). Since the bison were free to roam, return to the same site could take years.

Grassland vegetation is generally found on gently sloping or flat terrain. Mycorrhizal and other fungi, decomposition rates, the occurrence of heavy rains, frost, snow, hail or high winds, allelopathic effects of plants, diseases, insect activities and infestations, predator-prey relationships, annual migrations, animal population buildups, grazing, browsing, trampling, defecating, wallowing, digging, and burrowing activities all act either singly or collectively in the development of grassland (Vogl 1974).

Fire caused by lightning is another part of the steady state equation. Natural fires often combine with climatic, edaphic, and biotic conditions to maintain more or less permanent grasslands. Although grassland climates with dry seasons and periodic droughts favour fire, they also favour grass whether there are fires or not. Grassland vegetation responds to fire through renewed and vigorous growth. Collectively, fires, climate and grazing by herbivores like the bison maintained a diverse grassland devoid of the large stands of shrub and matted dead grass which now dominate many of our grasslands.

## ENTER PEOPLE

Although pre-European settlement filled all niches across the land, disease and famine kept the population in check. People, although initially superimposed, with time became part of the biological factor within the steady state equation. Each group had to learn about and deeply understand the landscape it occupied in order to survive—migration of fish, mammals, and birds, the properties of plants. Nelson's (1983) discussion of the Koyukon in the Northern Forest is an excellent account of such learning and understanding. The local minerals flowed through the system.

Ca-ion had marked time in the limestone ledge since the Palaeozoic seas covered the land. Time to an atom, locked in a rock, does not pass. The break came when a bur-oak root nosed down a crack and began prying and sucking. In the flash of a century the rock decayed, and Ca-ion was pulled out and up into the world of living things. It helped build a flower, which became an acorn, which fattened a deer, which fed an Indian, all in a single year. From its berth in the Indian's bones, Ca-ion joined in chase and flight, feast and famine, hope and fear. When the Indian took his leave of the prairie, Ca-ion moldered briefly underground, only to embark on a second trip through the bloodstream of the land. (Leopold 1966).

People also acquired the control and use of fire. Hence, with the arrival of people, fires were either deliberately set or, later, deliberately prevented. The earlier human economies collectively may be called fire economies. The manipulated fires helped to further set the prairie landscape (Sauer 1950; Eiseley 1954; Vogl 1974; Pyne 1984). "Natural vegetation" conceals long and steady pressure by human action on plant assemblages (Sauer 1950).

## EUROPEAN SETTLEMENT

Initially the first arrivals adopted the fire practice used by the Native Peoples. However, these were techniques for transients—for trappers, hunters, explorers, and military expeditions. But the character of the Euro-American settlement meant that such practices would serve only a transitional phase in the occupation of the Great Plains (Pyne 1984). The long-range settlement of the grasslands by the Euro-Americans replaced nomads with settlers and converted wildland to farms and fields. Domestic cereals replaced wild grasses, fenced-in domesticated livestock replaced free-roaming bison, a sedentary social order replaced a more mobile society, private land ownership with fixed titles replaced communal use of common land, barbwire replaced the unlimited expanse, the linear export of resources replaced the cyclical use of resources, Gross National Product replaced self-sufficient sustainability, the Big Bad Wolf of Little Red Riding Hood replaced the Medicine Wolf of the Blackfoot, the Swiss bank account replaced survival, and the singing in the quick shower with perfumed soap and deodorants replaced chanting and praying in the hours-long sweatlodge with sage and sweetgrass.

European farming practices, developed in forested environments, were superimposed on prairie landscapes. Narrow Father sky-related spiritual reality was superimposed on vast Mother earth-related spiritual reality. Although controlled fire replaced broadcast fire, combustion remained, nevertheless, fundamental to the energy flow of the ecosystem. However, it now resides in the cylinders of tractor engines rather than the free-burning flames of open fires (Pyne 1984) and in the pellets of the fertilizer bags rather than the ashes of burned prairie. The contrast between two world views or *Weltanschauungen* became all too clear.

If we ever want to see pre-European settlement prairie, broadcast fire will be mandatory. Fire is intrinsic to the native prairies of North America. Pyne (1984) noted that it has proved almost impossible to reestablish tallgrass prairies that resemble preColumbian grasslands without fire; fire is a manageable, cheap, and effective agent for promoting native grasses over exotics and for checking the invasion of grasslands by bush and trees.

Since today's society has a different intellectual environment, "thick with new scientific concepts and environmental perceptions" (Pyne 1984), from that of the First People, a different, culturally distinct ecological landscape with a different 'naturalness' will result, because of different expectations of what the grasslands 'ought to be'. The presumed natural scene of the pre-Columbian 'prairie' is just as much an artifact as a 1995 'prairie' will be.

## TODAY

What about the effect of the prairie landscape on our vision of life, our *Weltanschauung*, our spiritual well-being? Only to white humans is nature a 'wilderness'. In reality, what the Europeans saw before them was not a wilderness, an empty land. It was the artifact of a civilisation whose relationship to the living world was perceived by the Native Peoples in terms that Europeans would not or could not grasp at all. The relationship of the Native Peoples to the environment was existential. They lived in intimacy with their surroundings. Their field of vision was deep and wide. When travelling through the landscape, they could explain that it was not just a place on a map, but a whole series of locations set into stories remembered from their own experiences or recounted by their parents and grandparents (Raffan 1993).

There is also presence. Polosmak (1994), overseeing the recovery of the contents of a 2,400-year-old tomb of an Altay woman in the treeless grassland of the Ukok Plateau, Siberia, expressed the feeling that thoughts and ideas do not vanish. They still exist in the layers of the atmosphere that blanket the earth. The souls of the Altay are still there. We would see so much more if only we would explore terrain which was common to our ancestors. Even though today's ranchers and farmers view their property differently, just ask those who have lived on their property for several generations. They talk about their land in terms of a whole series of locations set into stories remembered from their own experiences or recounted by their parents and grandparents as well.

However, we must be realistic. The preColumbian hunter/nomad had no means to store food for very long. Food gathering had to be carried out all the time. Even though excess killing was difficult without guns and horses, while, conversely, climate changes would have led to the demise of animals such as mammoth and other Pleistocene mammals anyway, there was, no doubt, overkill and waste. Nevertheless, because of having to know about plants and animals, the relationship of pre-Columbian people with the land was communal and intimate. Their behaviour was in tune, albeit not necessarily in balance, with their environment. The newcomers came from economies based on exploitation of the land in which they were often exploited. They now saw opportunities to be the exploiters. Hence, they interpreted the landscape within their own psyche, which usually meant without caring about the intrinsic spiritual geography, without listening to the voices of the old ones.

Imagine yourself being separated from your environment year round by a few millimetres of hide rather than by metres thick walls of brick, concrete, glass, and plastic. Imagine yourself being separated from the elements by pelts that took skill to acquire rather than by cloth woven from fossil fuels. Imagine taking your sustenance from the earth of your immediate surrounding landscape rather than just from the nearest supermarket. Imagine your body being made up of elements (remember the "Ca-ion" story?) supplied by local water, plants, and animals rather than of elements procured from New Zealand sheep, Indian chutney, French wine, or Californian vegetables. Then, we were of the immediate earth. Now, our bodies are less sensitive to the rotations and vibrations induced in the molecules of our bodies by absorption of possible electromagnetic radiation and microclimatic nuances within our home area. The cation ratios within our bodies differ from that of our surrounding landscape.

Naturally, at one time, being physically in tune with the landscape where we lived, we would also be spiritually in tune with this landscape. The landscape helped us make sense of life, understand who we were and why we were here, of life and death, and of well-being and disease. Today, living in a concrete, glass, and plastic landscape, it may not matter much if we not only import our food from elsewhere, but also import our spirituality from the desert regions of the Middle East. However, the stories of Lot and Mary do not make much sense in the landscape of White Buffalo Woman and Star Face. The worldview of pre-European people living within the prairie landscape incorporated elaborate knowledge of the infinite reciprocal relationships between human beings and the natural and spiritual entities of their cosmos. Reality (Nelson 1983) is the world as it is perceived by the mind through the medium of the senses. Reality in nature is not just what we see, but what we have learned to see.

## QUO VADIS?

The use of land has shifted from communal to private property. The market has changed from local to global. Transport has changed from what people themselves or their packdogs could carry under their own power to wheeled and winged conveniences driven by fossil fuel power. Naturally our concept of prairie has changed. Euro-Americans just cannot create a 'Buffalo Commons' (Matthews 1994) as part of a long-term series of land use changes for the prairies. There is already a 4,000-ha ranch in Montana earning a comfortable profit from hunting and tourism (Hodgson 1994). Will we be part of nature or exploiter of nature (White 1967)? What people do about their ecology depends on what they think about themselves in relation to things around them.

Middle Eastern desert doctrines have de-sanctified the earth and placed humans in dominance over it. This has given us a society based on a philosophy emphasizing technology worship, economic expansion and commodity accumulation. Taken all together, we can never go back to what it was in preColumbian days. The question to ask is what are we aiming for? Will we enter a repeating cycle of wholeness, i.e. circular sustainability, or will we export resources, i.e. linear sustainability? If the former, a major reappraisal will be required; if the latter, a major effort will have to be mounted to minimize impact. Of course, that is not to say that we cannot come up with a new paradigm to share and sustainably use the prairies on today's physical and spiritual terms. We must be honest with our own Euro-Canadian views, i.e. biased urban perceptions, of the environment and our self-interest as we develop our use of the prairies.

Agriculture, be it crops or non-free roaming cattle, will most likely remain an important component of the prairies. Applying ecologic sustainability principles will help to create the steady state. Through protected areas and ecosystem management we will be able to 'preserve' some parts of the landscape. It must be realised, of course, that without preColumbian presence of nomadic hunter/gatherers who used fire as a management tool, a different, but nevertheless satisfactory, prairie can be maintained. Finally, aboriginal culture is a potent source of cultural energy for everyone, not just aboriginal people (Sik-ooh-kotoki Friendship Society 1995).

However, we want to introduce another idea into Sharing the Prairies. Polosmak (1994) believes that "thoughts and ideas do not vanish, they still exist in the layers of the atmosphere that blanket the earth."

Euro-Canadians generally deny this 'presence' by calling it 'pre-history.' But it is an intrinsic part of everyone, regardless of ancestry, presently living on the prairies.

A major step into becoming aware of this 'presence' is the knowledge and acceptance of preColumbian geographic names. It is our contention that the 10,000 year history of one part of the present day population (the *Nitsitapii*) and the 500 year long history of the other part of the present day population (the *Napikoan*) of the Prairie Landscape can be integrated to form a larger whole. Euro-Canadians must become aware that to the *Nitsitapii* all landscape features, such as mountains, rivers, trees, and rocks, are sacred keepers of physical and spiritual knowledge. The Native places of power to heal and strengthen one's spirit may well be able to help Euro-Canadians find inner harmony in preference to financial reward and completeness rather than achievement. Are we listening to this knowledge or are we only exploiting the landscape for economic gain?

The real and spiritual geography of the land appeared in names, songs and visions. For a deeper appreciation of the prairie landscape we must develop a pre-settlement, that is, traditional map with as many traditional named features as possible identified. Often, these names tell us about the landscape, for example:

| *Sik-ooh-kotoks* | Place of Black Rocks (Lethbridge) |
| *Mek-kia-towaghs* | Painted Rock, Medicine Stone |
| *Napi-aotzi-kagh-tzipi* | The River The Old Man Played Upon |
| *Nina-stokis* | The Chief (Chief Mountain) |
| *O-muk-otsi-mokoyi* | Big Grass Meadow (Stirling Lake) |
| *Omah-koh-pawah-koyi* | Big Ridge (Milk River Ridge) |

For non-Natives, place names have no significance beyond identifying a certain place or a particular feature. To the aboriginal people, place names are a manifestation of the special relationship between them and the rest of the universe. By not examining this dimension of the prairies, much of the knowledge open to all people remains trapped (Sik-ooh-kotoki Friendship Society 1995).

When we integrate the knowledge of different world views, we can really share. Understanding prairie ecosystem dynamics, understanding the application of ecological sustainability principles rather than market demand to agriculture, and understanding the pre-settlement culture of the prairie landscape, will together 'feed' the aesthetic, physical, and spiritual needs of us all.

## LITERATURE CITED

Borchert, J.R. 1950. The climate of the central North American grassland. Annals of the Association of American Geographers 40: 1-39.

Connell, E.S. 1984. Son of the morning star. North Point Press, San Francisco, California.

Dormaar, J.F. 1994. Geospirituality. Going to the Sun No. 25: 19-20.

Eiseley, L.C. 1954. Man, the fire-maker. Scientific American 191: 52-57.

Higgins, K.F. 1984. Lightning fires in North Dakota grasslands and in pine-savannah lands of South Dakota and Montana. Journal of Range Management 37: 100-104.

Hodgson, B. 1994. Buffalo: Back home on the range. National Geographic 186: 64-89.

Houle, R. 1992. The spiritual legacy of the ancient ones. Pp. 43-73 *In* Land, Spirit, Power - First Nations at the National Gallery of Canada (D. Nemiroff, R. Houle and C. Townsend-Gault, eds.). National Gallery of Canada, Ottawa, Ontario.

Hughes, J.D. 1983. American Indian ecology. Texas Western Press, University of Texas, El Paso, Texas.

Joffe, J.S. 1949. Pedology. Pedology Publications, New Brunswick, New Jersey.

Leopold, A. 1966. A Sand County almanac. Oxford University Press, New York, New York.

Matthews, A. 1994. Slow death beyond the 98th meridian. Outside 19: 70-76.

Nelson, R. 1983. Make prayers to the Raven: A Koyukon view of the northern forest. University of Chicago Press, Chicago, Illinois.

Polosmak, N. 1995. A mummy unearthed from the pastures of heaven. National Geographic 186: 80-103.

Pyne, S.J. 1984. "These conflagrated prairies" - A cultural fire history of the grasslands. Pp. 131-137 *In* The prairie: Past, present and future (G.K. Clambey and R.H. Pemble, eds.). Proceedings of the ninth North American Prairie Conference. Tri-College University Center for Environmental Studies, North Dakota State University, Fargo, North Dakota.

Raffan, J. 1993. Where God began. Equinox 12: 45-57.

Sauer, C.O. 1950. Grassland climax, fire, and man. Journal of Range Management 3: 16-21.

Sik-ooh-kotoki Friendship Society. 1995. "Draft" Aboriginal tourism action plan for the southern Alberta region.

Vogl, R.J. 1974. Effects of fire on grasslands. Pp. 139-194 *In* Fire and ecosystems (T.T. Kozlowski and C.E. Ahlgren, eds.). Academic Press Inc., New York, New York.

White, Jr., L. 1967. The historical roots of our ecologic crisis. Science 155: 1203-1207.

# WATER AND PRAIRIE RIPARIAN ECOSYSTEMS

## Kevin Van Tighem

*Ecosystem Management Specialist, Waterton Lakes National Park, Waterton Park, Alberta T0K 2M0*

## 1. WHAT IS A RIPARIAN AREA?

The dictionary says that "riparian" means "of or relating to a riverbank". One publication by the U.S. Environmental Protection Agency describes riparian areas as "thin lines of green" (Chaney *et al.* 1993b). This description captures a key attribute of riparian areas: they are linear, narrow, and occupy only a very small part of the landscape.

A riparian area, for the purposes of this paper, is the floodplain of a creek or river, the floor of a coulee, or any place where water usually flows for part of the year.

In a riparian area the important ecological processes relate to the balance between erosion and deposition by water, and the seasonal abundance of surface and groundwater. There are often trees and shrubs there, because they need more water than rainfall can provide in the prairies. The vegetation is often diverse because different parts of the riparian area are of different depositional ages and moisture regimes. Riparian areas are frequently lush, diverse and attractive.

## 2. THE IMPORTANCE OF RIPARIAN AREAS

Riparian habitats may occupy less than 2% of the western landscape (Chaney *et al.* 1993b) but their ecological, cultural and economic importance far exceeds that of most other habitat types on the prairies (Bradley *et al.* 1991; World Wildlife Fund 1989).

The highest densities of breeding birds anywhere in Canada are in prairie riparian forests (Savoy 1991), and various studies have shown that up to 90% of all the birds, mammals and other vertebrate species that occur naturally in grassland regions depend on riparian habitats for all or part of their life cycles (Thomas *et al.* 1979).

Humans are drawn to riparian area for recreation such as hunting, bird watching, fishing and canoeing. Stands of cottonwoods offer shade and shelter during the long, blazing summer, while choke cherry, saskatoon and currants are important seasonally for berry-picking. Parks, campgrounds and private recreation sites tend to be located in riparian areas.

Riparian areas remain highly important for plains Indians for hunting, culturally important plants, and shelter; several major reserves are centred on riparian areas.

Livestock require water and shelter from both sun and severe winter weather, all of which are available in riparian areas. Riparian areas are generally the most productive range sites in prairie Canada, when they are properly managed. On the Waldron Ranch in western Alberta, for example, forage production on a recovering riparian area was 2 1/2 times greater than on nearby upland pasture (Barry Adams, Alberta Public Lands, pers. comm.).

Riparian areas play a vital role in providing for both the quantity and quality of water. Lush vegetation filters out sediments during spring floods, while the combination of spring flooding, sustained summer flows and porous sediments make healthy riparian areas important for recharging water tables.

## 3. WHAT MAKES RIPARIAN AREAS WORK?

Irrigators like to talk about "water, sun, and the hand of man" as being the key to economic well-being in the southern prairies. It would be fair to talk about water, landscape and predictable seasonal cycles as being the key to the ecological well-being of southern Alberta's riparian ecosystems. The hand of man is the wild card, beneficial in some cases and disruptive in others.

If we are going to talk about, or plan for, the well-being of riparian ecosystems, then we need to understand how they work.

## Climate

Nature provides a continental climate through most of our prairie watersheds except for small parts of their mountain headwaters. Cold winters result in the accumulation of snow, especially at higher elevations. Most precipitation, however, falls as rain in May and June. Peak temperatures are in July and August.

Streamflow peaks in May and June and declines from July through October. In streams with healthy watersheds, the decline is generally slower than in streams where water runs off rapidly because of extensive urbanization or sustained, heavy grazing or widespread cultivation. Water that goes into the ground, in other words, is available longer than water that flows over the ground.

Spring floods have been a natural factor in the evolution of riparian areas for millennia, as have the slow trailing off of water flows through the summer, and the freezing over of winter's much reduced flows. The things that live in riparian areas are adapted to seasonal floods and seasonal scarcity, because if they were not, they would have vanished long ago.

## Water

Water obeys the law of gravity and in doing so, converts potential energy into kinetic energy. In other words, it becomes capable of doing work.

The work water does usually involves rearranging the landscape. Where the power of the water is greater than the resistance of the material over which it flows, it erodes that material. Where the power of water is weaker, it deposits material it has eroded.

The faster the flow of the water, the greater its energy and therefore the greater its ability to do work. For every two-fold increase in water velocity, there is a four-fold increase in energy and a 64-fold increase in its ability to move sediment. When engineers straighten out a channel, they are forcing the water to flow faster and so they normally have to armour the new channel with large boulders and riprap. By speeding up the water they've made it much more powerful, so they have to compensate by putting in more resistant material.

Each watershed generates a predictable amount of water through the year, and each watershed contains parent materials — rock, glacial till, lake bed clays — in its own distinctive pattern. The interaction between the two is what results in the unique appearance of any particular riparian landscape. The amount of twisting and turning of the stream channel and the normal speed of the current are both the product of centuries of compromise between water and land.

In spring, when lots of water is trying to come down the channel, streams adjust by speeding up, eroding their channels, and overflowing the channels to spread across the floodplain. The fast water has more energy and thus it can erode and carry more material, but when the stream escapes the channel it slows down as it spreads across the vegetated floodplain, loses energy, and deposits material. In addition, at any given point the water in the channel is flowing at different speeds; at the same time as fast water on the outside of a bend may be eroding the bank, slow water on the inside of the same bend may be depositing material from further upstream.

So each spring flood brings changes to the floodplain. The curves and meanders in the stream migrate, floodplain pools are re-filled, and fresh sediment is deposited on point bars and flooded areas. That's the work that spring floods do in a healthy prairie river.

Not all water is created equal. Clean, clear water has more potential to erode and carry material than water that is muddy and already using energy to carry sediment. Where clean water cuts like a carving knife, eroding rapidly into sediment, dirty water spreads like a butter knife. Most natural spring floods are of the butter knife variety; brown silty water that spreads out and works the whole floodplain. Where dams slow the flow of water they reduce its ability to do the work of carrying sediment, so the sediment drops into the reservoir. The water coming out of the dam is clearer than would otherwise be the case, and so the water is more likely to act as a carving knife, cutting down into the floodplain rather than spreading out across it.

## Vegetation and Animals

The balance between water and landscape is modified by the effects of vegetation cover.

Raw earth is easily eroded but soil covered with plants and tied together by roots is much more resistant to erosion. Where a spring flood might cut several feet of material from the outside of a bend in one year, it may take several floods to wash out a well-rooted old cottonwood.

Range managers know that for every gram of above-ground material, the average grass plant may have up to three grams of below-ground material. Cut off the top, and the roots die back until they are in balance with the amount of green material remaining. The same applies to most vegetation; plants can only sustain as much root as the amount of top provides.

Herbivory (grazing and browsing), then, is another important process affecting the way in which riparian ecosystems function. If grasses and shrubs are continually cropped so that they remain in a low state of vigour, then there will be less root material tying the soil together and less resistance to the erosive power of water. If the grazing action of animals is intermittent or light, then plants will have the ability to grow and replenish their energy reserves, maintaining strong root systems that hold the soil against erosion (Chaney *et al.* 1993a, 1993b).

Many plants are adapted to, and depend upon, the seasonal cycle of erosion and replenishment that typifies a prairie riparian ecosystem. Sandbar willow, for example, requires newly-deposited sediment to become established and grow. Cottonwoods release their seeds just as spring floodwaters are receding, and are therefore able to take advantage of the new silt deposited along the high water mark, as well as the availability of moisture and freedom from competition by other plants (Bradley *et al.* 1991). Young willows and cottonwoods slow the flow of water in subsequent floods and as a result they encourage the deposition of more silt and the building up of streambanks on the inside of each curve. Since both species are relatively short-lived, they depend on the continuing dynamic of flooding, erosion and deposition to maintain their populations; for many of the things that live beside streams, floods are not disasters but, instead, are sources of life and renewal.

The relationship between vegetation and riparian ecosystem is complex and multifaceted. Consider, for example, the scarcity of above-ground vegetative matter in the dry prairies. The one place where abundant new green material is produced year after year is in the canopies of the poplars, willows and other trees and shrubs that line prairie streams and rivers. Each fall, when those streams are flowing most slowly, countless billions of leaves fall into the water, become sodden, and sink. Through the months that follow, those leaves form the organic basis of much of the in-stream ecosystem. The decaying organic material releases nutrients and is consumed by microbes, small invertebrates and other animals which in turn are consumed by larger ones which become food for fish. Outside the stream, wildlife use trees for dens, canopies for food, and shrubbery for shelter. In turn, they have an impact on the vegetation (through herbivory) and the landscape (through erosion, trampling and in some cases like beavers, active modification) (Hunt 1988).

## The Upshot: Riparian ecosystems

A riparian ecosystem is a place where natural processes such as flooding, erosion and deposition, vegetation succession, herbivory and deciduous leaf-fall interact to create a dynamic system of exceptional natural diversity. The floodplain is in a state of dynamic equilibrium, having evolved through the predictable seasonal interactions between running water and parent material. Streamflows peak in spring, reworking the floodplain, and then gradually shrink back to reduced flows through late summer and fall. Plants are adapted to the cycles and, in fact, modify the ways in which these cycles work. Grazing animals, beavers and fire affect vegetation, and the result is further modification to the way in which the riparian system works.

Processes and cycles operate at various scales: flooding tends to be regular and predictable although intensity varies from one year to the next; beavers are local and ephemeral, occurring in one area for a period of years and then moving on only to recolonize the area again a few years later; while grazing animals like bison and elk historically fluctuated in numbers seasonally, sometimes causing intensive short-term grazing and trampling impacts, and at other times being completely absent for many consecutive months.

In seeking to conserve or restore riparian ecosystems, we need to keep the natural processes that create and sustain them foremost in our minds. If we want to sustain those ecosystems in all their vitality and dynamism, then we should not be focussing narrowly on protecting trees, regulating streamflows or excluding cattle. Instead, the focus must be on restoring the natural range of variation in water flows, sedimentation, the action of herbivores, and the other natural processes that give rise to the things we value about riparian ecosystems.

Cottonwood trees, herons, trout, clean water and happy cows are symptoms of a well-managed, healthy ecosystem. They are the outputs of natural processes that are working well and within the normal range of variability. If we sustain the processes, then we can count on the outputs. If we simply try and manage the outputs de-coupled from the processes, we can count on being very busy, very frustrated, and frequently disillusioned.

# 4. CHALLENGES IN MANAGING RIPARIAN ECOSYSTEMS

A century and a half of rapid agricultural and urban development have resulted in substantial change to the processes that historically sustained riparian ecosystems in prairie Canada. The natural range of variation in stream flow, sedimentation, herbivory and other processes has been altered, and new processes of change have been introduced.

## Water Management

Water, through the twentieth century, has been recognized as the chief limiting factor to human economy in prairie Canada. This is a semi-arid region; little water falls from the sky. It was recognized as early as the turn of the century that if more water were available, this region's rich grassland soils and hot summers could yield abundant crops (Environment Council of Alberta 1988).

If water won't fall from the sky when we need it, then it makes sense to look for surface water and see if we can't put that to work for us. In some cases, however, surface water can be in the wrong location. The past century has seen the draining and cultivation of many areas that formerly held shallow sloughs or were subject to periodic spring flooding. By modifying the process by which water interacts with landscape, however, wetland drainage or consolidation inevitably result in decreased groundwater recharge, losses in wildlife habitat, and downstream erosion due to the accelerated runoff. Solve one resource problem; get several other resource problems.

Most rivers and streams peak before the main part of the prairie growing season; by the time crops need water, most has flowed by. The solution of choice has been to manage surface water by damming major rivers or diverting their spring flows into off-stream reservoirs so that the spring floods can be held and redistributed into irrigation systems throughout the summer.

These are management actions that focus on a single resource: water. It is worthwhile examining them, however, from an ecosystem perspective: in terms of the natural processes these actions modify.

The cultivation and draining of upland areas interferes with natural processes by forcing surface water rapidly out of the watershed, reducing groundwater recharge and increasing downstream erosion. Damming rivers interferes with natural processes by trapping sediment and, as a result, turning butter-knife spring floods into butcher-knife spring floods which cut river channels down into their floodplains instead of spreading the flow across the floodplains. In addition, the use of water for irrigation in mid-summer results in much more pronounced reductions in summer flow in rivers. The distribution, timing and intensity of water movement through the landscape, in other words, are all affected by intensive water management.

When a sediment-depleted stream cuts down into its floodplain, it draws down the water table too. The lowered water table, compounded by diminished summer flows, can result in floodplain plants not being able to get the moisture they need. The result is die-back of the most water-dependent plants. Drs. Stewart Rood and John Mahoney of the University of Lethbridge documented the results: up to 55% of the cottonwoods along the St. Mary's River and 25% along the Waterton River have died downstream from major irrigation dams (Rood and Mahoney 1990).

Once the water has been changed by loss of sediment, and its flow patterns have been changed by interruption of normal flooding regimes, an inevitable result is that the way in which a stream meanders and rearranges its floodplain will change too. It no longer has the same tools to do the work it used to do. Plants that were dependent on erosion and new deposition to create the environments they need for seedling establishment inevitably become more uncommon. Bradley *et al.* (1991) point out that even while mature cottonwood stands, province-wide, appear to have remained common through the middle part of this century in Alberta, young cottonwoods are uncommon.

Cottonwoods provide denning habitat for many birds and mammals, roosting and nesting habitat for herons, eagles and other species, and much of the organic material that enriches the aquatic ecosystems of prairie rivers. As prairie streams entrench because of the increased bed erosion resulting from watershed damage and on-stream dams and diversions, former riparian areas are left high and dry by receding water tables, resulting in loss of shrubs and trees and, consequently, of ecological diversity and many of the attributes valued by humans. The action of beavers, sustainable in a healthy riparian system, becomes destructive as they exhaust available food supplies that may not be replaced at the same rate as under the natural water regime.

## Cattle Management

Ecologically, cows are different from bison and elk. Cattle have a stronger affinity to riparian and wetland areas than bison and elk, both of which tend to be upland grazers. The differences are frequently compounded by management practices. Where bison and elk formerly ranged across entire landscapes, concentrating seasonally upon different areas, cattle are held on discrete units of land because of a land tenure system introduced to the prairies in the 1880s. In many cases, this results in the same riparian area being grazed repeatedly through several seasons, year after year.

Cattle congregating in riparian areas, especially when they are held there for extended periods, can be extremely harmful (Chaney *et al.* 1993a). Repeated grazing of riparian pasture results in the dieback of roots, which in turn makes the soil less resistant to erosion. Cattle preferentially graze juvenile willows and poplars, with the result that riparian forests are less able to replenish themselves. Trampling and hoof action weaken stream banks and expose raw soil, again altering the balance between the erosive power of water and the resistant characteristics of the terrain (Serecon Consultants 1992). Heavy grazing of uplands can reduce vegetation cover and increase the rate at which water, and sediment, washes off the watershed.

Historically, riparian areas have commonly been considered sacrifice areas (Chaney *et al.* 1993a, 1993b; Clarey *et al.* 1991). Besides being an environmental problem, livestock impacts become an economic problem when chronically degraded riparian pastures, which should be the most productive range units in a cattle operation, become buttercup farms littered with decaying cottonwoods or are maintained in poor range condition (Chaney *et al.* 1993a; 1993b).

Herbivory is one of the natural processes that shapes riparian ecosystems. In other words, impacts arise not from the fact that herbivory occurs but from changes to the timing, intensity and return interval of herbivory. Cows aren't the problem; how they're managed is.

## Plant colonization

Agriculture imported more than just new herbivores to the prairie West; it also added numerous species of plant. Some, like leafy spurge, tall buttercup, sweetclover and awnless brome, are well-adapted to riparian environments. Unlike native plants, however, these exotic weeds arrived in Canada without a complement of insects and diseases. Few native animals feed on exotic weeds. As a result, new weeds frequently have a competitive advantage over native plants because they are largely exempted from such ecological processes as parasitism, disease and predation. The problem is compounded where ecosystem function has been impaired so that native plants can no longer vigorously compete with the invaders. Extensive stands of leafy spurge now exist along the St. Mary's and Oldman River. Another weed, sweetclover, has been directly implicated in reducing the survival of cottonwood seedlings (C. Bradley, per. comm.).

New weed invasions continue to occur, with seeds and other disseminules arriving on construction equipment, as crop seed contaminants, in livestock forage and on recreational vehicles and boats. Chemical control of infestations is generally unsuccessful when the conditions that give weeds a competitive advantage persist and when the supply of weed seeds cannot be cut off.

## Synergy

No single process is responsible for the diversity, productivity and aesthetic qualities of prairie Canada's riparian ecosystem. By the same token, no one modification to any of these ecological processes acts in isolation from any other. A river that has been dammed for irrigation, had much of its headwaters cultivated and drained, and is used along its entire length for cattle ranching will be highly vulnerable to weed invasion, because each of the modifications multiplies the effects of the others. Stresses are cumulative and they build upon one another. Conversely, of course, any actions we take to restore the natural range of variability to riparian ecosystems can be cumulative too.

## 5. HOW ARE RIPARIAN AREAS DOING IN ALBERTA?

Riparian areas in Alberta, for the most part, are in poor condition. There are very few exceptions.

A 1992 environmental audit conducted for the Alberta Cattle Commission identified degradation of riparian areas by domestic cattle as one of the most significant environmental problem areas associated with cattle ranching in Alberta: "There is a definite environmental concern with riparian areas and cattle access to water. Direct access of cattle to water sources can lead to pollution of the water source, erosion, siltation, degradation of the stream banks, and alteration and destruction of riparian vegetation.... Reducing degradation of stream banks due to cattle access should be a high priority." (Serecon Consultants 1992)

The Prairie Conservation Action Plan goes so far as to suggest that riparian areas are in critical shape: "Due to water and land management practices, they have become some of the most threatened ecosystems in arid and semi-arid regions of the world." (World Wildlife Fund 1989)

Studies on the Milk, St. Mary's and Waterton Rivers (Bradley and Smith 1986; Rood and Mahoney 1990) have shown measurable, sometimes drastic, declines in the extent and vigour of cottonwood forests downstream from water management projects because of drought stress resulting from floodplain degradation, summer de-watering of rivers, and reproductive failure due to the de-coupling of floodplain processes from normal flooding and sediment regimes (Bradley *et al.* 1991). The extent of the damage caused by on-stream dams is so major and so well documented that a Federal Environmental Review of the Oldman River Dam recommended that the dam be decommissioned.

Almost half the species at risk identified to date by the Committee on the Status of Endangered Wildlife in Canada are from prairie Canada, and many of those depend for at least a part of their life cycle on riparian ecosystems.

Bull trout occupy less than one-third of their previous southern Alberta range, due to habitat degradation and the truncation of populations through construction of on-stream dams (Fitch 1994). The range of walleye and lake sturgeon has been reduced in prairie rivers due to dams and water quality problems.

Leafy spurge, knapweed, Canada thistle, purple loosestrife and other noxious weeds continue to spread across many riparian areas in southern Alberta, largely due to vegetation damage by cattle and deterioration of natural ecosystem functions.

The signs of riparian ecosystem stress are widespread and well-documented, but are not always readily apparent to the public who see degraded cottonwood stands as park-like, and have come to accept hummocky, eroded streambanks as normal. The prairie climate is highly variable, but we tend to manage for maximum sustained yield, leaving very little in reserve for the inevitable dry (as opposed to "rainy") day. One result is that we have

chronically-stressed riparian ecosystems and, when droughts occur, our degraded systems have little reserve or resilience left in them to compensate.

## 6. ECOSYSTEM MANAGEMENT: BETTER DIAGNOSIS; BETTER TREATMENT

Ecosystem management focusses our attention on the causes of ecosystem changes, not the effects. Just as cottonwood trees, herons, trout, clean water and happy cows are symptoms of a well-managed, healthy ecosystem; so are leafy spurge, buttercups, starlings, slack water and missing bull trout symptoms of an ecosystem that has been knocked out of whack.

Spraying weeds, shooting starlings, releasing a little more water and stocking trout are ways of treating the symptoms, but they do little to deal substantively with the causes, and they offer no prospect of future ecosystem health.

An ecosystem-based approach seeks to restore something closer to the normal range of variability to the natural processes that control the ecosystem. If leafy spurge has a competitive advantage because it lacks predators and parasites, an ecologically-based approach is to place it on a more even footing with the native species with which it competes by adding predation and parasitism—two natural processes—back into the equation.

If range condition is chronically depressed and cows are eating all the baby cottonwoods, a simple solution might be to fence the cows out or, alternatively, write the floodplain off as a sacrifice area. An ecosystem-based approach looks for ways to more closely approximate the natural range of variability in herbivory. There are any number of grazing systems which could more closely reflect the conditions that healthy riparian ecosystems evolved under, including winter grazing, deferred grazing, rest-rotation or short-season intensive grazing. The key may be to recognize riparian pastures as ecologically-distinct grazing units and to manage them separately from upland pastures (Lorne Fitch and Barry Adams, pers. comm.)

If aging cottonwoods are turning into starling apartment houses, a simple approach might be to plant trees, put up bluebird boxes or pay the kids a penny for each starling they can shoot. An ecologically-based approach looks for the causes of cottonwood decline and look to restore the regenerative processes. This may be a daunting challenge where rivers have been blocked by major on-stream dams that deplete the sediment load of the streams, but if the operation of those dams is adjusted to more closely approximate a normal flow regime, the managed river will at least have a flow regime more compatible with the ecology of plants and communities that evolved under natural flow regimes.

It is all well and good to focus on ecosystem processes, rather than individual resource problems, as the way to restore or conserve the vitality of prairie Canada's riparian ecosystems, but how does one do put this into action on a broad scale?

There are several examples around today of successful, or promising, ecosystem-based initiatives or programs. I will highlight only a few.

## Cows and Fish

Cows and Fish is a cooperative project involving the Alberta Cattle Commission, Trout Unlimited Canada, individual ranchers and staff from Alberta Public Lands and Alberta Fish and Wildlife Services.

To date, six demonstration sites have been established in southwestern Alberta, while case histories are being compiled on a number of sites where riparian areas have been maintained in good health by the range management practices of their owners or managers. What is happening on those demonstration sites is that traditional season-long or extended-season grazing patterns are being replaced by patterns that better approximate natural grazing regimes and that are sensitive to the riparian processes at play in each area.

Cows and Fish offers ranchers an opportunity to work cooperatively and build goodwill with other constituencies who, in many parts of the American West, for example, have the potential to be potent adversaries. More importantly, it offers hope that sustainable patterns of herbivory can yield more economic benefits to ranchers while at the same time restoring health and vitality to riparian areas in the future.

## Conservation & Management Strategy for Riparian Forests in Southern Alberta

This strategy was developed by after extensive public review and peer evaluation in 1992. One of the great strengths of this strategy is that it is science-based; before it was prepared, an extensive review of the biology and status of riparian forests was completed (Bradley *et al.* 1991), focussing on the regenerative and life-sustaining processes that influence their well-being.

The strategy promotes specific actions that can be incorporated into existing programs and initiatives related to land and water management in southern Alberta, and places public education at the top of the list of specific goals. Although conservation strategies often tend to be top-down and expert-driven, the focus on public education recognizes that landholders and interest groups will ultimately be the ones who choose the solutions that work, and that their choices need to be informed by a solid understanding of ecological processes and the underlying issues that can lead either to riparian degradation or restoration.

## Canadian Heritage Rivers Program

Every prairie province is now a full participant in the Canadian Heritage Rivers Program (CHRS), which is a cooperative program for commemorating and managing river reaches that are nationally significant for natural, cultural or recreational reasons. Although rivers selected for the system receive no legal protection, there is a requirement that the government or agencies having jurisdiction over the river prepare a management plan that will ensure the river's heritage character will be maintained, before that river can be formally designated a Canadian Heritage River.

Alberta has established a process for nominating rivers to the system (Lounds *et al.* 1992) that offers considerable potential for improving the health of riparian systems. Alberta's approach is grassroots-driven; before the provincial government will nominate a river to the system it has to receive a recommendation that has been endorsed by local authorities representing at least half the people and three-quarters of the land base in the vicinity of the river.

Advocacy of heritage river recognition for local rivers, under Alberta's system, may provide a powerful impetus for communities and interest groups to educate one another about the special values of prairie riparian areas and to develop innovative management regimes that will maintain those special values by restoring conditions closer to the natural processes that created those values.

## Instream Flow Needs (IFN) Studies

Some southern Alberta rivers—for example, the Belly, St. Mary's and Waterton—have been evaluated scientifically to determine the minimum instream flows (IFNs) required to sustain fish populations (Locke 1994). This work acknowledges that southern Alberta rivers have been severely over-engineered and over-allocated, but it is only a first step. Certainly there is no evidence that current IFN studies have led to any changes in how river water is managed; flows are routinely reduced to well below recommended minimums.

For instream flow needs studies to deliver lasting benefits to riparian ecosystems two improvements are required. On the one hand, water legislation needs to be amended to make maintenance of riparian health a legal requirement that is at least equal in priority to providing water for licensed water users. This may result from of the current round of public consultation and expert review of the province's draft new water legislation. Limited transfer of water licenses between license holders, with provision for the government to hold back up to a set percentage of the licensed water at the time of transfer may provide a non-expropriative tool for Albertans to restore flows to over-allocated rivers.

The other improvement to IFN studies requires that we transfer the focus from one ecosystem output, such as fish, and determine instead what seasonal flows of water and sediment are required to sustain all ecosystem components including floodplain vegetation, fish, riparian recreation, wildlife. Fish, after all, require more than just water at the right temperature and with an adequate supply of oxygen. They need large woody debris from washed-out old cottonwoods, spring freshets to trigger spawning movements and leaf litter to support their food chain. The whole system has to work, if we really are to have any hope of sustaining fisheries.

## The Natural Resources Conservation Board

A new regulatory body was established as a result of Ralph Klein's leadership in responding to public concern that major projects in Alberta were not receiving adequate review for potential social or environmental impacts. The Natural Resources Conservation Board (NRCB) has been in existence for less than three years, but they have already demonstrated their ability to incorporate ecosystem-based thinking into regulatory decision-making sometimes with exceptionally enlightened and challenging results (Kennett 1994).

The NRCB process involves review of environmental impact studies, commissioned expert studies of outstanding issues and public consultation to determine the public interest before a decision is rendered or recommendations are forwarded to government. NRCB reviews are legally required for major dams and water development projects and should provide opportunities to plan for the maintenance or restoration of ecological processes that have been impaired by previous water development projects that took place with no, or only the most narrowly-focussed, environmental review.

## Biological Control of Noxious Weeds

Agriculture Canada, Alberta Agriculture, Food and Rural Development, and Parks Canada continue to experiment with insects that feed upon or parasitize noxious weeds such as leafy spurge, toadflax and knapweed. Unlike chemical control, which treats the symptom but not the cause, biological control serves to restore balance through the natural processes that control other plant populations: predation, parasitism and herbivory. Biological control is a pragmatic compromise unpopular with those who still believe that Pandora could have put everything back into the box she opened. It is only part of the equation, however. Other processes that contribute to weed infestations include localized over-grazing and the opening of raw soil by heavy equipment. Weed infestations need to be fought on several fronts, focussing on what ecosystem processes give rise to them, but biological control is already showing benefits at least in the case of leafy spurge.

## 7. CONCLUSION: PRINCIPLES AND PRIORITIES FOR RIPARIAN ECOSYSTEMS

If we are to achieve a future where prairie Canada's riparian ecosystems are as rich, diverse, healthy and productive as they are capable of being, then the following ecosystem management principles may prove useful in choosing among the management options available to prairie Canadians:

- Grass, clean water, trees, fish, and wildlife are all products of healthy ecosystems. Ecosystem products are the result of a variety of processes; things like the timing, duration and amount of water flow, predation, herbivory, erosion, deposition. If the processes are impaired or no longer operating within their normal range of variability, then the ecosystem will respond by showing signs of distress or degradation. Management that focuses on one or more ecosystem outputs and ignores underlying processes is not likely to be successful. Ecosystem-based management is more likely to lead to riparian health than water management, or range management, or any other sectoral form of resource management.

- It makes sense to avoid high-intervention solutions such as putting wire around trees, stocking fish or water engineering, except as temporary, stopgap measures. Focus energy and resources instead on actions that will restore the natural range of variation within the ecological processes that drive riparian ecosystems. The best options will always be those that move towards a self-sustaining system, not expensive and technology-dependent management regimes vulnerable to technical breakdowns or changes in budget priorities.

- Practise adaptive management, based on an understanding of ecosystem processes, at the working level. Many ranchers have been doing this for years on upland pastures and the health and diversity of much of Alberta's surviving native grassland show the benefits of their care and intelligence. We need to recognize riparian ecosystems as being more dynamic and driven by a different suite of processes, and take on the challenge of finding ways to manage them as well as we do our uplands. Cows and Fish is an exemplary first step in this direction.

- Water legislation needs to be strengthened so that the health and vitality of riparian ecosystems are mandatory considerations in land and water planning. In the development of those plans, the responsible agencies need to engage the public in defining valued attributes of riparian systems, evaluate the ecological processes that give rise to those valued attributes, and then calculate instream flow needs based on that information. New water legislation that entrenches the status quo is not an option. Legislation should serve the whole public interest, and it should recognize and respond to our collective responsibility as custodians of living ecosystems.

- The Milk, lower Red Deer and South Saskatchewan should be designated as candidate heritage rivers for Alberta. They have all played, and continue to play, vital roles in Canada's heritage,

after all and their ecological significance has increased as riparian areas have been lost or degraded throughout the Great Plains of North America. Promoting their formal recognition will provide the communities that share their watersheds with a positive opportunity to collaborate on the study, celebration and restoration of their home rivers.

## ACKNOWLEDGEMENTS

This paper benefited from critical review by Dr. Peter Achuff, Cheryl Bradley, Lorne Fitch and Dr. Stewart Rood. Their kindness is appreciated.

## LITERATURE CITED

Bradley C. and D. Smith. 1986. Plains cottonwood recruitment and survival on a prairie river meandering floodplain, Milk River, Southern Alberta and Northern Montana. Can.J.Botany 64: 1433-1442.

Bradley C., F. Reintjes and J. Mahoney. 1991. The biology and status of riparian poplars in southern Alberta. World Wildlife Fund Canada and Forestry, Lands and Wildlife, Fish and Wildlife Division.

Canadian Heritage Rivers Board. 1993. Annual Report 1992/1993: Canadian Heritage Rivers System. Environment Canada. ISBN 0-662-60075-4.

Chaney E., W. Elmore and W. Platts. 1993a. Livestock Grazing on Western Riparian Areas. U.S. Environmental Protection Agency publication.

Chaney E., W. Elmore and W. Platts. 1993b. Managing change: Livestock grazing on western riparian areas. U.S. Environmental Protection Agency Publication, Northwest Resource Information Centre, Inc.

Clarey W.P., E.D. McArthur, D. Bedundah and C.L. Wambolt (eds.). 1991. Proceedings of the Symposium on Ecology and Management of Riparian Shrub Communities. U.S. Dept. of Agriculture, Forest Service, Intermountain Research Station. Gen. Tech. Rep. INT-289.

Environmental Council of Alberta. 1988. Agricultural considerations for today and tomorrow. Discussion Paper, Rural Environment Sub-committee, Public

Advisory Committees to the Environment Council of Alberta. ECA88-PA/CS-S6.

Fitch L. 1994. Status and distribution of bull trout in southern Alberta. Paper presented at the 1994 Friends of the Bull Trout Conference, Calgary, Alberta.

Hunt C.E. 1988. Down By The River: The impact of federal water projects and policies on biological diversity. National Wildlife Federation, Island Press.

Kennett S. 1994. The NRCB's West Castle decision: Sustainable development decision-making in practice. Resources 46: 1-5.

Locke A. 1994. Belly, St. Mary and Waterton River instream flow needs. Notes, presentation to the Blood Tribe Council, Standoff, Alberta, Nov. 25.

Lounds M., S. Klassen, G. Hanna, H. Siebert, J. Webber, B. Free, C. Bradley, S. Ryan, B. MacDonald. 1992. Canadian Heritage Rivers System: Advisory Committee Report to the Honorable Ralph Klein.

Rood S.B. and J.M. Mahoney. 1990. Collapse of river valley forests downstream from dams in western Prairies: Probable causes and prospects for mitigation. Environmental Management 14: 451-464.

Savoy E. 1991. The importance of riparian forests to prairie birds: A case study from Dinosaur Provincial Park. *In* The biology and management of southern Alberta's cottonwoods (S. Rood and J. Mahoney, eds.). May 3-4, University of Lethbridge.

Serecon Management Consultants. 1992. Environmental Risk Assessment for the Alberta Beef Cattle Industry. Report prepared for the Alberta Cattle Commission.

Thomas J.W., C. Maser and J.E. Rodiek. 1979. Wildlife habitat in managed rangelands: The Great Basin of southeastern Oregon. U.S. Department of Agriculture, Forest Service, Pacific Northwest Research Station. Gen. Tech. Report PNW-80.

World Wildlife Fund Canada. 1989. Prairie Conservation Action Plan, 1989-1994. World Wildlife Fund Canada publication.

# ECOSYSTEM MANAGEMENT: CONCLUDING SUMMARY

## Lorne Fitch and John Dormaar
*Theme Reporters*

## A. HOW HAS THE WORKSHOP IMPROVED OUR UNDERSTANDING?

1) Define ecosystem integrity.

2) Challenge current paradigms or preconceptions and generalizations.

3) More sharing of ecosystem information; interjurisdictional, interdisciplinary, partnerships.

- Need local, regional, national, international scales to E.M.

- Lack of information should not prevent protective action.

- We need to work out our human part in the ecosystem.

- Understanding limits that nature will put on us.

- Risk involved in proceeding without good information.

- Put money into education.

- More sharing of information on ecosystem information. Interjurisdictional, interdisciplinary, partnerships, networking.

## B. HOW CAN IT BE APPLIED?

1) Farmers generally do not perceive the spectrum of benefits therefore they need inducement or incentives to change. The urban majority concurs and is willing to pay the cost but instruments to achieve this are lacking.

2) Which benchmarks are the key ones to monitor?

3) What are the practical actions to begin the process; what is possible and do-able?

- We are all part of the problem (trampling flowers we are looking for, harassing farmers)

- Information for cause and effect; should have enough information.

- The costs should be equally distributed between rural and urban.

- Interdisciplinary teams: soil, hydrology, economists etc.

- Need for benchmarks and monitoring. Indicators.

- Define priorities of research so we can focus on an intended goal.

- Demonstrate good examples (e.g. ranching) and bad examples.

- Practical actions to begin the process.

- Limits must be set for human growth.

## C. WHAT ARE THE FUNDAMENTAL CHARACTERISTICS?

1) How to maintain human populations without destroying the ecosystem; humans are part of the ecosystem

2) It is an approach; it is a way of thinking.

3) Single species management tactics are not ecosystem management strategies.

- Where humans fit into ecosystem.

- Making our use of the ecosystem more efficient.

- Way of thinking how we measure our goals. Process inter-relationships, broad view.

- The choices are up to society. This is a managed environment, how are we going to do this.

- Ecological mechanisms need to be understood.

## D. WHERE DO WE GO FROM HERE?

1) Reduce impediments to change; must recognize that government policies have had paramount influence on land use, therefore change needs appropriate policies and programs.

2) Use practical applied knowledge; leader/follower concept.

3) The public is ready for action.

4) Mother Nature bats first -and last.

- Never let fear and common sense stand in our way.

- Look for ways to work together.

- Communicate, make priorities.

- More forums, local, regional, international.

- Public ready for good advice.

- Lets work on improving policy.

- Develop demonstration areas to educate.

- Use practical, applied knowledge.

- Need right people who can integrate and work with many types of people.

- Create model of whole ecosystem before we go forward with our ideas.

It is truly amazing how so many know so much about so little. The matter isn't ignorance. In fact 90% of what they know just plain isn't so. The more scanty the knowledge the greater the certainty.

# 5.0  POLICIES AND PROGRAMS AFFECTING PRAIRIE CONSERVATION

# APPLYING PLANNING AND DECISION-MAKING TOOLS TO PROTECT SPECIES AND HABITAT: AN ALBERTA EXAMPLE

## John Thompson

*Senior Manager, Strategic and Regional Support Division, Alberta Environmental Protection,*
*3rd Floor, Oxbridge Place, 9820-106 Street, Edmonton, Alberta T5K 2J6*

In recent years, the practice of resource management has become increasing complex. Initially, the single concern of resource managers was to allocate resources to provide employment and income for individuals and industries. However, multiple use management practices were later adopted in order to recognize interactions among various types of resources, such as forests and wildlife. Within the last decade, resource managers have been given asked to protect rare, endangered and threatened species and habitats within the context of multiple use management. With publication of the Brundtland report in 1987, sustainable development has been added to the list of resource management objectives. And looking to the future, biodiversity is likely to become the next new objective for management of natural resources.

Given that the list of management objectives seems to be ever expanding and sometimes contains apparently conflicting or inconsistent directions, resource managers are persistently dogged with a very important question: How do you balance the objectives of habitat conservation and protection of endangered species against other economic, social, political and environmental objectives?

Of course there are no simple answers to this question, but there are some important tools that have evolved to help resource managers make trade-offs amongst these various management objectives. The purpose of this paper is to describe how these planning and decision-making tools are being developed and applied to resource management issues in Alberta, using the specific example of the Fox Creek-Knight Subregional Integrated Resource Plan and a threatened species: the woodland caribou.

## STUDY AREA

The planning area for the southwest Regional management Area (RMA) of the Fox Creek-Knight Subregional IRP covers an area of about 1,540 square kilometres (km²) in west central Alberta near the Town of Fox Creek. As shown in Figure 1, the area includes much of the upper reaches of the Little Smoky River basin which is relatively undeveloped and undisturbed at the present time. The need to undertake a resource plan is based on the variety of important and valuable resources in this area.

The upper water shed of the Little Smoky River is one of many areas in the province that are representative of the Upper Foothills Natural Subregion. However, of these sites, the Little Smoky River Valley is an excellent representative of a diverse Level 1 natural history themes for the Subregion, has very low levels of environmental disturbance and few land use dispositions, and contains a unique combination of caribou, wetlands and fish resources. Preliminary studies being conducted for AEP as background to developing a protected areas system for Alberta suggest that this area is worthy of designation as a protected area.

Residents of local communities and the surrounding region residents use the area for fishing, boating, hunting, camping and other forms of recreation. In recognition of the importance of this area, establishment of a "Little Smoky Boreal Forest Primitive Area" has been proposed. This could contribute towards future tourism development in the region and would help maintain important recreation opportunities.

The Little Smoky River contains one of the most significant, unexploited Arctic grayling populations in Alberta. The fishery has produced catch rates well above those of other rivers and streams in the region. While efforts have been made to protect the fishery by restricting angling to catch-and-release, the future success of the fishery is dependent on maintaining existing habitat.

The study area is home to a small herd of woodland caribou (60 to 100 animals) which were designated as a threatened species in Alberta in 1986. There is concern that timber harvesting and energy development in about 340 km² of key winter habitat could have significant

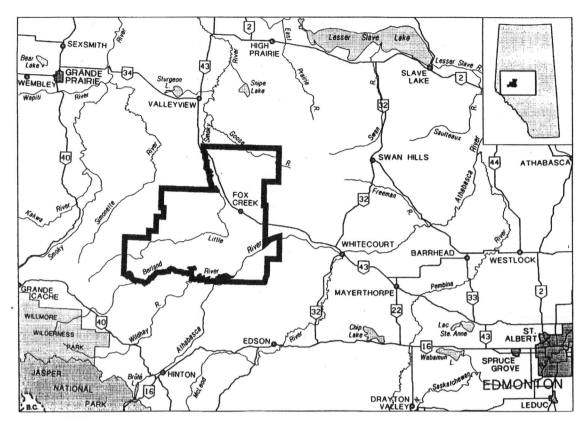

Figure 1. Fox Creek - Knight I. R. P. regional location.

impacts on caribou by causing a reduction in food sources, increased competition from other ungulates, and greater predation by wolves.

The study area is regarded as having high potential for discovering and developing considerable reserves of natural gas, although there is only one operating gas well. About 90% of the area has been leased for oil and gas development. Gas reserves are estimated to amount to 2.9 billion cubic metres.

Timber resources in the area have been allocated as part of a Forest Management Agreement (FMA) with the Alberta Newsprint Company which is located in Whitecourt. There are also three quota holders which are entitled to a portion of the annual allowable cut in the FMA. These include two sawmills and another pulp mill.

Each of these resources is important in their own right, but development of timber and energy resources will limit the extent to which the ecological resources of the region can be conserved. Similarly, protection of the ecological resources will preclude certain resource harvesting activities that would have significant economic implications for the local communities, the region and the province. The need to find a balance between conservation and development has triggered the planning process being undertaken in this area.

## PLANNING PROCESS

The Integrated Resource Planning (IRP) process was developed in Alberta as a means of providing direction for the management of public resources. For the Fox Creek-Knight area, this process is being coordinated by a planning team, which consists of representatives from Alberta Energy (AE) and various divisions within Alberta Environmental Protection (AEP). The planning team is responsible for gather and providing information, undertakes consultations with stakeholders and the general public, and formulates draft management plans.

At the outset of the process, a workshop was conducted with key stakeholders (28 organizations) to clarify issues and identify important values to be considered in the plan. This workshop produced several recommendations which were subsequently endorsed by assistant deputy ministers (ADMs) from AE, AEP, and Alberta Economic Development and Tourism (AEDT). These

Table 1. Summary of the general intent of proposed plan alternatives for the Southwest RMA of the Fox Creek-Knight Subregional IRP.

| | |
|---|---|
| Alternative 1 | Zone Little Smoky River corridor for recreation and allow timber harvesting and allow oil and gas activities in rest of area. Mitigate the impact of activities along the corridor. |
| Alternative 2 | Protect some key caribou habitat but allow zone boundaries to move over time as needs for habitat change. Allow some activity consistent with maintaining the remote quality of the area. |
| Alternative 3 | Provide permanent wildland recreation/tourism area. Forestry and oil and gas development phased out of key areas. Recreation management is the priority over caribou management. |
| Alternative 4 | Protect riparian habitat and provide wildland recreation corridor along Little Smoky River. For the remainder of the area, modified practices will be followed by industry in recognition of the caribou management needs. |

recommendations included resolving timber shortfalls with timber companies, managing the area to maintain the Little Smoky caribou herd, and managing the area to conserve unique wildland nature of the planning area through delineation of a special conservation area. These recommendations provided the context for developing management alternatives for the area.

A technical working group which represented the 28 stakeholder organizations was then established. This group was given the responsibility of defining the specific objectives of the plan and to work with the planning team to develop four alternative proposals for the area. These alternatives were then to be evaluated and a preferred option to be selected. The recommended plan for the area was then to be endorsed by the ADMs before being sent for public review.

At the time this paper was presented, the technical working group was still in the process of refining the four alternatives and defining the types of activities that could occur in each of the designated zones. Details about the four alternatives must be considered preliminary and are listed here only to provide a context for describing the types of evaluations that are being prepared.

## FOUR ALTERNATIVES

The technical working group developed four alternatives that vary considerably in terms of the degree of protection provided for woodland caribou and the extent to which forestry and oil and gas development would be allowed in certain parts of the study area. The general intent of the four alternatives is summarized in Table 1.

Refinement of these alternatives was done by defining a system of zones within the area. These zones, which identify permitted land use activities, were based on the Eastern Slopes Policy of Alberta but were adapted to meet the special concerns of the region. The land areas falling within each types of zone for each alternative plan are described in Table 2. These are preliminary estimates that have been included to show the major differences among the four alternatives.

Table 2. Zonation of proposed planning alternatives for the Southwest RMA of the Fox Creek-Knight Subregional IRP.

| Zone | Zone Name | Alternative 1 | Alternative 2 | Alternative 3 | Alternative 4 |
|---|---|---|---|---|---|
| | | (%) | | | |
| 1a | Prime protection | 0 | 10 | 20 | 0 |
| 1b | Protection | 0 | 14 | 9 | 0 |
| 2a | Riparian habitat | 0 | 4 | 4 | 7 |
| 2c | Critical caribou habitat | 93 | 72 | 50 | 73 |
| 4a | Wildland recreation | 7 | 0 | 17 | 7 |
| | Other | 0 | 0 | 0 | 13 |

## PLANNING AND DECISION MAKING TOOLS

Three different planning and decision making tools were used to assist the planning team in trying to make trade-offs among the four alternatives and to identify a preferred alternative. These tools ranged from a highly-structured but narrowly-focused assessment of economic effects to less-structured methods that consider a wider range of management objectives. Each of these approaches is described below in terms of its effectiveness in assisting the decision making process and the practical problems inherent in each approach. Preliminary information from the Fox Creek-Knight evaluations have been included to demonstrate how each method was used and the types of information that result.

### Benefit/Cost Analysis

One of the most conventional tools used to evaluate the implications of various alternatives is benefit/cost analysis. This approach can be used to measure, in dollar terms, the benefits and costs of the proposed alternatives on each of the major resources. In this way it is possible to identify the alternative that provides the maximum benefits and least costs for all resources.

While benefit/cost analysis has been used extensively in evaluating such things as energy export projects, there are limited examples in Canada and Alberta where this approach has been used to evaluate alternative natural resource management plans or projects. As a result, resource economists have to find innovative ways to apply economic concepts to measure the value of public goods. For timber resources, the standard approach is to assess potential costs in terms of any losses in industry income due to possible reductions in the annual allowable cut AAC and to determine the extent to which Crown stumpage fees (royalties) may be reduced. Potential impacts on energy resources can also be measured in terms of losses of Crown energy royalties and land bonus bids.

For non-market resources, like fish and wildlife, more unconventional approaches to valuation are employed. For example, the benefits of maintaining a caribou herd can be measured in terms of the extent to which Alberta residents would be willing to pay to protect this species and by examining the comparative costs of trying to protecting caribou at locations elsewhere in the province. The potential costs of a loss of fisheries resources can be measured by determining the higher costs faced by anglers having to travel to a different site which had similar fishing characteristics or by the costs of mitigating or replacing damaged fisheries habitat. In the case of assessing the value of ecological and natural history features, the value of one site can be assessed relative to the costs associated protecting similar sites elsewhere in the province.

While these methods were used in the Fox Creek-Knight Subregional Plan, they were not particularly successful. For all resources there was insufficient information to conduct a rigorous benefit/cost analysis. Three types of problems were encountered. First, there was incomplete information about the amount of resources in the region and the extent to which these resources are being used. It was difficult to estimate the size of oil and gas reserves or the actual amount of timber in key areas, and there were no statistics on current use of the fishery.

A second problem was that it was very difficult to estimate the extent to which implementation of each of the four plans would actually affect the resources of the area. Will protection of some old growth forest be sufficient to sustain the caribou herd in the long run? How will forestry operations affect the watershed and key fisheries habitat? How quickly will energy development occur in the region?

The third problem relates to the difficulty of assigning resource values. There was considerable debate about the value of timber that has already been committed to specific companies. For ecological and natural history resources, there was very little information on the relative costs of trying to protect similar features elsewhere in the province. For valuing caribou, there was a recently-completed study in Saskatchewan but it is unclear whether similar Albertans have the same values.

A general summary of the results of the benefits and costs of the four alternatives is provided in Table 3. The table shows that it was not possible to calculate benefits or costs in many cases. And, where estimates are shown, the range in these values was very broad. Thus, benefit/cost analysis proved to be of limited value in determining a preferred alternative, although it did provide some insights into some of the costs that would be associated with protection of caribou habitat and maintaining the existing watershed.

In general, the most important advantage of using benefit/cost analysis is that it is a long-established evaluation process that uses dollars as a common unit of measurement. The effects of risk and uncertainty can be

Table 3. Preliminary results of benefit/cost analysis in millions of 1994 dollars.

| Resource | Alternative 1 | Alternative 2 | Alternative 3 | Alternative 4 |
|---|---|---|---|---|
| Forestry | 0 | 0 | -$22 to -$100 | 0 |
| Energy | 0 | -$9 to -$12 | -$25 | 0 |
| Caribou | -$5 to -$8 | ? | 0 | ? |
| Fishery | ? | ? | 0 | ? |
| Ecological-Natural History Features | ? | ? | ? | ? |

readily dealt with by using discount rates to express future effects in today's terms and by conducting sensitivity analyses on the main assumptions. However, as shown in this example, many effects cannot be measured in dollar terms, especially those related to environmental and ecological values. In addition, benefit/cost analysis is only useful in measuring economic efficiency and does not deal with whether resource allocations are fair. Another limitation is that benefit/cost analyses are usually only conducted using a provincial accounting perspective so regional or local impacts are not identified.

## Multi-Objective Evaluations

The purpose of this tool is to allow the implications of alternative plans to be evaluated in terms of a wide variety of management objectives. This approach to evaluation evolved in the late 1960's as part of transportation planning and was widely used in support of urban planning in the US and Great Britain in the 1970's (Lichfield *et al.* 1975). Within Alberta, multi-objective type evaluations have been used infrequently and the potential for using this approach to evaluate regional resource management plans has only recently been recognized.

Two key types of information are used in multi-objective evaluations. Technical information is required to estimate the extent to which various plans will address the key management objectives for a particular problem. This information is typically provided by consultants, government staff or other specialists. Information on values is then used to identify which of the various management objectives are most important, and these values are often obtained through some sort of public involvement process. By combining the technical and value information together, the alternative that does the best job of achieving the most important management objectives can be identified.

For the Fox Creek-Knight evaluation, a five step evaluation process was used. The first step, and one of the most difficult, was to identify the key management objectives to be used in the evaluation. Initially the planning team identified 90 different objectives based on current legislation and policies. However, after considerable discussion, these were reduced to 17 broad objectives within five main categories or accounts. These five accounts are shown in Table 4.

The second step was to determine how well each alternative satisfied each of the 17 objectives. This task was

Table 4. Preliminary results of the multi-objective evaluation.

| Account | Weights | Alternative 1 | Alternative 2 | Alternative 3 | Alternative 4 |
|---|---|---|---|---|---|
| Environmental | 38% | 76 | 90 | 137 | 69 |
| Economic Development | 23% | 109 | 86 | 69 | 103 |
| Government Finances | 15% | 75 | 52 | 37 | 75 |
| Client/Industry | 6% | 30 | 18 | 12 | 27 |
| Social | 18% | 37 | 53 | 68 | 51 |
| TOTAL | 100% | 327 | 299 | 323 | 325 |

completed by the planning team using a combination of technical information and professional judgment. Although technical evaluations of various objectives often use different types of measurement that are difficult to compare, this approach used a five point ordinal ranking scale for each objective. Thus, each alternative was given a score of 1 to 5 for each objective, where 5 represented the most desirable result and a 1 represented the least desirable.

The third step involved determining the relative importance of various objectives and was also undertaken by the planning team. Working together, the planning team allocated 100 points among the individual objectives. These points are a measure of the weight that each objective has in making the final decision. As shown in Table 4, 38% of the points were assigned to various environmental factors.

In the fourth step, the weights and ordinal rankings were combined and then added to produce a total score for each alternative. The results of this process are summarized in Table 4 which shows that the total scores for alternatives 1, 3 and 4 were all very close. Examination of the results shows that Alternative 3 was the most effective in achieving the environmental and social objectives of the desired plan, while Alternative 1 scored best in terms economic development, government revenues and impacts on industry.

The last step in the process involved undertaking a sensitivity analysis to determine how changes in the weights assigned to the various objectives would affect the overall scores for the four alternatives. This was done to determine which objectives were the most important in affecting the overall scoring, and thereby identify the key trade-offs to be made by decision-makers. For example, assigning greater weights to environmental objectives showed that Alternative 3 would be superior while any reduction in environmental concerns would favour Alternative 1.

Overall, multi-objective evaluations are useful tools because they allow comparison of data of different types and can use professional judgment to overcome difficulties where there is limited technical information available. This tool readily allows decision-makers to identify the issues and trade-offs that are of greatest importance to each resource management decision. On the other hand, the selection of objective weights is a subjective assessment and there is no guarantee that a consensus on weights can be reached, especially if different groups have significantly different view on the

importance of the various management objectives. And, as shown in this case, the results may not necessarily show that one alternative is best.

## Risk Analysis

Risk analysis is very much like multi-objective analysis. The main difference between the two approaches is that risk analysis identifies the alternative that minimizes the adverse consequences rather than the one that best achieves the desirable objective. Risk analysis, as practiced by resource planners (Kepner, 1976) and described below, has been periodically used in support of integrated resource planning in Alberta during the last decade.

For the Fox Creek-Knight study, a five step process was used to estimate the risks posed by each of the four alternatives. The first step was to identify potential adverse consequences of the various alternatives and the planning team was able to identify 23 different types of adverse consequences. A partial list of these is provided as Table 5. The second step involved assessing the probability that each type of adverse consequence would occur. This assessment was conducted by the planning team, based on their professional judgment, and probabilities were assigned using a 10 point ordinal ranking scale. Thus, consequences that were considered inevitable were given a 10 while improbable consequences were assigned a 1. Step three consisted of estimating the severity or significance of the various adverse consequences. This was also completed by the planning team using a 10 point scale where small or insignificant effects were assigned a 1 and significant concerns were rated as a 10.

In the fourth step, the measures of probability and severity were combined and added to provide an overall measure of the extent of risk associated with each alternative. A sample of these calculations is shown in Table 5. Total scores were then compared to identify those alternatives with the smallest and greatest risks. In this case, Alternative 2 was considered to pose the greatest risk in terms of potential adverse consequences while Alternative 4 offered the least risk.

As a tool, risk assessment is an important means for understanding the potential downside for various resource management alternatives and can be used to compare a variety of different risks or concerns. It also provides a useful way of identifying the key risks or uncertainties associated with a particular resource management decision. In using this tool, there are a number

Table 5. Preliminary results of risk analysis where total scores (T) are based on probability of occurrence (P) and severity of consequences (S).

| Risk | Alternative 1 | | | Alternative 2 | | | Alternative 3 | | | Alternative 4 | | |
|------|---|---|---|---|---|---|---|---|---|---|---|---|
| | P | S | T | P | S | T | P | S | T | P | S | T |
| Decline of caribou and habitat | 8 | 10 | 80 | 8 | 10 | 80 | 6 | 10 | 60 | 9 | 10 | 90 |
| Loss of riparian habitat | 5 | 8 | 40 | 4 | 8 | 32 | 2 | 8 | 16 | 4 | 8 | 32 |
| No protection of Upper Foothills Subregion | 6 | 10 | 60 | 5 | 10 | 50 | 4 | 10 | 40 | 10 | 6 | 60 |
| Decrease in timber activities/revenues | 5 | 10 | 50 | 8 | 10 | 80 | 10 | 10 | 100 | 2 | 10 | 20 |
| Decrease in oil & gas activities/revenues | 5 | 10 | 50 | 10 | 10 | 100 | 10 | 10 | 100 | 4 | 10 | 40 |
| Total Scores | | 280 | | | 342 | | | 316 | | | 242 | |

of key concerns. This approach can be highly subjective and adverse consequences must be defined as being more than just a change from the status quo, especially where some sort of corrective action may be required. There should also be an assessment of which of these adverse consequences are more important that others. And, even if risk assessment is done correctly, there is no guarantee that one alternative will better that the others.

## SUMMARY AND CONCLUSIONS

The three types of planning and decision-making tools used to evaluate planning options for the southwest RMA of the Fox Creek-Knight Subregional Integrated Resource Plan demonstrate a variety of approaches that resource managers can use to find a balance between conflicting objectives. While none of these approaches has magically provided a simple solution to a very complex problem, they do provide an analytical framework that forces resource managers to answer some key questions that might otherwise be passed over. For example, use of multi-objectives evaluations requires that resource managers explicitly specify the range of objectives they are trying to achieve. Economic tools require resource managers to explicitly consider the dollar costs associated with various alternatives. Risk analysis forces managers to explicitly assess the implications of making the wrong decision.

Another benefit of using these analytical tools is that they help identify the key pieces of information required to make good decisions. In the case of the Fox Creek-Knight IRP, this meant collecting specific information on such things as the value of a woodland caribou herd, the magnitude of gas reserves, the standing volumes of timber in potentially affected areas, and the likely affects of economic development on the long-term survival of the woodland caribou herd. This additional information proved very information for both the economic and multi-objective evaluations, while the lack of information in some key areas were identified as uncertainties that were considered as part of the risk assessment.

The third benefit of using these planning and decision making tools is that they help resource managers identify and understand the key trade-offs that need to be made. In this example, the preferred alternative, regardless of the tool being used, hinged on the relative importance placed on honouring existing forestry and oil and gas commitments or protecting the woodland caribou. All other concerns were of secondary importance, and the tools showed how a slight change in priority from one concern to another would favour one alternative plan over another. While the tools cannot by themselves come up with a final solution, the results can be used to effectively guide and focus any ensuing discussions required to reach a final decision.

In comparing these tools, it should be evident that each approach measures different things in different ways. Consequently, it is not possible to categorically say that one approach is better than another. The best tool depends on the types of questions being asked and the availability of information required as input. In complicated situations, such as Fox Creek-Knight, it may be advisable to use one or more of these approaches.

But even with these tools, the Fox Creek-Knight study has identified a number of problems that resources managers must face before these tools can be used to maximum effect. One concern is there is often a lack of biophysical data and knowledge of ecological processes. Lack of information can make it very difficult to determine how well one alternative will achieve a particular environmental objective or to know the probability or severity of a potential environmental risk. Yet, all methods require this type of information especially when a threatened or endangered species is involved.

A second concern arises if benefit/cost analysis or other economic approaches are to be used. While resource managers are often concerned with the economic costs of precluding or limited economic development in a particular area, it is very difficult to make these calculations. Economic approaches measure the flow of benefits and costs over time and it is hard to predict the rate at which forestry and energy resources will be harvested or extracted in a given area. Similarly, it is nearly impossible to measure the worth of fish, wildlife or other ecological resources. Thus, benefit/cost analysis should not be the only tool used to evaluate management decisions, especially in relation to threatened or endangered species. It should be used as one of several tools if environmental values are to receive adequate consideration in the final decision.

One of the real difficulties in using multi-objective evaluations lies in determining the relative importance (weight) of conflicting resource management objectives. For the Fox Creek-Knight study this was done by a planning team consisting of people from various government agencies, but it could also have been done by a selected group of stakeholders or representatives of the general public. Each of these groups is likely to produce a different set of weights and priorities, possibly leading to different conclusions. Although there is no right way for setting objective weights, public values are of considerable importance. Thus, multi-objective evaluations should be integrated with public consultation in determining what objectives are of greatest importance in a given region.

The last observation is that, regardless of what process is used, final decisions on key trade-offs are made by elected officials. Politicians are ultimately responsible for determining resource management priorities in any situation, but they too are faced with having to reconcile conflicting advice and information from different lobby groups and to consider provincial as well as regional priorities. Through the use of planning and decision-making tools, resource planning teams can provide politicians with structured evaluations of alternatives that explicitly identify the key trade-offs to be made. Such information can, in turn, lead to better-informed decisions that can be made sooner and with a better understanding of consequences.

## LITERATURE CITED

Kepner, C.H., and B.B. Tregoe. 1976. The rational manager: A systematic approach to problems solving and decision making. Princeton, New Jersey.

Lichfield, N., P. Kettle, and M. Whitbread. 1975. Evaluation in the planning process. Pergamon Press, Oxford.

# A STRATEGY FOR SUSTAINABLE DEVELOPMENT IN AGRICULTURE

## Allen Tyrchniewicz

*Great Plains Project, International Institute for Sustainable Development,*
*161 Portage Ave. East, 6th Floor, Winnipeg, Manitoba R3B 0Y4.*

The Great Plains region of North America (Fig. 1) is considered by many to be the bread basket for the world, but this region is facing many difficulties. Recent and impending policy changes, such as GATT, the North American Free Trade Agreement, and the Western Grain Transportation Act have affected the region in a way that is yet to be determined. Rural depopulation has had a pronounced effect on the Great Plains and its inhabitants. Concern is also being raised with the quality of the natural resources of the Great Plains. While these are just a few of the issues facing the Great Plains, they do relay the existance of impending change to the region.

At the International Institute for Sustainable Development (IISD) we feel that, since a change is about to occur, it should be under the guidelines of sustainable development. The Great Plains project is IISD's first attempt to use the knowledge gained from our program areas to promote sustainable development within a particular ecozone such as the Prairies.

The Great Plains project had four objectives when it was initiated. The first objective was to identify critical issues in the Great Plains as viewed by the stakeholders and determine the sustainability of Canada's prairies. The second objective was to provide some guidelines for the resolution of the issues through principles and criteria of sustainable development. The third objective was to use the principles and criteria developed by the second objective to gain a better understanding of the effects of current agricultural and trade policies on the Great Plains of Canada. The final objective of the project was to make recommendations to policy-makers on how to improve the policies and program, to meet the needs of sustainable development.

To give you an idea on how we are doing at meeting our original objectives, I will provide you with a bit of history on the project. To ensure the project was relevant to the needs of the stakeholders of the Great Plains, we tried to include many of their views in our research. This involved organizing meetings, workshops, conferences as well as setting up an advisory committee to help guide the project. The project staff also travelled across the Canadian prairies to meet with researchers and other stakeholders. The visits with the researchers were very useful because they gave us a better idea of the condition of the prairies as well as ideas on what could be done to improve the conditions.

At our workshops, stakeholders were brought together to discuss the issues affecting the Great Plains from a sustainable development perspective. Participants included federal and provincial government officials from agriculture, environment and natural resources, producer, conservation and environmental groups. The workshops had two purposes, first to introduce IISD's concepts on sustainable development to the participants and to determine IISD's niche in the Canadian Prairies.

The advisory committee consists of seven members, all of who have been a great help to the project. There is representation from government, education, business, as well as a producer group. The purpose of the committee is to guide the project as mentioned earlier but also to provide insight as to what is happening on the Canadian prairies. In this respect, by acting as a sound board for ideas coming out of the project, the committee can ensure the work is relevant to the needs of the prairies.

Figure 1. Map of Great Plains.

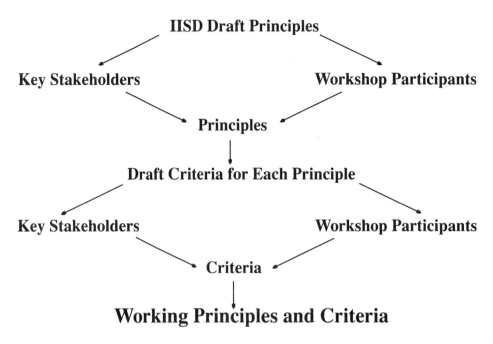

Figure 2. Development of principles and criteria of the International Institute for Sustainable Development (IISD).

The discussions with stakeholders and workshop participants led to a recognized need for principles and criteria for sustainable development that could be used on the Canadian Prairies. Figure 2 shows a chart of the process to show the development of these principles and criteria.

The process started by presenting IISD's Winnipeg Principles, the Manitoba RoundTables principles and other principles, to the participants and asking for comments. The participants developed a set of principles they could call their own, and then drafted criteria for each principle. It is important to note that these are working or draft principles and criteria and not set in stone. As the need to change them arises, they will be modified to meet the demands. These principles and criteria led to the development of a framework (Fig. 3) that used the principles and criteria as a yardstick to measure the effectiveness of agricultural policies and programs.

The consultations resulted in IISD's first paper on sustainable agriculture entitled "Sustainable Development of the Great Plains: Policy Analysis", released in May 94. In this document the major issues facing the prairies are outlined, as well as the principles and criteria for sustainable development and the policy framework.

The framework was used to evaluate 4 policies of the Canadian prairies: the Western Grain Transportation Act, which proved to be unsustainable; Supply Management

of Eggs, which also proved to be unsustainable, but not to the same extent; The Permnant Cover Program of PFRA, which proved to be sustainable under the present conditions; and the North American Waterfowl management Plan, which was considered sustainable.

The other recent publication coming from the Great Plains project was "Sustainability of Canada's Agrifood System: A Prairie Perspective". IISD, together with the University of Manitoba released this document on sustainable agriculture. The staff of the faculty of Agricultural and Food Sciences combined their efforts to produce this scientific look at sustainable development in the Canadian Prairies. This document offers suggestions to ensure the sustainability of the Canadian prairies through the research conducted at the University.

IISD is promoting and vetting its work through conferences and workshops through the Great Plains. The first international conference that the Great Plains project co-hosted was a Leadership Forum with the Global Tomorrow Coalition in Minneapolis to discuss sustainable development of the Great Plains. Leaders from Canada and the United States attended to learn what type of developments were under way and their role in the sustainable development of the Great Plains. The Premier of Manitoba, Gary Filmon, and the Executive Director of Manitoba's sustainable Development Coordination Unit, Bob Sopuck, attended and discussed

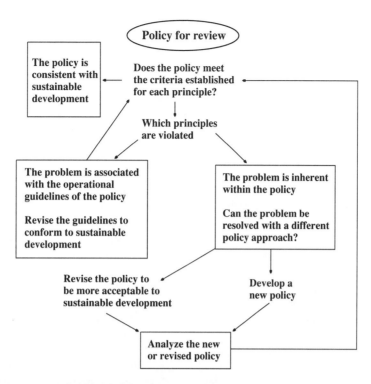

Figure 3. International Institute for Sustainable Development's evaluation policy framework.

Manitoba's Sustainable Development Act. The Attorney General of Minnesota, Hubert Humphrey III, also offered his comments on sustainable development.

The next conference for the Great Plains project is Planning for a sustainable Future: The Case of the North American Great Plains". This is scheduled for May 8-10 of 95 in Lincoln Nebraska. The focus of this conference is on the issues facing the North American Great Plains and ensuring the scientific research agenda meets the needs of the stakeholders.

IISD is also cohosting Sustainable Development on the Great Plains" with the Winnipeg Chamber of Commerce. This conference is scheduled for August 8-10, 1995. The focus is to bring sustainable development to the forefront on the issues of the Canadian Prairies as well as the rest of the Great Plains of North America. The conference is targetted to producers, urbanities, as well as policy-makers and researchers.

I have just given a quick sketch of the project, but I should mention what it is coming up in the future. We will further our efforts on making detailed suggestions in the case of agriculture policy. While much of our work todate has been with the Canadian prairies, we are now focussing on expanding our research to other Great Plains regions. We have started work in the United States with the conference in Minneapolis and Nebraska, but this could also be applied in such regions as the Ukraine and ties in well with IISD's work on Poverty and Empowerment in areas of Africa. The framework developed in the workshops need not be restricted to agriculture. Other resource sectors can use this work as well. In fact we are in the process of usingthe framework to evaluate the Ethanol industry and its sustainability.

While the work is still being refined, it is a good step in the right direction, and is being released on an on-going basis through documents and conferences. Perhaps the most important lesson learnt through this process is that consensus building is appropriate for sustainable development and in the right environment works very well.

# CONSERVATION INITIATIVES: IS THE RHETORIC TRANSLATING INTO APPLIED ACTION?

## Peter Lee

*Environmental Protection, Alberta Parks Services, 8th Foor, Standard Life Centre, 10405 Jasper Ave., Edmonton, Alberta T5J 3N4*

Many say there is considerable reason for pessimism when pondering the question "is the conservation rhetoric translating into applied action?." Many are pessimistic especially for the prairie and parkland regions. The 1994 Science Assessment for Biodiversity in Canada stated that because of agricultural conversion the loss of native habitat has been significant: we have less than 13% of shortgrass prairie left, only 19% of mixed-grass prairie left, 16% of aspen parkland and almost none of the tall grass prairie remains in a native state. That report also states that the loss of habitat to agriculture accounts for the endangerment of a disproportionably high number of species in Canada.

What some think is cause for even more pessimism is the really short space of time over which these major changes have occurred. We're only really talking about the last century. Many of us can recall conversations with our parents and grandparents, the pioneers who started all these changes to prairie ecosystem dynamics —only a very short time ago.

And in reaction to these changes, we have had a plethora of rhetoric. A whole smorgasbord of conservation plans, programs and initiatives, especially over the last quarter century.

So there is the pessimistic view on conservation initiatives and many who would answer NO to the question: "Is the rhetoric translating into applied action?" These people view all conservation initiatives sarcastically as "Another great moment in evolution, where nothing really changes for the better—only temporary blips to politically satisfy a few whiners and complainers."

I want to take a look at conservation initiatives in the major areas of today's conservation rhetoric—sustainable development and the North American Free trade Agreement, ecosystem management, biodiversity conservation, Special Places 2000. And I want to make some observations and look at the conservation rhetoric in terms of over-riding lessons that we perhaps can learn.

Brundtland succinctly defined sustainable development as that which meets the needs of the present without compromising the ability of future generations to meet their own needs. The definition sounds so easy. And indeed, Environment Canada indicated that sustainable development now dominates the international and national agenda. Sustainable development suggests a comprehensive strategy involving:

- an ecosystem approach to problem definition and problem solving;

- the integration of environment and the economy is now a strong consideration;

- improved decision-making;

- capital resources management - living off the "interest" of natural resources; and

- anticipation and prevention.

"Great rhetoric! Blah, blah, blah! Nice concept. We'll see what we can do." Meanwhile the Canadian east coast fishery collapses.

Along with international and national implementation of sustainable development, there is a simultaneous globalization of the economy that many rhetorically say will positively affect conservation. The question of international competitiveness, for example, is becoming more prominent:

- Countries that are taking the lead on tough environmental standards are developing products and technologies which will eventually provide them with a head start as suppliers for world markets for sustainable practices and products;

- In the North America Free Trade Agreement, the optimists are saying that environmental considerations are being integrated; and

- Increased green protectionism in Europe, for example, has resulted in pressure for trade barriers and boycotting of products and processes deemed to be unsustainable.

More rhetoric?? Well, those who have looked at the North American Free Trade Agreement (NAFTA), for example, have totally different points of view on the effects on Canada's environment:

- A critical look would conclude that under NAFTA, Canada abdicates forever its right to use important regulatory tools to manage Canadian resources in a sustainable manner and in the Canadian public interest, if such tools discriminate against US goods. A sympathetic look would conclude instead that Canada can still enact any environmental regulation whatsoever, as long as it is not discriminatory against US goods.

- A critical look would conclude that the NAFTA deal guarantees the US perpetual access to a proportionate share of Canadian resources. A sympathetic look agrees with this, but dismisses it as irrelevant as Canada should never ration its resources, but should simply succumb to the machinations of the marketplace.

- A critical look would conclude that Canadian attempts to protect the environment are vulnerable to attack by U.S. business interests as non-tariff barriers to trade. A sympathetic look would conclude instead that the deal changes nothing about this - this was already in effect.

- A critical look would conclude that new economic pressures will be created to reduce costs by lowering environmental standards. A sympathetic look just says to resist the pressure—no problem!

More rhetoric?? I don't know. And nobody will really know for at least one more generation.

Canada made a major public relations coup when it successfully pushed the international community to sign the Biological Diversity Convention. And Canada valiantly forged ahead with preparing its own made in Canada biodiversity strategy. The present draft strategy has fine, fine rhetoric when it suggests a biodiversity vision for Canada: "A society that lives and develops as a part of nature, values the diversity of life, takes no more than can be replenished and leaves to future generations a nurturing and dynamic world, rich in its bio-diversity." 'Pretty high falutin stuff: Biodiversity—The frantic, pulsating quest for life.' The strategy has goals related to conservation, sustainable use, understanding and education, incentives and equitable sharing.

A critical look at both the international biodiversity convention and Canada's biodiversity strategy takes away a warm and fuzzy feeling:

- The international convention has the classic loop-hole phrase - "as far as possible and as appropriate" which begins all the list of commitments.

- Canada's draft biodiversity strategy has the loop-hole phrase "governments will pursue the implementation in accordance with their policies, plans and fiscal capabilities." AND the Canadian strategy has NO ACTION ITEMS AND NO TIMELINES.

So we can easily criticize the rhetoric. But what's wrong with rhetoric anyway? Rhetoric is just the art or science of using words that are frequently over-ornate or ostentatious language intended to attract attention. What's the point about rhetoric? The point is that rhetoric is contested political terrain. Who can use words and what they are taken to mean is contested political terrain. Some words and phrases, like sustainable development, ecosystem management, gain acceptance as 'good' in the public arena, so all sides want to appropriate the words to their causes.

With all the rhetoric over sustainable development, I still don't know if it is **sustainable** development OR sustainable **development**. Is ecosystem management **managing for ecosystems** OR is it **managing ecosystems for the needs of humans**. The words are the same, the meanings are completely different BECAUSE we all have different visions, different philosophies and different world views.

So if rhetoric is most often interpreted in two totally opposite ways, what is its value? What do we do with it? How do we translate it into applied action?

Well, first we must continually question the rhetoric. We must recognize that most of it is just rhetoric. We must always question the so-called sacred truths. Truths like: nature is infinite; science and technology will solve all our problems; all of nature is at our disposal; we can manage the planet, and; pollution is the price of progress. Let's add to the list of so-called sacred truths the phrases ecosystem management, sustainable development, biodiversity conservation and others as they come along. And let us recognize that definition of words and phrases are simply political tools. Neither inherently good nor bad, just tools that we need to recognize and capitalize on when necessary.

We are just about to enter a major rhetorical phase here in Alberta with the hot political potato of Protected Areas. On the one hand, the rhetoric says that Alberta exceeds all other Canadian jurisdictions and ranks fairly high with the rest of the world, in terms of total and proportional areas dedicated as protected areas. On the other hand, its only because of National Parks that the figure is high and not because the province has done much. In fact, 80% of our present protected areas in Alberta were established before 1930, before Alberta gained control of natural resources from the federal government.

And when you take a closer look at the distribution of Protected Areas, Alberta has an inequitable distribution and representation of Protected Areas, with most areas being in the Rocky Mountains and northern boreal forest. Less than 1% of the grassland and even less in the foothills regions is under a protected area status.

There are many international and national rhetorical drivers for the establishment of a comprehensive system of Protected Areas to represent the full environmental diversity of every jurisdiction, like provinces and nations. The World Wildlife Fund has been the main non-government driver for a comprehensive system of protected areas across Canada.

Here in Alberta, as with every other jurisdiction in Canada, the response has been to develop a made-in-Alberta response to the drivers for Protected Areas. In Alberta, there has developed the requirement to fulfil a number of goals within a protected areas system other than protection:

- preservation;

- outdoor recreation;

- heritage appreciation; and

- tourism/economic development.

But the great sounding rhetoric is not without its critics. And the political power of the critics has substantially driven the definition of Special Places and will continue to drive its implementation, at least for the short term.

The powerful negative issues about SP2000 that have come to my attention include these:

- Special Places 2000 is definitely driven, we are continually told, by 'eco-terrorists,' in cooperation with government bureaucrats interested in expanding their authority and securing their jobs;

- The government is, at best, lukewarm in its support and in fact is the last province in Canada to have such a strategy. There is no political support;

- The implementation process is so cumbersome, it is designed to not produce results, just more rhetoric. A deliberate government strategy to not implement anything;

- Special Places 2000 will conflict with all those interested in timber cutting, grazing, off highway vehicle users and hunting;

- It is just more rhetoric and in conflict with the multitude of other rhetoric, such as the Forest Conservation Strategy, Wetlands Policy, Caribou Management Task Force and so on. So who needs just more rhetoric; and

- The perennial favourite - We can't afford it! So we can't even think about doing it.

So things can look pretty negative. Just more endless chatter, more rhetoric.

On the other hand, there are some positive signals, even for the protected areas issue in Alberta. Some constructive individuals have taken the 'bull by the horns' and actually looked at consensus options for some areas, including in southern Alberta.

The South Country Protected Areas Project people concluded from their discussions with both ends of the spectrum that:

- The large majority of landholders were willing and interested in discussing conservation values and management of areas;

- Person-to-person conversations are an effective way to explore common ground;

- Visions for the areas are similar among ranchers, conservationists and regional public land managers;

- There is a lack of agreement on how to realize this vision; and

- There is strong agreement over the off highway vehicle issue.

There does also appear to be a prickly consensus formed between the oil and gas industry and conservationists on the issue of protected areas.

So you go up and down like a yo-yo when looking at the rhetoric versus applied action. And often you just feel like you're sinking in rhetoric.

And is it surprising that you feel like you are sinking when you look at the problems? We've even examined the symptoms and causes of loss of wilderness in Alberta. There are surface causes, underlying causes, root causes and meta-root causes. They range from a blame on our economics in that the perceived economic benefits of development outweigh the benefits of conservation, every time, hands down. The single biggest obstacle to conservation is the perception that conservation costs money and jobs. They also range from a blame on economics to a blame on our collective values and beliefs. Values and beliefs that are reflected in the Alberta Report magazine when they said a few weeks ago that they are concentrating on real news, like the "current **unholy** alliance between the Alberta oil industry, the environmental lobby and Premier Ralph Klein .... **sacrificing** its resource industries on the **alter of eco-idolatry**." That statement is definitely a values' and beliefs' statement. How do you deal with or circumvent these extraordinarily negative values and beliefs?

And if you just look at the big conservation problems facing us globally, they are overwhelming. Jay Hare, the internationally famed conservationist from Alberta—advisor to President Clinton and past president of the International Wildlife Federation—lists the major global issues: population growth, global warming, biodepletion, pollution and consumption. Big stuff! Even Mr. Hare 's solutions are too big for most people:

- A new environmental world order;

- Environmental literacy; and

- Empowerment of all people.

He suggests that the biggest impediment to progress is the lack of awareness amongst the public and the most important force for change, at least rapid change, is the power of the consumer.

So there is an endless list of frustrations and problems for any conservation initiative—ideological opposition, no resources, bureaucracy, no political support.

Faced with these frustrations and problems and the endless rhetoric, what can you do? We certainly know that those who want to do nothing can find enough uncertainty to avoid doing anything. Then thank God, there are those who just want to get their roller skates on and get going. And they always amaze me. They do whatever it takes, whatever dog and pony show is necessary. Where do they get their inspiration? Some get their inspiration from conservation heroes and their past. Some get their inspiration from future generations—their kids and grandkids. Some get their inspiration from working with like-minded people. Some people make major conservation decisions over a cup of coffee at their kitchen table with a few friends. Many get their inspiration from those wild species and spaces—both small and large. Some use their inspiration to implement conservation initiatives through negotiation. Some use their inspiration and just apply their 'plain ole common sense.' Some get emotional and really enter the major conservation battles—for those battles take immense emotional commitment. Some just touch nature and show others, especially children, to touch nature. Because they know that touching is understanding and once you understand you will act. Some apply their personal conservation vision, use their guts or fortitude mixed with a hefty dose of savvy and accomplish great things. Others work at broad societal levels to try to effect a total cultural transformation towards more conservation.

The real applied action though, the real move from rhetoric to action is going to come from everybody. And believe it or not, when we listen to everybody there is a very strong conservation message. I enjoyed Dr. Angus Reid's talk to some politicians a few years ago that he titled "Ripples, Waves and Tides." He looked at long term polling trends on Canadian's attitudes towards the environment—trends over 20 years. He dispelled several myths including:

- There is an understanding among Canadians as to the notion of sustainable development. This is a myth - they do not understand it. It is just rhetoric.

- Another myth is that the environment is an issue that is meant for the bourgeois—when tough economic times come and Canadians have to tighten their belts, this issue will evaporate from the opinion screen.

- This is just a media thing and once editors get tired with this and move on to another issue, so too will the public. Wrong again, says Angus Reid.

He concluded that, as a society in Canada, we are facing not a ripple and not a wave, but a tidal wave on the issue of Canadians' opinions on the environment. "The undercurrents are strong, they are gaining momentum and the sea change is on the horizon."

Recent polls in Alberta done within the last year are even more interesting. Double the number of Albertans than 20 years ago believe that land use is a major environmental problem. And who does the public believe? Well, they don't believe business and they rate politicians and the media as believably the same. Albertans mostly believe scientists/professors first and environmental groups second. If we just look at Protected Areas, the last June poll commissioned by the World Wildlife Fund showed a high percentage of Albertans favouring Protected Areas, with no substantial difference between urban and rural dwellers.

So when we look at the rhetorical examples of sustainable development, ecosystem management, biodiversity conservation, Special Places 2000 and whether there is sufficient applied action, I have no answer. What I do find interesting though is what are the lessons that we learn from examining the question. The lessons I learned are these:

- Unless the rhetoric can be cast as good for the economy or at least linked to the economy it is not going anywhere - until at least there is some major catastrophic ecological event - much more major than the collapse of ecosystem segments, like the east coast fishery.

- New "signals" are required in the marketplace to link conservation with competitiveness and jobs. Unfortunately, the pending collapse of the east coast fishery did not send the right economic signal soon enough to change harvest to prevent a total collapse. And even this catastrophic event does not seem sufficient to send the right economic signals to stop the collapse of the west coast

salmon fishery. The escalation of biodepletion in tropical forests due to over-harvesting of timber does not send the proper economic signals to prevent even first world countries like Canada from allocating 100% and over 100% of its timber resources for harvesting. So new economic signals are required.

- We always have to explore common ground. There seems, for example, to be significant common ground between the ranching community and the environmental community to make some real progress here in Alberta.

- Using the power of the consumer is the most rapid way to effect change. Resource harvesters, in whatever industry, will respond quickly to consumer demands.

- We need to use voluntary + regulatory means. Voluntary means alone is usually the no-results approach. As Martin Luther King said, "legislation cannot change the heart, but what it does is restrain the heartless."

- All conservation initiatives require champions and they seem to arise every now and then. People who supply their blood, sweat, tears and their vision, guts and savvy.

- A critical mass is necessary and perhaps imminent and this can trigger massive demands for change. I like to think we are nearing a critical mass. We just need to talk to that one more person.

- Real actions will require incorporation of conservation into our cultures, into our collective world view. This is possible, especially in a country like Canada. It has to part of our collective mythology, our psyche. Other countries have done it.

- Rhetoric seems to always and necessarily precede action, so I guess we're stuck with it. Lets use it, but not get lost in it. Rhetoric is not an end in itself, only a means to an end.

# THE GREAT PLAINS PROJECT

## Larry Simpson

*Nature Conservancy of Canada, 3400 Western Canadian Place,*
*707 - 8 Ave. SW, Calgary, Alberta T2P 1H5*

The Nature Conservancy of Canada (NCC) has been conserving important natural landscapes coast to coast in Canada for 33 years. To date, we have completed over 560 projects and are now completing a project every 2 weeks. The NCC conserves by acquiring funds to purchase lands, accepting donations of lands or by structuring conservation covenants to protect biologically important aspects of productive ranching operations.

## THE CASE FOR PRIVATE CONSERVANCY IN CANADA

Approximately 95% of Canada's land base is not arable or usable for agriculture. The remaining 5% which is arable, has historically housed a substantial portion of Canada's biodiversity. Since Confederation, more than 80% of Canada's arable land base has been significantly or completely transformed. The remaining intact arable land comprises approximately 1% of Canada's total area and contains more than 70% of Canada's known terrestrial imperilled species. It is estimated that approximately half of this important land is owned by private interests.

Our forbearers homesteaded and took ownership of the richest lands they could find. Those natural remnants that remain on private land are often the most biologically diverse and continue to be transformed at an alarming rate when compared with federal and provincial lands. These remnant areas of biological diversity are also gene banks with enormous potential in the fields of agriculture and medicine alone.

Explaining why it is important to conserve remnant natural features that exist on private land makes it is necessary to revisit the World Conservation Strategy. Commissioned in 1980-81 by the United Nations, it was clear that the world had reached one billion in human population for the first time in the mid-1800's. It was also clear that another 5 billion people will be added to our population within the next human generation. It became obvious that humanity needed to arrive at a consensus regarding guiding principles that, if followed, would ensure a biologically sustainable future. The guiding principles are as follows: 1. Maintain the quality of our air, water and soil. 2. Use our resources sustainably. 3. Conserve biodiversity at the ecosystem level.

The Conservancy's Great Plains Project focuses on the third point, conserving biodiversity on the Canadian Prairies. While the Conservancy does not advocate biodiversity can be conserved by protecting 10% or 12% of each ecosystem, these numbers can be used as guidelines in determining conservation progress. Although many landscapes are well managed, less than half of 1% of Canada's Prairie and Parkland landscapes are formally managed with conservation as the priority.

If Canada is to achieve its biodiversity commitments, it must deal with privately owned remnants of natural lands within Canada's arable land base.

## THE CASE FOR PRIVATE CONSERVANCY IN THE PRAIRIES

About 2% of the earth's surface is temperate grassland like the Canadian Prairies. It is flat, fertile, relatively easy to modify with mechanized equipment making it one of the most heavily impacted natural systems in Canada and throughout the world.

In the Parkland Region of Canada, an ecosystem found nowhere else in the world, where over 70% of the land is privately owned, we find that as of 1994 less than 13% remains intact. The Northern Fescue region of Alberta and Saskatchewan, also an ecosystem found nowhere else in the world, is similarly impacted with only 5% remaining. The Mixed Grass and Tall Grass Prairie also occurs in the U.S. However, in Canada less than 1/5 of 1% of the Tall Grass Prairie still exists while over 20% of the Mixed Grass prairie remains.

To better understand the magnitude of loss of native prairie, imagine you are taking your family or friends for a drive from Calgary to Lethbridge and the landscape is forested. After driving two hours, your family and friends will have seen less than 1% of the forest standing. Likewise, if you were to drive from Edmonton to Winnipeg a trip of approximately 16 hours, less than 13% of the way would be lined with forest. Because we replace native grass with other forms of grass (e.g. wheat or barley), the landscape looks similar and, unlike forests, the changes aren't immediately obvious.

## THE GREAT PLAINS PROJECT

The Great Plains Project is designed to conserve key landscapes from the Eastern Slopes of Alberta to the Tall Grass Prairie of Manitoba in cooperation with the people of Canada. The Conservancy, through the Great Plains Project, will pursue practical, pragmatic opportunities to conserve important landscapes and recognizes that it must be conducted in co-existence with existing rights of owners.

The Project has been designed to co-exist with well managed ranching operations. The plant and animal communities in the prairies evolved and were shaped by the forces of fire and grazing. While fire, for the most part, no longer is allowed to play a significant role in shaping plant communities on the prairies, well managed grazing can contribute to the maintenance of biodiversity. Because many of the most productive landscapes are privately owned, one of our largest challenges will be to conserve large blocks of well managed rangeland. Landscapes conserved will continue to contribute to the agricultural economy while providing an obvious and important byproduct that NCC is most interested in, the conservation of plant and animal diversity.

Many of the landscapes acquired will also be subject to provincial surface rights acts. These acts allow oil and gas companies the ability to pursue their duly acquired mineral interests. Over 100,000 wells have been drilled on the Prairie and Parkland regions of Canada since the oil and gas industry began in the 1950's modifying

approximately 5% of the landscape. With some exceptions, it appears that the oil and gas sector has not played a significant role in transforming the prairie landscape. However, the oil and gas sector and others interested in conservation are working together on ways to reduce impacts on native prairie.

The process for securing important landscapes will vary. In some cases it may require the Conservancy purchase some sites, particularly if they are environmentally sensitive and outright acquisition is the only option considered logical to conserve them. Title and stewardship of some of these properties will be maintained by the Conservancy while other properties will be transferred to like-minded organizations.

The majority of lands, however, will be secured using conservation covenants or easements to secure limits to use on property with important biological values. For example, if a rancher wished to place a conservation covenant on his or her ranch it might limit certain uses such as, subdivision, wetland drainage, stream diversion, or the clear cutting of woodlands. The rancher would still own the land and could ranch it productively but, certain limits to use to protect rangeland and wildlife would be held by the Conservancy. Purchase or conservation covenants keep the lands productive and contributing to our agricultural economy and yet still achieve substantial conservation gains.

## SUMMARY

The Great Plains Project is designed to focus conservation efforts on one of the most heavily impacted landscapes in our country: the private land base of the Prairie and Parkland regions. In addition, this project provides companies, private foundations, individuals and governments, the opportunity to demonstrate leadership and leave a biological and agricultural legacy in addition to preserving a way of life.

# SUFFIELD NATIONAL WILDLIFE AREA - ECOLOGICAL INVENTORY

## Garry Trottier

*Canadian Wildlife Service, 4999-98 Ave. Edmonton, Alberta T6B 2X3*

On the 11th of March 1992 the Department of National Defence and the Department of Environment signed a Memorandum of Understanding to protect 440 km² of Canadian Forces Base Suffield as a National Wildlife Area. Located in the Mixed Prairie Ecoregion of Alberta, this protected site is equal in area to Grasslands National Park, thus it is a significant contribution to the protected area goals of the Prairie Conservation Action Plan. Development of a management plan awaits conclusion of legislative procedures for officially designating the National Wildlife Area. In the meantime, an ecological inventory has been initiated to provide information on the elements, states, and relationships of the grassland ecosystem.

# PUBLIC LAND'S - CATTLE INDUSTRY AND ALBERTA GOVERNMENT PROMOTE CONFLICT OVER CO-OPERATION

## Cliff Wallis

President, Alberta Wilderness Association

*Cottonwood Consultants Ltd., 615 Deercroft Way S.E., Calgary, Alberta T2J 5V4*

## INTRODUCTION

Millions of Albertans who are the rightful owners of public lands are being shut out of the use of and decision-making for their lands. Since day to day administration of public lands was moved from Environmental Protection to Agriculture in 1993, the Alberta Government has shifted from representing this broad public interest to pandering increasingly to the economic interests of a small rural elite.

The government has spent millions of taxpayer dollars acquiring private lands for parks, wildlife areas and recreation when there are over fifteen thousand square miles of public lands in the settled part of Alberta that should be freely available for the protection of biodiversity, recreation and the wise use of all Albertans. Alberta's public lands represent one of the greatest opportunities for long-term biodiversity and wildland protection in the Canadian prairies.

## BACKGROUND

For the record, the following background (Alberta Environmental Protection 1994) is provided to give some context the public lands issue:

- 8,750 square miles of Alberta Public Land is designated suitable for grazing, over half of this is in southern Alberta.

- Alberta public rangelands shelter some of the largest surviving tracts of intact aspen parkland, fescue grasslands and mixed grasslands. These provide habitat for significant populations of rare and endangered species and for numerous common species.

- Most cattlemen in Alberta do not have a public grazing lease. Many such cattlemen feel that the current system is unfair because they do not have the opportunity to acquire a lease except through assignment.

- Virtually all public land available for grazing is allocated (Table 1).

- The majority of existing leases are reissued to incumbent lessees for further ten year periods. Leaseholders argue that long-term leases and the security of tenure promote good stewardship and conservation. Shorter-term leases are seen by others as a means of government re-enforcing stewardship and redistributing improperly managed leases.

- CAPP (Canadian Association of Petroleum Producers) feels that surface compensation payments are excessive on public land. In most cases, this exceeds the grazing lessee's total annual costs for rent and taxes and significantly increases the assignment value of the lease. In Saskatchewan, public land under a surface lease is removed from the lease and the lessee paid a flat fee for nuisance and inconvenience.

Alberta Environmental Protection (1994) compared Alberta and Saskatchewan on their approaches to public lands (Table 2) and further elucidates on some principles to be applied to public lands:

*These lands will be managed using ecologically sound practices. The primary use of these lands will be for grazing domestic livestock. Other members of the public have a legitimate interest in other multiple use opportunities for these lands. Public direction for policy development is vital to any major policy development. There should not be an advantage in benefits or costs for public land grazing users over private grazing users. Special care should be taken to avoid the adverse public reactions which accompanied the 1987 grazing lease conversion task force hearings.*

Table 1. Dispositions on Public Land in Alberta

| Public Lands in the White (Settled) Area: | acres |
|---|---|
| Land under agricultural disposition | 6.8 million |
| Special Areas | 3.0 million* |
| Vacant | 2.7 million+ |
| Parks, Wilderness Areas | 2.5 million* |
| Total | 15 million |

| | number |
|---|---|
| Agricultural Dispositions Leading to Title | 1,832 |
| Agricultural Dispositions Not Leading to Title | 6,824 |
| Non-Agricultural(Mineral Surface, Recreation Leases) | 27,173 |
| Grazing Reserves | 32 |
| Total | 35,861 |

\* many of these are also under agricultural disposition
+ largely lands unsuitable for grazing

## DISCUSSION

A small group of Alberta cattlemen have hijacked public lands and the processes that were designed to allow the public to have a say in the future of public lands. The history of government commitment to the recommendations on public lands from its own appointed bodies has been dismal.

Despite an outpouring of public input, the 1987 Grazing Lease Conversion Task Force report was largely ignored by the Alberta government because of pressure from cattlemen (Grazing Lease Conversion Task Force 1987).

An August, 1990 recommendation made to the Minister of Alberta Forestry, Lands and Wildlife on public access has similarly not been implemented. This report recommended that the Public Lands Act be amended so that the public would be assured a right of reasonable access to public land under grazing lease disposition (Fish and Wildlife Advisory Committee on Access/Trespass 1990).

A November 1993 recommendation made to the Minister of Alberta Environmental Protection by his multi-stakeholder public advisory committee (Subcommittee on Public Land Management 1993) has not been acted upon. They recommended:

*The subcommittee on Public Land Management advises that the government as represented by the departments of Agriculture, Food and Rural Development (AFRD) and Environmental Protection (EP), design and propose a methodology for delivering a Public Land Management Strategy for Alberta. It is further recommended that the process which would produce such a strategy should fulfil the following requirements:*

*1. public involvement must play a strong role;*

*2. AFRD and EP interests must be seen as equal partners;*

*3. the role of government must be viewed principally as facilitative;*

*4. the outcome must be geared to defining roles and responsibilities of departments for policy development in the White Area;*

*5. and the outcome should articulate the jurisdiction for public lands administered by other agencies/departments.*

The resulting lack of action on the principles outlined in the background to this paper (Alberta Environmental Protection 1994), and on several recommendations made to government by its own appointed bodies has increasingly frustrated Alberta conservation and recreation organizations. By taking this stance, the government is promoting a conflict model for resolving these issues. This will probably mean that the cattle industry will control the agenda over the short-term as evidenced by

Table 2. Comparison of Public Lands administration — Alberta and Saskatchewan

| Public Lands Grazing Lease Rates (per Animal Unit Month) | |
|---|---|
| Alberta | $1.18 - 2.37 |
| Saskatchewan | $4.79 |

| Assistance for Range Improvements | |
|---|---|
| Alberta | - rental reduction up to 50% of improvement cost<br>- ability to sell improvement on lease cancellation |
| Saskatchewan | - no direct assistance<br>- rent can be frozen for up to 5 years to compensate for improvements<br>- no compensation on transfer of lease |

| Assignment of Public Lands Leases | |
|---|---|
| Alberta | - can sell lease rights<br>- assignment fee of $3 - 85/AUM paid to Government of Alberta<br>- can sublet at a higher fee than being charged by province |
| Saskatchewan | - no sale or subletting allowed<br>- assignments must be approved by province<br>- assignment fee is one year rental or $200<br>- deeded land must be part of assignment |

the partial transfer of management responsibility over public lands from Alberta Environmental Protection to Agriculture, Food and Rural Development. However, the long-term outlook is not clear. Ultimately, the increasing polarization and the sheer weight of numbers of urban residents will likely overwhelm the relatively small ranching community.

The outlook for prairie conservation will not necessarily be positive if the principal conflict comes from off-highway vehicle users and other recreationists who have little interest in sustainable land management. A better model for resolving these issues would be to have the cattle industry come to the table and, with the environmental community, promote a Public Land Conservation Strategy that would recognize:

1. a broader societal interest in conserving and using public lands;

2. the right of the public to have reasonable access to public lands;

3. the role of public lands and the types of management that would protect biodiversity; and

4. the role of grazing in Public Land conservation.

There should not be an advantage in benefits or costs for Public Land grazing users over private grazing users.

We cannot afford to give up any more of the Public Land base in the Grassland and Parkland regions to a single focus sector like agriculture. Agriculture's contribution to the Alberta economy has declined and other forms of economic activity (e.g. tourism) continue to contribute ever increasingly to Alberta's economy. While they have an important role to play in managing and conserving public lands, the ranching community should not have exclusive rights over these areas.

The public and the conservation community will apply ever increasing amounts of pressure until this situation is resolved. The concept of dominant public use that gives priority to recreation, wildlife and watershed uses will continue to be advanced by the conservation community.

Obstructionism and stonewalling by the cattle industry will only come back to haunt them. Their numbers are small and decreasing relative to the Alberta population. It is in their own self-interest and the interest of prairie conservation to work cooperatively with the environmental community and the rest of Albertans to come up with defensible solutions to public lands conflicts. The hand of cooperation has been extended by the provincial conservation community but it has been rebuffed on every occasion by the Alberta Cattle Commission. The ball is in their court. In this case even the bad guys have been wearing white hats.

I would like to close with some thoughts from William Kittredge, a member of a long-time ranching family in southeastern Oregon (Kittredge 1994):

*"When I heard that our ranch in Warner, along with two others out in the deserts to the east, was for sale and that the Nature Conservancy was interested, I was surprised by the degree to which I was moved and excited . . . Maybe, I thought, this would be a second chance at paradise in my true heartland, an actual shot at reimagining desire. What did I really want? A process, I think, with everybody involved — ranchers, townspeople, conservationists — all taking part in the reimagining . . .*

*There's no use sighting in the scopes on the deer rifles, not anymore. This invasion will not be frightened away. There is not a thing for the people in my old homeland to do now but work out some accommodation with the thronging, invading world . . . It's time we gave something back to the natural systems of order that have supported us, some care and tenderness . . . Our isolations are gone, in the West and everywhere. We need to give some time to the art of cherishing the things we adore, before they simply vanish. Maybe it will be like learning a skill: how to live in paradise."*

## LITERATURE CITED

Alberta Environmental Protection. 1994. Public land grazing lease issues: Access/trespass, surface rights compensation and rental rates. Discussion Paper. Alberta Environmental Protection, Edmonton.

Fish and Wildlife Advisory Committee on Access/Trespass. 1990. Public access to Crown Lands held under grazing disposition. Alberta Forestry, Lands and Wildlife, Edmonton.

Grazing Lease Conversion Task Force. 1987. Grazing Lease Conversion Task Force Report. Alberta Forestry, Lands and Wildlife, Edmonton.

Kittredge, William. 1994. Second chance at paradise. Audubon May-June: 70-78.

Subcommittee on Public Land Management. 1993. Proposal for a Public Land Management Strategy for Alberta. Alberta Environmental Protection, Edmonton.

# PUBLIC LAND'S CONFLICTS: THE SASKATCHEWAN EXPERIENCE

## Lorne Scott, MLA

*Indian Head-Wolseley, Box 550, Indian Head, Saskatchewan S0G 2K0*

## INTRODUCTION

In Saskatchewan, about 85% of the land south of the forest fringe is privately owned. In some areas, such as the Regina Plains, less than one percent is crownland.

A small percentage of the fifteen percent of crownland in southern Saskatchewan is found in Provincial Parks, with the majority equalling several million acres of crownland used for agricultures leases.

I would like to focus my comments on crownland grazing leases. I will cover three main issues, including (1) public access, (2) conservation of native habitat and wildlife and (3) equitable sharing of resources.

## Access to Public Lands

- lessees control access

- interest groups, whether hunters or berry pickers, are encouraged to ask permission to enter grazing leases, even if they are not posted.

- most lessees allow public access with some conditions (livestock) -"drive on trails only" or "access by foot only".

- some lessees hand out cards to hunters who ask permission and ask the hunters to report any problems they encounter.

- a few lessees choose to post all of the public land to NO Access

Thanks to cooperation and respect between the lessees and the public, access to crownland in Saskatchewan is working relatively well. This cooperation is perhaps enhanced by the representation of farmers and ranchers on the Saskatchewan Game Advisory Committee, which determines hunting season dates and game bag limits.

## Conservation of Native Habitats and Wildlife

Throughout history on the prairies, the ranchers have, in general, been good stewards of the grasslands. As far back as about 1908, when government brought in the Homestead Act which promoted settlement and breaking of the prairies, the cattlemen and women bemoaned the breaking and loss of the productive and diverse grasslands.

In the decades since, the ranchers have consistently stood by the productive native range land. They did not succumb to the "experts" who promoted breaking the prairies and planting exotic grasses. They resisted government subsidies which would reward people who broke arid, fragile and erodible land, and provide them with more income through crop insurance programs.

Also, with a stroke of the pen, governments could throw all of our crownland up for sale as happened in 1981.

In 1984, the Saskatchewan government proclaimed the Wildlife Habitat Protection Act. This Act prohibits the sale or breaking and clearing of 3.4 million acres of crownland. The Act is NOT to protect native grasslands from ranchers and grazing, but rather, to protect the land from government policies and politics. Under the Wildlife Habitat Protection Act lessees can continue to graze livestock, as they have for years, under long term leases.

Our public grazing lands continue to support a variety of wildlife species under the stewardship of the lessees. Again, cooperation and a little give and take, has benefitted everyone involved. At the request of some lessees, about 143 quarters were removed from the Act because these quarters of land were adjacent to ranch headquarters, contained water supplies, wintering pens, etc. Basically, they formed an integral part of the ranch operation.

The Wildlife Habitat Protection Act is unique in a number of ways. It provides long term security for lessees, protects important wildlife habitat, does ***not*** change current land use practices and does not cost the tax payer a lot of money.

## Effect on Oil and Gas Development

In general oil and gas companies can explore and drill on crown lands including those designated under the Wildlife Habitat Protection Act. However, land disturbance must be kept to a minimum and on certain lands which are especially important because of endangered species or other reasons, oil development may be excluded. In both the Great Sandhills and the Manitou Sand Hills, land use reviews have lead to decisions to exclude oil and gas development from some areas.

Permits are required to drill for oil and gas on WHPA lands. These permits may contain special conditions. For example, development is kept away from Ferruginous hawks or Prairie Falcon nests, and tree cutting is kept to a minimum. Where there are specific concerns, environmental monitors are required to ensure that seismic or drilling crews follow specified conditions, and to search for possible problems like hawk nests.

## Revenue from Crownlands

Lessees of Sask Crownlands pay a fee based on the use - grazing fees are $5.40 per animal unit, monthly (one of the highest rates in North America). The typical use, grazing, requires fees based on the allowable stocking rate of that land and price of cattle. If other uses are approved, fees would be based on that use.

Because the lease typically covers use of the land for certain agricultural purposes, revenue from surface rights rentals for mineral development goes to the government. However, in recognition that the presence of a well poses some nuisance for the lessee, he receives $100 per well or 30% of his lease fee, whichever is smaller. The lessee also receives $100 per new well in the year of drilling. This fee is deducted from his rent owing. This policy is a significant change from policy in the 1980's when about half of affected leasees received more revenue from oil and gas activity than they paid in lease fees.

One time access for seismic work is between the lessee and the seismic company. Any fees for access are paid directly to the lessee.

## Economic Sustainability

In the long term, maintenance of extensive areas of native grasslands requires that they have economic value. We will not and do not want to displace the people from millions of acres of southern Saskatchewan and Alberta to create wilderness parks. Grazing is a natural component of the ecology of our grasslands. Most of our grasses evolved under and are adapted to, grazing regimes. Indeed many species grow more vigorously when grazed. Of course, extensive grazing can weaken the plants and impoverish rangeland.

The key to maintaining native grasslands is thus a continuing market for livestock, especially for range fed livestock, and grazing systems which produce a good economic return to the producer while maintaining a good grassland community. Society has an important role in developing such grazing regimes and encouraging their use. Partnerships such as the North American Wildlife Management Plan are currently doing that.

## CONCLUSION - GOALS

I believe all of us here share the same goal of maintaining diverse and productive prairie ecosystems.

Our goal should be balance between economic, environmental, and social interests which achieve long term sustainable use and preservation of our grasslands. To achieve our goal, we must all work together cooperatively and objectively. We need to listen to and respect, everyone's point of view. Failure to do so will result in ever increasing conflict between interest groups, resulting in the continued loss of the very thing we all want to protect—healthy, diverse, and productive prairie grassland ecosystems.

Thank you.

# ALBERTA PUBLIC LAND'S—WELFARE FOR ELITE CATTLE PRODUCERS

## Darrel Rowledge

*2428 Capitol Hill Cr., NW, Calgary, Alberta T2M 4C2*

As its title implies, this session deals with conflicts; conflicts that can arise because of differences in background, interest, purpose, needs, desires, goals, vision, philosophy, and even conflicts of process, method, and practice.

Unfortunately, conflicts can be difficult, divisive, and distracting. In fact, they can be so difficult that they go unresolved for years. They can divide communities, friends and even families. And they almost always distract us from the things we would really prefer to be doing.

While it is seldom obvious to the players involved, a pervasive but almost imperceptible factor can influence and often severely impair our perceptions, and hence our attitudes. That factor is context. Our proximity to the various issues can actually have reasonable, well intended people *"unable to see the forest for the trees."* The tendency to get bogged down on minute details and points of disagreement tends to impose obstacles that can easily become insurmountable.

Resolving *"conflicts"* therefore, almost always requires a return to perspective. In other words, *moving forward* almost always requires *a step back* to examine the picture in its greater context.

The primary focus of this presentation  dealing with *public land conflicts*  will therefore be aimed at regaining a more contextual perspective; regarding not just public land and its background and foundational proportions, but beginning with that of our own (AWA) position. An examination of the various conflict issues from within proper context will then be both appropriate and, hopefully, more productive.

First, our organization and positions: It must be emphasised that our organization, our people, and the AWA positions on this issue, are ***not:***

- *against agriculture;*

- *anti-cattle;*

- *anti-ranching;*

- *anti-grazing;*

- *against the leasing of public land for grazing; or*

- *in any way, a "minority" opinion.*

In fact, the AWA recognizes the importance of the large grazers, and in the absence of bison, and with appropriate limitations, cattle can play an important role in the ecosystem.

Moreover, this position is not new. The AWA was in significant part, founded by ranchers Floyd Stromstead, Willie Michalsky, and Steve Dixon and the organization is still strongly supported by ranchers, as well as representatives of the various other sectors of Alberta Society.

Finally, it is important to acknowledge that the views represented here are not merely the position of the AWA; they in are in complete agreement with virtually all conservation and public interest groups, with the vast majority of the Alberta public, and even with the majority views from the agricultural and ranching communities. This fact has been consistently reflected in the various public processes that have been struck to deal with these issues and conflicts.

In keeping with the need to provide proper context, there is a housekeeping matter of some significance because it relates directly to the perspective being presented: that is, the inappropriate title ascribed to this session ("Crown Land Conflicts"). The land referred to is not "crown" land, it does not belong to the royal family, it has never been referred to as such at any level in either federal or Alberta legislation, and the use of this kind of title is a distortion of both history and law.

These are ***PUBLIC LANDS***, they belong to Albertans, and are currently administered under the "*Public* Lands Act." This, at the provincial level, was formerly the *Provincial* Lands Act, and prior to the Natural Resources Transfer of 1930, they were administered federally, by the Minister of the Interior, under the _Dominion_ Lands Act. Thus the term "crown" is inaccurate. This is a concern because the use of the term "Crown" implies something other than "public ownership." Without postulating about motives or intent, we propose that the term "crown" simply be acknowledged as anachronistic, and, in the interest of maintaining an accurate perspective, to replace it with the correct term "public" land.

Another significant issue having to do with perspective relates to the wholly distorted portrayal of this issue as something of an urban vs. rural issue, or as an anti-agriculture issue. Nothing could be further from the truth.

Those holding grazing leases to these public lands are _not_ typical of either the "rural" community, or of "agriculture."

In fact, those holding leases to graze these public lands are not even representative of cattle producers:

> The average cattle producer does _not_ have a grazing lease;

> In fact, about 85% of cattle producers do not have grazing leases.

Our perspective must, therefore, reflect this fundamental reality: Those holding grazing leases represent a very, very tiny proportion of Albertans (1/4 of 1%). More importantly, it is clearly an elite group; not just in relation to agriculture, but a small minority even among cattle producers!

These few leaseholders are very fortunate. They not only have exclusive access to grazing on these public lands allowing them to expand their operations that grazing access is significantly subsidized. Grazing lease rates in the white area are $1.18 to $2.40 per AUM. Average market value for comparable private lease is about $10.00 per AUM, or at least 4 times higher!

Obviously, for those fortunate enough to have a grazing lease, this exclusive ability, and the significant public subsidy, provides a great advantage over the majority of cattle producers. And it is an advantage over more than just their neighbours and other local producers; other jurisdictions, both nationally and internationally, have much higher fees (about twice Alberta's).

The matter of this subsidization is increasingly becoming a conflict issue, not just because of the inequity, but because in these days of drastic fiscal restraint, increasing user fees, and massive cutbacks to health, education, and virtually all government services, subsidies of all kinds are being cut back or eliminated.

Without digressing into other issues, however, the significant point is the clear demonstration that these conflicts are not _"rural vs. urban."_ Moreover, in all of the various processes that have been designed and undertaken to examine and resolve these issues, a significant _rural_ and _cattle based_ representation has recorded their position opposite that of lease holders. The general public only reinforces that fact.

If the causes of disagreement stopped here, the situation may well have lacked sufficient concern or friction to ever amount to much. However, the presence of several other issues of further and even greater disparity have raised fundamental questions about the whole arrangement. And once again, in the midst of today's cutbacks, basic questions about fairness are being asked; both in private and in the press.

In fact, the conflict issues go so much further that some are now publicly demanding that the entire relationship be re-established from scratch. Cuts to education, healthcare, and essentially all government assistance, in conjunction with recent moves by leaseholders over the last decade, and increasingly in the past few months have pushed the issue to open, and potentially very ugly, confrontation.

In 1986 the "Grazing Conversion Policy" engineered and pushed by leaseholders and the government sought to sell this public land; but the only people who could even bid were the leaseholders. Public outrage was so significant that a Provincial Task Force was struck to hear the views of all concerned. In their final report, the Provincial Task Force not only demanded that the "Conversion Policy" be rescinded, they identified several significant sources of conflict:

First, much of the public was astonished to find that surface royalties were going to the leaseholder. Every year, tens of millions of dollars that ought to have been going to the owners of the land the public has been going into the pockets of the leaseholders. In many, many cases the amounts vastly exceed the cost of the lease, and in some cases these yearly payments equal what it would cost to actually _buy_ comparable land! With no justification whatsoever, individuals fortunate enough to be lease holders are reaping a further windfall; literally being subsidized to the tune of hundreds of thousands per year!

While this windfall has been publicly denounced as "cowboy welfare," that term is clearly unfair because the vast majority of "cowboys" do not receive it. It would perhaps be more appropriately termed "elite cowboy welfare." The 1987 task force recommended that the issue be reviewed, yet it continues, and every attempt to entertain that review is deliberately rejected.

The second major issue confronted by the Provincial Task Force, and one that has now become untenable in the extreme, is the issue of public access. While the "conversion policy" was rescinded (as per the Task Force recommendation), there remains an attempt to secure defacto "ownership" of this public land this time without even having to pay for it at all. The tiny and very fortunate elite who have a subsidized arrangement to lease the grass from public land, are taking a position that they ought to control all public access. No trespassing signs are regularly found, several leaseholders have been attempting to charge for access (usually through various side arrangements to avoid breaking the law), and in the fall of 1994, a court injunction was sought to keep the public from their own land.

The 1987 Provincial Task Force not only visited this issue, they recommended:

- Foot access at all times; and

- Vehicle use restricted to established roads or designated trails, or, by permission of the occupant to off-road lands.

This land belongs to the public, and they do not require permission of a subsidized leaseholder to enjoy it. Neither the public, nor the AWA has even requested unrestricted use, and vehicles should be restricted as per the Task Force report.

Since the Provincial Task Force report, and in the broader context, a further issue of concern is the transfer of jurisdiction to Agriculture, which took place in 1993. This transfer is not only a betrayal of the government's word, it is clearly a move that will severely impair our ability to responsibly and equitably steward this vital public land. It moves authority away from the "multiple use" policy of the past, and to that of a single use mandate.

Finally, an issue of continuing and serious concern arises because of the practices of the Alberta Cattle Commission. Unfortunately, the Cattle Commission consistently chooses to represent the tiny lease holder elite over its rank and file, and they have betrayed every effort and process to legitimately deal with these issues. Their retracting support for the sub-committee position is only the latest example. Perhaps with the benefit of proper context, they will revisit their position.

In closing, it is the continuing belief and position of the Alberta Wilderness Association, that accepting and following through on the results of open, honest, and legitimate process is essential if we are to resolve these conflicts. As we have accepted, and will accept now, the recommendations of the past initiatives, we remain open to any legitimate, renewed effort; this with the single proviso that there be an absolute and unequivocal comitment to enact it.

# HABITAT PROGRAMS UNDER THE NORTH AMERICAN WATERFOWL MANAGEMENT PLAN: ALBERTA PRAIRIE CARE

## Leslie Wetter

*Alberta Provincial Agrologist, Ducks Unlimited Canada,*
*#202, 10470 - 176 St., Edmonton, Alberta T5S 1L3*

## INTRODUCTION

The Alberta Prairie CARE (APC) program is a wildlife habitat enhancement program under the Prairie Habitat Joint Venture (PHJV) within the North American Waterfowl Management Plan (NAWMP). Funding is secured through plan members; members include the US and Canadian federal governments, Provincial and State governments as well as non-governmental organizations such as Ducks Unlimited Inc. (US), Ducks Unlimited Canada and Wildlife Habitat Canada. In Alberta the program is jointly delivered by Ducks Unlimited Canada and Alberta Environmental Protection. Similar programs exist in Saskatchewan and Manitoba, although delivery partnerships differ. The program consists of direct, geographically targeted, wildlife habitat enhancement, creation, conservation and restoration programs as well as educational programs directed at resource professionals and landowners. Acreage accomplishments for habitat securement under the PHJV from 1986 to 1994 are presented in Table 1.

## HABITAT SELECTION

Habitat programs are focused in areas which constitute the "best of the best" in terms of wetland density and permanence. Alberta Prairie CARE is wetland driven: an ecosystem approach with a focus on the waterfowl resource is used. Care is taken to preserve habitat for non-game species of migratory wetland birds as well as resident mammals. Program delivery is focused in high quality areas within landscapes of varying size (approx. 10 townships) The program is delivered on a proactive rather than a reactive basis, the best habitat lands are actively pursued. In Alberta APC is currently working in approximately twenty landscapes. Total acreage and securement accomplishments in a typical landscape "Thomas Lake" are described in Table 2. Program goals are 65% complete for the Thomas Lake Landscape.

## HABITAT SECUREMENT

Habitat securement is accomplished through a number of tools. These include purchase, lease and management agreements. Purchase and lease are used on private lands while management agreements are used on private and public lands. Purchase lands are managed exclusively for wildlife or for land use exchange on privately held agricultural land. Under the Land Use Exchange Program (LUEP), portions of purchased lands of low

Table 1. Land securement under the Prairie Habitat Joint Venture (PHJV), 1986-1994[1].

| | Alberta[1] | Saskatchewan[1] | Manitoba[2] | Total |
|---|---|---|---|---|
| Upland (acres) | | | | |
| Acquisition | 24,736 | 33,217 | 9,669 | 67,622 |
| Securement (other) | 141,529 | 206,333 | 73,341 | 421,203 |
| | | | | |
| Wetland (acres) | | | | |
| Acquisition | 6,609 | 9,621 | 1,557 | 17,787 |
| Securement (other) | 83,254 | 63,427 | 20,917 | 167,598 |
| | | | | |
| Total | 256,128 | 312,598 | 105,484 | 674,210 |

[1]From: National Reporting System, PHJV 1986-1994: Canadian Wildlife Services, Environment Canada.
[2]From: Manitoba Habitat Heritage Corporation 1986-1994 per. comm.

Table 2. Thomas Lake landscape: Land use statistics.

| | Area within landscape (acres) |
|---|---|
| Total upland | 218,386 |
| Total wetland | 17,066 |

| | Area secured within landscape (acres) |
|---|---|
| Planned grazing | 1,622 |
| Delayed hay | 879 |
| Lease | 2,836 |
| Purchase | |
| Cultivated | 1,902 |
| Natural Area | 1,405 |
| Total purchase | 3,307 |
| Total land secured | 8,644 |
| % of total landscape secured | 3.7% |

Source: Ducks Unlimited, Camrose District Office

habitat quality, but high agricultural quality are exchanged for modified management of high habitat lands on adjoining properties. Land title does not transfer under LUEP. Lease is used as a short term securement on critical habitat lands for exclusive wildlife use while management agreements are used to create multiple use projects on private and public lands. An example of a management agreement is the creation of planned grazing systems which set stocking levels and timing of use.

Other land securement tools which are currently under investigation are Conservation Easements and Profit a Prendres. Conservation Easements are not available in the prairie provinces at present although legislative reform is being sought to permit their use. Profit a Prendre legislation exists and has historically been used as a tool to promote development, however the rights to own agricultural productivity on land without taking title of the land makes this tool appropriate for conservation purposes. Both Conservation Easements and Profit a Prendres allow certain values of the land to be split off from the title and held in perpetuity. A sale or

transfer of the land leaves these instruments in place. Wetland habitat is preserved and protected using personal contracts with landowners. Conservation Easements would be an appropriate tool to secure wetlands as water cannot be privately owned, and therefore, Profit a Prendres are not applicable.

## HABITAT ENHANCEMENT

In many cases habitat is restored on formerly cultivated or drained land. This necessitates the planting of perennial cover. On those lands which are secured for exclusive wildlife use, native grasses and shrubs are planted. Seed sources of native ecovars are currently being developed in cooperation with agricultural researchers. On land which will be used for exchange purposes or to supplement planned grazing systems, tame species of grass are used which are appropriate to the planned use, such as early spring grazing. Grazing systems are created through fencing, stock watering and creation of spring grazing paddocks to relieve pressure on native or wetland areas. These tools are aimed at manipulating the timing of grazing as well as improving grazing distribution. Drained wetlands are restored using inexpensive ditch plugs. Wetlands are created by building dams that impound runoff or irrigation spillwater.

## EXTENSION/EDUCATION

In addition to focused habitat programs an education/extension program is offered province wide to landowners. This program promotes farming techniques on annual cropland or on perennial forage which minimize agricultural impacts on wildlife. The techniques must be neutral or positive to the overall farm revenue. Techniques vary and are flexible in recognizing the changing nature of the farm economy. For example, in the early 1990's direct seeding of spring and winter annual crop was promoted. With a projected increase in cattle numbers in the mid '90's, techniques which aid in cattle distribution, such as remote off stream water sources for livestock, are being encouraged. Direct expenditures on extension programs under the PHJV are listed in Table 3. Extension programs have differed by province reflecting the high proportion of annual cultivation in Saskatchewan and Manitoba and the larger cattle numbers in Alberta.

Table 3. Extension expenditures by province under the Prairie Habitat Joint Venture (PHJV)[1].

| Alberta | Saskatchewan | Manitoba | Total |
|---------|--------------|----------|-------|
| $393,175 | $807,400 | $528,700 | $1,729,275 |

[1]From: National Reporting System, PHJV 1986-1994: Canadian Wildlife Services, Environment Canada.

## ALBERTA PRAIRIE CARE CONTRASTED WITH THE CONSERVATION RESERVE PROGRAM AND THE PERMANENT COVER PROGRAM

The end results of the Alberta Prairie CARE (APC) program, the Conservation Reserve Program (CRP) and the Permanent Cover Program (PCP) are similar. Changes in land use occur which result in the conservation of soil, water and wildlife. The differences are largely ones of intent. The objectives of APC are different than CRP or PCP. Alberta Prairie CARE is aimed at creating and maintaining habitat for wetland-dependent species of wildlife. The CRP and PCP programs are aimed at establishing permanent cover on erodible cropland. Programs under APC are aimed not only at cropland conversion but management of existing tame and native perennial vegetation, and as a result have a broader focus. APC is more geographically limited than the CRP or PCP; the program is focused in areas with a substantial wetland base. An additional difference is funding; APC funding is derived from a number of sources, private as well as public. Under the CRP and PCP funding is solely public. Land security under CRP and PCP is enhanced by a cross indexing to agricultural support programs. Land which is enrolled is not eligible for government assistance for annual cropping; this enhances the security of personal contracts under CRP and PCP. Alberta Prairie CARE is driven by the land security issue to investigate new instruments to secure land. Under the PCP, agricultural use such as haying or grazing is permitted. Under the CRP, use is not permitted except in emergency situations. Under APC, use may be permitted; however level and timing of use are controlled.

## CONCLUSION

Alberta Prairie CARE is a wildlife program aimed at enhancing habitat for waterfowl and other wetland-dependent species. In the process, habitat for many other non targeted wildlife species is improved. An indirect consequence of habitat creation is the conservation of land and water resources.

# CONSERVATION THROUGH THE PERMANENT COVER PROGRAMS

## Paula Brand

*Prairie Farm Rehabilitation Association, Rm. 832, Harry Hays Bldg., 220 - 4th Ave. SE, Calgary, Alberta T2G 4X3.*

Since 1989, the Prairie Farm Rehabilitation Association (PFRA) has been administering the Permanent Cover Programs across the Prairies. The programs have encouraged the conversion of lands marginal for annual cultivation and cereal production to long term forages. Program participants enter into a 10 or 21 land use agreement, maintaining the land under cover, in exchange for a one time contract payment. While they forgo crop insurance, grazing and haying of the land is allowed. Approximately 1.3 million acres across the Prairies have been enrolled at a program cost of $66.4 million. Initially 50.7 million acres of land were identified and targeted as "marginal".

Many economic and environmental benefits were realized once forages were seeded on these sites. The economic benefits of Permanent Cover Programs (PCP) on other government programs have been estimated. As well, the economic value of the environmental benefits gained, from specifically wind erosion and productivity loss reductions have also been estimated. A recent participant survey attempted to capture the benefits to producers participating in the programs.

## GOVERNMENT BENEFITS

The primary objective of the PCPs was soil conservation. Eligible lands included Agricultural Capability 4, 5 & 6. Yield reductions and exportation implications were considered serious benefits because PCP lands were lands of lower quality and therefore the impact on total cereal production was small.

A 1992 PFRA study (PFRA 1992) examined the reduction in direct transfer payments that result from the decrease in cultivated acres due to changes resulting from PCP. Ongoing and ad hoc programs were effected by PCP. Programs such as Net Income Stabilization Account (NISA), Gross Revenue Insurance Plan, (GRIP), Crop Insurance, Farm Support Adjustment Measure II (FSAMII), and Western Grain Transportation Act (WGTA) were examined. The total savings to the Federal government of all programs is estimated to be $23.1 million annually. This does not include contributions to these programs by provincial governments.

## PRODUCTIVITY BENEFITS

Land degradation was common on all sites enrolled in PCP. An estimated 80% of the sites were sandy textured soils, prone to drought and severe wind erosion potential because of low or poor moisture-holding capacity. Annual soil erosion rates, on PCP lands while annually cropped across the soil zones is estimated at:

| | |
|---|---|
| Brown | 8 - 23 tons/ac |
| Dark Brown | 3 - 13 tons/ac |
| Black | <3 tons/ac |
| Gray | <1 ton/ac |

Seeding forages has a significant impact on erosion rates, especially in the drier soil zones. Soil erosion under a continuous forage system is reduced to <1 ton/ac. PCP had minor impact on wind erosion in the Gray soil zone. However, wind erosion is not a major factor, as the area is affected by other soil degradation processes.

The effects of soil loss on production were estimated from "Assessment of the Economic value of Topsoil" by K.J. Greer, J.J. Schoneau and D.W. Anderson, of the Soil Science Department, University of Saskatchewan. The report provided a computer generated production percent loss compared to a theoretical no soil loss production. The percent losses of this analysis are based on wheat production for normal moisture conditions for unfertilized soils.

The process developed by Greer et al. was applied to PCP type lands, where between two and five million dollars of soil productivity was saved by converting the land to permanent cover (Brand and Bonneau 1994). It is important to note this saving is occurring to the future owner/manager of the soil not to the current farmer or the government.

## PRODUCER BENEFITS

A survey of approximately 501 PCP clients was conducted in March of 1994 by Western Opinion Research, Inc. The objectives of the survey were to determine present and intended land use, identify PCP client information need, and determine landowner perception of the costs and benefits of PCP.

A summary of survey results indicates:

- PCP clients describe themselves as 59% mixed, 34% livestock, 4% grain, 3% other;

- Main reasons for enrolling include physical land problems, no money in grain, wanting to seed forages, needed hay, and money;

- 94% rated the success of their forage establishment as good or better than expected;

- Most common establishment problem was weeds (47%), followed by drought (35%);

- Future Plans include keeping land in forage as long as possible (93%);

- 18% plan to return PCP land to annual cropping after contract expires;

- 21% said additional information on wildlife habitat enhancement would be "very valuable," 36% "somewhat valuable".

Survey participants were asked to assess the Impact of PCP on their farm operations. Participants cited:

| | |
|---|---|
| increase in: | amount of wildlife habitat (65%), size of livestock herd (64%), net farm income (56%); |
| decrease in: | soil erosion (74%), operating costs (70%), purchased feed (60%); |
| net change in: | operating costs (75%), soil erosion (75%), wildlife habitat (67%); purchased feed (66%), herd size (65%), farm income (63%). |

Participants were asked to describe their management of PCP lands:

| | |
|---|---|
| Haying: | 79% reported haying on PCP land, average 152 acres, yield 1.8 tons/ac, one cut (76%), 85% feed to own livestock; |
| Grazing: | 64% reported grazing on PCP land, average 192 acres, 96% beef cattle, seasonal grazing - (72% fall, 47% spring); |
| Other: | 4% reported other uses - mainly wildlife habitat. |

## CONCLUSION

By all accounts the Permanent Cover Programs were very successful. The financial benefits to both the government and individual producers are well documented. The environmental benefits, while more difficult to demonstrate quantitatively, are well accepted in terms of decrease soil erosion and increased wildlife habitat. PCP was a timely program, however future programs, if any, will definitely be impacted by impending changes to agriculture policy and government fiscal constraints.

## LITERATURE CITED

Brand, P. and M. Bonneau. 1994. Environmental benefits of Permanent Cover Programs - an assessment of the economics of wind erosion reduction. PFRA, Calgary (Unpublished report).

PFRA. 1992. Potential impact of Permanent Cover Programs on Federal Government expenditures. PFRA Draft Report, July.

# THE CONSERVATION RESERVE PROGRAM - PAST, PRESENT, AND FUTURE

## James W. Stutzman and Robert F. Johnson Jr.

*U. S. Fish and Wildlife Service, Benton Lake NWR, Box 450, Black Eagle, Montana 59414*

## INTRODUCTION

The Conservation Reserve Program (CRP) was established under the 1985 Food Security Act. Landowners were paid to remove highly erodible and other environmentally sensitive lands from crop production for ten years and convert them to perennial vegetation. More than 375,000 farmers in 47 states have enrolled 36.4 million acres in the program. More than two-thirds of CRP acreage is located in the Great Plains and Prairie Regions.

The CRP has provided significant benefits to landowners and the environment. Soil erosion has been reduced and water quality improved. It has also provided extraordinary benefits to wildlife. Agricultural commodity payments have been reduced and landowner satisfaction with the program has been high. The CRP is the most successful conservation program of the 20th century.

## HISTORY OF THE CONSERVATION RESERVE PROGRAM

The Conservation Reserve Program was created by the Conservation Title of the 1985 Food Security Act. The primary goal of the program was to take highly erodible land (HEL) out of production. Estimates indicated that more than 102 million acres of HEL were eligible for the CRP. Congress limited the program to 25% of a county's cropland which reduced the total eligible HEL acreage to 70 million acres. Landowners would

Table 1. Conservation Reserve Program goals

1. Remove highly erodible land from production.
2. Protect the nation's long term food and fiber producing capability.
3. Reduce sedimentation.
4. Improve water quality.
5. Enhance fish and wildlife habitat.
6. Reduce surplus farm commodity production.
7. Provide income support for farmers.

enroll their land into the CRP for ten years and receive an annual rental payment. The Federal government would provide up to 50% of the cost of establishing perennial cover on the acres that were accepted into the CRP and the landowner would be responsible for maintaining the cover at his own expense for the duration of the contract. The program goal was to enroll up to 45 million acres in the CRP between 1986 and 1990 (Table 1).

Twelve sign-ups were held and 36.5 million acres were enrolled which represented 8% of all U.S. cropland. The first sign-up included land in capability class II - IV having an annual erosion rate greater than 3T (three times the tolerance value of the soil) or land in capability class VI - VIII (Tables 2 and 3).

Landowners submitted bids to the U.S. Department of Agriculture (USDA) indicating the acreage that they would retire and the amount per acre they would be willing to accept annually in compensation. USDA then accepted the lowest bids in the multi-county pool in which the landowner's farm was located. The idea

Table 2. The Conservation Reserve Program contract summary

|  | Total enrolled acres (Millions) | Number of contracts (Thousands) | Total value of contract[1] (Billions, $) | Average contract size (acres) | Average value of contract[2] (Thousands, $) |
|---|---|---|---|---|---|
| U.S | 36 | 375 | 20 | 97 | 52 |
| Montana | 3 | 8 | 1 | 360 | 142 |

[1]Value of contract is the total rental payment plus cost share.

[2]Average value of contract is the full amount paid over the term of the contract (usually 10 years).

Table 3. Major Conservation Reserve Program cover types.

| | National | Montana |
|---|---|---|
| Enrolled acres seeded with introduced grasses | 21,385,876 | 2,493,903 |
| Enrolled acres seeded with native grasses | 8,459,403 | 295,453 |
| Enrolled acres planted with trees | 2,321,193 | 190 |

behind bidding was to get the cheapest conservation benefits by taking the lowest bid. Actually, the only genuine bidding occurred among first round participants who did not know that USDA had decided to put an upper limit on accepted bids in order to prevent outlandish payments. The caps remained essentially unchanged in subsequent sign-ups, and as this knowledge became widespread the distribution of bids received converged to the cap level in each pool. The cap rate, in effect, became the going price for cropping rights on fragile land and low bids disappeared. The potential savings from the bidding process was lost (Cochrane and Runge 1992).

Subsequent sign-ups targeted watersheds and wetlands. The last sign-up was in June of 1992. Congress has not appropriated funds for additional enrollments since then.

Average annual rental rates ranged from $40.35/acre in the southern plains to $74.17/acre in the corn belt. The maximum annual rental rate was $200/acre and the minimum annual rental rate was $4.00/acre. The overall average of all contracts nationwide was $56.55. The average cost share per contract was $3,665.

Table 4. Highly erodible land (HEL) in the CRP.

| | National | Montana |
|---|---|---|
| | —— million acres —— | |
| Enrolled acres | 36 | 3 |
| Enrolled HEL acres | 35 | 3 |

## CONSERVATION RESERVE PROGRAM BENEFITS

### Soil Erosion

Estimates of soil saved range upward to 693.4 million tons/year. The average erosion rate on land enrolled in the CRP has been reduced from 18 tons/acre/year before CRP to 1.4 tons/acre/year with CRP. In Montana, the average erosion rate on CRP acres has been reduced from 14.5 tons/acre/year before CRP to 1.5 tons/acre/year with CRP (Tables 4 and 5).

### Water Quality

USDA's Economic Research Service (ERS) estimates that sediment flow into waterways has been cut by 100 million tons/year. Estimates of water quality benefits include a reduction of total suspended sediment by 33,980,000 tons or 11%, 123 million tons of nitrogen or 14.4% and 25.2 million tons of phosphorus or 13.3%.

In North Dakota, the CRP has improved water quality in many lakes that support recreational fishing. Prior to the CRP, a winter with heavy snowfall like the winter of 1993-94 would cause complete winterkill in approximately 40 lakes statewide. During spring 1994 surveys, partial winterkill was found in 15 lakes, a much smaller impact than expected. Winterkill is the result of high nutrient runoff causing plant and algal growth that decomposes and consumes oxygen to the point where fish cannot survive. CRP acres slow runoff, reduce erosion and ultimately save lakes from winterkill. The North Dakota Game and Fish Department saved $480,000 in fish restocking costs in 1994 and anglers gained three additional years of recreational opportunity that would have been lost if the lakes had to be restocked.

Table 5. The Conservation Reserve Program (CRP) saves soil.

| | National | Montana |
|---|---|---|
| Average erosion rate before CRP (tons/acre/year) | 18.6 | 14.5 |
| Average erosion rate with CRP | 1.4 | 1.5 |
| Total soil saved per year (Million tons) | 693.4 | 37.2 |

The CRP could also be used to manage saline seeps. The utilization of deep-rooted perennial forage crops in upslope recharge areas is a proven reclamation technique. A significant decrease in the size of the seeps occurs within five years when 80% of the recharge area is seeded to alfalfa. The CRP offers a definite opportunity to increase plant water use over dryland summer fallow farming on sites where recharge areas are also highly erodible.

## Wildlife Benefits

One of the initial objectives of the Conservation Reserve Program was to enhance habitat for fish and wildlife populations. The actual benefits to wildlife have been significant (Table 6).

Several passerine species that breed in the temperate grasslands of North America and winter in the Neotropics have shown significant population declines in the past 25 years. The continued conversion of perennial grassland to cropland is a suspected cause of the population declines. The lark bunting (*Calamospiza melanocorys*) and the grasshopper sparrow (*Ammodramus savannarum*) declined by nearly 50% during that period. Research in Montana, Minnesota, North Dakota and South Dakota has found that the lark bunting was the most abundant bird in CRP fields and the grasshopper sparrow was the second most abundant (Johnson and Schwartz 1993) (Table 7).

Preliminary results from an ongoing CRP study conducted by Dr. R.J. Robel of Kansas State University in Indiana, Iowa, Kansas, Michigan, Missouri, Nebraska, and Wisconsin indicate that in 1992 and 1993 CRP

Table 6. Six features of the Conservation Reserve Program most valuable to wildlife.

1. Large acreage size.
2. Nationwide distribution with a prairie emphasis.
3. Creation of large blocks of habitat.
4. Inclusion of unique land types (eg. cropped wetlands).
5. Relatively undisturbed vegetation.
6. Establishment of suitable cover types.

fields supported 21 times more nests and 32 times more successful nests than rowcrop fields. The most common species in CRP fields were song sparrows (*Melospiza melodia*), field sparrows (*Spizella pusilla*), dickcissels (*Spiza americana*), and grasshopper sparrows.

In the main ring-necked pheasant (*Phasianus colchicus*) belt states of Iowa, Kansas, Minnesota, South Dakota, North Dakota, Montana, Colorado, and Nebraska, the pheasant population has increased 31% from 11.5 to 14.8 million birds as a result of the CRP. Some states have experienced pheasant increases of 60 to 100%. In areas where winterkill is the main factor limiting pheasant numbers, heavy CRP cover has been crucial during severe winters. With improved production conditions, CRP acres could produce as many as 18 to 20 million pheasants, which is nearly double the pre-CRP population throughout the main pheasant states.

Several grassland-dependent waterfowl species, notably mallards (*Anas platyrhynchos*), northern pintails

Table 7. Grassland bird response to the Conservation Reserve Program (CRP).

| | Average densities[1] | | Average annual change (%) |
| | Cropland | CRP fields | Central region |
| Species | 1990-91 | 1990-91 | 1966-90 (bbs) |
|---|---|---|---|
| Lark bunting | 4 | 23 | -4 |
| Baird's sparrow | 0 | 2 | -3 |
| Western meadowlark | 4 | 8 | -<1 |
| Clay-colored sparrow | 0 | 5 | -2 |
| Bobolink | 1 | 4 | -3 |
| Savannah sparrow | 2 | 6 | 1 |
| Grasshopper sparrow | 1 | 21 | -5 |

From Johnson and Schwartz 1993.
[1]Indicated pairs/100 ha.

(*Anas acuta*), and blue-winged teal (*Anas discors*), have declined since the 1970's. Persistent drought conditions in many areas of the prairie pothole region, continued conversion of grassland to cropland, and high predator populations have combined to significantly reduce waterfowl production.

Studies in Minnesota and North Dakota from 1989 - 1991 found that waterfowl nest success ranged from 12 to 60% in CRP fields and from 3 to 12% on U.S. Fish and Wildlife Service Waterfowl Production Areas (WPA). Overall nest success was 23.1% in CRP fields and 8.2% on WPA's (Kantrud 1993) (Table 8).

During the spring and summer of 1994 approximately 10,000 acres of CRP in North and South Dakota and northeastern Montana were searched for nests. Analysis indicates that waterfowl nest densities approached one nest per 2.6 acres of CRP cover. Nest success was close to 30% for all species combined. Extrapolating this nest density and success to the three million acres of CRP with similar wetland densities and breeding duck populations represents somewhere around three million hatched ducklings.

Similar nest success figures were found on a sample of WPAs that were searched in 1994. Water conditions were significantly better in 1994, and large CRP acreages may have influenced nest success on WPA's by

Table 8. Mayfield nest success rates for major duck species in the prairie pothole regions of Minnesota and North Dakota, 1989-1991.[1]

| Species | CRP[2] | WPA[3] |
|---|---|---|
| Mallard | 25 | 10 |
| Northern pintail | 37 | 4 |
| Blue-winged teal | 12 | 9 |
| Northern shoveler | 15 | 12 |
| Gadwall | 60 | 3 |

Adapted from Kantrud 1993.

[1]Estimates were made by pooling all nests and therefore may be biased.

[2]Conservation Reserve Program.

[3]Waterfowl Protection Area.

substantially increasing available habitat and spreading out predators.

The CRP has also provided significant benefits to endangered species. In California, several endangered species such as the San Joaquin kit fox (*Vulpes macrotis mutica*), giant kangaroo rat (*Dipodomys ingens*), and blunt-nosed leopard lizard (*Gambelia silus*), are benefitting from the grassland habitat created by the CRP.

In Idaho, which supports the largest remaining population of Columbian sharp-tailed grouse (*Tympanuchus phasianellus columbianus*), outside of Canada, this species occupied less than 10% of its historic range. Populations were stagnant and it was considered a candidate for Federal listing as a threatened species.

The CRP created 600,000 acres of grassland habitat in southeast Idaho. The Columbian sharptail breeding range has increased dramatically and the statewide population has increased between 200 and 300%. Two-thirds of the new leks discovered in the state were found on CRP lands, and biologists have established two new populations of grouse in areas of the state where they have not existed for many years. Every state in the northwest is interested in obtaining Columbian sharptails from Idaho to reestablish extirpated populations. In Oregon there were no Columbian sharptails prior to the CRP program, and there are now breeding populations. This type of positive response to CRP could make the Endangered Species Act a non-issue for this species.

The greater prairie chicken (*Tympanuchus cupido*), formerly a state listed endangered species in Colorado, was changed to threatened status in late 1993 because of substantial population and range increases due, in part, to CRP habitat.

The CRP may prevent the endangered species "train wrecks" that Secretary of the Interior Bruce Babbitt frequently talks about. These occur when conditions get so bad and population numbers get so low that there are no alternatives to listing a species as endangered. If grassland species can increase on CRP lands over a wide area we may be able to avoid the listing process with all the problems and expense that go along with it. Species that are already listed may do well enough to be delisted. This is a benefit of the CRP that could be significant, and may also represent an enormous financial saving. The problems with government regulation, landowner relationships, and private property rights that could be avoided may also be significant.

Big game species have also benefited from the CRP. In Cimmaron County, Oklahoma a small population of pronghorn antelope (*Antilocapra americana*), had existed for years. When county landowners enrolled the maximum acreage in the CRP, the pronghorn population increased by 300%. The primary reason for the increase was the increased grass cover and forage provided by the CRP fields.

In San Luis Obispo County, California, Tule Elk (*Cervus canadensis*), and pronghorn antelope have been successfully reintroduced with the CRP providing much of the new habitat base for these species.

## Financial Returns

Economic analysis of Federal Farm Program payments in North Dakota, South Dakota, Montana, Nebraska, Kansas, and Colorado for 1991 indicated that without CRP the Federal government would have paid out $16 million more and would have received no natural resource or wildlife habitat benefits. Fifteen million acres of wildlife habitat and $124 million in natural resource benefits in addition to the direct saving of $16 million were the benefits of CRP in these states.

Increased pheasant populations in South Dakota attracted almost 48,000 nonresident and 80,000 resident hunters in 1993. These hunters spent more than $50 million while hunting in the state. In Jones County alone, increased hunting activity that was a direct result of the CRP, generated an estimated $1 million in the first six days of the 1993 pheasant season.

According to USDA economists, the CRP will provide between $3.4 and $11 billion in environmental benefits over the life of the program. National Biological Survey (NBS) economists estimate that the CRP will generate more than $13 billion in resource-based benefits to society.

## THE FUTURE

The CRP is not without problems. Many of the CRP acres in Montana were seeded to monotypic stands of crested wheatgrass, which provides very poor wildlife habitat.

Successful stand establishment in some areas due to drought conditions has been a problem. Some landowners have been receiving CRP payments for five years or more and they have not succeeded in establishing cover on their CRP acres.

Weed control has been a problem in some areas, especially with seed mixtures that included legumes. USDA regulations have allowed these areas to be mowed, but the vegetation could not be removed. Heavy amounts of litter that were left on the fields created problems with survival of desirable species, and the weed problems increased.

The threat of wildfires on large unbroken CRP tracts has been a concern in many areas, and many fires have started as the result of lightning strikes and high winds causing power lines to arc.

In many areas of the northern great plains emergency haying of CRP stands has been authorized almost yearly. Haying was allowed during the peak of the nesting season.

The economic impact of the CRP on rural communities has been mixed. Farm families, rural landowners, and recreationists have benefited financially from the CRP. In North Dakota, studies have indicated that 21% of CRP contract holders were able to continue farming as a direct result of the CRP. Farmers as a group have seen higher income with increased commodity prices that result from removing land from production (Gustafson 1994).

Agribusiness firms have suffered in the short term with reduced purchases of fertilizer, seed, and equipment.

The future of the CRP is uncertain. The first contracts begin to expire in 1995, and by the year 2000 less than three million acres will remain in the CRP. Several bills have been introduced into the U.S. Senate and House of Representatives to extend the CRP. On August 26, 1994, Secretary of Agriculture Mike Espy extended the CRP contracts that would expire in 1995 for one year.

Support for extending the CRP is widespread among many environmental and farm groups. The current deficit reduction activities in Washington make it very difficult to predict what will happen. Many people look at the $1.8 billion annual price tag for the CRP and feel it is simply too expensive.

The Congress will begin debate on the 1995 Farm Bill in the near future, and the fate of the CRP will be decided during that process.

Deficit reduction laws passed by Congress in the past few years have capped the entire Federal budget for discretionary spending. Any new legislation by Congress that authorizes additional Federal spending must be offset by spending reductions elsewhere.

Two Federal agencies monitor and enforce these budget cuts. The Office of Management and Budget (OMB) performs this function for the Executive Branch and the Congressional Budget Office (CBO) performs it for Congress. At the beginning of 1994 both agencies considered CRP to be a ten year program that begins to wind down in 1995. The reauthorization of the CRP in the 1995 Farm Bill would be considered a new spending authorization which would require cuts in other USDA programs. This would force a confrontation between conservationist and commodity interests over a program now strongly supported by both.

On December 14, 1994, USDA announced that it intends to offer CRP participants the opportunity to modify and extend their contracts for up to an additional ten years when current contracts expire.

CBO has made a preliminary determination that over the next five years USDA will extend a portion of the expiring contracts to end up with about 15 million acres in the CRP. This would be less than half of the acreage currently enrolled in the program. CBO has assumed that, in the absence of new legislation, that USDA will selectively extend existing contracts to reduce the size of the CRP, to retarget it geographically, and to enhance its environmental benefits.

Surveys indicate that without a CRP extension, 53 to 63% of CRP acres would be returned to crop production, 24% would be used for hay or livestock grazing, and the remainder would be kept in trees or grass for wildlife or other uses. A substantial increase in crop prices may result in up to 74% of CRP acres being returned to crop production.

If contract holders were offered extensions with 100% or more of current rent, contracts on 80% of CRP acres would be extended.

The CRP has been the most successful conservation program in the history of the United States. The natural resource benefits have been extraordinary, wildlife populations have flourished on CRP stands, soil erosion has been reduced, water quality has improved, and agricultural subsidy payments have been reduced.

No other conservation program has been as successful as the CRP over such a large scale in such a short period of time. The CRP can be a lasting natural resource legacy of the 20th century.

## LITERATURE CITED

Cochrane, W.W. and C.F. Runge. 1992. Reforming farm policy toward a national agenda. Iowa State Univ. Press, Ames, Iowa..

Johnson, D. H. and M. D. Schwartz. 1993. The Conservation Reserve Program and grassland birds. Conservation Biology 7: 934-937.

Kantrud, H.A. 1993. Duck nest success on Conservation Reserve Program land in the Prairie Pothole Region. Journal of Soil and Water Conservation 48: 238-242.

Gustafson, C.R. 1994. Impact of the Conservation Reserve Program on rural economies. Presented at the CRP Policy Options Workshop, Arlington, Virginia, February 1994.

# NATIVE RANGE ON PUBLIC LAND IN ALBERTA

## Keith Lyseng

*Agriculture, Food and Rural Development, Public Land Management Branch, Edmonton, Alberta*

## INTRODUCTION

Good morning ladies and gentlemen! It is a pleasure to be with you today to talk about native range on public land in Alberta. My name is Keith Lyseng and I am a Land Management Specialist with Public Lands in Agriculture, Food and Rural Development.

You know, being in government, I can say we are honestly trying to do what is best for the resources and people of Alberta. But sometimes it reminds me of when my grandfather went in a nursing home. He was getting older and was quite frail, so during the day the staff would help him get dress and help him to a day room where they had activities. The first day he was there, he would start to lean over sideways, and the staff would come running over and straighten him up. Then he would lean over the other way, and they would come and straighten him up. This happened time after time. That night, dad and I went to visit him. Dad asked him how his first day had gone. Grandpa smiled and said "You know, this is sure a nice place and the staff mean well, but they just don't let you fart!".

I hope as managers of public rangeland, we can see the big picture and understand what the resource users really need and want. One of our primary functions in Public Lands is to act as facilitators in the use and management of native range. However I will discuss that in more detail, later.

My presentation today will contain:

- a description of public land in Alberta

- the role of Public Lands in Agriculture, Food and Rural Development (AFRD)

- a description of the administration and management of public land in the White Area

- a brief description of the grazing contracts issued on public land

- a discussion of some of the "range issues"

- and finally close with some opportunities and threats to the management of native range.

## SOMETHING ABOUT PUBLIC LANDS IN ALBERTA

Alberta's rangelands are extensive and diverse native plant communities that provide for a wide range of needs such as livestock grazing, wildlife habitat, natural areas and watershed. Rangeland ecosystems developed over thousands of years, adapting to soils, climate, and the presence of fire and grazing that ensured a dominance of grass.

The beauty of these native prairie landscapes are becoming more recognized and sought after by both urban and rural populations. Native rangeland agriculture differs from arable agriculture by being extensively managed, with relatively low input cost of labour and capital, limited production techniques, and a low financial return per acre. With appropriate range management practices, rangelands yield a stable flow of products while maintaining the integrity and resilience of the soil, vegetation, and water resources.

Alberta contains approximately 163.4 million acres. About 28% of this area, or about 46 million acres is privately owned. The remainder is Crown land, owned and controlled by provincial or federal departments. Approximately 6% or about just over 10 million acres is classified as public lands and is managed by Public Lands in the Department of Agriculture, Food and Rural Development.

Although public land is scattered throughout the White area, most of the public land is concentrated in the northern third and southern third of Alberta.

A 1992 Statistics Canada report, indicated that about 46% of land occupied for grazing is found in the mixed grass prairie, about 7% in the fescue prairie, about 23% in the aspen parkland and about 23% in the boreal forest. This roughly corresponds to the areas of public land in the White Area.

Provincial grazing leases comprise some 5.2 million acres of Alberta's public lands providing over 1.2 million Animal Unit Months (or AUMs) of grazing. Provincially they play an important role in developing and diversifying Alberta's economy. These grazing agreements offer an extensive pasture area for the livestock industry and the grazing of native range in particular is an important part of southern Alberta's ranching industry.

Considering public grazing leases alone, which is 33% of Alberta's rangeland, livestock production generates 200 million dollars annually in primary benefits and 540 million dollars in secondary benefits (Rudd and Wehrahn 1990).

## ROLE OF PUBLIC LANDS IN AGRICULTURE, FOOD AND RURAL DEVELOPMENT

The role of Public Lands staff in Agriculture, Food and Rural Development in native range management is to maintain a healthy range plant community in partnership with the grazing disposition holders whose livelihood depends on that range. A key goal of range management is to maintain plant vigour and vegetative cover, thereby protecting the soil and forage resource. Management of public lands is guided by the integrated resource management philosophy that considers other resource values like watershed, fish and wildlife, and recreation in addition to livestock grazing.

Today, **deregulation** is a term that seems to be in vogue. "Get government out of the face of Industry" is a phrase we hear daily. This is a practice that has been used for decades by Public Lands in dealing with lease holders. We set some rules, facilitate use of the land, but then get out of their face and work with them as partners in native range management.

## ADMINISTRATION AND MANAGEMENT

In the spring of 1993, the Department of Forestry, Lands and Wildlife was dissolved. A formal accord between the Minister of Environmental Protection and the Minister of Agriculture, Food and Rural Development was signed. Management of public land in the White Area became the responsibility of Agriculture,

Food and Rural Development, while the administration would be performed by the Department of Environmental Protection. By that agreement, Alberta Environmental Protection, Land Administration Division handles the administration of all public land covered by the *Public Lands Act*. They handle the legal and legislated requirements associated with legal contract issuance and maintenance, the public land computer registry, and day to day service to the public on administration issues.

Land and Forest Service is responsible for the management of the public land in the Green Area, and Public Lands in Agriculture, Food and Rural Development manages the public land in the White Area or settled area (except for the Special Areas).

Now I would like to discuss grazing contracts issued on public land:

There are five types of contracts issued for grazing:

1. Grazing Leases
2. Grazing Permits
3. Head Tax Grazing Permits
4. Grazing Licences
5. Forest Reserve Permits

These contracts are usually issued in different circumstances, depending on the land uses that have been determined for an area. On public land there are over 5,600 grazing dispositions in the province.

### Grazing Leases (Table 1)

This is the most common grazing contract issued on public land. There are about 5300 grazing leases covering about 5 million acres on public land in the White area. Leases can be held by individuals, corporations, or by grazing associations which are often called community pastures.

Leases are usually issued for a term of 1 to 10 years, with an option for renewal if all conditions of the lease are meet and fees are paid. The usual term is 10 years.

Persons can obtain grazing leases either by assignment from an existing lease holder or by competing for and securing an unallocated parcel of public land. For areas of native range, very few parcels are unallocated. If a parcel does become available, they are normally allocated by auction or tender.

Table 1. Characteristics of grazing leases in Alberta.

| | |
|---|---|
| Term | Up to 10 years. |
| Public access | The lessee has the right to restrict public access. |
| Subletting | The lessee must own the livestock. |
| Transfer | The lessee can sell (assign) the lease rights. |
| Collateral | The lessee can use the lease as collateral for mortgages (conditional surrender). |
| Surface rights compensation | The lessee has the right to negotiate compensation. |
| Charges | Standard grazing rental and taxes. |

Grazing lease holders must pay taxes to the local authority and must follow proper range management practices (no overgrazing, fenced,).

The lease holder also negotiates surface rights compensation for any oil and gas development on his lease.

Public land in the White Area is also managed for multiple use. The lease holder as well as other disposition holders is given additional responsibilities to act as the stewards of the native prairie resource.

The annual rental (Table 2) is based on a formula that considers the average annual weight gain of cattle, the average price of cattle and the grazing capacity of the land.

The 1995 fees per AUM are $2.79 for Southern Alberta, $2.32 for Cental Alberta, and $1.39 for Northern Alberta. For Head Tax and Forest Reserve permits, the rates are $3.50 in Southern Alberta, $3.00 in Central Alberta, and $2.05 in Northern Alberta.

## Grazing Permits (Table 3)

Grazing permits are issued annually, usually on lands reserved for other purposes, or where the best long term use is not grazing. The Permittee does not have the right to restrict access but can use the permit as collateral and can negotiate surface compensation with oil and gas developers. The permittee can assign the permit rights and must pay the local taxes.

## Head Tax Permit (Table 4)

Head tax permits are issued for a specific period of time for the grazing of livestock. These permits convey no interest in the land so the permittee cannot restrict access and does not pay local taxes. There are two types of Head Tax Permits—those issued on Grazing Reserves, and those issued on vacant public land.

## Grazing Licences (Table 5)

Licences are issued for up to 10 years. The licencee does not have the right to restrict access or assign the licence. The licencee is recognized as an occupant under the *Surface Rights Act* and can negotiate compensation. Local taxes are paid only if the licence is outside a Forest Management Area.

Table 2. Alberta grazing rentals in 1995 by region (cost per animal-unit-month).

| | Southern | Central | Northern |
|---|---|---|---|
| | | $ | |
| Grazing leases, permits, and licences | 2.79 | 2.32 | 1.39 |
| Forest reserve and head tax permit rates | 3.50 | 3.00 | 2.05 |

Table 3. Characteristics of grazing permit rights in Alberta.

| | |
|---|---|
| Term | Annual. |
| Public access | Permittee does not have the right to restrict public access. |
| Subletting | Permittee must own the livestock. |
| Collateral | Permittee can use the grazing permit as collateral for mortgages (conditional surrender). |
| Surface rights compensation | Permittee has the right to negotiate compensation. |
| Transfer | Permittee can sell (assign) the permit rights. |
| Charges | Standard grazing rental and taxes. |

## Forest Reserve Permits (Table 6)

This is an annual grazing disposition given out only in the Forest Reserves. It is very similar to the Head Tax Permits in that it does not allow the permittee to control access or negotiate surface rights compensation. The permittee does not pay taxes and is not allowed to transfer or assign the permit.

## SOME RANGE ISSUES

Range resource management (i.e. maintaining a healthy, productive and sustainable range) for livestock grazing remains a key issue. Drought conditions over the past decade, and man made problems caused by overgrazing, points toward the need for better range management province wide. Management emphasis includes:

- adjusting stocking levels for drought effects and larger cows with earlier calves,

- implementation of planned grazing systems that build in periods of deferral and rest for rangeland,

- tame pasture development for complementary grazing systems,

- brush management,

- and fencing and water developments to improve livestock distribution. (Turnbull *et al.* 1993).

A stockman's course put on by Public Lands staff in southern Alberta has been very well attended by may users groups and deals with the fundamentals of range management.

There are a number of issues facing lease holders, Albertans, and public land managers and administrators concerning native range management.

Table 4. Characteristics of the head tax permits in Alberta.

| | |
|---|---|
| Term | Specified period of use. |
| Public access | Conveys no interest to the land; therefore, the permittee cannot restrict public access. |
| Subletting | Not allowed. |
| Collateral | Not allowed. |
| Surface rights compensation | No interest in the land but occupancy is recognized under the Surface Rights Act. |
| Transfer | Not allowed. |
| Charges | Permittees pay fees based on a per-head per-month charge; do not pay municipal taxes. |
| Note | These permits are used primarily on grazing reserves. |

Table 5. Characteristics of grazing licences in Alberta.

| Term | Up to 10 years. |
|---|---|
| Public access | The licencee does not have the right to restrict public access. |
| Subletting | The licencee must own the livestock. |
| Collateral | Should not be considered as collateral. |
| Surface rights compensation | The licencee has the right to negotiate compensation. |
| Transfer | Licences are not assignable. |
| Charges | Standard grazing rental; taxes are payable by the licencee only if the licence is outside a forest management area. |

## GRAZING OF THE NATIVE RANGE

Some question the grazing of native range and would like to restrict cattle from using it. To preserve the species composition and "protect" the range, these people feel cattle should be removed. You can see some of these initiatives south of the border. However grazing of the range can be very complimentary with conservation objectives and if managed properly is part of the good range management. Let me explain:

A significant portion of Alberta rangelands have been maintained in a healthy state through a high standard of range management. There has only briefly been a "pristine" condition where the range was not periodically eaten. The native range evolved under grazing pressures from a variety of animals. Many historians have documented the great buffalo kills of the mid 1800s. Sherm Ewing, a long time cattleman, public land lease holder, and recent author, wrote in his book "The Range" that buffalo were virtually extinct by 1879. As Mr. Ewing states in his book, after the buffalo were gone, there was a gap of several decades where there was very little grazing of the native range. This was a period of under use and correlates very closely to the arrival of the early

settlers. This was a time as Mr. Ewing describes his fathers generation as telling of grass near waist height. This growth and lack of use was a short period of transition and totally abnormal. Unfortunately, some people use these times as the threshold for comparison of range health. Mr. Ewings contention is that "range today is a damn sight better than it was in 1864 when the buffalo still roamed free". Studies done by University and Government staff agree that moderate grazing pressure and good range management practices are essential in protecting species diversification and range health (Range Notes, Feb. 1993).

However, after this short period of under use, came a period of severe overuse. The late 1800s and early 1900s were marked by unrestricted year-round grazing, which lead to substantial deterioration of many range areas. Overgrazing continued in some areas because of heavy grazing pressure, improper timing, or prolonged duration of use. Unrestricted public grazing of some areas of southern Alberta lasted until the mid 1930s when these practices were abandoned, but not before the range had been severely impacted. Some of these overgrazed lands have taken decades to recover. With proper range management practices, range condition is now

Table 6. Characteristics of the forest reserve permit rights in Alberta.

| Term | Annual (long-term security established under preference quota[1]) |
|---|---|
| Public access | Permittee does not have the right to restrict public access. |
| Subletting | Permittee must own the livestock. |
| Surface rights compensation | Permittee can not negotiate compensation for surface rights. |
| Transfer | Not allowed. |
| Charges | Same fees as head tax permit, but permittee does not pay municipal taxes. |

[1]After a permittee has held a temporary permit for three years, a preference quota can be established that guarantees him a set level of animal-unit-months (minimum 100 - maximum 1,000).

much improved. The terrible results of the "public grazing" experience was a major factor in the change to a system of leaseholder tenure.

Another issue is public access to rangeland. As is the trend elsewhere in North American, our large (and growing) urban population is discovering the beauty and appeal of native grasslands which it may prefer to regard as "wildlands". Retention and protection of native prairie has become a prominent issue. As the population of Alberta grows, the demand for use of these open spaces will increase. The increasingly important task of both public land administrators and lease holders is how to integrate these uses.

## ACCESS TO PUBLIC LANDS

Access to public lands under a grazing lease requires permission from the grazing leaseholder. For a Grazing licence, no permission is required because no rights to the land have been given to the licence holder. The Justice Department has determined that a grazing lease holder has the right to restrict access on his grazing lease. There is no change planned to removing the right of the grazing leaseholder to control access. We recognize grazing lease holders as the resident stewards of the land. Most lease holders closely monitor the range and are concerned about it's protection and potential overuse. Livestock producers are also in the best position to control access to protect the investment from which they are earning a living. Generally, leaseholders control over access does not pose a problem for recreationalists, as in most cases they will be given permission to enter the land. A survey by the Alberta Cattle Commission shows that approximately 80% of grazing lease holders would permit reasonable access to their grazing lease land.

Unrestricted access to public land under a grazing lease would not be beneficial for the native range or practical for the rancher who must be able to protect his investments. All terrain vehicles criss-crossing a sensitive range, without attention to livestock or sensitive landscapes is everyones' worst fear. However total restriction of access by leaseholders after cattle have been removed from the lease is also unreasonable. Foot access by conscientious members of the public when the lease holders cattle have been removed should be quite acceptable. Each user has valid concerns but must recognize the valid concerns of others.

Public Lands supports a program called "Use Respect". This encourages both the public and leaseholders to use respect when dealing with each other. We encourage leaseholders to provide reasonable access.

Surface Rights Compensation on grazing leases is another issue that is of concern to members of the public. Compensation under the *Surface Rights Act* is paid for "loss of use, adverse effect, nuisance, inconvenience, and noise". The rancher does experience extra work and costs resulting from oil and gas exploration and development. However there are a number of cases where the compensation for surface revenue far exceeds the fees paid for grazing rental and taxes on the lease. This is seen by some members of the public as "windfall" profits.

There are over 8,500 agricultural dispositions and over 27,000 non-agricultural dispositions in the White Area. Not all these non-agricultural dispositions are covered by the *Surface Rights Act*. It is important to note that 98% of all non-agricultural dispositions occur on top of an agricultural disposition.

## OPPORTUNITIES/THREATS/ IMPLICATIONS

Conservation and agricultural efforts must be recognized as being tied together. The "buzz" words of the last few years have been "ecosystem" management and "sustainable" agriculture. Those working on sustainable agriculture tend to focus on ecosystem functions (i.e. looking at maintaining soil organic matter and fertility, reducing soil erosion, and controlling ground water pollution). Until we all realize that sustainable agricultural practices and conserving threatened grassland biodiversity are intertwined problems, solutions to user conflicts will elude us.

The biggest threat to the management of native prairie is a breakdown in communication between user groups. With this breakdown will come a call to government to legislate single uses. Slogans like we hear coming from south of the border—"Cattle free by '93"; "Cattle galore by '94"; "No Cattle Alive by '95"; show us the confrontation that has evolved. We have been warned. Now it is up to all concerned to make their cases understood and to deal with other users with respect and in a constructive fashion. Public Lands in Agriculture, Food and Rural Development is a partner in this information and decision-making process. However if this process fails, and negotiations are replaced with hardened positions and litigation, we will then be faced with the confrontational situations. We are at a crossroads where we can choose to accommodate multiple users or entrench a single use. If we are forced to entrench a single use—are you confident it will be your use?

## LITERATURE CITED

Turnbull, M.G., B.W. Adams, M.L. Anderson, and L. Cole. 1993. Alberta rangeland resources. Pp. 31-37 *In* Managing Canadian rangeland for sustainability and profitability (F. Taha, Z. Abouguendia, and R. Horton, eds.). Proceedings of the First Interprovincial Range Conference, Saskatoon.

Ewing, S. 1990. The Range. Mountain Press Publ. Calgary.

Land Administration Statistics. 1993. Department of Environmental Protection Annual Report, 1992-93. Deptartment of Environmental Protection, Alberta.

Rudd, L. and R. Wehrhahn. 1990. A profile of Alberta's cattle industry. Alberta Agriculture, Food and Rural Development internal working paper.

Willoughby, M. 1993. Species diversity and how it is affected by livestock grazing in Alberta. Range Notes No. 13, Alberta Agriculture, Food and Rural Development, Public Lands, Edmonton, Alberta.

Wilson, S. 1986. The future of ranching and range management in Alberta, Canada. Rangelands 1: 21-22.

# AGRICULTURAL CROWN LAND MANAGEMENT IN SASKATCHEWAN

## Greg R. Haase

*Sakatchewan Agriculture and Food, 3085 Albert St., Regina, Saskatchewan S4S 0B1*

## INTRODUCTION

We are at a crossroads in Saskatchewan with respect to agricultural Crown land management. We can continue on the road we have travelled for the last fifty years and minimize non-agricultural uses or we can chose the road that recognizes other demands and achieves an integrated resource use. The choice is ours. There are risks with both choices but choosing the first risks having the second imposed at a later date. The increasing urbanization we have will see agriculture ultimately lose if we wait for an imposed resolution. Taking a proactive approach at this time will allow a more balanced approach to the management of this important resource.

## THE RESOURCE

In Saskatchewan we have approximately 8.8 million acres of agricultural Crown land. This land is largely a cumulation of land transferred from the federal government in 1930 and the remnants of the 1970's Land Bank program. It is comprised of approximately 950 thousand acres of cultivation, 600 thousand acres tame forage and 6.3 million acres of grazing. The balance is either unsuitable for agricultural production or is unclassified. This resource brings in approximately $25 to $30 million annually and ranks agricultural Crown land as the fourth largest resource revenue generator in the province, behind oil, potash, and natural gas, while ahead of uranium, forests and game, coal, and other minerals.

## GRAZING LAND

The grazing land is the largest component of the land we administer and it is indeed the most fragile in many ways. A recent re-assessment of all the grazing land in the province indicated that there is approximately 15.6 million acres in total. The 6.9 million acres of grazing and forage represents nearly one half of all the assessed grazing in the province. Programs targeting this Crown resource have a significant impact on the entire industry.

Since our province was settled, native lands have been put under the plough at a steady rate. While this rate has slowed over the past number of years, it continued to grow into the 1990's. Correspondingly, more grazing lands have fallen victim to the plough from the post settlement years to present. Figure 1 illustrates these trends.

While grazing land continues to disappear, livestock numbers continue to grow. As well, increases in livestock size and performance have increased the grazing pressure on the remaining resource. Figure 2 estimates the cumulative effect of these industry trends. This pressure placed on the resource is beginning to strain the bounds of sustainability. It is only through the use of annual forage, fall stubble grazing and/or seeding down more tame forage that the resource can sustain itself at current rates.

## ORGANIZATION

Agricultural Crown land is administered by the Lands and Regulatory Management Branch of Saskatchewan Agriculture and Food. In addition to the responsibility for the leasing and sale of Crown land, this branch is responsible for the veterinary and dairy laboratories, community pastures and the environmental regulations pertaining to pollution by livestock and proper farming practices.

For the purposes of Crown land management, the province is divided into four regions with a regional manager in each region, two land agrologists, and one or two agreement co-ordinators. The land agrologists deal with all field work related to land use, lease inspections, price and rental verification, and most client interaction. The agreement co-ordinators prepare all agreements and manage inventory control.

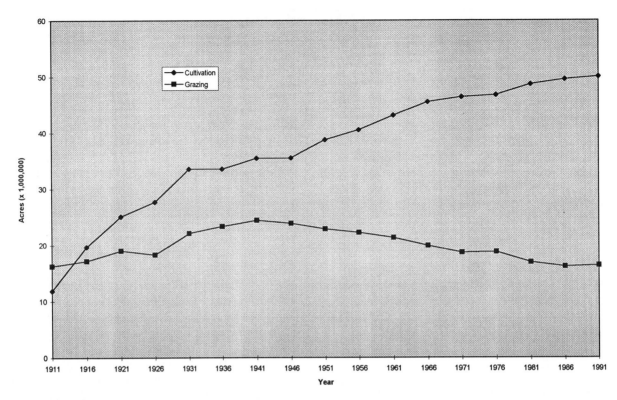

Figure 1. Comparison of cultivated land versus grazing land over time.

Each region is self sufficient operationally, preparing and completing all lease and sale agreements, advertising all land, and generally dealing with their local clientele. All billing is done by a separate branch in head office. Our section works very closely with the rangeland staff of the Extension branch in developing range plans and working with producers who seek assistance in the management of their grazing units.

## GRAZING RENT

The mathematical formula used to establish grazing and hay rent on agricultural Crown land is established by regulation under authority of the Provincial Lands Act. The theory behind it is to charge a fee for the use of the land based on an appropriate share of the value of the product produced. It is based on research and fluctuates with the price of cattle from July 1 to November 30 of the preceding year. The formula is as follows:

Annual rent
= The weighted value of beef
x 46 pounds
x Productivity rating of the lease
x A factor to adjust for constant stocking
x The percentage share
x The number of acres in lease

Where:

- "x" means multiplied by;

- "The weighted value of beef" means the average price as reported by Agriculture Canada for markets in Saskatchewan from July 1 to November 30 of the previous calendar year, weighted as follows:

| | |
|---|---|
| Calves | 61.02% |
| Feeders | 21.52% |
| Cows | 17.46%; |

- "46 pounds" represents the average pounds of beef produced from one animal-unit-month (an animal-unit-month is the amount of feed required to feed a 1,000 pound cow with a calf less than 6 months of age for one month.);

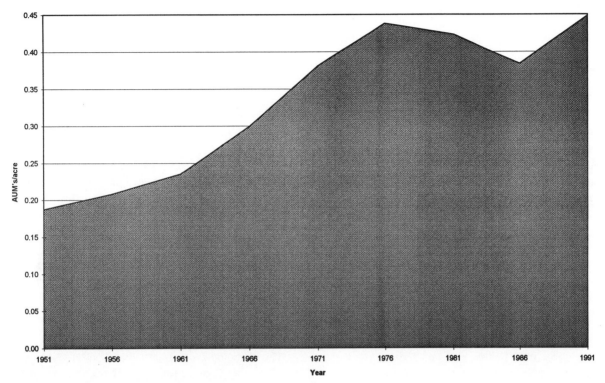

**Grazing Pressure**

Figure 2. Grazing pressure on Saskatchewan rangelands over time.

- "Productivity rating of the lease" means the average number of animal unit months per acre the lease is rated at; leases are rated in accordance with the most current grazing assessment techniques taking into account the types of plants growing on the lease, their forage value and their production under the long term average climate; this rating is based on the potential of the lease (i.e. the amount of forage that will grow under proper management, ensuring the lease remains in excellent condition); management of the lease will affect whether or not the potential is reached;

- "A factor to adjust for constant stocking" means a factor which adjusts the rent to account for constant stocking in each year (range scientists have concluded that the only way that potential productivity can be reached without adjusting stocking rates in each year under grazing is to stock at 80% of the potential; this factor for grazing land, therefore, is 80% and allows producers to maintain a constant size herd on their lease in all but prolonged and extreme drought conditions; this factor is 200% for hay land because there is no loss from trampling and no requirement to leave the same amount of carryover on hay land;

- "The percentage share" means the value, determined by the minister, that represents a fair return to Saskatchewan (currently 12.764858%).

## POLICIES

### Lease Policy

Saskatchewan has one lease policy that allows for the allocation of new leases, the assignment of existing leases, and the renewal of expiring leases. This policy resulted from a major revision in 1994.

*Allocations*

Land for lease is advertised province wide in January of each year. Applications are accepted by the land agrologist. The land is targeted to individuals who are 23 to 35 years old, in close proximity to the land, and who have average size land holdings. Applications are scored to the targeted criteria and allocated by the land agrologist. Allocations are subject to appeal to an independent land appeal board.

*Assignments*

Existing leases can be assigned to family members or individuals purchasing the farm or ranch. The only difference between an assignment to a family member and a purchaser is the assignment fee; the family member pays $200, while the non-family member pays the greater of $200 or one additional years rental.

*Renewals*

Expiring leases are renewed for a maximum of 33 years providing the lessee is still actively managing and operating the farm or ranch and has all accounts with Saskatchewan Agriculture and Food in an acceptable status.

## Sales

Crown land that is eligible for sale is available to lessees upon their request. Vacant Crown land that is eligible for sale is advertised for tender in November of each year. The highest bid over an upset value is the successful bidder. All land is sold based on comparable land sales. Lands are reserved from sale for reasons such as important wildlife habitat, sand and gravel deposits, heritage sites, fragility etc.

## Land Development

Crown land may still be developed for cultivation or tame forage providing the land is suitable and providing the lessee has an acceptable plan for development. Virtually no Crown land is developed for cultivation any more, as the vast majority of land owned by the Crown is of marginal quality. Minimal amounts of land is developed for tame forage since there is no direct financial assistance and since there is a better understanding of the limitations of tame forage.

This policy also provides for the conversion of marginal cultivated land and for the reduced stocking of poorer condition grazing lands.

## THREATS

A number of issues threaten the status quo of agricultural Crown land administration. As indicated earlier, left unsolved, these issues will likely result an in imposed resolution to any land use disputes and it will likely be to agricultures detriment.

## Increasing Multi-use Demands

The increasing urban influence that is expanding in our province results in an increased demand for non-agricultural activities. These activities range from industrial uses to non consumptive eco-tourism.

## Non-sustainable Land Use

Although most agricultural lessees take excellent care of their Crown land, some have not. An increasingly environmentally aware public is beginning to demand that all Crown land be managed properly.

## Tenure Conflicts

Throughout Crown land history, producers have argued over Crown land tenure; everyone wants some. Economic pressures and increased awareness can amplify debates over these issues.

## Non-compliance of Lease Terms

The changing face of agriculture causes us to reflect on the restrictions of lease use. The traditional cultivation versus grazing is complicated by diversification efforts such as game farming, custom grazing, outfitting, etc. The traditional lease agreement either did not contemplate these activities or restricts them.

## Revenue Objectives

The public and lessees have debated for decades over what level of rent should be charged for agricultural Crown land. This debate continues and is enhanced by the province's fiscal position.

## Access

Agricultural lessees in our province control access to their Crown land. Most lessees will honor reasonable requests for access, however, individuals who refuse, fuel requests to take this right away.

## OPPORTUNITIES

Saskatchewan lessees have a number of advantages that equal or surpass their counterparts in other provinces.

## Security

Lessees receive a 33-year lease regardless of age, provided they actively manage and operate a farm. This provides significant security.

The lease is assignable which allows the lessee to keep his farm or ranch together and pass it on to the next generation or sell it as a unit.

## Access

Just as the loss of control of access is a threat, the fact that lessees do control it is an opportunity.

## Agricultural Awareness

The largest city in Saskatchewan has less than 200 thousand people, many of whom are one generation from the farm. This, coupled with a strong agricultural industry, provides an agricultural awareness second to none.

## Environmental Awareness

The average Saskatchewan resident is becoming increasingly environmentally aware. This has resulted in an increased awareness of proper land management that is paying direct dividends in the management of Crown owned land.

## Opportunities for Public Input

The public has more input than ever before with respect to the management of resources. Reconciling this input will result in improved understanding and acceptance of land use policies.

## Stability in Tenure Management

Past administrations have purchased land only to be followed by administrations which sold it. This has been a reflection of the division in opinion in our society. Current economic conditions in conjunction with current land use policies recognize there is a role for both private and public ownership of land which in turn has resulted in fewer problems.

## IMPLICATIONS

The public must decide what it wants with respect to the 8.8 million acres of Crown owned agricultural land. What land should be sold, what should be kept, what it should be used for, and what it should return all must be debated publicly. This process, if managed properly, will result in sound land use policies that will have public acceptance. This in turn will result in improved land use that accommodates different demands in a truly sustainable fashion.

When the day is done all Saskatchewan residents, regardless of background, share the same ideal with respect to Crown land management. Farmer, rancher, environmentalist, agrologist, biologist and ecologist alike all want to leave it in better condition than when we received it. We simply need to more frequently discuss, in order that we better understand that we do indeed share common goals.

# MANITOBA'S NATIVE CROWN LANDS

## James Bezan

*Executive Officer, Manitoba Cattle Producers Association,*
*3-2033 Portage Avenue, Winnipeg, Manitoba R3J OK8*

I would like to thank Peggy Strankman and the conference organizers for inviting me today. I believe that we have some excellent opportunity to build consensus and look at the problems that we have in dealing with the area of native rangelands. It is something that I have a very strong interest in as a producer and also as a person that represents the cattle industry in Manitoba. My presentation today was put together with the assistance of Gil Lahaie from the Crown Lands Branch of Manitoba Agriculture. Gil sends his regrets since he could not attend. There is a major meeting of Policy Managers and Crown Land Reps in Manitoba, and he felt that was his priority.

I want to do a quick overview of what rangeland we have in Manitoba. Although we are not to the same degree of size as Alberta or Saskatchewan, we still have a significant amount of land in Crown Land management for agriculture purposes. In Manitoba we have Aspen Parkland of over a million acres, grasslands in the upland area of 126,000 acres and lowland grasslands of 223,000 acres. There is improvement going on in Manitoba. There are 120,000 acres that are in tame forage. About 105,000 acres are mainly marsh areas that we consider unusable. The rated carrying capacity is 750,000 animal-unit-month's (AUM) or well over 150,000 cattle and horses. This represents over 20% of the cattle industry in Manitoba. Capacities are underestimated by about 20,000 head. We are trying to keep our stock rates down to make sure that this is a more sustainable resource, taking into consideration the fluctuations that we have in drought conditions, precipitation and other problems on a year to year basis.

The Crown Land area in Manitoba is primarily found in the north, central, and south eastern corner. That is also where the majority of native range land is found. Much of it exists in the Interlake Region, around Lake Manitoba and Lake Winnipeg, and by the Riding Mountain and Duck Mountain Provincial Parks. Some of it has been improved. The vast majority of this land is aspen woodlands consisting of black and white popular with some birch and oak. We do have tame forage that has been improved through a number of different methodologies. This was mainly done to increase our

productivity. There is no doubt that this has also benefited wildlife, especially ungulates.

Brush cover is a problem on Crown Land that we are trying to control. Aspen encroachment is one of the major problems that we have on Crown Land areas. It has been a major concern brought forward by different wildlife groups, as well as Manitoba Natural Resources and the Natural Resource Institute at the University of Manitoba. We have to control aspen encroachment because it is starting to infringe on habitat of many desirable species that we have in the province.

The scope of what we have in leases is over 1.6 million acres in Forage Leases. Fifty thousand of those are annual permits and 18,000 are actual cropping permits. Cropping leases exist primarily along floodways around Winnipeg, which are considered Crown Lands and those are the areas that are actually cropped. About 3,000 producers in Manitoba have Crown Land Permits and that represents about 25% of cattle producers in Manitoba. The availability of those lands requires an inter-departmental multi-use decision that involves Manitoba Natural Resources' Wildlife Branch, Manitoba Agriculture staff from the Crown Lands Branch and also from the policy area of Manitoba Agriculture. We always make sure that the land has more than one user, and these areas are used for grazing, hay and cropping. We do allow land development, but monitor this.

There is tenure via lease or permit. Most of it is through lease, but there are other considerations given. We do have quite a bit of security with these leases. They are issued for a lifetime or until the lease holder is 65 years of age. The lease-holder has the ability to transfer their lease if the operation is sold. They have the ability to transfer it to their family members from generation to generation; this has been the most popular way of handling it. They do have the opportunity to purchase the lease after they have had it for two years. Only the lease holder can purchase land. Nobody else is allowed to.

When we look at our rates, they are quite a bit different from Saskatchewan. Manitoba is very competitive with our rates. Its an arbitrary calculation which is based on a cost recovery system of the government. We look at the administration costs of the Crown Lands Branch and take 75% of that cost and divide that by the AUM's to come up with our lease fee of $1.39 this year, plus municipal taxes. Most of the leases have a tax base which is usually equal to the AUM charge.

Before a person can lease Crown Land in Manitoba, they have to go through a tenure process. Applications are made, and allocations scored. Manitoba Agriculture looks at your need for land, at your herd size and whether or not your existing forage base can support that; and they look on whether or not you have off-farm income. Younger farmers get a bit of a break. Preference is given to those who live near-by to the land.

The sale of Crown Land was reinstituted back in 1979. The province reviews the needs by all departments on whether or not that land is going to be for sale, taking into consideration Special Places, wildlife and all the other interest groups that are out there before that land is going to be approved for sale. Since 1979 there were over 320,000 acres applied for and of that about two thirds were approved for sale.

Many people may not look very favourably upon the sale of Crown Land. But, in Manitoba we don't have any control of access. There has been considerable abuse on this land by off-road travel, by poachers, and through rustling activities. Producers want to secure control and for that reason have bought the land so they do have the ability to control who's out there. They are not necessarily cutting down on access, but want to know who's there. There is a big difference of knowing who's there and who's not. When people have to ask permission to go on land and enter that area, they are going to be more responsible in their activities.

I want to highlight some of the management activities that are going on in Manitoba. There are no incentives offered in Manitoba. There was a program under the Farming for Tomorrow Program which we had in Manitoba. The Crown Rangeland Management Program was only available on Crown Land. It involved a complete planning process that was put in place in conjunction with livestock specialists, forage specialists, Crown Land representatives, and the producer; together with some involvement from Natural Resources to determine what should happen on this land to make it more productive and still keep in mind the multi-use aspect of it. We looked at rotational grazing, sod seeding, livestock

access lanes, and brush control, and it was very well received.

Through the Manitoba Cattle Producers Association, in conjunction with the Crown Lands Branch of Manitoba Agriculture, we have reapplied for funding for this program under the Canada-Manitoba Agreement on Agricultural Sustainability which is the Green Plan. We have applied and are awaiting approval.

When we had the program, it worked to bring a producer together with his local land representative, all the different people including non-government groups and the farm management specialist to help implement it. It took in consideration a broad base of how that operation interacted with that chunk of Crown Land. We were looking at extending the grazing season through complimentary grazing, improving grazing distribution, at matching pasture to livestock requirements, managed by range types, and controlling leg brush invasion which is a big problem in Manitoba. Semi-intensive improvements were made and we managed those improvements to the maximum.

Every person that cooperated was recognized through the program. They put together a workbook that the producer used as his plan of action on how he was going to manage once they went through the process of consulting. This may not be what this conference wants to look at, but we did go into range areas, and improve those pastures with tame species. We are looking at using more native species in those areas but we are trying to improve productivity and also look at improving areas that might have been degraded. We put together some improved watering sites and often used solar pumping systems.

A good example of the type of brush invasions that we have is swampy birch which we are trying to control. We are doing it through pulse grazing, and again are controlling aspen encroachment using chemical control. Burning in Manitoba is not a real viable option since we have such vast areas of Aspen Parkland. Occasionally we have fires that get away. We're not talking just about burning a large portion of the range, but about fire invading operations, burning houses down, and everything else on site. Its an area which requires careful management.

The program did some clearing to put in place cross fences so we can properly manage that range rather than graze continuously. Because of the heavy timber that we have in Manitoba and the underbrush that makes it difficult for cattle to get into some areas of those native rangelands, we have put access trails in where the cattle can get through the pastures and get back into the areas that may not be accessible and increase forage utilization.

We recognize the efforts of the producer and, hopefully, he will be held up as an example in the area. Through this program, we tried to work with leaders in the community; people that are considered on the leading edge of what they are doing, and work closely with them. Producers will always sit back and watch and wait to see who is going to take the initiative in new technologies and new innovation, and after they see it implemented successfully on the neighbours operation, they may take it home and use it on their own ranch.

One of the key issues is communicating with producers and educating them. Crown Lands is doing that through their newsletter and Manitoba Cattle Producers Association does it through our Manitoba Beef magazine. Producers can take the initiatives that we are talking about and implement them, learn about them. The big issue is that education is going to be a key to the success of what we are trying to accomplish. Producers want to help, they just need to know how. Extension work is going to be a major activity in this whole area.

In Manitoba we were getting involved in the endangered spaces campaign with the World Wildlife Fund. Manitoba was being coordinated through the Sustainable Development Unit of the Manitoba Government which reported directly to the Premier. There was faulty communications down the line between World Wildlife Fund, to the Sustainable Development Unit, to Crown Lands Branch and to the producer level. There had been the identification of Crown Land that is going to be put aside for this program.

One of the areas that we were concerned about regarding Crown Lands, was that there was going to be some restrictions put in place like hydro development, mining, logging and other commercial activities. Other commercial activities were never defined and in some cases entire ranches had been identified as a special areas. We want assurances that ranching activities are not exempt from these areas before the cattle industry will give its support to this particular strategy.

Many conversation programs out there are shooting themselves in the foot. More producers reject them versus producers you are going to actually help. Whenever we see programs introduced through different organizations and agencies that places a caveat on the use of that land, there are more producers that draw away from it; express interest at first but draw away from it because of the caveat.

Producers by nature want to leave the land in a better condition than what they found it in. They want to be sure it is sustainable and can be passed from generation to generation. I know that this is the way my dad approaches the whole area of ranching, that is the way I approach it, and there is more and more people out there that are thinking along the same lines.

Recently I got the feeling that I should be doing something environmental. I went to the Beefeater and ordered their prime rib. If you wanted to do something to really make sure that native rangelands are out there, eat beef. The cattle industry is the only reason that we still have native land to protect. If you want sustainability, and grazing has proven to be sustainable over time, then support the industry that is making use of these resources in that fashion.

# DOMINANT USE OR MULTIPLE USE OF PUBLIC LANDS IN THE UNITED STATES: ARE MAJOR CHANGES UNDERWAY?

## Thomas France and Michael Roy

*National Wildlife Federation, Northern Rockies Natural Resource Center,*
*240 North Higgins, Missoula, Montana 59802*

Sharing the public lands of the western United States, particularly the prairies, periodically gains visibility in the public eye. From the so-called "Sagebrush Rebellion" of the late 1970's and early 80's to today's "Wise Use Movement," we occasionally find highly charged conflict bubbling to the surface as the myriad stakeholders in the public estate debate the appropriate uses of these lands. This conflict now seems to threaten the very foundation of nearly a century of conservation efforts.

This paper presents a brief outline of our interpretation, as a non-governmental organization, of how management of public lands in the western United States has evolved over time, and what impact the current adverse political climate may have on the future of prairie conservation.

Depending on one's perspective, the United States is either blessed or burdened with an enormous base of public lands; at over 730 million acres, approximately one third of the nation is in the public domain. The management of these lands, and questions concerning who profits from and who pays for the resources they produce, have been a source of continuing controversy throughout the 20th century.

There are presently four major public land managing systems in place in the U.S., each growing out of separate traditions, each with their own constituencies and advocates, and each with a different legislative mission. These four systems are the National Park System, the National Wildlife Refuge System, the National Forests, and public lands managed by the Bureau of Land Management[1] (BLM). Early on, the U.S. recognized the need to preserve and protect the national treasures we now call our national parks. Yellowstone Park, established three years before the battle at the Little Big Horn in 1876, was the world's first national park. Since then

Congress has added several hundred units to the National Park System. Many parks were carved out of the public land base, but some, especially in recent years, have been purchased. In 1926, Congress passed the Park Service Organic Act, which established the two purposes of the system: recreation for the general public and the protection of park resources for future generations.

During the first decade of this century, the U.S. also began acquiring and reserving lands for wildlife protection, and thus began the evolution of the National Wildlife Refuge System. The "dominant use" of the refuge system is wildlife, and other uses, by law, must be "compatible" with wildlife protection. The first mission of the refuge system was waterfowl protection, and as such, most refuge lands have been purchased, although there are significant exceptions. In the West, Franklin Roosevelt created four large refuges, including the Charles M. Russell in Montana, by carving them out of public lands. The Alaska National Lands Bill, signed in the waning hours of the Carter Administration, also added tens of millions of acres of public lands to both the National Wildlife Refuge System and the National Park System.

Because the parks and the refuges were established with a relatively well-defined mission—a dominant use —their management has been only moderately controversial. This is less true of the two largest land management systems, both of which are managed for multiple uses: the national forest system, administered by the U.S. Forest Service, and lands administered by the BLM.

The federal government began establishing the national forest system in the 1890's, primarily as reserves and primarily to protect public forest lands from plunder by logging, mining and railroad companies. Gifford Pinchot, the father of the Forest Service, changed this

---

[1] Other federal agencies, including the Departments of Defense and Energy and the Bureau of Reclamation, have management responsibilities over significant land bases. For the most part, however, these agencies have not been given any land management goals by Congress and public uses are managed as secondary purposes.

original mission. As a European-trained forester, and with Teddy Roosevelt's strong support, Pinchot had the Forest Service moved to the Department of Agriculture, where he established a management philosophy of sustainable timber production. To jump ahead, this philosophy was given statutory recognition in 1960 when Congress passed the Multiple Use-Sustained Yield Act. In passing this law, Congress envisioned a steady supply of timber coming off the national forests, but within a management system that did not compromise wildlife, clean water or recreation, the other multiple-use values recognized by the law. This multiple-use vision was further refined in the planning requirements of the National Forest Management Act in 1976.

Finally, there are the lands nobody wanted for any purpose, which are now the public lands managed by the BLM. Under the homestead acts, congressional policy was to move public lands into the private domain. Despite these efforts, millions of acres could not even be given away. Decades of unrestricted competition for rangelands had already resulted in extremes of overgrazing and soil erosion by the time the first efforts were made, in large part with the support of the livestock industry, to place some limits on rangeland use through the passage of the Taylor Grazing Act in 1934. And it was not until 1976 that the Congress passed the Federal Land Management and Policy Act (FLPMA), a true organic act for the BLM. The FLPMA stated that the nation's policy was to retain public lands and that such lands would be managed under principles of multiple use and sustained yield.

The prospectus for this conference suggested that the Clinton administration has attempted to shift the multiple-use philosophies of the Forest Service and BLM to a dominant-use orientation. However, for all of its political missteps, one thing the Clinton Administration has not tried to do, or even contemplated doing, has been to change the statutory direction for either the Forest Service or the BLM. Even under the last Congress, such a proposal would have been a political disaster, such that neither the administration or the environmental community have suggested it. A multiple-use management strategy will remain the statutory basis for both the Forest Service and the BLM for the foreseeable future.

But the Clinton administration has suggested changes in public land management that would decrease the emphasis placed on commodity production. What has been the driving force behind these suggestions? In a single word, the primary catalyst has been science. The past two decades have seen a small revolution in the bio-

logical sciences, and this revolution has captured the technicians and biologists and foresters that staff both the BLM and the Forest Service. In turn, these professionals have shifted agency priorities. And as these priorities have changed, the politics surrounding public land management has intensified. The Clinton administration inherited these changes, and perhaps to its regret, it has tried to harness them and give them life by sweeping policy announcements.

There is perhaps no better example of this than the controversy that has raged around proposed changes in range management on BLM and Forest Service lands. Not long ago, range conservationists estimated carrying capacity by looking at all of the forage available in a pasture—the "big pile of hay" approach to range management. In general, riparian areas, for all their value to fisheries, wildlife and water quality and quantity, were treated no differently than other grazing lands.

In fact, as recently as 1985, U.S. Fish and Wildlife Service managers at the 800,000-acre Charles M. Russell National Wildlife Refuge in Montana, operating under a management philosophy that gave first priority to wildlife, proposed, adopted and claimed as a great victory a management plan that conceded riparian areas to livestock. Under the management plan, the Fish and Wildlife Service declined to build water developments away from riparian areas, reasoning that livestock would concentrate themselves in creek bottoms, thus leaving upland areas available for wildlife. Now, the CMR plan was a victory in that stocking rates were significantly reduced, and reduced over the determined opposition of grazing permittees who had operated on the refuge for decades. But the science on which the plan was based, even in 1985, would not be credible today.

Across the West, range scientists and wildlife biologists have reconstructed their vision of the landscape and the biota it supports. Public land agencies have recognized that riparian areas, which comprise less than one percent of the West's land base, are critical habitats for most of our wildlife species. With the scientist's recognition of this fact, managers have been forced to reshape the "art" of range management, and with this reshaping has come real and sharp conflict with powerful livestock interests.

Even before our scientific view of the range changed, other issues clearly posed challenges to public land managers. The cost of grazing privileges was embarrassingly low, and there was a general perception that a few livestock permittees had too much control over the management of public lands. But it was only when the agency's own range scientists and biologists began identifying problems and suggesting new approaches that serious and widespread conflicts began to develop.

This conflict began in earnest in the second half of the 1980's, long before Bill Clinton. Long enough before Bill Clinton, in fact, that a community of agency experts, agency reformers, and environmental non-governmental organizations had already accepted both the science and the need for reform as a given. The new administration, which had promised change, readily acquiesced to the demand that reform move forward, and initially saw political advantage in this stance. But it seems fair to say that neither reformers nor Clinton administration officials ever saw this change as an assault on the basic principle of multiple-use management. Rather, it was the desire for fairer allocation of uses and the need for "better" management that drove both the Department of Interior and the Forest Service to propose substantial changes in range policy.

Similarly, changing science has played a critical role in the debate raging over forest practices. While the public has known for years that clear-cutting was devastating many national forests, it was only when the scientific community began quantifying the damage and suggesting new approaches to minimize such problems that a new forestry based on ecosystem concepts began to emerge that was endorsed by Forest Service policymakers. Concepts like habitat fragmentation, biological diversity, and viable populations, coupled with the recognition that important indicator species were on the edge of extinction, forced even hardened foresters to recognize that a tree farm mentality would not meet multiple-use and viability mandates for protecting terrestrial and aquatic species. The result has been the emergence of a new science, one with which we are actually trying to manage forests rather than trees.

Unfortunately, even the scientific and conservation communities have been, until recently, very slow to recognize the value of conservation of prairie ecosystems to preservation of biological diversity. While forest ecosystems, for example the late successional forests of the Pacific Northwest, have been in the public eye for a quarter century or more, we have only recently begun to seriously take stock of our prairie resources. Perhaps due to this late response, we now find 55 prairie species listed under the U.S. Endangered Species Act, and over 700 additional prairie species are candidates for listing. For example, the range of the black-tailed prairie dog—

arguably, along with the bison, the most ecologically significant prairie herbivore—has been reduced to less than three quarters of a million acres in the northern prairies (only a few tenths of one percent of its historic distribution), and range contractions are ongoing. With prairie dog declines we have seen similar losses in a suite of prairie dog associates, from the burrowing owl to the swift fox. Some are even concerned that some game species, in particular prairie grouse in Montana, are declining due to human-caused habitat fragmentation and degradation.

With this said, it is clear that both agency scientific staffs and the conservation community must redouble their efforts to assess conditions in prairie ecosystems and to transfer the current enthusiasm for "ecosystem management" from the forests to the prairies.

While prairie conservation has thus far taken a back seat to forest conservation, and though science has been the driving and irresistible force in shaping federal land management policies, public interest and advocacy for reform has also been increasing. And public advocates have quickly seized upon the new science as an important tool for change.

Again, we need look no farther than Montana for an example. Last year, using the Forest Service's own data, which showed that livestock grazing was having a severe impact on many riparian areas, the National and Montana Wildlife Federations sued the Beaverhead National Forest over its grazing program. The result of this suit was the quick capitulation of the Forest Service as to the legal issues, and a settlement proposal that secured a comprehensive reform program scheduled to be phased in over the next ten years. Similar actions on both forest and range issues by individuals and NGO's have played a fundamental role in moving land management forward in a manner based on emerging biological information. This advocacy began long before the inauguration of Bill Clinton and will likely long outlast him.

It is clear that however one orders recent history in terms of the interplay between science, management and policy, the Clinton Administration has run hard up against an extraordinarily difficult political situation over both its forest and range initiatives. Traditional resource industries such as grazing, mining and logging have organized their workers, and hostility to any new federal land policies is widespread across the West. This fierce political opposition has forced the Administration to back away from some initiatives, particularly in regard to range reform. The new Republican majorities in Congress are now talking about their own new approaches to public land management, some of which will probably be adopted to the detriment of the environment.

But as long as it is science that is driving land management agencies to propose reforms, it seems the backlash that is occurring, much like its predecessor in Sagebrush rebellion times, is a little like King Canute ordering back the tide. The facts won't go away, and the facts say we need to change our approach or risk a long-term loss of diversity and productivity in public lands ecosystems, with unknown costs to prairie wildlife, plant and human communities. Positive change in public land management may well be slower as a result of last November's elections, but it will not stop.

# MEASURING PROGRESS, AN ENDANGERED SPACES GOAL

## Presented by: Gail Whelan Enns[1] and Dawn Mitchell[2]

[1]*Coordinator, Manitoba Endangered Spaces Campaign,*
*63 Albert St., Suite 411, Winnipeg, Manitoba R3B 1G4*
[2]*Coordinator, Alberta Endangered Spaces Campaign, World Wildlife Fund Canada,*
*1035, 510 - 5th Street SW, Calgary, Alberta T2P 3S2.*

The **Endangered Spaces** campaign has a specific, measurable goal: **to conserve Canada's biological diversity by protecting a representative sample of each of the country's terrestrial and one-third of its marine natural regions by the year 2000, with completion of the marine system by the year 2010**. Progress toward this goal is achieved by establishing parks or other protected areas which limit the impact of human activity on natural ecosystems and the wildlife species they sustain.

Achieving this goal will likely involve setting aside at least 12% of Canada's lands and waters, a target in the federal Green Plan. Since data on the size of protected areas has been more readily available than data on representation, this target has been the focus of public attention. Nonetheless, representation, not percentage, is the **Endangered Spaces** goal and progress reporting by the World Wildlife Fund (WWF) has increasingly reflected this fact since the campaign launch in 1989.

By itself, a protected areas system is not sufficient to conserve Canada's biological diversity. We must also ensure that human activity on the rest of our lands and waters maintains their productive capacity. Nevertheless, if we want to hang onto our rich heritage of genes, species, and habitats, it is essential that we protect examples of the full range of Canada's natural ecosystems (Noss 1992, 1995).

There is also special urgency to protected areas goals. For example, more than one-quarter of Canada's terrestrial natural regions have already been altered to the point that the preferred option of designating one large representative wilderness area is simply gone. If Canada really is to meet the Biodiversity Convention challenge, we must dramatically accelerate the pace of protecting our wild places.

To measure progress in this regard, we need three things:

1) a map showing each jurisdiction's terrestrial and marine (where developed) natural regions,

2) criteria for representing a natural region,

3) standards for judging when an area is protected.

## 1. NATURAL REGIONS MAPS

A reference map depicting a terrestrial natural regions framework for protected areas planning is now in use in every jurisdiction. The Northwest Territories, on a provisional basis, is using the natural regions classification of Parks Canada. Natural marine region frameworks have been developed for national marine park planning by Parks Canada and the province of British Columbia has included within its ecoregion framework marine regions off the Pacific coast.

Mapping natural regions is a technical exercise based on information regarding soils, landforms, climate and vegetation. Since each jurisdiction has conducted this exercise independently, two discrepancies are visible when all the maps are brought together for the country. First, natural region boundaries don't always fit together across the borders between the twelve provinces and territories. Second, the federal government uses its own natural regions map, not the provincial and territorial maps, for planning the national parks system.

Recognizing these discrepancies, WWF assesses the performance of each jurisdiction according to the natural regions map used by that jurisdiction in protected areas system planning. As illustrated in the following pages, this means measuring progress in terms of action taken to represent over 400 terrestrial and marine natural regions.

## 2. CRITERIA FOR REPRESENTATION

With protected area planning now framed by natural regions, all jurisdictions have recognized representation as an underlying principle for enlarging their protected areas system. Criteria for achieving representation have also been developed by many jurisdictions but not all are based on ecological principles. For example, some jurisdictions still judge representation of natural regions on the simple basis of presence or absence of protected areas, yet, without an accompanying methodology and ecological inventory to guide the location, size and configuration of the protected areas, there is no way to ensure that they capture the full suite of biophysical elements present in the larger natural region.

Some Canadian jurisdictions have developed more detailed criteria for achieving representation under the auspices of a "gap analysis" methodology. This is an important component of a protected areas system plan and is intended to "facilitate the identification of gaps in the existing protected areas system" (British Columbia Ministry of Environment, Lands and Parks 1993). In British Columbia, the gap analysis is being implemented to advance the goal of identifying areas of natural diversity for representation, as well as areas of cultural heritage and recreational value. Natural values are given priority where it is not possible to achieve representation of all values. In Alberta, a three level system of natural history themes has been developed for use in their gap analysis (Achuff and Wallis 1992). There are twenty Level 1 themes that reflect broad landform/lifeform complexes across the province and protected area targets (in sq. km) have been established for the relevant themes in each natural region. It is recognized that the targets are to be used as guidelines and that they are not intended to capture the full complement of a natural region's biodiversity nor the habitat requirements of wide-ranging wildlife.

World Wildlife Fund Canada has undertaken an independent assessment of representation. Representation was assessed using a gap analysis methodology developed from three pilot projects and a synthesis report by specialists in ecological land classification, in an effort to achieve a consistent science-based approach across all jurisdictions. In relying on these projects commissioned by the Canadian Council on Ecological Areas (CCEA), WWF has adopted the recommendations of the CCEA as outlined in two other reports: *Framework For Developing a Nation-wide System of Ecological Areas: Part 1 - A Strategy* (CCEA 1992), and *A First Approximation of Principles and Criteria to Make Canada's Protected Area Systems Representative of the Nation's Ecological Diversity* (Peterson and Peterson 1991). They recommend that representation be based on "enduring features of the environment..., relatively stable landforms and seaforms and their accompanying

plant and animal communities". In comparison to other analyses, the gap analysis undertaken by WWF assumes that the protection of a natural region's characteristic enduring features, that is, the natural region's eco-diversity, will ensure the maintenance of biodiversity and ecological processes. WWF argues for a protected areas system as the cornerstone of a comprehensive land management strategy.

## 2.1 Identification of Enduring Features

The gap analysis methodology conducted by WWF recognizes that ecosystem dynamics and biodiversity interact with and are influenced by climate, physiography, topography, geology and edaphic conditions. Climate and broad physiographic types are delineated by natural region boundaries. Within each natural region, additional units can be identified which represent the variation in landforms that characterize a natural region. WWF identifies these "enduring features" of the landscape at the 1:1,000,000 scale. Once mapped, the distribution of these units is an important consideration in assessing the degree to which existing protected areas contribute towards the ecological representation of a natural region. The identification of enduring features within natural regions incorporates sources of information used in the gap analysis adapted by WWF (WWF 1995). These are summarized in Figure 1. Additional sources include Bostock (1970) and Rowe (1972).

## 2.2 Assessment of Representation

A two-step approach was taken in order to assess natural region representation: 1) assess representation of each enduring feature and 2) assess representation of enduring features collectively for the whole of the natural region, including consideration of ecological integrity values (Noss 1995). The following principles were employed in the assessment of natural region representation (for definitions of terminology used in WWF methodology and for operating assumptions, see Appendix I):

- to represent all enduring features, preferably in a way which maximizes habitat variation;

- to favour larger parks that more easily maintain natural integrity than an assemblage of smaller parks;

- to maintain natural disturbance regimes and ecological processes; and

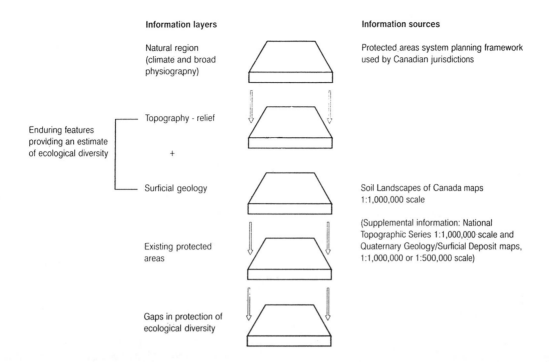

**Information layers**

Natural region
(climate and broad
physiograpny)

Enduring features
providing an estimate
of ecological diversity

Topography - relief

+

Surficial geology

Existing protected
areas

Gaps in protection of
ecological diversity

**Information sources**

Protected areas system planning framework
used by Canadian jurisdictions

Soil Landscapes of Canada maps
1:1,000,000 scale

(Supplemental information: National
Topographic Series 1:1,000,000 scale and
Quaternary Geology/Surficial Deposit maps,
1:1,000,000 or 1:500,000 scale)

Figure 1. Overlay of the landscape themes and data sources used in WWF gap analysis procedure. Enduring features of the landscape (topography-relief and surficial geography) provide the basis for assessing protection of ecological diversity within each natural region. Climate and large scale physiographic variation are accounted for by natural region boundaries. (Adapted from: Agriculture Canada 1990)

- to maintain habitat requirements for the long-term survival of wide-ranging species.

The assessment of natural region representation is based on the enduring feature rankings:

- **Little or No Representation**: None of the major enduring features are **moderately or adequately captured** and less than 80% of features are **partially captured**.

- **Partially Represented**: (1) Up to 50% of the major enduring features are either **nearly or adequately captured** and at least 50% of the remaining features are at least **partially captured**; (2) A significant majority (at least 80%) of all features are **partially captured**.

- **Moderately Represented**: At least 50% of the major enduring features are **adequately captured,** and a majority (at least 80%) of the remaining features are either **moderately or partially captured**.

- **Represented** - All of the enduring features are judged to be **adequately captured** in existing protected areas.

Gap analysis is a recent technique still in its developing stages for use in protected areas system design. As a result, methodologies often vary in relation to the available data. There are important characteristics of the gap analysis methodology undertaken by WWF:

- The analysis identifies enduring features at 1:1,000,000 scale.

- The primary data sources used to identify enduring features are available for the entire country.

- Emphasis is placed on long-term planning of protected areas systems based on enduring features in order that eco-diversity is maintained (Rowe 1993, WWF 1995).

More detailed descriptions of the gap analysis conducted by WWF are available by calling or writing World Wildlife Fund Canada and requesting a copy of 'A Protected Areas Gap Analysis Methodology: Planning for the Conservation of Biodiversity'.

## 3. PROTECTION STANDARDS

Capturing a subset of a natural region's enduring features within one or more conservation sites is not enough to ensure that these attributes will be secure in the long term. For this to happen, another criterion must be met: ecological integrity. The CCEA defines integrity as "the capability of a protected area to support and maintain assemblages of organisms (communities) that have a composition, form and functional organization comparable to that of similar ecosystem types of the region."

To date, there are no nationally agreed upon standards in Canada to determine when an area is adequately protected in these terms. The principle standard used in this report, consistent with the World Conservation Union (IUCN), and broadly supported by Canadians, is that no industrial activities be permitted, especially logging, mining, hydroelectric, oil and gas development. Agriculture, hunting, recreational development and other activities can also have unacceptable impacts on natural ecosystems through their direct effects on habitat and wildlife populations, and through access provided to the backcountry within the protected area. However, if properly regulated, these impacts can be considerably less than industrial activity. Decisions regarding when these impacts are, or are not, acceptable are best taken at a site-specific level and WWF relies on the advice of local campaign partner organizations in determining which sites permitting such uses are to be recorded as "protected" in this report.

A second protection standard is the long-term security of a particular site through its conservation designation. Here too, there is no universally accepted standard. The **Endangered Spaces** campaign goal is not confined solely to sites with "park" or "wilderness" designations. However, the conservation site must have some form of long-term legal status and a specified management authority in order to qualify as "protected." These criteria still leave a wide range of protection mechanisms ranging from private lands managed by conservation organizations through easements or restricted covenants, to nature reserve zones in official municipal plans, to National Parks established by Parliament under the *National Parks Act*.

For each jurisdiction, this report tabulates the total area of lands and waters reserved through various conservation designations, such as parks, ecological reserves and wildlife areas. It also calculates the portion of this reserved area that is judged to be protected; sites with legal status where logging, mining, hydroelectric and oil and gas development are disallowed.

A third factor, intertwining representation and integrity, is that of the size and configuration of protected areas. Principles of island biogeography provide the basis for standard-setting, whereby one large circular site, such as an intact watershed, is preferable to tiny unconnected, linear sites. Adjacent land use also needs to be compatible with protected area goals, especially in smaller sites. In practice, WWF believes that one large wilderness area along with one or more smaller sites, which add representative elements missing from the wilderness areas, will be needed to meet Endangered Spaces objectives in a natural region. Further information regarding the design of protected areas systems in relation to ecological integrity principles can be obtained by contacting WWF and requesting a copy of: *Maintaining Ecological Integrity in Representative Reserve Networks* (Noss 1995).

Available data are not sufficient for this standard to be rigorously applied throughout this report. However, it already underlies protected areas targets in some jurisdictions and as more data become available future Progress Reports will employ these higher standards.

## LITERATURE CITED

Achuff, P. and Wallis, C. 1992. Report 3 - Natural regions and natural history themes: Targets for Alberta. Prepared for Alberta Tourism, Parks and Recreation and Alberta Forestry, Lands and Wildlife.

Agriculture Canada. 1990. Soil landscapes of Canada series. Various Authors.

British Columbia Ministry of Environment, Lands and Parks. 1993. Gap Analysis Workbook for Regional Protected Areas Teams. Working Draft-June 1993.

Bostock, H.S. 1970. Physiographic subdivisions of Canada. Pp. 10-30 *In* Geology and economic minerals of Canada (R.J.W. Douglas(ed.). Geological Survey of Canada, Dept. of Energy, Mines and Resources, Queen's Printer, Ottawa. Accompanying map - Physiographic Regions of Canada (1:5,000,000 scale).

Canadian Council on Ecological Areas. 1992. Framework for developing a nation-wide system of ecological areas: Part 1 - A strategy. Prepared by the Canadian Council on Ecological Areas Systems Framework Task Force for the St. John's, Newfoundland Annual Meeting.

Noss, R. 1992. The Wildlands Project Land Conservation Strategy. Wild Earth: 10-21.

Noss, R. 1995. Maintaining ecological integrity in representative reserve networks. WWF Canada-WWF United States Discussion Paper. Toronto, Canada.

Peterson, E.B. and Peterson, N.M. 1991. A first approximation of principles and criteria to make Canada's protected areas systems representative of the nation's ecological diversity. Canadian Council on Ecological Areas. Occasional Papers.

Rowe, J.S. 1972. Forest Regions of Canada. Canadian Forestry Service, Ottawa.

Rowe, J.S. 1993. Eco-diversity, the key to biodiversity. Prepared for the Fredericton Symposium/Workshop, Atlantic Region Protected Areas Working Group, 11 June 1993.

World Wildlife Fund Canada. 1995. Protected areas gap analysis methodology: Planning for the conservation of biodiversity. WWF Canada Discussion Paper.

# APPENDIX I

## Gap Analysis Definitions

Natural Region - A geographical area define by each jurisdiction for purposes of protected areas system planning, that has broad similarities in land form, geology, climate and macro-vegetation cover.

Enduring Feature - Similar to land form. A landscape element or unit within a natural region that has relatively uniform origin and texture of surficial deposits, edaphic conditions and topography-relief.

Ecological Diversity - The variety and variability of ecosystems, where ecosystem is defined as an enduring feature of the landscape (land form) together with an associated assemblage of organisms (community) (Rowe 1993).

Biological Diversity - the variety and variability among living organisms, and the ecological complexes in which they occur (Davis et al. 1990). Species and genetic diversity resulting from the evolution over time of biota and enduring features. Hence, ecological diversity gives rise to biological diversity.

Ecological Integrity - A geographical site exhibits a higher quality of ecological integrity when natural process and disturbance regimes can be expected to continue over long periods of time, thereby maintain the natural regions' compliment of biological diversity. A protected areas system nestled within a comprehensive land management scheme must be able to support and maintain all ecosystem types (ecological diversity) of a natural regions.

"Those of use who wander around in the outdoors recognize that land form - the shape and substances of the land - is the key to ecodiveristy and hence to biodiversity." (Rowe 1993)

## Gap Analysis Operating Assumptions

1. Natural region boundaries use for protected areas system planning by Canada's 13 jurisdictions reflect broad variation in climate and physiography across the nation.

2. Achieving representation of the full range of enduring features (Eco-Diversity) within a natural region will provide significant habitat protection for native species potentially occupying that natural region.

3. Protected areas designed to accommodate the habitat requirements of large carnivores or wide ranging herbivores while maintaining ecological processes will protect a significant proportion of a region's biological diversity.

4. Single large protected sites are likely to exhibit higher levels of ecological integrity than collections of small, fragmented sites.

# MOVING FROM REACTIONISM TO CONSTRUCTIVE EDUCATION: A CRITIQUE OF THE CANADIAN ENVIRONMENTAL LOBBY

## Peter Jonker

*Environmental Science and Technology, Extension Division, University of Saskatchewan,*
*Rm 126 Kirk Hall, Saskatoon, Saskatchewan S7N 0W0*

## INTRODUCTION

This title is somewhat presumptuous for three reasons: first, because I'm not an expert on the Canadian environmental lobby; second, because the critique is very cursory and offered more for illustrative value; and third, because most of what I present is not new. Nevertheless, it is amazing how poorly we allow some basic ecological knowledge to change our habituated ways of thinking and doing. I believe this subject matter to be very important and, after feeling compelled to explore it myself, now feel equally compelled to share my thoughts with others.

So, this paper offers a cursory critique of the Canadian environmental lobby; suggests that environmental groups, with a view to aligning and strengthening the Canadian environmental lobby, must develop and communicate a unified vision of a sustainable, global community of all ecosystem participants; and, recommends for individuals a framework for developing this unified vision. My essential message is this: In order to align and strengthen all our lobbying activities, we must develop and communicate a *vision* of a sustainable, global community of all ecosystem participants.

The rapid growth of a Canadian environmental movement since the nineteen fifties is characterized by an increasing number of people formally coalescing around environmental issues. Although history will remember this as the "environmental movement," the actual people it embraces represent, in fact, not only great diversity of backgrounds and experience, but also a surprisingly wide range of opinions and approaches to how perceived environmental problems ought to be framed and solved. In a manner somewhat reminiscent of the Great Reformation which saw an explosion of religious denominations and sects, a plethora of environmental interest groups have sprung up. So congested with diverse opinions is this arena of public discussion that one wonders sometimes what commonalities, if any, serve to keep them oriented together toward some overall shared goal or destiny.

There is good reason for concern that, amidst this fray of opinions and calls of alarm, a core environmental message is quite lost on the unconnected public whom we are attempting to bring on side. Is it our message that we should prevent waste and live austere, frugal lives? Or, is it that we should develop technologies to convert all such so-called waste into alternative human resources and hence follow an alternative avenue to economic growth? Is it that we should hurry to save untouched representative wilderness everywhere before the exploiters get in and ruin it forever? Or is it that we should develop more parks for human recreation, escape, and learning? Is it that we should save and respect all species for their adapted roles within ecological systems? Or, is it that we should protect maximum diversity of gene pools as productive fishing holes for future commercial interests? Does good environmentalism, as some suggest, really create jobs? What do we mean by "the environment" anyway?

By reacting and criticizing we create a sense of alarm and urgency. This is great for attracting initial attention from an ecologically naive public. But, this is now also resulting in a backlash from industry, and we must demand more of ourselves. We do well to heed Roszak's (1993) observation, "As shortsighted, deceptive, and plain vicious as the new anti-environmental counterattack may be, to some degree the ecologists have only themselves to blame for their vulnerability. Their habitual reliance on gloom, apocalyptic panic, and the psychology of shame takes a heavy toll on public confidence."

## POLLING ENVIRONMENTAL GROUPS

With these concerns in mind, I sent letters to the 25 Canadian environmental organizations listed in *"Associations Canada, 1992"*, In the letter I identified my objectives and invited each to forward documents or statements describing its vision, values, mission, goals and philosophy. My request to them is based on my following beliefs:

(1) That an organization's public image is largely created by its public actions and rationale, and

(2) that to be effective a lobby must be driven by a mission and set of values from which flow the organization's goals, public actions and supporting arguments.

Without an articulated vision and values an organization's goals, objectives and public arguments are likely to be less connected over time and more reactionary. Without communicating its mission and values in support of its public actions, an organization's public image becomes ad hoc and less credible.

Eleven lobby organizations responded. These were the World Wildlife Fund (WWF), Canadian Nature Federation (CNF), Canadian Parks And Wilderness Society (CPAWS), Alberta Wilderness Association (AWA), Federation of Alberta Naturalists (FAN), Grasslands Naturalists (GR NAT), Friends of Nature Conservation Society (FNCS), World Home Environmentalists Network (WHEN), Saskatchewan Environmental Society (SES), Citizens Association to Save the Environment (CASE), and Canadians for a Clean Environment (CCE).

In reviewing the submitted documents, I was interested in the following questions:

1. Does the organization *articulate* a vision of a sustainably functioning future society?

2. Does it *articulate* the organizational values that underlie its vision?

3. Does it *articulate* a mission, goals, and/or objectives?

4. Are its mission, goals, objectives congruent with its vision?

5. To what degree does its vision appear to drive its mission, goals, objectives?

Under these questions, the returned information is summarized as follows:

## 1. Does the organization articulate a vision of a sustainably functioning future society?

WWF: Yes - A future in which humans live in harmony with nature.

CNF: No

CPAWS: Yes - A healthy ecosphere where people experience and respect natural ecosystems.

AWA: Yes

(1) There will be a comprehensive system of protected wild areas;

(2) There will be a society with decision-making process, policies, and laws that recognizes the value of nature for its own sake;

(3) Alberta people will be aware and enabled to protect wild areas and wildlife; and,

(4) The AWA will have sufficient resources to speak independently on wilderness issues.

Gr.Nat: No

FAN: No

FNCS: Yes -To maintaining the balance of nature for the mutual benefit of people and their plant and animal friends.

WHEN: No

SES: Yes -A conserver society - one in which a stable population uses renewable resources and recyclable materials to create and sustain a high-quality lifestyle that does not erode the environment that supports it.

CCE: No

CASE: Yes - A conserver, sustainable society.

## 2. Does it articulate the organizational values that underlie its vision?

WWF: No

CNF: Yes

(1) All species have a right to exist whether or not they are judges to be useful to humans;

(2) Humans are an integral part of natural ecosystems; and,

(3) Our existence must be guided by sound ecological principles.

CPAWS: No

AWA: Yes

(1) Ecocentredness: we recognize the inherent importance of Nature and humankind's place in it, and the role

of the AWA is to be an advocate for
that which cannot speak for itself;

(2) Integrity: We conduct our advocacy
with truth, honesty, respect for others
and within the full limits of the law;

(3) Respectfulness: We develop rapport
with individuals and communities
through active listening, openness, and
free access to information in a democra
tic way;

(4) Participation: We promote effective
environmental decision making
through an empowered and knowl
edgeable public that is inclusive of all
segments of society;

(5) Tenacity: We will steadfastly advocate
for Nature in a manner true to our
principles through innovation, persistence, and passion; and,

(6) Passion: We are free to feel,
demonstrate and encourage an emotional and spiritual connectedness
with Nature.

Gr.Nat:  No
FAN:  No
FNCS:  No
WHEN:  Yes -Conserverism, recycling, organic
food production, trees, pollution-free
drinking water, vegetarianism, low
impact transportation, empowerment of
individuals, political action.
SES:  No
CCE:  No
CASE:  Yes -Reverence for life in all its glorious
and different forms; without that rever-
ence we are lost. Biological diversity
has to be maintained and enhanced.

## 3. Does it articulate its mission, goals, or objectives?

WWF:  Yes -To conserve wild animals, plants
and habitats for their own sake and for
the long-term benefit of people. Its mission for the 1990's specifically is To
achieve the conservation of nature and
ecological processes by:
(1) Preserving genetic, species and
ecosystem diversity;
(2) Ensuring that the use of renewable
natural resources is sustainable both
now and in the longer term, for the
benefit of all life on earth; and

(3) Promoting action to reduce, to a
minimum, pollution and the wasteful
exploitation and consumption of
resources and energy.

CNF:  Yes
(1) To conserve the environment so
that the integrity of natural ecosystems
is maintained; and,
(2) To promote the understanding,
awareness, and enjoyment of nature.

CPAWS:  Yes -The care and protection of natural
ecosystems in parks and wilderness
areas by means of conservation, education, advocacy, and action.

AWA:  Yes  To be an advocate for wild Alberta
through awareness and action.

Gr.Nat:  Yes  To encourage "the study, conservation  and protection of all components.

FAN:  Yes  Encouraging Albertans ...

FNCS:  Yes -To maintain the balance of nature
with particular concern for the world's
fast-disappearing old-growth forests.

WHEN:  Yes -To provide educational information
to people about environmental issues
and thus support them in bringing about
practical, positive environment changes
in their own lives and communities.

SES:  Yes (implied) - To work toward making
the environment last, using it wisely,
keeping it healthy, and keeping it beautiful.

CASE:  Yes  Soil and water conservation of the
natural world.

CCE:  Yes (implied)  To lobby and educate in
favour of waste management, against air
and water pollution, against the introduction of foreign species, and against
ozone depletion.

## 4. Are its mission, goals, objectives congruent with its vision?

WWF:  Yes
CNF:  Yes
CPAWS:  Ambiguous: Do not address the dilemma
caused by separating natural from
unnatural

AWA:  Incomplete: Inadequately addresses the
question, What is role of people in
wilderness?

Gr.Nat:  Cannot assess (no vision)
FAN:  Cannot assess (no vision)
FNCS:  Incomplete: Seems to be narrowly
restricted only to saving old growth
forests

WHEN:    Cannot assess (no vision)
SES:     Yes
CCE:     Cannot assess (no vision)
CASE:    Incomplete: Seems to assume and accept the urban consumer paradigm

## 5. To what degree does its vision appear to drive its mission, goals, objectives, actions?

WWF:     Low: assumes mostly lobby, info-gathering, and info-sharing roles
CNF:     Zero: no vision
CPAWS:   Low: assumes largely a protectionist posture
AWA:     Low: assumes largely a protectionist posture
Gr.Nat:  Zero: no vision
FAN:     Zero: no vision
FNCS:    Low: mission too limited; fails to place humans in "natural" ecosystems
WHEN:    Zero: no vision
SES:     Moderate: but fails to place humans in "natural" ecosystems
CCE:     Zero: no vision
CASE:    Moderate: but fails to place humans in "natural" ecosystems

## VISION AS THE INTEGRATING FACTOR

It is evident from these results that public image for the majority of respondents is generated more by mission, goals, and/or objectives than by vision. Almost half of the organizations did not articulate a vision, and of the remainder who did four are considered to have low congruence between their vision and actions and two only moderate congruence. In addition, only four of the eleven respondents articulated values underlying their public actions and postures. All respondents, however, were able to identify a mission, goals, and/or objectives.

One problem that emerges from a lack of vision is inability to articulate more than alarmist reactions. A healthy individual or group will be able to rationalize suggested solutions in terms of a clear vision of how things ought to be. Such vision should drive the *entire* solution process—not only prompting alarmist reactions but also setting goals and objectives, and then implementing action and evaluation plans. Without a clear vision it is nigh impossible to move beyond alarmist reaction.

The public face of an organization is, and must necessarily, be made up of two main components: its visible *actions* in the community of its operations blended with the *rationale* it deploys in support of its actions. The rationale is the thinking that goes on behind the action. Consider the popular phrase, "Act locally, think globally." I suggest we improve this to say, "Act locally, think globally and infinitely." Thinking globally and infinitely is eco-centric thinking. When our local actions are informed (rationalized) by best current understanding of global interrelationships and our desire to sustain these infinitely, then these actions are eco-centrically grounded.

We fall short on the thinking component of our public image, the publicly visible argument or rationale that explains our visible public protests and postures. This rationale should be driven by both a set of values and a vision. Action is to rationale what a mushroom is to its mycelia; values and vision comprise their vascular fluids. Action can be appreciated, but only the rationale can convey the integrated sense of it.

The proposed framework is intended to help individuals connect to their values and vision. It begins with the recognition that an organization is comprised firstly of its individual members, and that the vision and values internal to it precipitate from the knowledge and values of these members. My proposed framework for strengthening the collective environmental lobby focuses on the two main areas of individual neglect: knowledge and values.

The immediate question then is, Where should such a vision be grounded so that it is not just another opinion free-floating in a sea of personal beliefs? The answer is ecology. Ecology is considered here in its broadest meaning: the science that studies relationship dynamics of life systems. As such, it does not restrict itself to so-called natural landscapes; it includes humans, as it includes all. It is holistic as no other science can be; it is the umbrella science embracing all disciplines of study. Deep ecologist, Peter Berg (1990), correctly observed that "the pro-active element of "What should we do instead?" [is] obviously not going to be provided by environmentalism but by ecology." Similarly, Orr (1992) observed that "The basis of ecological literacy ... is the interrelatedness of life grounded in the study of natural history, ecology, and thermodynamics."

A vision grounded in ecology is an eco-centric vision. Its articulation should form the heart of our environmental lobby.

## BASIC KNOWLEDGE

Ecology offers some basic or "primary knowledge" as well as derivative knowledge. Primary knowledge answers at least three fundamental questions:

1. What is the real world?
2. How does an experience of the real world differ from the real world itself?
3. What rules enable sustained functioning of the real world?

    Derivative knowledge answers questions such as:

> What is the human proper place?
> What is the proper place for other species?
> How should we define community, jobs, right-to-life, health, technology, culture?

The real world is everything; everything happening in space and time. When we take a moment to consider this statement we may begin to glimpse how awesome this is. This is truly big, truly incomprehensible! Nevertheless, ecologically true. Everything happening right this split second, throughout the whole universe in a microtome's slice of time, *is* the real world. Furthermore, since all "things" are connected by energy flowing only one way through the universe (i.e. toward entropy), therefore one cannot but conclude that *all* of the past, since time immemorial, contributes to this present and is also to be included in the real world.

Contrast this to our perceived world, or our "environment." Environment is a subject-dependent perception of a minuscule fragment of the total dynamic occurring in the universe. In as much as distinct species have distinct sensory abilities and ranges, so is its environment unique to each species. And, it is universally true that for all species perception is extremely limited by the fact that each has limited sensory apparatuses and narrow sensitivity ranges. True, we humans have expanded our sensitivity and memory thresholds somewhat through technology, but in the total real world context this enhancement is almost insignificant. The real world and the perceived environment are very different entities.

A third primary knowledge addresses the question, What rules governing inter-species relations (including humans) enable sustained functioning of the real world? Daniel Quinn (1993) articulates a cardinal rule with three corollaries. The cardinal rule is, "No one species shall make the life of the world its own." The corollaries are:

1. Do not exterminate competitors;
2. Do not eliminate a competitor's food supply - consume only what you need for yourself; and,
3. Do not cut off a competitor's access to her/his food supply.

These prompt the following important derivative knowledge.

## 1. Human's Place

The human's place, as that of any other species, is not to dominate, but to participate as an equal player.

## 2. Defining Community

In everyday discourse we have become so accustomed to linking this term to human groupings (such as community associations, church communities, recreational communities, villages, towns, and cities), that we have forgotten about the largest portion of our family which includes all other species, organisms, and ecological "things." A true-to-life definition of community, one that is ecologically sound, embraces all things that interact within the dynamic ecosphere. Since all things interact, no matter how one defines "things," therefore community ultimately embraces the whole. All of the ecosphere, in the most holistic sense thinkable, ought ultimately to be considered a "community."

A community of the whole was strongly felt by traditional Indigenous peoples whose lives were relatively little insulated from ecological cycles. It is clearly implicit, for example, in Black Elk's frequently cited introduction to his life's story (Neihardt, 1961): "It is the story of all life that is holy and is good to tell, and of us two-leggeds sharing in it with the four-leggeds and the wings of the air and all green things; for these are children of one mother and their father is one Spirit."

## 3. Defining Jobs

From an ecological perspective, a job is described by niche or role. Darling and Dasmann (1972) defined niche as "an individual's or species' place in a biotic community." They further suggest that "It is defined in terms of the surrounding environment, ...and the role played by the organism within it." In other words: where you live and what you do for a living, your "job." My job as an adult educator permits me (via money as an intermediary) access to whatever it is I need to sustain myself. I don't see this to be *essentially* different from that of another species. A squirrel's job, for example, includes cutting, gathering, burying, nest building, quarreling, churring, and whatever else she must do to sustain herself for the duration of her job as a squirrel. It is deceiving to suggest merely that species are interdependent; it is species' jobs that are interdependent.

Contrary to Quinn's rule, we humans do not now confine our activities to mere food predation; since the discovery of agriculture we commenced job predation. The technologies that we humans (especially of western industrial cultures) are developing to steal the jobs (or portions of jobs) of other species, are becoming at the same time more and more exact in their ability to target the yield of human advantage and increasingly global in scale of impact. Our European predecessors thus turned resident Indigenous peoples into economic slaves to serve our appetites for beaver and bison; we thus preyed upon tall-grass prairie soils to yield year upon year of grain; we thus continue to enslave select tree species to yield us paper and timber, and disinherit those species that are unable; we thus just now stumbled all over our Canadian corporate and government selves to complete our biodiversity strategies and generously help Costa Ricans conduct an exhaustive catalogue of rainforest species. The history of western industrial cultures, from an ecocentric perspective, is a litany of (job-) colonization, (job-) oppression, (job-)displacement, (job-)disinheritance, and outright genocide for thousands of species evolved over countless years to occupy those jobs.

We would do well to think more critically about the daily appeals of politicians and others to the overriding importance of "job-creation." Ecological relationships are all about relationships among the jobs of diverse species living together in one global community dependent on a relatively fixed (limited) amount of energy offered by the sun. Job creation, ecocentrism suggests, ought not to be restricted to creation of human jobs. Instead, it should be about supporting the jobs, and the natural evolution of jobs, of all species that make up the community mosaic of the ecosphere.

tle that has found seasonal refuge in my window sill have this right? The elm tree by the sidewalk? Or the bark beetle larva gnawing intricate channels between bark and wood? The question is complex if approached from a human-centered, individualistic starting point. The ecocentric view suggests that life is larger than individual organisms or species, and therefore, that life is an attribute not resident within any individual. Rowe (1993) stated "that the ecosphere and its sectoral ecosystems are the creative entities of primary value, and that they are the source of life." He elsewhere elaborated (Rowe, 1992) that, "... if the ecosphere is considered as the bearer of life, then we do violence to it by dividing it into biotic and abiotic, animate and inanimate, organic and inorganic, even "living" and "dead."

An ecocentric definition of community and of life directs us to equate right-to-life as a right ultimately of the ecosphere and its sectoral ecosystems that we call landscapes and waterscapes—the right to keep on being that dynamic whole of trillions of perpetually interacting entities and processes.

Thus, right-to-life certainly does **not** mean the right of all individual organisms to uninterrupted existence (as, for example, some anti-hunting sentiments and vegetarians seem to suggest); it also does *not* mean that matters of pregnancy and birth of any species, including humans, must be left to take their so-called natural courses. Both unconstrained reproduction and wholesale elimination of any species is destructive to the ecosphere.

It *does* mean that all species have a right to exercise their jobs in ecosphere dynamics, and that all individual species members (including humans) ought to accept reproductive management as desirable, and do so with total sensitivity and dignity. If the Hippocratic Oath, born from a human-centered approach, were to be re-phrased from an ecocentric point of view, we would become better equipped to handle recurring issues such as birth control, euthanasia, and right-to-die.

## 4. Defining Life and Right to Life

Right-to-life is of course a most laudable concept. But what "life" are we talking about? Is it my grandmother's right to be maintained on a life-support system? Is it the right of a two-week or 4-month old fetus to continue to exist and develop? Or, of the mother carrying it? Is it a right my family's dog has? Does the lady bird bee-

## 5. Defining Health

An ecocentric view suggests that, as with life, health is an attribute not resident in the individual, but resident in the ecosphere as a whole. The individual has only an experience of health: that is, the feeling of well-being. This reality underlies an apparent paradox: whereas average human life expectancy has greatly increased in recent times, which most would suggest is an indicator of generally improved health, we are nevertheless generally *feeling* increasingly ill. Our feeling increasing illness, I suspect, is likely our response to declining health of manufactured environments we have surrounded ourselves with, and the increasing stress resulting from human overpopulation. This declining health, in turn, reflects the inability of the ecosphere to cope with these artificial environments.

An ecocentric view suggests that pursuit of health, like support of life, requires us to practice ethical constraint upon ourselves rather than unbounded pursuit of self-serving goals. As Leopold (1949) observed, "Health is the capacity of the land for self-renewal. Conservation is our effort to understand and preserve this capacity."

Saskatchewan Health's "Wellness Report" (1992) made a very small step in the right direction with the statement "An expanded view of health considers factors such as housing, employment, education and the environment." But this is far short of the fundamental and sweeping change required first within our individual minds, and then expressed in de-constructing and re-constructing our environments to render them ecologically friendly.

## 6. Defining Technology

A technology is a *design* by which a species and/or individual interacts with its environment. Considering this definition, technology is not restricted to human invention. A bird's nest is a technology, as is a squirrel's design to cut cones from tree tops and then store them within middens. A beaver's ability to engineer dams in order to raise water level to store its winter food and ensure safe winter temperature within its lodge is every bit as good a technology as designing a suit for survival in space. Every species has developed technologies to manage the probable changes it is challenged to manage.

## 7. Defining Culture

Culture is the sum total of all the technologies characteristic of a species, any species. Human culture includes all the tool and technological designs and innovations created and employed by us, whether at work, at home, the road, on water, in the air, or in space. Similarly, the sum total of all technologies characteristic of magpies comprise its culture. Perhaps the reason we humans distinguish human culture from animal culture by referring to the latter as "habits," may have more to

do with our insistent effort to position ourselves apart from and above other species—a transgression of Quinn's rule for sustainable living.

## VALUES

In addition to basic knowledge to frame a vision of sustainable living, we must be transformed by essential values. I suggest two primary values, and several derivative values. The primary values underlying a vision of sustained living in the universe are:

1. The value of respect for all components of and participants in the ecosphere; and,
2. The value of the universe as the entity of life.

The following essential derivative values are adapted from Orr (1992) and Miller (1988):

- Equality of rights for all species;
- Empowerment of all species;
- Genetic diversity;
- Careful, ecologically friendly design;
- Peace, justice, fairness;
- Decentralized control;
- Democratic participation:
- Small scale and simplicity of action and design;
- Roles that contribute to the well-being of all species; and
- Longest term solutions to conflicts and problems.

## ECOSYSTEM MANAGEMENT PRINCIPLES

For purposes of management, the following three principles should be applied:

1. The rights of all species are equal
2. The rights of individual organisms are subject to limits that support the whole system
3. In conflict resolution, the ultimate arbiter should be ecosystem integrity (i.e. the indefinite sustaining of all processes and roles).

Principles 2 and 3 are, by the way, recognized in *A Wildlife Policy for Canada, 1990*, in the statement, "The maintenance of viable natural populations of wildlife always takes precedence over their use by people."

The draft discussion document, "Prairie ecosystem management: an Alberta perspective", circulated at the opening of this conference, offers four prairie ecosystem management principles. Based on the above knowledge and values I would constructively amend them slightly and add a fifth, so that they read as follows:

1. Ecosystem management maintains and restores native prairie so all resident species can continue to derive all the benefits that flow from it (ecological, economic, and social);

2. Ecosystem management attempts to perpetuate a fullest spectrum of ecosystem processes;

3. Ecosystem management applies eco-centric knowledge to prairie management, monitors the results, and adapts as required;

4. Ecosystem management is supra-disciplinary and inter-jurisdictional; and,

5. Ecosystem management is directed and constrained by eco-centric values.


## CONCLUSION

The upshot of all of the above is that we humans should conduct a whole lot more self-management and a whole lot less environmental management. In our everyday experience most humans transgress all of Quin's rules; in fact our educational and economic institutions condition our young people into perpetuating such transgression. Smith (1992) said it succinctly: "Few publicly question the commonly shared assumptions about unlimited growth and expanding individual opportunities that undergird schools. ...The central preoccupation of most educational debate over the previous decade has been America's competitiveness in an international market."

Massey Lecturer, Ursala Franklin (1990) similarly observed:

> "... if somebody robs a store, it's a crime and the state is all set and ready to nab the criminal. But if somebody steals from the commons and from the future, it's seen as entrepreneurial activity and the state cheers and gives them tax concessions rather than arresting them."

In conclusion, my essential message is this: in order to align and strengthen all our lobbying activities, we must develop and communicate a *vision* of a sustainable, global community of all ecosystem participants. A most immediate and inescapable implication is that the basic knowledge and values by which species govern themselves should be applied also by us humans to ourselves. We environmentalists, as individuals and groups, are in the best position both to bring this message and to enact it. We can become most effective if we embrace this knowledge and these values, and consistently base our public critique and argument on them.


## LITERATURE CITED

Berg, Peter. 1990. Bioregional and wild: a new cultural image. Pp. 22-30 *In* Turtle talk: Voices for a sustainable future (C. Plant and J. Plant, eds.). New Society Publishers, Lilloet, British Columbia.

Darling, F.F. and R.F. Dasmann. 1972. The ecosystem view of human society. Pp. 41-46 *In* The ecology of man: An ecosystem approach (R.L. Smith ed.). Harper & Row, New York, New York.

Franklin, Ursala. 1990. The real world of technology. CBC Massey Lectures Series. CBC Enterprises, Toronto, Ontario.

Leopold, Aldo. 1949. A Sand County almanac. Oxford University Press, New York, New York.

Miller, John P. 1988. The holistic curriculum. OISE Press. Toronto, Ontario.

Neihardt, J.G. 1961. Black Elk speaks: Being the life story of a Holy Man of the Oglala Sioux. University of Nebraska Press. Lincoln, Nebraska.

Orr, David. W. 1992. Ecological literacy: Education and the transition to a postmodern world. State University of New York Press. Albany, New York.

Quinn, Daniel. 1993. Ishmael. Bantam Publishers.

Roszak, Theodore. 1993. The voice of the earth: An exploration of ecopsychology. Simon & Schuster, New York, New York.

Rowe, J. Stan. 1992. Saskatchewan's endangered spaces: The essential ecocentric approach. Chapter 1 *In*

Saskatchewan's endangered spaces: An introduction. (P. Jonker, ed.). University of Saskatchewan Extension Division, Saskatoon, Saskatchewan.

Rowe, J. Stan. 1993. Forum: Stan Rowe on the ecological perspective in a changing world. Hastings Bridge. Fall, 1993.

Saskatchewan Health. 1992. A Saskatchewan vision for health: A framework for change. Saskatchewan Health. (Also known as the "Wellness Report"). Regina, Saskatchewan.

Smith, G.A. 1992. Education and the environment: Learning to live with limits. State University of New York Press, Albany, New York.

# POLICIES AND PROGRAMS: CONCLUDING SUMMARY

**Richard Laing**
*Theme Reporter*
**Don Ferguson**
*Theme Recorder*

## INTRODUCTION

In a final working group session, participants were asked to identify commonalities and differences heard during the conference regarding the effects of policies and programs on the prairie landscape. For presentation purposes, the group's discussion is presented in the following sections in 4 categories, which are: (1) Barriers to participating in the development of effective policies and programs; (2) Using effective multiple-use approaches; (3) Improving communication; and (4) Improving economic policies.

## BARRIERS TO PARTICIPATING IN THE DEVELOPMENT OF POLICIES AND PROGRAMS

Workshop participants identified several critical barrier which limit or prevent members of the public and stakeholders from effectively participating in the development of government policies and programs which significantly affect the conservation of prairie wildlife and the sustainable use of renewable resources. These barriers identified included:

- Lack of knowledge and understanding by individual and groups of the processes which exist to receive their input regarding development of new, or modifications to existing policies and programs;

- Excess demand on time of individuals and groups who would like to participate in policy and program development processes but are overloaded with other processes; and

- A perception by individuals and groups that their input will not have a significant influence in their design or implementation or policies and programs.

## USING EFFECTIVE MULTIPLE-USE APPROACHES

Workshop participants supported the development of effective multiple-use approaches to achieve the conservation and sustainable use of prairie resources. Many felt that existing processes had only limited success and that models that have been successful, such as the NAWMP, should be highlighted.

Improvements to multiple-use processes are required involving members of the public and stakeholder. The following concepts should be included in multiple-use processes:

- Prairie resources are shared resources;

- The costs of conservation must be shared among all beneficiaries;

- Solutions must be found to specific concerns of landowners and producers, such as wildlife crop damage;

- Planning and analysis are required to determine appropriate and dominant land uses; and

- Integration of policies must be ensured in order to avoid conflicting objectives.

## IMPROVING COMMUNICATION

Many workshop participants felt that this was crucial to achieving conservation goals and reducing or avoiding conflicts among resource users. In order to advance communication, the following issues needed to be resolved:

- Communication must be user friendly; communication must not be initiated by language barriers such as the use of technical terms and legalese, Landowners\producers and members of conservation groups, scientists and others must all improve their ability to communicate using common languages in order to facilitate understanding of issues;

- Respect for each others views must be developed through better communication, increased trust and understanding; and

- A greater respect and appreciation for traditional knowledge is needed.

## IMPROVING ECONOMIC POLICIES AND PROGRAMS

Many workshop participants discussed the impacts of economic policies and programs on prairie resources. The debate was complex and did not result in consensus about the future application or role of economic policies and programs in shaping the prairie landscape. Some individuals felt that economic policies and programs should be widely implemented to achieve conservation goals. Others felt that economic policies usually meant government subsidies, and such subsidies were not only unreliable given our current public debt problems, but also unnecessary.

There was also considerable discussion regarding the need to link policies and programs to the constraints and opportunities of the landscape, and not simply to commodity markets. Most participates felt that economic policies had been developed without adequate consideration of their impacts on prairie landscape.

There was consensus on several aspects regarding current economic policies and programs; for instance:

- Economic subsidies have had the effect of overvaluing some resource uses encouraging undesirable resource use practices;

- Economic policies and programs, other than direct subsidies, have not been adequately researched to determine their role in achieving conservation goals; and

- If economic policies and programs are to continue, they must be designed and implemented to ensure that they support prairie conservation objectives in addition to social and economic objectives.

## SUMMARY

Workshop participants unanimously concluded that public policies and programs have been and will continue to be critical elements in the management of prairie resources and in shaping the prairie landscape. Given the importance of policies and programs, all participants agreed for the need to continue to improve the effectiveness of our multi-stakeholder decision-making processes and improve and enhance communication to increase respect and understanding among residents of the prairies.

# 6.0 ENDANGERED SPECIES

# ENDANGERED SPECIES CONSERVATION

## Geoffrey L. Holroyd

*Canadian Wildlife Service, Room 200, 4999-98 Ave, Edmonton, Alberta T6B 2X3*

## INTRODUCTION

The number of species on Canada's endangered species list, which includes many species of prairie wildlife, continues to grow each year and only a few have been removed or downlisted. In 1994, 39% of the birds (9 of 23 species and subspecies) that were listed as endangered, threatened and vulnerable occurred on the Canadian prairies. In addition 10 prairie species of mammals and more plants are listed. The percentage of species listed from the prairies declined since 1989 when 50% of the listed species of birds occurred on the prairies. However, the decline in percent is only because species are being added to the list from other regions faster than from the prairies. The absolute number of species has not declined.

Why are so many prairie species listed? While most species' declines are caused by several factors, primary factors can be identified in many cases. Overhunting in the last century is the cause of low populations for three species that bred on or migrated through the prairies: trumpeter swan (*Cygnus buccinator*), whooping crane (*Grus americana*) and eskimo curlew (*Numenius borealis*). One endangered species, mountain plover (*Charadrius montanus*), breeds in Canada at low numbers because it is at the northern fringe of its range and should be listed as vulnerable, not endangered. Toxic chemicals caused the decline of the peregrine falcon (*Falco peregrinus*) and are of concern to the Cooper's hawk (*Accipiter cooperii*). Habitat related issues are the primary cause of declines in eight other species: piping plover (*Charadrius melodus*) , long-billed curlew (*Numenius americanus*), ferruginous hawk (*Buteo regalis*), burrowing owl (*Speotyto cunicularia*), short-eared owl (*Asio flammeus*), loggerhead shrike (*Lanius ludovicianus*), Baird's sparrow (*Ammodramus bairdii*), and swift fox (*Vulpes velox*).

If habitat issues are so important in endangered species conservation, what is the status of prairie habitats? The loss of wetland habitat has been documented in many publications (e.g. CWS 1985). Waterfowl numbers are half what they were in the 1950's and 40% of prairie wetlands have been drained. In response to these declines, the North American Waterfowl Management Plan (NAWMP) was initiated in 1985 at a cost of $1.5 billion. Over 75% of the prairies have been ploughed or paved (WWF 1988). About 75% of mixed grass and parkland ecoregions, 90% of fescue grasslands, and 99% of tall grass prairie are gone in Canada. Thus, it is no coincidence that most of the prairie wildlife in jeopardy are upland species not wetland species.

The conversion of native grasslands to cultivation is still encouraged by agricultural subsidies and programs, and by continued expansion of irrigation in Alberta. With less than one quarter of the prairies in a natural state, endangered species recovery is likely to be more difficult in the future. Wildlife agencies need to continue building a dialogue with agricultural agencies which affect land use practises on most of the prairies.

So, what are we doing about this growing problem? This paper reviews endangered species recovery plans and teams, the role of habitat conservation, and compares other approaches to endangered species conservation so as to enhance current practises. Many of the ideas in this paper were discussed at the working sessions on endangered species at the Lethbridge workshop.

## RECOVERY TEAMS

Recovery teams are required for all species that are listed as endangered and threatened by COSEWIC. The appointments to the team are made by the national committee of federal, provincial and territorial wildlife directors that is called RENEW (REcovery of Nationally Endangered Wildlife). The RENEW strategy calls for recovery plans to be drafted by the team within one year of a species being listed as endangered (RENEW 1988); the strategy states that it addresses the need "to react quickly to endangered species affected by sudden emergencies" (ibid, page 11).

However, the experience of two prairie recovery teams indicates that the approval of recovery plans has been very slow and cumbersome. The draft recovery plans for the ferruginous hawk and burrowing owl were commissioned by WWF's Wild West committee in 1988 in anticipation of the formation of RENEW and in recognition of the plight of these species. The recovery teams for these two species gave their technical endorsement of these two species plans in 1990. However, the plans were printed in December 1994 and May 1995 (ferruginous hawk and burrowing owl, respectively). Clearly the approval of recovery plans is an extremely slow process that requires streamlining and shortening.

Each plan focuses on the actions needed to recover populations of the species. Common concerns of the single species approach are to increase our knowledge of the status of the species through inventories, determine the life history of the species, its interactions with other species, how and why the populations change over time, the species' habitat needs and how these needs can be met through habitat protection, restoration and management.

## SINGLE SPECIES CONCERNS

The working sessions at the workshop identified conservation issues for several species and species groups. The sage grouse (*Centrocercus urophasianus*) session identified the need to determine the effect of grazing systems, particularly rotation grazing on sage grouse and its habitat. Predation by coyotes (*Canis latrans*) was of concern but its impact is unknown. Finally, we need to know more about the life history of the sage grouse in Canada.

The current status of an established population of swift foxes is a major success story, brought about by co-operation amongst many individuals and agencies. However, we still need a better understanding of the ecology of the species and how the population interacts with the prairie environment under different human management practises such as grazing systems.

The plant and insect sessions focused on habitat conservancy as the key to conservation. There are too many species of plants and insects for a single species approach to work. Our knowledge base needs to be improved so that we know more about the distribution of species, the effect of fire management and water on these species complexes. We also need to know more about the community interactions of the many plant and insect species on the prairies.

The amphibian and reptile session focused on information needs and education of land owners and the public. We need to know more about the conservation requirements of these species and their biology. Public cooperation and participation is also needed to conduct an amphibian and reptile atlas. Legislative protection was deemed inappropriate.

The burrowing owl session discussed habitat loss and the critical role of Operation Burrowing Owl (OBO) in Alberta and Saskatchewan. OBO encourages landowners with burrowing owl habitat to sign voluntary agreements to conserve the pastures that support the owls for a period of five years. The burrowing owl's productivity is low due to habitat fragmentation and habitat degradation. Mortality factors that stem from human activities are pesticides, particularly carbofuran, roadkills and shooting. In addition, we know little of the migration and winter habitats and mortality of this species.

OBO is an example of how wildlife needs require integration with human land use activities. The owls need an unploughed pasture for nesting, and the landowners agree not to plough the pasture. Another example of the need to integrate wildlife needs into prairie agricultural practises is the prairie falcon (*Falco mexicanus*) which eats primarily ground squirrels. In the breeding season, 75% of the prey items and 94% of the biomass of the prairie falcon's diet are Richardson's ground squirrels (*Spermophilus richardsonii*) which live on only 2.9% of the prairies (in one study area south of Brooks). If prairie falcons are to breed successfully, ground squirrels must continue to live on native pasture. Likewise, piping plover conservation hinges on the protection of habitat for nest sites from cattle trampling and disturbance.

An additional concern of teams that are trying to recover migratory species, is the conservation needs south of Canada. Piping plover and whooping cranes are two species where U.S. cooperators work actively with Canadian Recovery Team members. For many other teams, including teams for the peregrine falcon, ferruginous hawk and burrowing owl, there is little formal contact with US, Mexican or Latin American agencies or individuals. Enhanced communication and cooperation is needed if international concerns are to be addressed by recovery efforts.

While recovery teams seem effective in learning new information about the species in jeopardy and have brought forward some new conservation techniques, they have done poorly at addressing habitat conservation needs of their species. The recovery efforts require a broader effort to tackle the complexities of habitat management.

## RECOVERY PLANS AND HABITAT

All recovery plans incorporate the maintenance of habitat. As stated earlier habitat is the primary cause of the declines of at least eight prairie species. The recovery of all endangered species involves some aspect of habitat conservation.

Despite the importance of habitat as a common thread in recovery plans, recovery teams have been unable to tackle many habitat problems because of the size and complexity of the topic. The lack of emphasis in habitat related work is reflected in the applications received by the Endangered Species Recovery Fund (ESRF), World Wildlife Fund Canada. In January 1995, there were 62 applications from across Canada, 13 from the prairies. Of the 49 projects from elsewhere in Canada, about 20 involved habitat research and conservation, and 5 involved habitat protection. From the prairies, only 2 of 13 involved habitat research and conservation, and 2 involved habitat protection. In terms of funding, only $40K of a total of $830K (5%) requested involved prairie habitat. In contrast, $542K of $2.7 million (20%) involved habitat issues from elsewhere in Canada. While many applications for non-habitat work are worthwhile, there is definitely a shortage of applications regarding prairie habitat issues.

While every working session on species or species groups identified the need to collect more information to have a better knowledge of populations and to determine habitat requirements, none of this information benefits the species if actions are not taken to benefit prairie wildlife. Wildlife will only prosper if our actions on the prairie take their needs into account. All wildlife habitat requirements can be met by natural native prairie. However, most prairie land is privately owned, and the owner has the final say on the actions affecting that land.

For landowners to take action, they need to be informed about the needs of wildlife and/or motivated to act accordingly. One route to provide this education is by having people directly involved in conservation action. Programs such as adopt a pond' or stream, collecting information for a wildlife atlas, and participation in youth and school programs will get landowners and their children involved in conservation action. OBO is the best example of the voluntary approach to landowners. In Alberta this program is being broadened to included other species (Scobie 1992).

## SPECIES, MULTI-SPECIES OR ECOSYSTEM APPROACH?

The working session on endangered species discussed at length the pros and cons of these three approaches to endangered species conservation. The current approach of single species recovery teams has many accomplishments but some shortcomings. The question is: Can we be more efficient at recovering endangered species by pooling our efforts? The pros and cons of each approach are summarized in Table 1.

### Single Species Approach

Current recovery plans typically include gathering information about a species in the following topics: population surveys, productivity, diet, habitat and conservation actions needed for recovery. Wildlife agencies are represented in the team together with some technical experts. Habitat conservation and management agencies are rarely represented, yet habitat protection and restoration are a necessary part of the recovery plan.

The single species approach has worked well for species that had specific threats and needed specific actions such as the release of captive bred peregrine falcons (Fyfe 1987) and translocation of trumpeter swans (Winkler 1991). For these and other species, direct action is needed to solve a particular need.

The process is reactive, that is, a recovery plan is developed only after the species' populations are perceived to have declined. The proactive components of agencies plans are developed outside the recovery team, for example NAWMP. The problem is that the number of species being listed by COSEWIC is increasing faster that RENEW's ability to write, approve and implement recovery plans. Where species co-occur, such as on the prairies, there is a redundancy in some actions particularly related to habitat. Another problem can be diverse and multiple messages sent to landowners, although the basic problem is that most landowners receive little contact. Usually before a species plan can be effective, we must learn more about the species ecology. The process can be very slow.

Table 1. Summary of the primary activities, pro's and con's of three approaches to endangered species conservation.

**Single species Approach:**
1. Increased population knowledge base through surveys and monitoring.
2. Increased life history knowledge base including: productivity, longevity and mortality parameters and interspecific interactions.
3. Habitat conservation, protection and restoration

| Pro's | Con's |
| --- | --- |
| - restricts the number of variables to a manageable size | - approach with highest cost per species |
| - less costly individual projects | - problem is often habitat conservation which is too |
| - previous success demonstrates that the approach works | large an issue for a single-species team |
| - high profile species can be used to promote education | - reactive process |
| | -shortage of people and dollars |
| | - species being added to the COSEWIC list faster than |
| | they can be covered with a recovery team |
| | - limited number of people to solve varied problems |

**Multiple Species Approach:**
3. Habitat conservation, protection and restoration
4. Public education including broad-based awareness, cooperation, and landowner stewardship

| Pro's | Con's |
| --- | --- |
| - more species benefit from actions | - may still require habitat actions that are broader in |
| - pooling of species specific efforts | implications |
| - more cost effective per species | - more costly than single species approach |
| - potential to be more preventative | - more complex than single species approach |
| - can link less charismatic to more charismatic species | - slower to implement than single species approach |

**Ecosystem Approach:**
3. Habitat conservation, protection and restoration
4. Public education including broad-based awareness, cooperation, landowner stewardship, and land ethics.
5. Policies to support voluntary landowner action and protection by land management agencies and to redirect other funding programs toward conservation objectives

| Pro's | Con's |
| --- | --- |
| - broad impacts and potential for broad range of wildlife benefits | - involves consensus with more partners |
| - most preventative (proactive) approach | - most complex |
| - can include keystone species such as ground squirrels | - most costly |
| - involve broader issues such as ethics and landowners' stewardship | - slowest to implement |
| - promote endangered habitat conservation | |
| - most efficient approach to tackle the effects of agricultural and socioeconomic | |

If we are to cope with the growing number of species listed by COSEWIC, the endangered species program must change from species management to a more efficient process. Two that have been suggested are multi-species management and ecosystem management.

## Multi-Species Management

On the prairies several species occupy overlapping habitats and they are threatened by common factors. For these co-occurring species, it may be possible to be more efficient by developing plans and actions that benefit several species together rather than attempt to conduct actions individually. For example, many threatened and endangered species occur on the prairie upland and many conservation actions will benefit more than one species (e.g., OBO, Scobie 1992). Such plans will require wider expertise and additional coordination. However, most prairie teams share some members so that communication between teams should be fairly simple. Such a multi-species approach should be more cost effective than single species actions that would result in duplication of effort. However the approach is still reactive, treating species once they are listed by COSEWIC.

## Ecosystem Approach

As identified earlier, the prairie ecozone is heavily affected by humans. An ecozone or ecosystem approach will be concerned with broad habitat issues not species specific issues. The ecosystem approach should include natural interactions of the full range of physical and biological components as well as the broad issues that affect land use activities and society's actions. Habitat conservation, protection, and restoration would be the major focus of this approach. An ecosystem team would be comprised of both wildlife and land use agencies and representatives of landowners. Topics such as agricultural policy, land use practises, taxation systems, subsidies, societal ethics, and others could be more effectively tackled by such an approach. The conservation strategy for riparian cottonwoods in southern Alberta is an excellent example of a plan that could be part of an ecosystem approach (WWF and AFW 1992). In southern Alberta three million acres of crown land provide the land base for current native wildlife populations. An ecosystem approach would involve promoting conservation land management on these public lands and on all suitable private lands.

An ecosystem approach would require broad expertise, with people familiar with biophysical, plant, animal,

social, economic and political issues. Such an approach would require greater collaboration and broader stakeholder communication. Examples in eastern Canada are Carolinian Canada where candidate sites for protection are selected based on habitat types; Great Lakes 2000 with a goal to restore 60% of the natural shoreline habitats; and the Atlantic Coastal Plan which is mandated to improve water quality and control contaminants (S. Nadeau, personal communication). It was pointed out in the session that B.C. Forestry is responsible for all species in the land that they use and they have hired biologists to work at integrating wildlife needs into forestry practises. Who uses the prairies and what are their responsibilities?

In contrast to single or multiple species approaches, the ecosystem approach would focus on human activities as well as broad natural physical and biological processes as well individual life histories. The ecosystem approach to endangered species could focus concern for habitat conservation to complement the species approach. Ecological keystone species such as ground squirrels and grasshoppers could receive higher profile in an ecosystem discussion than they do now in species teams. Ground squirrels are a keystone species because they are an important prey for several prairie predators such as prairie falcon, ferruginous hawk, Swainson's hawk (*Buteo swainsoni*), swift fox and badger (*Taxidea taxus*); they provide burrows for nesting burrowing owls and modify the grazing pressure on native grasslands. Grasshoppers are a major prey item for a wide variety of songbirds, microtines and even Swainson's Hawk.

## CONCLUSION

The ideal strategy to the recovery of endangered and threatened species will be to combine approaches. Single species management will always be required for urgent problems, while ecosystem management will achieve longer term sustainability of the prairies. Recovery teams need to be linked to broader programs to implement the endangered species habitat concerns. Single, high profile species can serve as the essential marketing tool for ecosystem conservation. So called mega fauna such as large mammals and charismatic species such as peregrine falcons can be used to convince society that ecosystem management actions are necessary to save wildlife. Waterfowl are being used to convince the public and politicians that wetland conservation is necessary. One result is the funding of the North American Waterfowl Management Plan, which is a wetland plan at least in part. Most of the public are familiar with the concept of endangered species. Endangered species should also be used to promote a prairie conservation plan. Since the wetlands are targeted by NAWMP, an upland plan would be complementary to NAWMP. Upland species such as Cooper's hawk, long-billed curlew, ferruginous hawk, burrowing owl, short-eared owl, loggerhead shrike, Baird's sparrow and swift fox make excellent star species for such conservation plans.

## ACKNOWLEDGEMENTS

I thank Clive Abbott, and Candice Phillips for their detailed notes on our session which allowed me to make this article more complete. The presentations and input of ideas from Simon Nadeau, and Stewart Rood, and the editorial comments of Ursula Banasch and Loney Dickson are greatly appreciated.

## LITERATURE CITED

Canadian Wildlife Service. 1985. North American Waterfowl Management Plan, draft November, 1985. Canadian Wildlife Service, Environment Canada, Ottawa, Ontario.

Fyfe, R. 1987. The peregrine falcon. Pp. 209-216 *In* Proceedings of the Workshop on Endangered Species in the Prairie Provinces (Holroyd, G.L., W.B. McGillivray, P.H.R. Stepney, D.M. Ealey, G.C. Trottier, and K.E. Eberhart, eds.). Natural History Occasional Paper No. 9. Provincial Museum of Alberta, Edmonton, Alberta.

Holroyd, G.L., H.L. Dickson, M. Regnier, and H.C. Smith. 1993. Proceedings of the Third Prairie Conservation and Endangered Species Workshop. Natural History Occasional Paper No. 19. Provincial Museum of Alberta, Edmonton.

RENEW. 1988. A strategy for the recovery of nationally endangered wildlife in Canada. Canadian Wildlife Service, Ottawa, Ontario.

Scobie, D. 1992. Operation Burrowing Owl, Alberta 1992 Annual Report. Alberta Fish and Game Association, Brooks, Alberta.

Winkler, T. 1991. The Elk Island National Park trumpeter swan reintroduction project. Pp. 208-210 *In* Proceedings of the Second Endangered Species and Prairie Conservation Workshop (G.L. Holroyd, G. Burns, and H.C. Smith, eds.). Natural History Occasional Paper No. 15. Provincial Museum of Alberta, Edmonton, Alberta.

World Wildlife Fund and Alberta Forestry Lands and Wildlife. 1992. Conservation and management strategy for riparian forests in southern Alberta. Alberta Forestry Lands and Wildlife, Edmonton, Alberta.

World Wildlife Fund Canada. 1988. Prairie Conservation Action Plan 1989-1994. WWF, Toronto, Ontario.

# ACTIVITIES OF THE PLANTS SUBCOMMITTEE (COSEWIC)

## Erich Haber

*Chairman, Plants Subcommittee (COSEWIC), National Botanical Services,*
*604 Wavell Avenue, Ottawa, Ontario K2A 3A8*

The Plants Subcommittee of the Committee on the Status of Endangered Wildlife in Canada (COSEWIC) currently has a "List of Plant Candidates for Status Report Preparation and Plants with Designated Status" that includes 498 vascular plants nationally. Since formation of the subcommittee in 1979, 84 vascular plants have had status designated and a total of about 110 status reports have been commissioned for which full reports were prepared. At the 1995 COSEWIC annual meeting, held 4-6 of April, there will be seven vascular plant reports presented for status designation, as well as one for a lichen from British Columbia. The seven vascular plants to be considered for designation are: Bolander's quillwort (*Isoetes bolanderi*), Nebraska sedge (*Carex nebrascensis*), Maclean's goldenweed (*Haplopappus macleanii*), hare-footed locoweed (*Oxytropis lagopus*), golden paintbrush (*Castilleja levisecta*), yellow montane violet (*Viola praemorsa*), and white wood aster (*Aster divaricatus*).

Through the efforts of status report authors in Alberta and Saskatchewan, there are a number of reports for these provinces in preparation or under review by the Plants Subcommittee. Reports in preparation include: Mackenzie hairgrass (*Deschampsia mackenzieana*), Indian tansy (*Tanacetum huronense* var. *floccosum*), and pinweed (*Lechea intermedia* var. *depauperata*). Reports on blue phlox (*Phlox alyssifolia*), dwarf fleabane (*Erigeron radicatus*), and rush pink (*Stephanomeria runcinata*) have been completed and are being revised. *Brickellia grandiflora*, a Waterton Lakes National Park plant, also has been completed recently and is under review.

Traditionally, the Plants Subcommittee has dealt only with vascular plants. This has changed during the past year and a half. Recent nation-wide emphasis on species risk assessment has stressed the need to include groups other than just vertebrates and vascular plants in this process. Consequently, the Plants Subcommittee has expanded its activities to include bryophytes and lichens. Some work is also underway to identify potential candidates of nationally significant algae.

Two new specialist groups within the Subcommittee have been established to include bryophyte and lichen specialists (four of each). These new groups are in addition to the larger group of vascular plant specialists consisting of nine members. As much as possible, members are chosen from across the country so as to reflect a broad coverage in expertise and the relative importance of different regions with regard to the number of species-at-risk in each region. New members are also included to reflect provincial interests, such as when new Conservation Data Centres (CDCs) and Natural Heritage Information Centres (NHICs) are formed.

Candidate lists are being developed by the recently formed lichen and bryophyte specialist groups. Selection of candidate taxa will be based on 1-5 occurrences, and perhaps 6-20 occurrences. Taxa with such low numbers of occurrences nationally are potentially at greatest risk due to their low frequency. These criteria are also used by the CDCs and NHICs provincially. The vascular plant list will also be updated this coming year. As better data become available on species-at-risk from CDCs and other workers in the provinces, the COSEWIC lists will be updated accordingly.

In vascular plants, the Subcommittee has been working closely with provincial CDCs and NHICs in British Columbia, Ontario, and Quebec to promote the development of status reports for nationally significant species that are also of concern provincially. This has been possible through funding provided by the Canadian Wildlife Federation which matches basic funds provided by agencies such as the Canadian Wildlife Service, Parks Canada, and Fisheries and Oceans Canada.

The Canadian Wildlife Service (CWS), which provides the Secretariat and the basic infrastructure support for COSEWIC, is presently looking into ways of more closely linking federal and provincial government departments and institutions, universities, and environmental non-governmental organisations. This is being done to promote a more integrated approach to gathering information on all groups of taxa so as to expedite the process of species and habitat risk assessment.

This past year, I have been assessing National Wildlife Areas and Migratory Bird Sanctuaries with regard to species-at-risk and for the presence of major invasive species that could potentially modify these federal lands. This work is being done on a contractual basis through the National Atlas Information Service (NAIS) of Natural Resources Canada under a letter of agreement with CWS. A report has been completed for CWS review. I will also be evaluating a fairly comprehensive database on arctic benthic marine algae to determine potential species-at-risk as candidates for COSEWIC status report preparation and to assess the value of these benthic algae in determining areas of high biological diversity in arctic waters. Such areas would be potentially significant marine habitats that might be candidates for conservation efforts. These projects are all related to or dependent on the process of risk assessment for species and habitats resulting from COSEWIC activities.

The emphasis on risk assessment has broadened to include a wider range of organisms and, therefore, a wider range of specialists involved in the process. This will provide a better information base for national risk assessment for both species and habitats.

In closing, I would like to acknowledge the various agencies that are actively involved in the work of COSEWIC. In addition to the Secretariat, which is operated through CWS, COSEWIC includes members from Parks Canada, Fisheries and Oceans Canada, every provincial and territorial wildlife department, and national conservation organizations—Canadian Nature Federation, Canadian Wildlife Federation, and World Wildlife Fund Canada. I would also like to thank the Canadian Museum of Nature, a COSEWIC member institution, for its continued support of the Plants Subcommittee.

# SASKATCHEWAN CONSERVATION DATA CENTRE - 1995 UPDATE

## Sheila M. Lamont

*Saskatchewan Conservation Data Centre, 326-3211 Albert Street, Regina, Saskatchewan S4S 5W6*

## GENERAL OVERVIEW

For those not familiar with the Saskatchewan Conservation Data Centre, it was set up in March of 1992 as the result of an agreement between the Government of Saskatchewan, The Nature Conservancy (TNC, U.S.A), and the Nature Conservancy of Canada, signed in October 1991. The Data Centre is a node in a network of centres which The Nature Conservancy coordinates. This network of centres extends throughout the United States, much of Canada and Central America. Most of the US offices are referred to as Heritage Programs, but their nature and purpose are the same as those of the Canadian Data Centres which are currently located in Quebec, B.C., Saskatchewan, Ontario and Manitoba (listed in order of the date of their establishment). These centres store information on sensitive elements of biodiversity: those plants, animals, and plant communities that through the nature of their occurrences are imperilled or are vulnerable to disturbance. Most centres use the Biological Conservation Data System (BCD), a computer database developed by The Nature Conservancy (U.S.A.), to store their data.

This report will deal with the status of the botanical and plant community aspects of the Saskatchewan Conservation Data Centre.

## THE GENERAL PROCEDURE AND THE VASCULAR FLORA

The initial task at a Data Centre is to develop what we refer to as an element tracking list, or in the case of the plant communities a community classification. For the vascular plants the botanist is supplied by the Nature Conservancy with an initial list developed by Kartesz, the senior author of the Synonymized Checklist of the Vascular Plants of North America, and a member of the committee working on the current Flora of North America project. The next task is to assign a subnational rank (SRANK), to each of the taxa that are placed on the tracking list and decide whether or not they will be "tracked." The ranking is based on the number of occurrences or locations at which the element occurs, the size

of the total population and the threat to its continued existence. Elements that are ranked S5 are abundant and secure. S4 indicates common and deemed secure. Those elements that are ranked S3, S2 and S1 are deemed to be sensitive to disturbance and their locations and status are "tracked" or recorded and monitored by the Data Centre. S1 is considered critically imperilled, S2 imperilled and S3 vulnerable to disturbance.

With the list of elements prepared, the next step is to obtain from the Nature Conservancy the codes which are assigned by TNC to each of the taxa, so that all the network refers to the same taxon by the same code, regardless of which synonym their floras may use to refer to the taxon. Once the code is obtained the information on the locations of each element, referred to as the element occurrences, can be entered into the database; the locations are mapped on 1:50,000 topographic maps, marked with the precision with which the location is known, and manual files are created to store a hard copy of all information and references to each element.

Saskatchewan's vascular plant tracking list currently has about 2,325 elements. This list is not final or complete. Some taxa whose synonymy is unresolved and the correct codes have not been determined have not been entered into the database. There are also some subspecific and varietal taxa whose status in the province is uncertain, and they have been placed on the list to remind us to determine which subspecific categories we have in our jurisdiction. Of those that are entered in the database about 460 taxa have been ranked "higher" than S4, they fall into the vulnerable to critically imperiled categories, and thus are tracked by the Data Centre. To date, in spite of the advantage of having access to the RARE database produced by Dr. Vernon Harms of the University of Saskatchewan as a basis to work from, only 66 elements, with about 500 element occurrences, have been entered into the database. About 20% of the 8,053 specimens recorded in RARE have been processed for entry into BCD. This figure is much lower than the goal we initially set, to complete the entry of available data in the first two, the "set-up" years, of operation of the Data Centre. Time was spent helping in field surveys for rare vascular plants being carried out by Saskatchewan Research Council and Saskatchewan

Parks. We have been stymied at the Data Centre by having to perform tasks related to the coordination of the centre after our Coordinator/Zoologist left us to join the Manitoba crew in July of 1994, by having to spend time working out the scenarios of continued funding for the data centre, and by trying to supply information on data requests without the benefit of having all the data already in the database.

The vascular plant tracking list has 202 taxa ranked S1, 32 ranked S1S2, 145 ranked S2, 46 are S2S3, 30 are S3 and 5 are ranked as S3S4. (See Table 1 for further information on ranking of Saskatchewan taxa.) There are also 6 other taxa reported for the province but not verified (SR), 4 whose status is unknown (SU) and 2 that have been classed as historical (SH). Some of the plants that are now classed as S3 or S3S4 will no doubt be placed in the category of not tracked when they have been thoroughly researched. The removal of some of these from the rare plant list for the province has already been recommended by Dr. Vernon Harms in the summary document which accompanied his database, but until over 100 occurrences have been verified for the province, the policy of the data centres has been to retain them on the tracking list. The subnational rank cannot be lower (less endangered) than the rank assigned globally.

Another category on the tracking list is W (for the tracked/not tracked criterion), which means that the taxon is on the "watch list." Although these are ranked S3S4 or S4 and their populations do not warrant keeping track of all occurrences, they are taxa that are sensitive to human activities, and their populations could be drastically altered in a short space of time, requiring that they become tracked taxa. We have placed one plant, the Pitcher Plant (*Sarracenia purpurea*), on the watch list.

There are 2,172 taxa on the list still not ranked (listed as S?). They are believed to be secure in the province, but there is still the possibility that some of these belong on the tracking list, so eventually a rank will be assigned to them all.

## GLOBAL RANKING

A list of 25 taxa has been assigned to SKCDC for determination of the global rank. These include Saskatchewan's endemics from the Athabasca Sand Dunes, and those species/subspecies/varieties for which the major part of the range falls within the province.

After consultation with the other provinces/states which have that entity within their jurisdiction we will judge the status and suggest the assigned rank. TNC and the other programs will review the suggestion and then the global rank is accepted or modified as necessary. Initial effort in recording element occurrences for the province was placed on those taxa with a global rank of imperiled or vulnerable (G1 - G3).

## PROBLEMS TO BE EXPECTED

In working with specimen data there are inherent difficulties. Often data recorded with the specimen is limited, making exact location impossible to pinpoint. On the other hand, sometimes the collector will record the location using more than one method, and sometimes the two or more methods do not result in the same location on the map. So there is a certain amount of judgement call to be made. If the collector can still be contacted, map locations may be verified. If not, and map location is not precise it is recorded on the map within a symbol that indicates the accuracy of the mapping.

## COSEWIC

The figures here, when compared with the number of vascular plants listed by COSEWIC which occur in Saskatchewan are vastly different. (These figures may be out of date since recent additions have not been checked for Saskatchewan range.) One limitation to the COSEWIC program is that people are required to write status reports before a species is considered for listing. That has not been happening at a very fast rate. The comparison here is not truly valid, because the COSEWIC list is mainly for nationally rare taxa, not for each province. The populations in the other provinces may be secure and this province may be on the edge of the range. However, this does not negate the comparison, but it emphasizes the need for each province to expend some effort to inventory what it has and what it needs to protect.

## NON-VASCULAR FLORA

A list of mosses expected within the province has been prepared. Because the expertise in this area is limited in our province, Dale Vitt with the University of Alberta

Table 1. Status of Saskatchewan Species[a]. (Saskatchewan Conservation Data Centre, June, 1995)

| NO. RANKED SPECIES[b] | SX | S1 | S1S2 | S2 | S2S3 | S3 | S3S4 | S4 | S4S5 | S5 | S? | Misc. | TOTAL |
|---|---|---|---|---|---|---|---|---|---|---|---|---|---|
| Mammals | 2 | 1 | 0 | 3 | 1 | 9 | 6 | 8 | 1 | 44 | 0 | 2 | 76 |
| Birds | 4 | 18 | 0 | 4 | 0 | 15 | 0 | 58 | 0 | 161 | 0 | 43 | 302 |
| Reptiles | 0 | 1 | 0 | 6 | 1 | 6 | 0 | 3 | 0 | 2 | 0 | 0 | 12 |
| Amphibians | 0 | 0 | 0 | 0 | 0 | 1 | 0 | 4 | 0 | 2 | 0 | 0 | 7 |
| Fishes | 0 | 0 | 1 | 1 | 3 | 3 | 17 | 0 | 2 | 28 | 2 | 8 | 66 |
| **VERTEBRATES** | 6 | 20 | 1 | 14 | 5 | 34 | 23 | 73 | 3 | 237 | 2 | 53 | 471 |
| Crayfish | 0 | 0 | 0 | 0 | 0 | 1 | 0 | 0 | 0 | 0 | 0 | 0 | 1 |
| Beetles | 0 | 0 | 0 | 0 | 0 | 0 | 0 | 0 | 0 | 0 | 0 | 0 | 20 |
| Butterflies/Skippers | 0 | 0 | 0 | 0 | 0 | 0 | 1 | 0 | 0 | 0 | 95 | 0 | 174 |
| Dragonflies | 0 | 0 | 0 | 0 | 0 | 0 | 0 | 0 | 0 | 0 | 186 | 0 | 186 |
| Unionid Mussels | 0 | 0 | 0 | 0 | 0 | 0 | 0 | 0 | 0 | 0 | 9 | 0 | 9 |
| **INVERTEBRATES** | 0 | 0 | 0 | 0 | 0 | 1 | 1 | 0 | 0 | 0 | 290 | 0 | 390 |
| Ferns & Fern Allies | 0 | 21 | 1 | 7 | 2 | 3 | 0 | 1 | 0 | 0 | 44 | 2 | 92 |
| Gymnosperms | 0 | 1 | 0 | 0 | 0 | 0 | 0 | 0 | 0 | 1 | 9 | 0 | 11 |
| Dicots | 0 | 107 | 15 | 80 | 34 | 20 | 3 | 4 | 0 | 3 | 1,308 | 16 | 1,590 |
| Monocots | 0 | 73 | 16 | 58 | 10 | 7 | 2 | 1 | 0 | 0 | 466 | 6 | 639 |
| **VASCULAR PLANTS** | 0 | 202 | 32 | 145 | 46 | 30 | 5 | 6 | 0 | 4 | 1,838 | 24 | 2,332 |
| Bryophytes | 0 | 0 | 0 | 0 | 0 | 0 | 0 | 0 | 0 | 0 | 240 | 0 | 240 |
| Lichens | 0 | 0 | 0 | 0 | 0 | 0 | 0 | 0 | 0 | 0 | 0 | 0 | 0 |
| Other Non-Vascular Plants | 0 | 0 | 0 | 0 | 0 | 0 | 0 | 0 | 0 | 0 | 0 | 0 | 0 |
| **NON-VASCULAR PLANTS** | 0 | 0 | 0 | 0 | 0 | 0 | 0 | 0 | 0 | 0 | 240 | 0 | 240 |
| **TOTAL SPECIES LIST** | 6 | 222 | 33 | 159 | 51 | 65 | 29 | 79 | 3 | 241 | 2,470 | 61 | 3,417 |

[a] Exotics, accidentals, hybrids and other non-standard entities are not included in these counts. Where totals do not match, species have been added to the list, but not yet ranked.
[b] Rank Key:
SX - Provincially extirpated
S1 - Provincially critically imperiled
S2 - Provincially imperiled
S3 - Provincially endangered
S4 - Provincially secure (long-term cause of concern)
S5 - Provincially secure (no cause for concern)
S? - Unranked

has agreed to help us to assign provincial (subnational) ranks to this list. A list of the lichens found within the province is currently being prepared from the literature. The Data Centre has not even begun to deal with the fungi, algae and the microflora.

## PRODUCTS

The vascular plant tracking list is available to those who are interested. Recent emphasis has been placed on attempts to make the list more useful to those who obtain it. More common names have been entered. The ecoregions within which they occur have been recorded for the tracked species, in order that regional lists can be drawn up for users interested only in a certain area of the province.

Numerous data requests have been replied to by the Data Centre. Most of these are from consultants considering the environmental impacts of proposed developments, however some of them have been from people seeking information or educational material.

An attempt is being made to fit rare taxa into the forest site types identified in the new forest site classification that has been developed for the province.

## COMMUNITY CLASSIFICATION

The Data Centre also tracks the plant communities of Saskatchewan with the focus on occurrences of rare community types and significant stands of all community types. The dynamic nature of community classification is illustrated in Figure 1. The community focus acts as the coarse-filter in the selection of areas for preservation. Someone at TNC estimated that by protecting good examples of all community types we would protect 85-90% of all species, but in order to do this communities must be listed and ranked and occurrences mapped. The communities must first be identified in a community classification built on existing information (reports, publications and data from previous vegetation studies) and input from other provincial experts. This is compared and standardized with classifications being developed in neighbouring provinces and states.

The Saskatchewan classification follows TNC vegetation structure, which is a modified version of the UNESCO (United Nations Educational, Scientific and Cultural Organization) National Vegetation classification. The **Classification structure** forms a hierarchy (class, subclass, group, formation, alliance (=cover type), community element (=association).

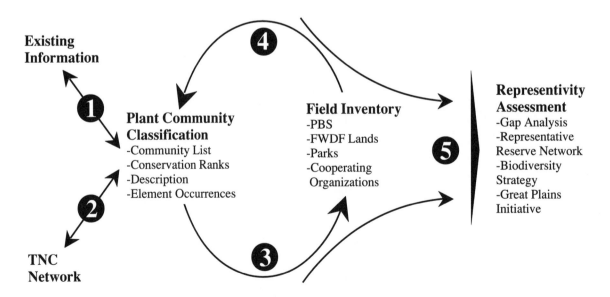

Figure 1. CDC community classification. Information cycling and feedback loops build the classification.

238

## CURRENT STATUS

The Data Centre's ecologist, Joyce Belcher, has completed the draft classification to the community level for terrestrial grasslands, and is working on drafts to the alliance level for the rest of Saskatchewan's vegetation (shrublands, forest, wetlands, etc).

Joyce is working closely with TNC to include Saskatchewan in standardized regional, (and ultimately continental) vegetation classifications. She participated in a meeting of TNC ecologists from the Great Plains provinces and States to develop one classification for the Great Plains of North America. This is in connection with the Great Plains Initiative which in addition to classifying and mapping vegetation has been involved in the identification of landscapes of significance, areas deemed worthy of protection.

Some new projects, focusing on prairie communities, will provide information that will improve the classification. These will include processing of pre-computer vegetation survey data and quantitative vegetation data that does exist.

The Prairie Biodiversity Survey focuses on landscape and community levels of biodiversity and will involve vegetation sampling in representative landscapes.

This data will improve the classification of prairie communities. A methodology/protocol for conducting community biodiversity surveys throughout the Saskatchewan prairies and beyond will be developed.

## SASKATCHEWAN'S RARE FLORA - EXAMPLES

A few examples of rare flora in Saskatchewan follow. The ram's-head lady's-slipper (*Cypripedium arietinum*) is globally ranked G3, vulnerable. In Saskatchewan it was initially ranked as S1, and still appears as S1 on our list. The number of known occurrences is now adequate to support the change of this to an S2. In addition to more sites being located, it was determined that a number of the occurrences are found within recreation sites or parks in the province. While this does not provide any legal protection to the plants, it was felt that it did provide some sites that were not as likely to be destroyed. (Subsequent to the conference, I reviewed a copy of revised EO specifications, which are criteria agreed upon to define an element occurrence, and how to rank those element occurrences, for *Cypripedium arietinum*. It would appear that some of the locations which I had recorded as separate occurrences, should be lumped into one occurrence because there does not appear to be any habitat discontinuity between them, even though there is considerable distance between colonies. In this case a decision on the number of occurrences to recognize will affect the provincial rank.)

Swamp lousewort (*Pedicularis macrodonta*) is globally ranked G4. Using specimen data it was ranked S2, but numerous additional occurrences have been reported and the rank will likely become at least S3 when processing is completed.

The remaining examples are all globally ranked G5.

Climbing bittersweet (*Celastrus scandens*) is known from only four locations in the extreme south (and east) of the province and is therefore ranked S1. This appears to be the northwestern corner of the range.

Downingia (*Downingia laeta*) is an ephemeral type of plant. It occupies drying margins of sloughs in heavy clay soils. Classed as imperiled (S1S2), it has only a few known sites in the southwestern corner of the province.

Douglas' hawthorn (*Crataegus douglasii*), identified by its dark fruits and the length of its thorns, is known in the province only from the Cypress Hills area. It is disjunct here from a Rocky Mountain range, and because of the limited extent of its occurrence in Saskatchewan is listed here as imperiled (S2).

Racemose milk vetch (*Astragalus racemosus*) is listed as imperiled (S2). It is found at a few locations in the south-central part of the province.

White rattlesnake-root (*Prenanthes alba*) is ranked S2. Its occurrence in the province appears to be limited to the southeastern edge.

Marsh felwort (*Lomatogonium rotatum*) is ranked S2. It is found on shores scattered throughout the southern half of the province.

Marsh bellflower (*Campanula aparinoides*) falls in S2S3 rank. I know a numerous other localities not supported by specimens, which will likely lower the rank of this species.

White twisted-stalk (*Streptopus amplexifolius* var. *americanus*) has a scattering of localities across the parkland, forest fringe. It is ranked S2S3.

Northern bush-honeysuckle (*Diervilla lonicera*) reaches the western edge of its range in east-central Saskatchewan. It is most common in the Pasquia Hills area and reaches as far west as Nipawin and Otter Rapids.

These are just some examples of the vascular plants we are tracking. I am limited here in presenting those for which we had illustrations available. Some of the rare plants that occur throughout, but are very scattered and few, as well as those endemic species that occur in the Lake Athabasca area go unrepresented due to the fact that I do not have slides of them.

# MANITOBA CONSERVATION DATA CENTRE:
# A TOOL FOR PLANT CONSERVATION

## Elizabeth Punter,

*Manitoba Conservation Data Centre, 1007 Century Street, Winnipeg,*
*Manitoba R3H 0W4*

The Manitoba Conservation Data Centre began operations in July 1994. The Centre is a joint inititiative of 4 partners: Manitoba Department of Natural Resources; Manitoba Museum of Man and Nature; Nature Conservancy of Canada; The Nature Conservancy (US). In addition, financial support has been provided by a number of companies, corporations and non-profit agencies.

The Manitoba Conservation Data Centre is located in Winnipeg and housed in the Land Information Centre of the Manitoba Department of Natural Resources but is not part of that department. The staff consist of the Manager, Carol Scott; Information Manager, Ken Donkersloot; Zoologist, Jim Duncan, Ecologist, Jason Greenall; Botanist, Liz Punter.

Setting conservation priorities is extremely complex on account of the hundreds of distinct ecosystems and thousands of taxa involved. To deal with this complexity, The Nature Conservancy created The Natural Heritage Network of data centres starting in 1974. These data centres manage computer-based data for species and plant communities.

The Manitoba Conservation Data Centre is one of a network of 86 data centres throughout North and South America and the Caribbean. In most US states, the data centres are called Natural Heritage Programs while in Canada and Latin America, they are known as Conservation Data Centres. Each data centre is associated with, or part of, a government agency responsible for natural resource management and protection.

The data centres use a methodology developed by The Nature Conservancy for the collection, management, and use of biological, ecological and related information. The computer system, Biological and Conservation Data system (BCD), developed by The Nature Conservancy, is used for data storage and retrieval, along with manual files, maps, and a library of reference material.

Data and information are obtained from scientific literature, reports, collections, knowledgeable individuals and field studies. Data are assembled on plant communities, plant and animal species and their biology, habitats, locations, conservation status, and management needs, and managed areas (parks, ecological reserves, wildlife management areas).

The Nature Conservancy has developed a method for establishing relative rarity and endangerment of elements (taxa and plant communities) throughout their entire range. Each element is given a Global Element Rank which is derived by consensus of scientists, The Nature Conservancy central staff, and data centre network staff. Important factors used in assigning Global Ranks are: total number of known, extant sites globally; abundance; size of range; number of known populations considered to be securely protected; and the ability of the taxon to persist at its known sites.

G1 = Critically imperiled globally because of extreme rarity (5 or fewer occurrences or very few remaining individual acres) or because of some factor(s) making it especially vulnerable to extinction.

G2 = Imperiled globally because of rarity (6 to 20 occurrences or few remaining individuals or acres) or because of some factor(s) making it very vulnerable to extinction throughout its range.

G3 = Either very rare and local throughout its range or found locally (even abundantly at some of its locations) in a restricted range or because of other factors making it vulnerable to extinction throughout its range in terms of occurrences, in the range of 21 to 100.

G4 = Apparently secure globally, though it may be quite rare in part of its range, especially at the periphery.

G5 = Demonstrably secure globally, though it may be quite rare in parts of its range, especially at the periphery.

Likewise, these same criteria can be used to rank elements at the national level (N ranks). Argus and Pryer (1990) used this ranking system as part of their methodology for the production of the list of rare vascular plants for Canada.

The data centres assign provincial or state ranks (S ranks) but consider only those factors within their political boundaries.

S1 = Critically imperiled in province because of extreme rarity (5 or fewer occurrences or very few remaining individuals or acres) or because of some factor(s) making it especially vulnerable to extirpation from the province.

S2 = Imperiled in province because of rarity (6 to 20 occurrences or few remaining individuals or acres) or because of some factor(s) making it very vulnerable to extirpation from the province.

S3 = Rare or uncommon in province (on the order of 21 to 100 occurrences).

S4 = Apparently secure in the province, with many occurrences.

S5 = Demonstrably secure in province and essentially ineradicable under present conditions.

Additional ranks - SX (extirpated), SH (historic), SR (reported), SRF (reported falsely), SE (exotic), SU (possibly in peril in province but status uncertain; need more information), S? (insufficient information to rank) can be assigned to taxa.

These provincial/state ranks are used by the data centres to set protection priorities for rare taxa and plant communities. Combination of the Global rank with the provincial rank can further refine protection priorities.

The plant communities represent the coarse filter for natural diversity. Identification and preservation of the best examples of all terrestrial and aquatic community types may preserve perhaps 85 to 90% of the biological diversity in the province (Anonymous 1988).

The remaining 10 to 15% of the plant taxa may fall through this coarse filter because they do not occur in a given plant community with enough regularity to ensure their protection. The fine filter for capturing this portion of the plant taxa is an inventory list of those species which are endangered, threatened, rare, peripheral, endemic, or otherwise of special concern within the province. The data centres track the individual occurrences of these inventoried taxa. During their early stages, the data centres concentrate their efforts on elements with the ranks S1 to S3, elements of high conservation priorities. The geographic locations of the occurrences of elements are plotted on 1:50,000 topographic maps and the geographic coordinates are stored in the data base, BCD .

This information can be used in the selection and design of conservation areas. Since the elements are ranked S1 to S3, and their geographic occurrence is known, the inventory system can indicate those places in the landscape that are supporting very rare to uncommon elements. These occurrences can be further evaluated in order to select those that constitute the best examples. The successful perpetuation of a rare species depends on our ability to document its distribution. No matter how much is known about a its niche, range, or habitat, a species cannot be preserved or managed unless the actual locations of its occurrences are known in the landscape (Jenkins 1981).

The mapping activities should also indicate those areas of the landscape where we have little or no information on biodiversity. These areas can then be a target for future inventory work.

To date the Manitoba Data Centre has compiled species lists of nonvascular and vascular plants, and a plant community classification for the province. Ranking of elements is underway; and documentation and mapping of occurrences; based on review of literature sources and collections are ongoing. It is expected to take about two years to populate the BCD system with this information. A Geographic Information System will also be used to store, manage and analyze spatial data.

The data collection and analyses will be an invaluable tool to Manitoba in setting conservation priorities, development planning, research, land and natural resource management, environmental impact review and other applications.

## LITERATURE CITED

Anonymous. 1988. The Natural Heritage Program operations manual. The Nature Conservancy, Arlington, Virginia.

Argus, G.W. and K.M. Pryer. 1990. Rare vascular plants in Canada: Our natural heritage. Canadian Museum of Nature, Ottawa.

Jenkins, R.E. 1981. Rare plant conservation through elements-of-diversity information. *In* Rare plant conservation: Geographical data organization (Morse, L.E. and M.S. Henifin, eds.). The New York Botanical Garden, Bronx, New York.

# THE STATUS OF RARE PLANT CONSERVATION IN ALBERTA

## Joyce Gould

*Alberta Environmental Protection, Natural Resources Service, Parks Management Support Division*
*8th Floor, 10405 Jasper Avenue, Edmonton, Alberta T5J 3N4.*

The aim of this presentation is to provide a summary of rare plant conservation activities in Alberta. This will be done, first by providing an overview of the main landscape units of the province followed by a discussion of the state of our knowledge of the flora of these units. I will then describe some of the current initiatives dealing with rare plant conservation in Alberta.

Alberta is a province of diversity. It encompasses six natural regions - Grassland, Parkland, Foothills, Boreal Forest, Mountains and Canadian Shield. These natural regions are further subdivided into 20 subregions, which reflect a diversity of climate, elevation, soils, vegetation, geology and landform.

We are fortunate to have a comprehensive, systematic account of the provincial vascular plants. This *Flora of Alberta* was first published by Ezra Moss in 1959 and subsequently updated, with the inclusion of distribution maps, by John Packer in 1983. In addition, there are several popular works dealing with vascular plants, mostly the commoner species, and particularly those species of the mountain and prairie regions. A new field guide for the boreal forest is due in May 1995.

We know a great deal about the vascular flora of certain areas of the province. The prairie and mountain regions are well explored; however, even here we are still finding species that are new to Alberta. For example, western spiderwort (*Tradescantia occidentalis*) was discovered in southern Alberta in 1986. Our knowledge is poor for the flora of areas such as wetlands, high alpine areas and the boreal forest largely because much of these regions is so inaccessible.

Compared to the vascular plants, the non-vascular component of the flora is less well-known. There are no comprehensive, systematic accounts for Alberta although a couple of popular guides exist that cover some of our species. Dr. Vitt, his students and colleagues at the University of Alberta are currently working on a summary of the rare mosses of the province. This work will be an important step toward consolidating our understanding of the ecology and distribution of these species. It will be another essential step in the march toward conservation of biodiversity in Alberta.

The scale of that biodiversity is significant. To date, 1,778 species of vascular plants, 601 species of mosses and 645 species of lichens have been identified to occur in the province.

The distribution patterns of some of our rare vascular species reflect the elements of a number of different floras. For example, we have representatives of the **Great Plains** flora such as soapweed (*Yucca glauca*). This species range just barely extends into Alberta; it is restricted to the dry mixed grassland of the extreme southern portion of the province. The soapweed is rare both in Alberta and in Canada. We also have species that are associated with the **northern boreal forest** such as slender-leaved sundew (*Drosera linearis*), another species that is rare. Many of our mountain species have an **arctic-alpine** distribution, such as woolly lousewort (*Pedicularis lanata*), but some are endemic, e.g., Kananaskis whitlow-grass (*Draba kananaskis*). The southwestern portion of the province has its own unique flora—it has affinities with the flora of the **Pacific Northwest** and in fact many of our rare vasculars, e.g., hispid paintbrush (*Castilleja hispida*), are restricted to this corner of the province.

Conservation of populations of species that are at the limits of their range is important for the conservation of genetic diversity. Many of these populations have a different genetic makeup than populations at the centre of their ranges and it is thought that many of these populations on the fringes of their distributions are better adapted to change. This adaptability could be especially important in light of global problems such as climate change. Some of our rare species have a more generalized distribution, but are rare wherever they are found, e.g., bog adder's-mouth (*Malaxis paludosa*).

Two publications deal specifically with the rare vascular plants of the province. The first, by David White and George Argus, was published by the National Museum in 1978. It listed approximately 350 species (20% of the known vascular flora) as rare. A species was defined as rare if it had a small population within the province. This publication was followed in 1984 by *Rare Vascular Plants of Alberta* by John Packer and Cheryl Bradley. They defined plants that had been collected in fewer than five localities as rare. Their list included 360 species (20% of the known vascular flora). They also suggested that some species were on the list only because collections were lacking from the northern and high mountainous areas. Since 1984 we have learned a great deal more about our boreal and mountainous regions—several species that are new to the province have been found and we have extended our knowledge about the distribution of several other rare species. In addition to the provincial publications, the National Museum has published *Rare Vascular Plants in Canada*. Here 125 species are listed as nationally rare. This total represents 7% of our vascular flora.

Substantial ongoing work is attempting to summarize and update our knowledge of rare vasculars in the province. In particular, our division, Alberta Parks Management Support, has developed a rare vascular plant database. This database houses all of the label information from seven herbaria in the province for all of the rare plants listed by Packer and Bradley. We also now have label information from the two national herbaria (National Museum and Agriculture-Food Canada). However, this database contains only the information listed on the original label—in some cases, there is a good deal of locational and habitat information; in other cases, the information is sparse, e.g., "Waterton Lakes National Park, summer". We have also developed a rare plant sighting summary sheet, which has been distributed to various botanists/naturalists in the province. Information that is submitted is then included in our database.

We recently initiated a joint effort with Parks Canada, specifically Waterton Lakes National Park and Alberta Region, on a pilot project entitled the Natural Heritage Information Centre. The centre is modelled after the conservation data centres of other provinces and the United States. We developed a series of linked databases to house information on location, status of species on provincial and national scales, sources of information, and habitat requirements, among other things. We also list information on managed areas and are able to show how many or even whether populations are contained within the boundaries of protected areas or other managed areas. The data centre information also shows where the population occurs within the managed areas and when it was last seen. This type of information is invaluable for management planning and decision making.

We also include information on the population-size, distribution, threats, etc. at that location. The information is currently mapped on 1:50,000 National Topographic Series map sheets although we are aiming to make the transition to a geographic information system (GIS) within the next few months.

We are now focusing on the Mountain and Foothill natural regions and the disjunct portion of Boreal Forest around Elk Island National Park. We are collecting and processing information on selected vascular plants, including the information in our rare vascular plant database, and on mosses, plant communities, invertebrates and vertebrates.

Alberta Parks staff, volunteers and consultants are also monitoring populations of some of our rare plants. Species currently being monitored include western blue flag (*Iris missouriensis*), upland evening-primrose (*Oenothera andina*), smooth boisduvalia (*Boisduvalia glabella*), yellow paintbrush (*Castilleja cusickii*), California oat grass (*Danthonia californica*), and one-spike oat grass (*Danthonia unispicata*).

We work closely with volunteer organizations such as the Alberta Native Plant Council (ANPC). The ANPC, along with the Federation of Alberta Naturalists, has produced a list of rare vascular species, which is currently under review. The ANPC is also aiming to produce a field guide to the rare vasculars of the province—our database has been made available for their use.

Reports have been prepared by individuals on several species of vascular plants for COSEWIC (Committee on the Status of Endangered Wildlife in Canada). The information housed in these reports is being incorporated into our information system.

Currently, no provincial or federal government agency has a mandate for the protection of plants. Plants are not included in the provincial *Wildlife Act* or any of its regulations and Alberta does not have endangered species legislation. Protection of plants is therefore accomplished through other means such as the protection of sites through designation as ecological reserves, natural areas, etc. One of our provincial natural areas, Big Sagebrush, was nominated specifically because of the large number of rare plants and the unique plant associations within its boudaries. The ANPC is the volunteer steward for this site.

Much can be done for the conservation of plants even without a legislated designation for either species or sites. However, our management decisions are only as good as the information which is used to make them. Right now, we have a lot to learn about rare plants in Alberta, particularly for the nonvascular species. We hope that through the continuation of our pilot project in conjunction with the workdone by ANPC and others, we will further our knowledge and build a solid information base that will assist land managers and others in making conservation decisions.

# AMPHIBIAN AND REPTILE CONSERVATION: ACTIONS AND PRIORITIES - RESULTS OF A WORKSHOP SESSION

## Steven Brechtel[1] and Andrew Didiuk[2]

[1]*Wildlife Management Division, Alberta Dept. of Environmental Protection, Edmonton, Alberta;*
[2] *Canadian Wildlife Service, Saskatoon, Saskatchewan.*

## INTRODUCTION

The amphibian and reptile session at the fourth Prairie Conservation and Endangered Species Workshop was divided into two sections. It began with three presentations summarising the current status of management and research programs in each of the prairie provinces. The final portion of the program was dedicated to an open workshop discussion of the actions which were needed to enhance the conservation of amphibians and reptiles in prairie Canada. Attendance at this session was very positive, with roughly 75 participants including landowners, researchers, industry representatives and government staff from across the prairies. A summary of the workshop discussion and the priorities for herp conservation programs is provided below.

## RESULTS

During the workshop, participants were provided with four general headings and asked to identify priority actions within each area of endeavour. Proposed actions were summarised on flip-charts and at the end of the session, participants were asked to review the actions, and indicate their highest priorities. The headings provided and the actions proposed, listed in general order of priority, are:

## Population, Demographics, Systematics

- Priority should be given to monitoring selected "index" or "sentinel" species/populations (eg. northern leopard frog) to determine if and why populations are declining.

- Action should be focused on defining the long term trends in populations (local, regional, and national).

- Detailed studies of demographics will help to determine the impact of mortality on populations.

## Habitat - Needs, Use, and Limiting Factors

- Priority should be given to enhancing the environmental impact assessment process. Incorporating more information about amphibians and reptiles will allow better informed assessments.

- The need to protect key habitats for amphibians and reptiles was identified.

- A variety of site-specific habitat (people) management ideas were proposed: snake crossings, culverts, speed bumps to slow traffic.

## Distribution and Range

- Priority should be given to creating and strengthening atlas-type programs to define the distribution and identify changes and trends in the range. Atlas programs enhance public awareness, encourage public involvement, facilitate monitoring, and provide an "early warning" system to identify problem areas.

- Methods should be established to allow researchers, managers, naturalists and others to "network" and share data and information.

## Communications, Education, Information

- Priority should be given to enacting and enforcing legislation that extends formal protection to amphibians and reptiles. Governments should "lead by example. Limits should be placed on the collection and possession.

- Priority should also be given to initiating and strengthening programs which involve active participation by the public:

  - monitoring programs (Atlases and less formal projects);

- Adopt-a-Pond programs involving groups with a specific site;

- school activities and educational resources; and

- youth group activities.

• Education programs dealing with amphibians and reptiles should be provided for land managers, industry and biologists. Programs should include both resource materials and workshops and should focus on both providing information and increasing awareness.

• Information/communications programs should focus on the positive role herps play in the ecosystem. This type of positive attention or "promotion" can help change traditional attitudes and may help attract resources for conservation initiatives.

• Information/communications programs are important in that they increase public awareness. This, in turn, may lead to an increasing public demand for appropriate management and protection by both governments and land managers.

## SUMMARY

Workshops, by their very nature, result in a broad sampling of the diverse opinions of the participants. There was, however, a surprising consensus of opinion which emerged during this session.

The majority of the actions proposed and much of the discussion that occurred focused on various ways to increase the understanding of the biology, status and needs of amphibians and reptiles. A wide variety of target audiences were identified including land managers, government regulators, landowners, industry, biologists, teachers and school children. Words and phrases such as "more information", "promotion", "positive attention" and "awareness" were used often during the discussion.

While it is risky to try to summarize the input from such a diverse audience, many of the participants suggested that:

• The highest priority action was to provide more and better information on the status, needs and ecological importance of amphibians and reptiles.

• This information would lead to increased understanding awareness and concern, and

• this awareness and concern would encourage landowners, managers, legislators and the public to more actively promote the conservation of amphibians and reptiles.

A second related theme which emerged was that the best method to increase information, understanding and concern was through programs which include **active** public participation. Formal atlas programs, roadside counts and extensive volunteer monitoring projects were all proposed. It was also suggested that improved awareness of herp conservation needs would lead to increased public demand for appropriate legislation and regulations to protect amphibians and reptiles and their habitats.

The amphibian and reptile workshop was well attended and provided some very clear direction on the priorities for herp conservation on the prairies. The challenge now will be to act on these priorities.

# AMPHIBIAN AND REPTILE CONSERVATION ACTIONS FOR SASKATCHEWAN

## Andrew B. Didiuk

*Saskatchewan Amphibian Monitoring Project and Saskatchewan Herpetology Atlas Project,
314 Egbert Avenue, Saskatoon, Saskatchewan S7N 1X1*

## INTRODUCTION

Nineteen species of amphibians and reptiles have been recorded in Saskatchewan (Secoy and Vincent 1976) compared to 18 species recorded in Alberta (Russell and Bauer 1993) and 22 in Manitoba (Preston 1982). We do not have the western montane species of Alberta [(eg. long-toed salamander (*Ambystoma macrodactylum*)] nor the eastern species of Manitoba which are at or near the northeastern edge of their North American range [eg. mudpuppy (*Necturus maculosus*)].

In Saskatchewan we do have seven species of amphibians and reptiles which are widespread and typical of the northern grasslands and southern boreal forests and which occur in all three prairie provinces [boreal chorus frog (*Pseudacris triseriata maculata*), wood frog (*Rana sylvatica*), northern leopard frog (*Rana pipiens*), Canadian toad (*Bufo hemiophrys*), tiger salamander (*Ambystoma tigrinum*), plains garter snake (*Thamnophis radix*), and red-sided garter snake (*Thamnophis sirtalis parietalis*)]. These are complemented by 12 species of more restricted southerly distribution which are at the extreme northern or northeastern edges of their North American ranges [great plains toad (*Bufo cognatus*), plains spadefoot toad (*Scaphiopus bombifrons*), wandering garter snake (*Thamnophis elegans vagrans*), eastern yellow-bellied racer (*Coluber constrictor flaviventris*), western hog-nosed snake (*Heterodon n. nasicus*), prairie rattlesnake (*Crotalus v. viridis*), bull snake (*Pituophis melanoleucus sayi*), smooth green snake (*Opheodrys vernalis*), northern red-bellied snake (*Storeria o. occipitomaculata*), western painted turtle (*Chelydra picta belli*), snapping turtle (*Chelydra serpentina*), and easter short-horned lizard (*Phrynosoma douglassi brevirostre*)]. In a province characterized by a strongly temperate climate (long cold winters, dry hot summers) we have an interesting diversity of amphibians and reptiles.

Saskatchewan is a region with extremely limited information regarding the distribution and status of amphibian and reptile populations (Secoy and Vincent 1976). The status and conservation of these species has been addressed within several national or regional perspectives (Cook 1970, 1974; Stewart 1974; Secoy 1987; Seburn 1992, Didiuk 1995). These attempts to assess the status and trends of amphibian and reptile populations have been severely limited by the lack of information regarding distribution and abundance for all species. Examination of these publications will provide an overview of the status and perceived risks to amphibians and reptiles of Saskatchewan.

The intent of this presentation is to propose activities which may, over the long-term, enhance our knowledge of amphibians and reptiles of Saskatchewan and to assist in our conservation efforts.

## CONSERVATION ACTIVITIES

### Species Distribution

#### Observer network

The encouragement and organization of a core group of naturalists who have an interest in amphibians and reptiles can provide new distribution information year after year. The cultivation of local contacts has proven successful in the detection of breeding of the plains spadefoot toad in southwestern Manitoba (W. Preston, pers. commun.) and in southern Saskatchewan (A. Didiuk, unpubl. data).

#### Solicitation of Reports

Reports of species, particularly those more readily identified by the general public, can be obtained from requests for observations in the media. Directed inquiries to rural agencies and selected rural media have proven to be more successful. Participation of provincial and federal wildlife agencies, and staff of other conservation organizations, can also provide important observations.

## Monitoring Projects

Observations of amphibians and reptiles obtained from monitoring efforts can provide new reports of occurrence at the onset of such projects, and additional reports if and when additional monitoring sites are established. The pilot project activities of the Saskatchewan Amphibian Monitoring Project in 1993 and 1994 have provided new and valuable records and it is anticipated many more will arise.

## Herpetology Atlas Project

The development of an atlas project similar to that being completed for Ontario will be an effective means of assessing the distribution of amphibians and reptiles in Saskatchewan and provide a basis for evaluating persistence of species throughout their ranges. The limited number of participants likely to be available in this province suggests this project will have to developed over many years. The Saskatchewan Herpetology Atlas Project is being initiated in 1995 with the first contributors arising from participants of the Saskatchewan Amphibian Monitoring Project.

## Regional Surveys

Regional assessments of amphibian and reptile populations, either through canvassing and documentation of reports (Hooper 1992) or through more structured surveys, can provide valuable descriptions of local herpetofauna. These could be effectively conducted by local natural history societies.

## Research Activities

Those conducting focused research projects or natural history studies of particular species should ensure their observations of occurrence of species are submitted to the Saskatchewan Herpetology Atlas Project data base.

## Environmental Impact Assessments

Environmental studies designed to assess potential impacts and recommend mitigative measures arising from proposed developments in most cases do not provide sufficient resources to adequately detect or assess amphibian and reptile populations. The level of effort for these species should be increased and the results of these surveys should be included in the Saskatchewan Herpetology Atlas Project data base.

## Biological Studies

### Amateur Naturalists

Natural history studies by individuals interested in amphibians and reptiles, or by natural history societies, should be encouraged. Funding requirements for these volunteer efforts will likely be minimal and could be provided by cooperative efforts of provincial agencies, natural history societies or other conservation organizations.

### Academic Research

There are many opportunities for original research including biogeography, population dynamics and habitat selection of the amphibians and reptiles of this province. Applied research addressing topics such as toxicology, identification of critical habitat requirements, habitat fragmentation and dispersal capability are necessary to support conservation and management actions. Conservation agencies and organizations can support these endeavours by provision of funds and staff or volunteers.

## Monitoring Programs

### Extensive Monitoring

The Saskatchewan Amphibian Monitoring Project is modeled after the Ontario and Wisconsin programs which use volunteer naturalists to monitor the relative abundance of amphibians. This project has completed two of its three years as a pilot project in Saskatchewan and it may become an annual contribution to national monitoring efforts. The success of this program will depend, like all other volunteer efforts, upon continued interest by, and encouragement of, volunteers.

### Intensive Monitoring

There are currently no intensive monitoring projects to track amphibian or reptile populations and environmental parameters on selected study area(s). This is an activity which could be initiated as academic research supported by provincial and federal government agencies and conservation organizations, and perhaps with assistance by volunteer help. An understanding of the long term changes in amphibian and reptile populations in response to environmental changes and anthropomorphic activities requires intensive monitoring.

## Conservation Issues

### Status Evaluations

Provincial and federal agencies should initiate efforts to evaluate the status of those species of amphibians and reptiles which may be at risk due to restricted range and/or low populations. An evaluation of all species should be conducted to allow an initial determination of those species which may be at risk. More resources would subsequently be required to better delineate distribution, abundance, critical habitat, risks and management opportunities. Local natural history societies could assist in these efforts through volunteer help and funding support.

### Habitat Protection

Provincial and federal government agencies should ensure those sites which are critical to maintenance of populations of amphibians and reptiles are adequately protected. Hibernacula of snakes, wetland breeding sites of great plains toads, and known ranges of eastern short-horned lizards, are of particular concern.

### Environmental Impact Assessments

Past environmental impact assessment activities have provided minimal resources for detecting, assessing and mitigating impacts upon amphibians and reptiles. Although this reflects the difficulty in studying these species due to their secretive behaviour, low density or irregular breeding, these species can be particularly vulnerable to land use changes. Restricted mobility, dependence upon wetlands for many species during a portion of the year, and aggregation of individuals during breeding and in winter for some species, result in many species being vulnerable to site disturbance. Increased resources to address reptiles and amphibians should be required by regulatory agencies during environmental assessments conducted by development proponents.

## Public Lands

Provincial and federal agencies should be encouraged to provide resources to assess populations of amphibians and reptiles on public lands, to determine those species which may be declining and at risk, and to determine habitat requirements of these species for incorporation in land management plans.

## Education Programs

### Schools and Youth Groups

Additional resource materials are required to portray the diversity and range of adaptations of amphibians and reptiles and to deliver conservation messages to our youth. The inherent fascination with these species provides an opportunity to attract and hold the interest of school children. Resource materials, in the form of text and video or film, are required to supplement Project Wild activities within the school system. Participation or field visits by school groups in monitoring efforts and local or regional herpetological investigations are desirable. Natural history societies and wildlife agency extension staff are appropriate sources of expertise and resources to develop and deliver these types of programs in cooperation with educators.

### Public Information

Active submission of reports, interviews or summaries to a variety of media outlets can serve to better inform the public regarding amphibians and reptiles. This can help deliver conservation messages to the public and to rectify popular misconceptions.

### Publications

A variety of text and graphical materials are required to provide information regarding the biology of amphibians and reptiles of Saskatchewan, conservation issues, and opportunities for study and conservation action. The current preparation of a revised and expanded version of Amphibians and Reptiles of Saskatchewan (Cook 1966) as part of the special publication series of Nature Saskatchewan will complement similar publications in adjacent provinces (Preston 1982; Russell and Bauer 1993).

## CONCLUSION

An increased interest and concern regarding "biodiversity" may encourage further interest in the amphibians and reptiles of Saskatchewan. The preceding description of conservation activities represents an ambitious program with only a few activities initiated in recent years.

Given the small number of individuals currently interested in herpetology in Saskatchewan, and its small and dispersed population, it is apparent that attainment of the above objectives will have to occur over many years. The immediate challenge is to begin now! I hope this presentation will serve to stimulate interest in, appreciation of, and coordinated study of amphibians and reptiles by students, biologists and the public.

## LITERATURE CITED

Cook, F. R. 1966. A guide to the amphibians and reptiles of Saskatchewan. Saskatchewan Museum of Natural History Paper Series No. 13, Regina, Saskatchewan.

Cook, F. R.. 1970. Rare or endangered Canadian amphibians and reptiles. Canadian Field Naturalist 84: 9-16

Cook, F. R. 1974. Review of the Canadian herpetological scene. *In* Proceedings of the Symposium on Canada's Threatened Species and Habitats. Canadian Wildlife Federation, Ottawa.

Didiuk, A. 1995. Status of amphibians of Saskatchewan. *In* Amphibians in Canada: Population status and decline. Report of Canadian Working Group, IUCN/SSC Declining Amphibians Population Task Force, Herpetological Conservation, SSAR. (In press)

Hooper, D. 1992. Turtles, snakes and salamanders of east-central Saskatchewan. Blue Jay 50: 72-75.

Preston, W. 1982. The amphibians and reptiles of Manitoba. Manitoba Museum of Man and Nature.

Russell, A. and A. Bauer. 1993. The amphibians and reptiles of Alberta. University of Calgary Press, Calgary, and University of Alberta, Edmonton, Alberta.

Seburn, C. N. 1992. The status of amphibian populations in Saskatchewan. Pp. 17-18 *In* Declines in Canadian amphibian populations: Designing a national monitoring strategy. Occasional Paper No. 76, Canadian Wildlife Service, Environment Canada.

Secoy, D. M. 1987. Status report on the reptiles and amphibians of Saskatchewan. Pp. 139-141 *In* Provincial Museum of Alberta Natural History Paper No. 9, Edmonton, Alberta.

Secoy, D. M. and T. K. Vincent. 1976. Distribution and population status of Saskatchewan's amphibians and reptiles. Report to the Saskatchewan Department of the Environment, Regina, Saskatchewan.

Stewart, D. 1974. Canadian endangered species. Gage Publishing Limited, Toronto, Ontario.

# ALBERTA'S AMPHIBIANS AND REPTILES: CURRENT RESEARCH AND CONSERVATION ISSUES

## G.L. Powell and A.P. Russell

*Department of Biological Sciences, The University of Calgary,*
*2500 University Dr. NW, Calgary, Alberta T2N 1N4*

Here we give brief accounts of current and recent research efforts, concerned with the ecology and distributions of native amphibians and reptiles, underway in Alberta, and discuss conservation efforts in this province relevant to these species. Although we concentrate upon prairie species, initiatives concerned with montane and boreal species will also be touched upon.

## THE ALBERTA HERPETOFAUNA

As would be expected in a high-latitude area with a continental climate, Alberta has a relatively small herpetofauna, consisting of ten species of amphibians (two salamanders and eight anurans) and eight species of reptile (one turtle, one lizard, and six snakes) (Russell and Bauer 1993). This fauna can be roughly divided into a prairie assemblage, a montane assemblage, and a boreal assemblage, although such species as the wood frog (*Rana sylvatica*) and the chorus frog (*Pseudacris triseriata*) are found in more than one assemblage (Russell and Bauer 1993). Alberta's herpetofauna can also be divided into widely-ranging species, such as the wood frog, the chorus frog, or the red-sided garter snake (*Thamnophis sirtalis parietalis*), and geographically-restricted species, such as the great plains toad (*Bufo cognatus*) and the short-horned lizard (*Phrynosoma douglassii brevirostre*), although this to some extent reflects the geographical extent of the biomes within which these species are found (Russell and Bauer 1993).

## SPECIES ACCOUNTS

### Leopard Frog (*Rana pipiens*)

The catastrophic decline in numbers and range experienced by this species in western Canada has been documented by Koonz (1992, 1993), Seburn (1992), Roberts (1992), and Orchard (1992). In Alberta it is placed on the Red List (having, or being considered for, classification as an Endangered Species in Alberta - Anon. 1991).

The decline in this province was marked by a severe restriction in geographical range as well as a reduction in numbers (Roberts 1992; Russell and Bauer 1993), and in an effort to determine where leopard frogs were still to be found (as well as to draw public attention to their status), Alberta Fish and Wildlife Services initiated a poster campaign requesting reports of leopard frog sightings. During the 1980's and early 1990's such independent agents as Cottonwood Consultants were also aware of the importance of leopard frog sightings and routinely included them in field surveys of appropriate habitat. Seburn (1992b, 1993) began field studies of two leopard frog populations, one south of Cypress Hills Provincial Park and one in the Empress area, concentrating upon demographic data and also attempting to determine dispersal potential. This work was continued in 1994 by Yaremko (1994).

Despite the efforts described above, the overall population status and distribution of the leopard frog in Alberta remain poorly known. Numbers appear to be highest in the lower Milk River drainage. Possibly volunteer monitoring initiatives (see below) will give us a more detailed picture of the species' situation over the province as a whole, to supplement the baseline quantitative work of Seburn (1992, 1993) and Yaremko (1994), so important for understanding the fine-grained processes affecting population sizes and potential for natural recovery of this species in Alberta.

### Long-Toed Salamander (*Ambystoma macrodactylum*)

This species is also on the Alberta Red List (Anon. 1991), and until fairly recently was poorly known in this province. At the behest of Alberta Fish and Wildlife Services, we began a demographic study of two populations of this species in the Bow Corridor, an area where many of the then-known populations of the species in Alberta are found (Russell and Bauer 1993) and which is currently under considerable development pressure. One of these populations had been previously examined by Cook (1991). Our demographic study, while still underway, has given evidence over the past four years of very large populations of this species in the Bow Corridor, although these can be strongly circumscribed in area (Powell *et al.* 1992). This effort has been expanded in the summer of 1995 by the first part of a two-part survey of the known populations of this species in Alberta; currently the populations between the Bow Corridor and the Montana border are being examined, following a preliminary literature and anecdotal data summary (Oseen *et al.* 1995), and funds are earmarked for a similar survey of the northern part of the range in 1996 (S. Brechtel, pers. comm., April 1995). Population studies on the species elsewhere in its Alberta range have just been concluded (Julie Fukumoto's demographic and management study in Waterton Lakes National Park - Fukumoto 1995) or are underway (Karen Graham, a graduate student of Dr. James Bogart at the University of Guelph, is conducting a population study in the Weldwood Forestry Management Area near Hinton, examining among other things the effect of forestry practices on the species). While the long-toed salamander is not a prairie species, and perhaps thus beyond the brief of this workshop, the recent work on it promoted by Alberta Fish and wildlife Services is a good model for how a poorly-known amphibian species, possibly at risk, should be examined.

## Western Hog-Nosed Snake (*Heterodon platyrhinos*)

Little is known of this species in Alberta; reports are uncommon (Pendlebury 1976; Russell and Bauer 1993) and the snake appears to be actually rare over much of its Alberta range, rather than simply seldom-encountered. Appropriately enough, it is on the Alberta Red List (Anon. 1991), and, like the leopard frog, has been the subject of a poster campaign on the part of Alberta Fish and Wildlife Services. Cottonwood Consultants were retained to search for hognosed snakes in the Bindloss and Milk River regions in 1989 and 1990, and despite considerable expenditure of effort captured only one snake (Cleve Werschler, pers. comm., Feb. 1995). Anecdotal reports indicating that hog-nosed snakes are relatively abundant in the Suffield Military Reserve are persistent, and now that the area is being examined by the Canadian Wildlife Service (Andrew Didiuk, pers. comm., May 1994) and by consultants retained by the Department of Defence, a better picture of hog-nosed snake numbers and ecology in Alberta may come our way.

## Eastern Short-Horned Lizard (*Phrynosoma douglassii*)

Like almost all of the species discussed here, the eastern short-horned lizard is on the Alberta Red List (Anon. 1991). It has been the subject of considerable research interest on the part of our laboratory, and as result its ecology and distribution in the province are tolerably well known (Powell 1982; Powell and Russell 1984, 1985a, 1985b, 1991a, 1991b). However, population trends have never been properly examined, so in the summer of 1991 we were funded (partly by Alberta Fish and Wildlife, and partly by the Recreation, Parks and Wildlife Foundation) to examine the statuses of populations over the known Alberta range (Powell and Russell 1992, 1993a). At the same time Wayne Smith, under contract to Alberta Fish and Wildlife, evaluated the habitat and status of the populations in the Manyberries block, which is the site of considerable oil and gas development (Smith 1993). Based upon our findings and those of Smith (1993), we initiated a three-year radiotelemetric study of home range size and overwintering strategy in the Manyberries Creek valley (Powell and Russell 1992, 1993a). This study, funded partly by Alberta Fish and Wildlife and partly by the Recreation, Parks and Wildlife Foundation, has yielded considerable data on habitat use and yearly activity schedule of the short-horned lizard in Alberta (Powell and Russell 1993c, 1994), which can be used in formulating habitat protection guidelines. In addition, the data gained on yearly activity schedule suggests that the species is in fact limited by climate, but not in the way we had previously thought (Powell and Russell 1985b, 1991a, 1991b, 1993a), which has led us to further suggestions concerning its protection (Powell and Russell 1994). This work is currently being enlarged upon by Janice James, an M.Sc. student of A.P. Russell's, who is using the technique to examine thermal ecology and movement of the species at Bow Island. Again, as in the cases of the leopard frog and the long-toed salamander, the worth of research on a reptile or amphibian species perceived as being at risk is evident.

## VOLUNTEER AMPHIBIAN MONITORING

In 1991, in response to the IUCN's Declining Amphibian Task Force mandate, a Canadian task force (DAPCAN) was organized to examine the problem in this country (Bishop and Petit 1992), and shortly thereafter a provincial effort was initiated (Powell and

Russell 1993b). A monitoring handbook (with tape of anuran calls) has been produced by David Seburn, under contract to Alberta Fish and Wildlife Services, and has been widely distributed to Fish and Wildlife workers and to interested amateur naturalist groups and individuals. At present we are analyzing the data from our 1994 respondents; the report will assess the utility of what is still considered to be a pilot project. The data are to go towards an amphibian atlas of Alberta. Ideally this pilot project will give rise to a widely-based network of observers across the province, and by the turn of the millennium we will be able to publish the first instalment of our atlas.

## CONCLUSIONS

We have discussed five research and conservation initiatives concerned with the Alberta herpetofauna, either focusing upon single species perceived to be at risk or upon a possible long-term loss of diversity. It must be stressed that, when dealing with such poorly-known (as a rule) elements of the fauna as amphibians and reptiles, research must precede or accompany any but the most basic conservation efforts. Amphibians and reptiles are generally the most inconspicuous terrestrial vertebrates in any community of which they form a part, and even such things as presence or absence can be difficult to ascertain. The ecological literature on some of our species (ie. short-horned lizards) is scanty, which leaves us with the option of doing it ourselves. Fortunately this option is one which has been actively supported by the appropriate agencies in Alberta over the last decade.

## ACKNOWLEDGEMENTS

Firstly, our apologies to anyone whose work in Alberta we may have missed or misrepresented - it was not intentional. Leslie Yaremko, Cleve Werschler, Wayne Smith, Karen Graham, Julie Fukumoto and Caroline Seburn were good enough to share with us the details of their research at one time or another, and we are grateful for this. Our thanks to Steve Brechtel for his seminal influence in this work.

## LITERATURE CITED

Anonymous. 1991. The status of Alberta wildlife. Pub. No. I/413, Alberta Forestry, Lands and Wildlife, Fish and Wildlife Division, Edmonton, Alberta.

Bishop, C.A. and K.E. Pettit (eds.). 1992. Declines in Canadian amphibian populations: Designing a national monitoring strategy. Canadian Wildlife Service Occasional Paper Number 76.

Cook., F.R. 1991. Endangered salamanders and the Seebe leasehold. A report to Lafarge Canada Inc., Exshaw, Alberta.

Koonz, W. 1992. Amphibians in Manitoba. Pp. 19-20 *In* Declines in Canadian amphibian populations: Designing a national monitoring strategy (C.A. Bishop and K.E. Pettit, eds.). Canadian Wildlife Service Occasional Paper Number 76.

Koonz, W. 1992. Amphibians in Manitoba. Pp. 273-275 *In* Proceedings of the Third Prairie Conservation and Endangered Species Workshop (G.L. Holroyd, H.L. Dickson, M. Regnier, and H.C. Smith, eds.). Provincial Museum of Alberta Natural History Occasional Paper No. 19.

Orchard, S.A. 1992. Amphibian population declines in British Columbia. Pp. 10-13 *In* Declines in Canadian amphibian populations: Designing a national monitoring strategy (C.A. Bishop, and K.E. Pettit eds.). Canadian Wildlife Service Occasional Paper Number 76.

Oseen, K., G.L. Powell, and A.P. Russell. 1995. The distribution of the long-toed salamander (*Ambystoma macrodactylum*) in southwestern Alberta. Alberta Environmental Protection, Fish and Wildlife Division.

Pendlebury, G.B. 1976. The western hognose snake, *Heterodon nasicus nasicus*, in Alberta. Canadian Field-Naturalist 91: 416-422.

Powell, G.L. 1982. The eastern short-horned lizard in Alberta: Basic field ecology of northern marginal populations. M.Sc. Thesis, University of Calgary, Calgary, Alberta.

Powell, G.L. and A.P. Russell. 1984. The diet of the eastern short-horned lizard (*Phrynosoma douglassi brevirostre*) in Alberta and its relationship to sexual size dimorphism. Canadian Journal of Zoology 62: 428-440.

Powell, G.L. and A.P. Russell. 1985a. Growth and sexual size dimorphism in Alberta populations of the eastern short-horned lizard, *Phrynosoma douglassi brevirostre*. Canadian Journal of Zoology 63: 139-154.

Powell, G.L. and A.P. Russell. 1985b. Field thermal ecology of the eastern short-horned lizard (*Phrynosoma douglassi brevirostre*) in southern Alberta. Canadian Journal of Zoology 63: 228-238.

Powell, G.L. and A.P. Russell. 1991a. Distribution of the eastern short-horned lizard, *Phrynosoma douglassi brevirostre*, in Alberta, Canada. Northwest Naturalist 72: 21-26.

Powell, G.L. and A.P. Russell. 1991b. Parturition and clutch characteristics of short-horned lizards (*Phrynosoma douglassii brevirostre*) from Alberta. Canadian Journal of Zoology 69: 2759-2764.

Powell, G.L. and A.P. Russell. 1992. A preliminary survey of the distribution and abundance of the eastern short-horned lizard (*Phrynosoma douglassii brevirostre*) in Alberta. To The Recreation, Parks and Wildlife Foundation of Alberta.

Powell, G.L. and A.P. Russell. 1993a. The range and status of the eastern short-horned lizard in the Canadian Prairies. Pp. 278-290 *In* Proceedings of the Third Prairie Conservation and Endangered Species Workshop (G.L. Holroyd, H.L. Dickson, M. Regnier, and H.C. Smith eds.). Provincial Museum of Alberta Natural History Occasional Paper No. 19.

Powell, G.L. and A.P. Russell. 1993b. Monitoring amphibian populations in Alberta: Are they declining? Pp. 276-277 *In* Proceedings of the Third Prairie Conservation and Endangered Species Workshop (G.L. Holroyd, H.L. Dickson, M. Regnier, and H.C. Smith, eds.). Provincial Museum of Alberta Natural History Occasional Paper No. 19.

Powell, G.L. and A.P. Russell. 1993c. A radiotelemetric study of movement and thermal ecology in an Alberta population of the eastern short-horned lizard (*Phrynosoma douglassii brevirostre*). To the Fish and Wildlife Branch, Alberta Forestry, Lands and Wildlife.

Powell, G.L. and A.P. Russell. 1994. A radiotelemetric study of movement, thermal ecology and hibernation site selection in an Alberta population of the eastern short-horned lizard (*Phrynosoma douglassii brevi-*

*rostre*). To Alberta Environmental Protection, Fish and Wildlife Division.

Powell, G.L., S.J. Nelson, and A.P. Russell. 1992. The Bow Valley long-toed salamander population study: A preliminary report on the 1992 field season. A report to Alberta Forestry, Lands and Wildlife, Fish and Wildlife Division, Edmonton, Alberta.

Powell, G.L., A.P. Russell, J.D. James, S.J. Nelson, and S.M. Watson. 1995. Population biology of the long-toed salamander (*Ambystoma macrodactylum*) in the Front Range of Alberta. *In* Amphibians in Canada: Population status and decline. (In press)

Russell, A.P. and A.M. Bauer. 1993. The amphibians and reptiles of Alberta. A Field Guide and Primer of Boreal Herpetology. University of Calgary Press, Calgary, Alberta.

Roberts, W. 1991. An action plan for the recovery of the northern leopard frog in Alberta. Pp. 199-200 *In* Proceedings of the Third Prairie Conservation and Endangered Species Workshop (G.L. Holroyd, G. Burns, and H.C. Smith, eds.). Provincial Museum of Alberta Natural History Occasional Paper No. 15.

Roberts, W. 1992. Declines in amphibian populations in Alberta. Pp. 14-16 *In* Declines in Canadian Amphibian Populations: Designing a National Monitoring Strategy (C.A. Bishop, and K.E. Pettit, eds.). Canadian Wildlife Service Occasional Paper Number 76.

Seburn, C.N.L. 1992. The status of amphibian populations in Saskatchewan. Pp. 17-18 *In* Declines in Canadian Amphibian Populations: Designing a National Monitoring Strategy (C.A. Bishop, and K.E. Pettit, eds.). Canadian Wildlife Service Occasional Paper Number 76.

Smith, W. 1993. An assessment of short-horned lizard habitat and use, Manyberries badlands, Alberta. A report to the Fish and Wildlife Branch, Alberta Forestry, Lands and Wildlife.

Yaremko, L. 1994. Northern leopard frog project. Field report 1994. A report to the Department of Environmental Protection, Fish and Wildlife Services, Edmonton, Alberta.

# THE FUTURE OF THE PEREGRINE FALCON (*FALCO PEREGRINUS ANATUM*) POPULATION IN ALBERTA

## Gordon Court[1], Steven Brechtel, Gary Erickson, and Bruce Treichel

*[1]Department of Environmental Protection, Natural Resources Service, Government of Alberta, 7th Floor, O.S. Longman Building, 6909-116 St., Edmonton, Alberta T6H 4P2*

## ABSTRACT

Eggshell thinning and organochlorine residues in egg contents and prey species were reviewed for peregrine falcons (*Falco peregrinus anatum)* nesting in the province of Alberta between 1968 and 1992. Shells from 118 eggs representing 58 clutches produced between 1983 and 1992 averaged 12.9% thinner than eggs produced by peregrines under "DDT Free" conditions (DDT - dichlorodipheyldichloroethylene). This average is 4% less than the thinning level considered critical for successful reproduction in this species. In the last decade, eggs from 16 of 58 clutches were thinned past critical levels, with the thinnest shell in the sample being 29% thinner than normal. Nevertheless, more than 72% of clutches sampled during this decade had shells thicker than the critical level, with some shells as thick as those produced under "DDT Free" conditions, indicating that the Alberta population is now viable despite the fact that birds in this population contain residues of a variety of organochlorine pollutants.

The geometric mean level of DDE (dichlorodipheyl-trichloroethane) residues in eggs from 86 nesting attempts between 1968 and 1992 was 8.29 ppm (wet weight). Levels of DDE and polychlorinated bi-phenyls (PCBs) in egg contents showed significant decreases over the last three decades. The geometric mean DDE level from the contents of eggs produced by peregrines from Alberta during the 1990's is less than half the level considered critical for sustaining a viable peregrine population.

All but two of 36 prey species sampled from three different areas of Alberta in 1991 showed measurable levels of organochlorines. Only 4 species, two gulls, an insectivorous passerine, and an omnivorous passerine contained DDE residues high enough to potentially affect breeding success of peregrines in the province. Only one of the gulls and the insectivorous passerine would be primary prey species taken by falcons. These data represent an improvement in the pollution status of prey species for the peregrine in Alberta since the 1970's and 1980's. Re-introduction programs for the peregrine in Alberta appear well grounded, as levels of pollution in peregrines and prey are not high enough to inhibit a population recovery.

## INTRODUCTION

The widespread decline of the peregrine falcon (*Falco peregrinus)* in North America has been attributed to reproductive failures following the indiscriminate use of certain chlorinated hydrocarbon pesticides, most notably DDT (summaries in Peakall 1976, Cade *et al.* 1988). The association between pesticide contamination and reproductive failure has been the focus of much of the research on this species over the last three decades (Ratcliffe 1967, Enderson and Berger 1968, Hickey 1969, Lincer *et al.* 1970, Ratcliffe 1970, Cade and Fyfe 1970, Cade *et al.* 1971, Peakall *et al.* 1975, Fyfe *et al.* 1976, Enderson *et al.* 1982). DDT was banned from use in Canada in 1969 and the United States in 1972 (Kiff 1988), but by 1975 the peregrine of continental North America, *Falco peregrinus anatum*, had been extirpated over its range east of the Rocky Mountains and south of the boreal forest (Fyfe *et al.* 1976). In Alberta, by the mid-1970's, less than 5 of 73 historical nest sites known at that time were occupied by breeding pairs, all of them north of the 56th parallel (Fyfe *et al.* 1976).

To reverse the downward trend in peregrine numbers in Canada, a breeding, re-introduction, and maintenance program for the species was initiated in the mid-1970's and continues to present (Fyfe 1976). Through fostering of captive-raised young to wild pairs and hack releases, the population in northern Alberta continues to grow and at least 6 new pairs have established in southern Alberta (Court 1993a). Present management objectives include enhancement of the southern Alberta population to 10 territorial pairs by 1997 and to 10 producing pairs by 2002 (Paetkau 1990). These goals are to be reached through hack releases of a large number of captive-raised young in southern Alberta in between 1991 and 1996 (Stubbs 1992).

A primary factor that may influence the ultimate success of this program continues to be the effects of foreign pollution. It has been established that much of the contamination in migrant Nearctic peregrine populations originates in Central and South America, where these falcons and many of their primary prey species spend the winter months (Henny *et al.* 1982, Fyfe *et al.* 1990). Many countries in Latin America continue to use persistent organochlorine pesticides (including DDT) now banned from use in Canada and the United States (Peakall 1976, Burton and Philogène 1988). Therefore, there exists concern as to whether continued exposure to foreign sources of pollution may inhibit the recovery of populations of *anatum* peregrines in Alberta despite re-introduction efforts.

One of the difficulties in predicting the success of the Southern Alberta Peregrine Falcon Re-Introduction Program is that there has been no recent review of toxicological data from the Alberta peregrine population. The majority of studies to date consist of periodic surveys of population size and breeding success (Cade and Fyfe 1970, Fyfe *et al.* 1976, White *et al.* 1990, Murphy 1990). Pesticide monitoring has consisted mainly of measuring pollutants in addled peregrine eggs and prey species collected prior to 1988 (Peakall *et al.* 1990, Baril *et al.* 1990). Here, we review data on pesticide residues in the contents of Alberta peregrine eggs dating from the 1960's to present, eggshell quality from nesting efforts over the last decade, and recent (1991) residue determinations in prey. We discuss the implications of these findings regarding the 'health' of the species in terms of pollutant levels and comment on the impact of these data on current re-introduction efforts for this species in Alberta.

## METHODS

Between 1983 and 1992, eggshell fragments were gathered from both unsuccessful and successful peregrine nests in Alberta by staff of the Alberta Fish and Wildlife Division (now Natural Resources Service), the Canadian Wildlife Service, and Parks Canada. Shell thickness was measured optically using a Leitz Wetzlar UWM Toolmaker's Microscope Micrometer, accurate to ±0.0025 mm. With fragment samples, mean eggshell thickness was determined from three chips selected at random from the collection at each nest. For whole eggs, measurements were from fresh chips taken at three places on the equator of the shell. Most measurements included the shell and shell membrane. In instances where shell membranes were absent, the average membrane thickness of 0.069 mm (Court *et al.* 1990) was added to the shell thickness. Where more than one egg from a clutch was available, a mean clutch thickness was calculated and this was included in the data analysis as a single egg representing a clutch.

For comparative purposes, a "DDT Free" mean eggshell thickness was determined for 40 eggs produced by captive peregrine falcons; these eggs were measured using precisely the same methods as outlined above for the wild eggs. The captive birds, housed in the Canadian Wildlife Service Endangered Species Facility at Wainwright Alberta, are fed locally-raised quail and pheasants, food sources known to contain only trace levels of organochlorines (Alberta Fish and Wildlife Division, unpublished data). Moreover, many of the falcons in the Wainwright facility are from the same genetic stock as wild birds in Alberta. Both wild and captive shell collections used in this analysis have been archived by the Alberta Fish and Wildlife Division, at the O.S. Longman Building in Edmonton.

Infertile peregrine eggs were collected incidentally on visits to eyries in Alberta dating from 1968. Egg contents were stored in acetone-rinsed vials, sealed with a foil-lined stopper, and frozen. Egg samples were analyzed for residues of selected organochlorine pesticides and polychlorinated bi-phenyl's (PCBs) at the following laboratories: the Alberta Environmental Centre in Vegreville, the Ontario Research Foundation at Sheridan Park in Ontario, the Canadian Wildlife Service in Ottawa, and the Food and Laboratory Services Branch of Alberta Agriculture in Edmonton. Methodology for analyses followed the procedures summarized by Won (1982).

All residues in egg contents and referenced values for residues in prey species are expressed as mg/kg (parts per million - ppm) wet weight of the samples. Residue data were skewed to the left, so for parametric statistical comparisons individual values were transformed to a $log^{10}$ scale. All means presented for residue data are geometric, unless stated otherwise. Eggshell thickness data were normally distributed, so no transformation was necessary and means for these data are arithmetic ± one standard deviation (SD). Statistical tests follow Sokal and Rohlf (1981). Differences among data sets were considered significant when the probability value *(P)* was ≤ 0.05.

## RESULTS

### Eggshell Thickness

Collections of eggshell fragments and whole shells allowed shell thickness measurements on 118 peregrine eggs representing 58 clutches produced in Alberta between 1983 and 1992 (Fig. 1). Mean shell thickness for eggs was 12.9% thinner than the average shell thickness for peregrine eggs produced under "DDT Free" conditions (0.296 ± 0.023 mm vs 0.340 ± 0.022 mm). Eggshells collected from wild nests ranged in thickness from 0.246 mm to 0.346 mm, with the thinnest shell in the sample 29% thinner than the "DDT Free" mean. The best wild-produced shell in the sample was 2% thicker than the "DDT Free" mean. More than two-thirds of the sample (42/58; 72%) included eggs with shells thicker than critical levels. In our sample, shell thickness was not significantly different for eggs collected in the 1980's versus those taken in the 1990's (Student's t-test, t = 0.753 P = 0.458).

Shells produced by the remnant wild peregrine population in northeastern Alberta between 1985 and 1992 averaged 0.298 ± 0.022 mm, 14% thinner than eggs from "DDT Free" conditions (Fig. 2). There was no significant difference in the thickness of shells produced by birds in this population and those from peregrines nesting

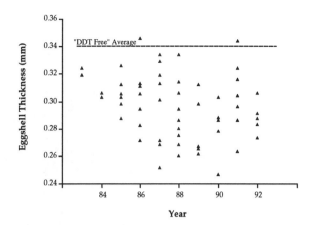

Figure 1. Shell thickness (mm) peregrine falcon eggs representing 58 clutches produced in Alberta between 1983 and 1992.

in southern Alberta (0.298 ± 0.022 mm (n=38) vs. 0.292 ± 0.022 mm (n = 19); Mann-Whitney U-Test Z =- 0.745 P = 0.45). There was no evidence to conclude that shell quality had improved in Northeastern Alberta between 1985 and 1992, as there was no significant difference in eggshell thickness among years in this sample (ANOVA, $F_{7,34}$= 0.991, $P$ = 0.45) (Fig. 2).

A series of eggshells was available for two female peregrines, each nesting on city buildings, for all of their breeding lives (Figures 3 and 4). The female nesting in

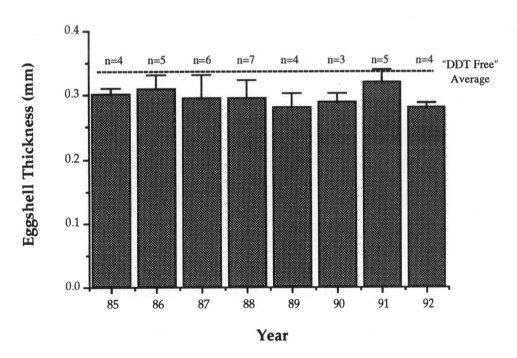

Figure 2. Arithmetic mean shell thickness (mm) for each year 1985 to 1992 for peregrine falcons nesting in Northeastern Alberta; n=38 clutches. Error bars=1 SD of the mean.

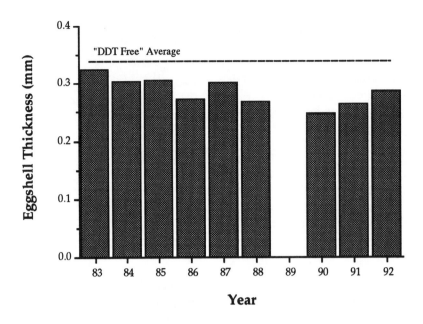

Figure 3. Average eggshell thickness for the same adult female peregrine falcon nesting on the AGT Toll Building in Edmonton, 1983 to 1992.

Edmonton produced eggs averaging 16% ($0.285 \pm 0.025$ mm) thinner than the "DDT Free" mean (Fig. 3), only 1% less than the critical level for successful nesting. This female crushed several of her eggs during her breeding life (Fish and Wildlife Division, unpublished data). The female in Calgary produced eggs averaging 12% ($0.300 \pm 0.019$ mm) thinner than normal. Although shell quality of these females fluctuated from year to year there was no significant trend in the quality of their eggshells through time.

## Organochlorine Residues in Eggs

Residue levels in egg contents were available for 86 peregrine breeding attempts between 1968 and 1992. Residues of the three most commonly detected

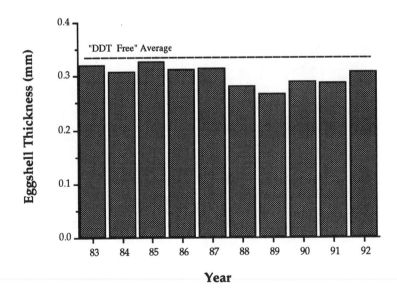

Figure 4. Average eggshell thickness for the same adult female peregrine falcon nesting in the downtown core of Calgary, 1983 to 1992.

organochlorines in egg contents are summarized in Table 1. There were significant differences in the mean levels of all three organochlorines considered in the analysis, with a reduction in the levels of DDE and PCBs in the last two decades. Most significantly, the geometric mean DDE level in the contents of eggs collected in 1990-92 (n = 17) is slightly more than half that for eggs collected in the 1970's (n = 14) (Table 1), and residues of this compound in peregrine eggs have decreased each year (Fig. 5).

Correlations between concentrations of organochlorine residues in eggs are presented in Table 2. A particularly strong correlation was observed between residues of DDE and dieldrin, but significant correlations were found between all of three organochlorine compounds detected in the samples.

In 1988, the adult female nesting in downtown Edmonton returned to her territory without a mate. She began 'dumping' a number of single eggs and these were collected in sequence and analyzed for pollutants and shell quality. In that year, this female was one of the most polluted falcons attempting to breed in the province, with a geometric mean DDE level in egg contents of 14.20 ppm and an average shell thickness for all eggs of $0.268 \pm 0.014$ mm, 21% thinner than the "DDT Free" mean. Measurements of eggshell thickness and DDE contents in the eggs showed that neither eggshell quality nor pollutant state of eggs improved with laying order (Fig. 6). In fact, the eighth egg laid by this female had the highest DDE content of all 11 eggs laid that spring, indicating that the bird was eating prey species on the breeding grounds that were polluted enough to have affected her reproduction.

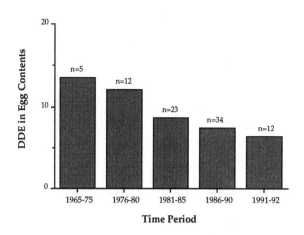

Figure 5. Geometric mean levels of DDE in the contents of peregrine eggs from 86 different breeding attempts in Alberta between 1965 and 1992.

## Organochlorine Residues in Prey Species

In their review of pollutant residues in peregrine prey in Canada for the 1980's, Baril *et al.* (1990), concluded that only three compounds, DDE, PCBs, and dieldrin, occur in sufficient concentrations to potentially affect the productivity of peregrine falcons. Residues of these compounds from whole body pools of 36 prey species from three different localities in south-central Alberta were summarized recently by Natural Resouce Services (Court 1993b). This sample consisted of whole body homogenates comprised of 201 adult and 10 juvenile individuals.

In brief summary: Only rock doves and northern flickers from the Red Deer River valley were free of detectable residues of all organochlorines. Three species of gull sampled showed elevated levels of DDE, as did the common tern. Other aquatic species, bufflehead and

Table 1. Levels of organochlorine residues in peregrine falcon eggs from 58 different breeding attempts in Alberta between 1968 and 1992.

| Era | *n* | DDE | PCB | Dieldrin |
|-----|-----|-----|-----|----------|
| | | | (ppm) | |
| 1968-1979 | 14 | 11.60 (1.86-63.40)[1] | 5.54 (1.87-13.47) | 0.43 (0.14-2.34) |
| 1980-1989 | 55 | 8.31 (1.51-41.00) | 3.95 (1.50-18.00) | 0.13 (0.00-1.52) |
| 1990-1992 | 17 | 6.21 (2.39-13.85) | 3.06 (1.11-9.86) | 0.12 (0.10-0.48) |
| All Years | 86 | 8.29 (1.51-63.40) | 3.97 (1.11-18.00) | 0.16 (0.00-2.34) |

[1]Geometric mean and range of values.
ANOVA using log-transformed values: DDE $F_{1,84} = 4.85$ $P=0.03$; PCB $F_{1,78}=11.75$ $P=0.0009$; Dieldrin $F_{1,73} =28.48$ $P=0.001$.

Table 2. Correlation coefficients (r values) between concentrations of different organochlorine compounds in peregrine falcon eggs from 86 different breeding attempts in Alberta between 1968 and 1992.

|  | DDE | PCB | Dieldrin |
|---|---|---|---|
| DDE | 1.00 |  |  |
| PCB | 0.40** | 1.00 |  |
| Dieldrin | 0.73** | 0.30** | 1.00 |

**$P<0.01$

eared grebe also showed elevated DDE levels, while the only shorebird in the sample to contain over 0.50 ppm DDE was the killdeer. The only passerines to show over 0.50 ppm DDE were two species of swallow and the American crow. Rough-winged swallow and American crow were the only terrestrial species to show mean DDE levels over 1.00 ppm. Only California and Bonaparte's gulls reached this level in the aquatic species sampled, and Bonaparte's gull pools averaged the highest DDE and PCB concentrations (3.57 ppm and 4.78 ppm respectively) of all species sampled. Although DDE and PCBs were present in the highest concentrations, dieldrin, heptachlor epoxide, DDT, DDD, hexachlorobenzene, mirex, and oxychlordane were also detected in the prey species sampled; none were high enough to have affected reproduction in peregrine falcons (Peakall *et al.* 1990).

## DISCUSSION

The reported variation in reproductive and population status of North American peregrine populations in recent years (Cade *et al.* 1988) and the on-going re-introduction of the species to Alberta, makes the results of any detailed inquiry of pesticide pollution in these birds important, and forces us to address a number of questions: (1) What body of evidence do we have to evaluate the levels of pollution in peregrines now nesting in Alberta and how well do the separate data sets (eggshell thickness, residues in eggs) support one another?; (2) From what we know of pollution in other populations, how severe is the present level of pollution in this population and how should these levels affect the productivity in Alberta?; (3) Do prey species contribute significantly to pollutant levels in peregrines on the breeding grounds?; (4) Is it possible to predict how the

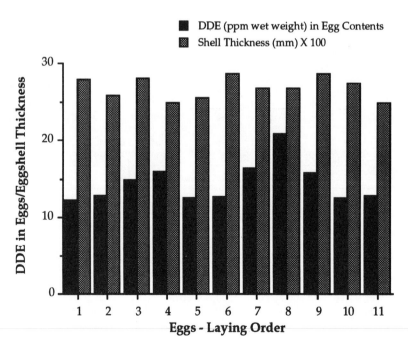

Figure 6. Shell thickness and DDE residues in egg contents for 11 eggs laid by the same adult female peregrine falcon nesting in the downtown core of Edmonton in 1988.

population is likely to respond in the near future?; and (5) Are re-introduction programs justified considering the present pollutant status of peregrines and their prey?

## Eggshell Thinning

DDE-induced eggshell thinning is recognized as the proximate cause of reproductive failure in polluted populations of the peregrine (Ratcliffe 1967, 1970, Hickey and Anderson 1968, Anderson and Hickey 1972). For this reason, collections of shells for thickness comparison are a useful means by which to evaluate potential pollution problems. The large collection of shell fragments and whole shells provided a representative average eggshell thickness for the Alberta population over the last decade and showed that these birds produce shells about 13% thinner than eggs produced by peregrines breeding in a pesticide-free environment. This degree of thinning is roughly similar to thinning percentages recorded for tundra peregrines in Greenland in the 1970's (Walker et al. 1973 - 14.1%) and the 1980's (Falk and Møller 1986 - 14.2%), and Alaska between 1979 and 1984 (Ambrose et al. 1988 - 13.6%). In recent years, all of these populations have shown recoveries from pesticide-induced declines (Cade et al. 1988).

Hickey and Anderson (1968) concluded that, for a number of bird species, eggshell thinning above 18% is associated with reproductive failure. For the peregrine, a recent review of 30 different studies of pollution in the species showed that populations declined or had been extirpated in every case where shell thinning had exceeded 17% below the pre-pesticide average thickness for each population (Peakall and Kiff 1988). As most pairs in Alberta now produce eggshells that are thicker than critical shell thinning levels, it is likely that a healthy peregrine population could be sustained in this region.

## Organochlorine Residues in Eggs

Ratcliffe (1970) reported that peregrines in Great Britain, failing through egg breakage, averaged only 13.7 ppm DDE in their eggs. More recently, Peakall et al. (1975, 1990) concluded that DDE residues in peregrine eggs averaging 15 to 20 ppm would experience reproductive failures. As peregrines nesting in Alberta during the last decade produced eggshells with only about 13% thinning, it was not unexpected to find a mean DDE level in the eggs below critical levels, at 8.29 ppm. In the last three years in Alberta, the geometric mean DDE level in Alberta dropped even further to about 6 ppm.

Relative to some other North American populations sampled in recent years (e.g.: Enderson et al. 1982), the mean DDE level in eggs produced by peregrines in Alberta over the last decade is encouragingly low. In fact, since 1980, less than 15% (9/72) of the eggs collected in Alberta contained DDE residues in the range likely to cause impaired reproductive performance. Peakall et al. (1990) noted that peregrine populations usually decline when more than 50% of pairs in a population produce eggs containing DDE in the critical range. Therefore, as concluded from data on shell thinning, the presence of productive peregrine pairs in the province is understandable in that most birds produce eggs with DDE residues below critical levels. Nevertheless, some pairs in Alberta will continue to fail each year as a direct result of egg breakages associated with DDE contamination. Such birds apparently tend to specialize on more contaminated prey species or are somehow more likely to accumulate pollutants (e.g.: a polluted wintering range); the adult female that nested in downtown Edmonton, "Arrow", is one such example. The preference for grebes and gulls by this pair (Follinsbee 1992) may have been related to the consistently poor quality of the eggs produced by this female (see below).

Mean levels of other organochlorines, PCBs and dieldrin, found in egg contents were below levels considered critical for the species (Peakall et al. 1990, Table 1). Maximum recorded levels of dieldrin were high enough to have affected reproduction of some individuals (see summary in Peakall et al. 1990); this was not true for PCBs. Interestingly, levels of all these compounds were correlated (Table 2), suggesting that individual falcons are exposed to most of these compounds collectively. Similar findings have been documented in other studies of polluted peregrine populations (Enderson et al. 1982, Newton et al. 1989, Court et al. 1990).

## Pollutant Levels in Prey and Reproductive Failure

DeWeese et al. (1986) reviewed studies of the effects of DDE in the diet of raptors and concluded that levels of DDE in prey species above 3.0 ppm (wet weight) are high enough to potentially affect the reproductive success of avian predators such as the peregrine falcon. Though based on small sample sizes, recent residue levels in prey from three different areas of south-eastern Alberta, show that only the Bonaparte's gull contained residues of this magnitude (Court 1993b). California gulls, rough-winged swallows, and American crows were the only other species to show DDE levels above

1.0 ppm (Court 1993b), and of this group only the swallow could be considered a common prey species of peregrine falcons (Enderson *et al.* 1982).

Baril *et al.* (1990) measured levels of organochlorines in Alberta peregrine prey collected in the 1980's. Although impossible to compare statistically to the samples taken in 1991, it is notable that far fewer family representatives from the 1991 samples had elevated levels of DDE (*i.e.:* over 1.0 ppm). In samples from the early 1980's, Baril *et al.* (1990) detected elevated levels in 6 of 13 families sampled. In the 1991 samples (Court 1993b), over 20 families were represented in the collection and only five species in three families, Laridae, Corvidae and Hirundinidae, averaged over 1.0 ppm DDE in whole body homogenates. Species that are cause for the greatest concern remain the Larids, particularly Bonaparte's gulls, a species that is used heavily along with Franklin's gulls by the remnant population in north-eastern Alberta (Johnson-Beaver 1979), and grebes, as they figure prominently (along with gulls) in the diet of urban peregrines (Follinsbee 1992). Peregrines feeding heavily on these species prior to egg laying would probably be at risk of reproductive failure.

Overall, collections from 1991 suggest an improvement in the pollutant status of most prey species in Alberta (Court 1993b). Some prey, however, are polluted enough with DDT residues to affect the reproductive success of peregrines on the breeding ground. The best evidence for this comes from the series of eggs taken from the female nesting on the AGT building in Edmonton in 1988. On a 'clean' diet, this animal would have been expected to dispose of as much as one-half of her body burden of DDE by laying the first four or five eggs in the sequence (Bogan and Newton 1977). In laying this series of 'dump' eggs, one would have expected DDE residues in egg contents to drop, with a commensurate improvement in eggshell quality; data in Figure 6 did not support this prediction. DDE residues were highest in eggs # 7 and # 8, a fact that clearly indicates that this bird was feeding on prey species on the breeding grounds that were polluted enough to cause her to lay eggs thinned close to critical levels. In a summary of the food habits of this pair of peregrines from 1983 to 1992, Follinsbee (1992) found that over 30% of the diet was composed of gulls, terns, and grebes and it is likely that the elevated organochlorine levels in these prey species contribute to the poor quality of the eggs produced by the AGT Edmonton pair each year.

## CONCLUSIONS AND RECOMMENDATIONS FOR FUTURE WORK

In a recent review of almost all chemical analyses of peregrine falcon eggs undertaken in Britain over the last three decades, Newton *et al.* (1989) concluded that viable populations of this species can exist in polluted environments when geometric mean levels of DDE in eggs are no higher than 15 ppm, shell thinning does not exceed 15-20% below normal, and productivity is greater than 0.6 young per territorial pair. Since 1980 in Alberta, the geometric mean level of DDE in egg contents was less than 8 ppm, shell thinning averages 13% below normal, and, in years when poor weather does not affect reproductive success, annual production averages over 1.5 young per territorial pair (Alberta Fish and Wildlife Division, unpublished reports). Therefore, recent pollutant and productivity data from Alberta indicate a viable peregrine population. Furthermore, this population is likely to show a recovery in the next few years, especially considering the large scale re-introduction of captive-raised peregrines now underway (Stubbs 1992). The release of a large number of these captive-raised birds seems particularly vital, as this program will complete the re-introduction of genetic stock of Alberta origin that has been 'archived' in captivity for more than 20 years.

This toxicological assessment has demonstrated, however, that peregrine falcons nesting in Alberta continue to accumulate significant amounts of organochlorine pesticide and PCB residues, so there is little room for complacency in the management of these chemicals and this species. Forecasts of reduced DDT use in Latin America are encouraging (Burton and Philogène 1988) and the drop in DDT residues in the tissues of Alberta peregrines and most of their prey in recent years suggests that the risks from this compound may be diminishing. In the decade to come, however, a proportion of the breeding pairs in Alberta will suffer reproductive failures each year as a direct result of organochlorine pollutants; hopefully this proportion will decrease with time. Moreover, many new compounds are licensed as biocides in Canada each decade and we still have little knowledge of the long term effects of PCBs on wildlife, compounds that continue to increase in concentration in the world's ecosystems. As peregrine falcon populations recover in Alberta it will be important to herald their return, but the species should still be considered as one of the most sensitive "barometers" of environmental health available. Efforts to recover pesticide samples (addled eggs, eggshell fragments, and representative prey species) from this population should remain a priority of biologists working on the species in Alberta over the next decade.

## ACKNOWLEDGMENTS

Logistical assistance and funding for field work was provided by the Department of Environmental Protection, Natural Resources Service (formerly Fish and Wildlife Services) - Government of Alberta, Parks Canada, and the Canadian Wildlife Service - Environment Canada. The authors would like to acknowledge the dedicated field work of many peregrine falcon researchers who collected the samples used in this analysis, including: Richard Fyfe, Harry Armbruster, Pat Paul, Rick Beaver, Lizzane Johnson-Beaver, Ursula Banasch, John Campbell Jr., John Follinsbee, Jon Jorgensen, Jeff Dixon, Geoff Holroyd, Brad Tomm, Grant Gunderson, Steve Brechtel, and Dave Moore. J. Somers of the Alberta Environmental Centre, V. Kadis of Alberta Agriculture, and D. Peakall of the Canadian Wildlife Service expedited the residue analysis of egg contents. Richard Fyfe expedited the analysis of eggs at the Ontario Research Foundation at Sheridan Park, Ontario. This evaluation was also supported by Petro-Canada, as part of their continuing support of peregrine falcon re-introduction in Alberta. We thank Mr. A. Muir of the Department of Mechanical Engineering, University of Alberta, for allowing us to use the microscope micrometer owned by his department. Phil Trefry and Helen Trefry of the Canadian Wildlife Service Endangered Species Facility in Wainwright kindly provided a sample of eggshells from captive peregrine falcons in their care. Dave Ealey edited a penultimate draft of this manuscript.

## LITERATURE CITED

Ambrose, R.E., C.J. Henny, R.E. Hunter, and J.A. Crawford. 1988. Organochlorines in Alaskan peregrine falcon eggs and their impact on productivity. Pp. 385-393 *In* Peregrine falcon populations: their management and recovery (Cade, T.J., J.H. Enderson, C.G. Thelander, and C.M. White, eds.). Proceedings of the 1985 International Peregrine Conference, Sacramento, Braun-Brumfeld, San Francisco, California.

Anderson, D.W. and J.J. Hickey. 1972. Eggshell changes in certain North American birds. Proceedings of the 15th International Ornithological Congress: 514-540.

Baril, A., J.E. Elliot, J.D. Somers, and G. Erickson. 1990. Residue levels of environmental contaminants in prey species of the peregrine falcon, *Falco peregrinus,* in Canada. Canadian Field-Naturalist 104: 273-284.

Bogan, J.A. and I. Newton. 1977. Redistribution of DDE in sparrowhawks during starvation. Bulletin of Environmental Contaminants and Toxicology 18: 317-321.

Burton, D.K. and B.J. R. Philogène. 1988. An overview of pesticide usage in Latin America. A report to the Canadian Wildlife Service Latin America Program. Environment Canada, Wildlife Toxicology Division, 100 Gamelin Boulevard, Hull, Quebec.

Cade, T.J. and Fyfe, R.W. 1970. The North American Peregrine Survey, 1970. Canadian Field-Naturalist 84: 231-245.

Cade, T.J., J.H. Enderson, C.G. Thelander, and C.M. White (Editors). 1988. Peregrine falcon populations: their management and recovery. Proceedings of the 1985 International Peregrine Conference, Sacramento. Braun-Brumfeld, San Francisco.

Cade, T.J., J.L. Lincer, C.M. White, D.G. Roseneau, and L.G. Swartz. 1971. DDE residues and eggshell changes in Alaskan falcons and hawks. Science 172: 955-957.

Court, G.S. 1993a. A Review of historical nesting records for the American peregrine falcon (*Falco peregrinus anatum*) in Alberta south of 56ºN: Priorities for surveying a recovering population. Unpublished Report, Department of Environmental Protection, Fish and Wildlife Division, Edmonton, Alberta.

Court, G.S. 1993b. A toxicological assessment of the American peregrine falcon (*Falco peregrinus anatum*) breeding in Alberta, Canada - 1968 to 1992. Occasional Paper No. 10. Department of Environmental Protection, Fish and Wildlife Division, Edmonton, Alberta.

Court, G.S., C.C. Gates, D.A. Boag, J.D. MacNeil, D.M. Bradley, A.C. Fesser, J.R. Patterson, G.B. Stenhouse, and L.W. Oliphant. 1990. A toxicological assessment of peregrine falcons (*Falco peregrinus tundrius*) breeding in the Keewatin District of the Northwest Territories, Canada. Canadian Field-Naturalist 104: 255–272.

DeWeese, L.R., L.C. McEwen, G.L. Hensler, and B.E. Petersen. 1986. Organochlorine contaminants in passeriformes and other avian prey of the peregrine falcon in the western United States. Environmental Toxicology and Chemistry 5: 675-693.

Enderson, J.H. and D.D. Berger. 1968. Chlorinated hydrocarbon residues in peregrines and their prey species from northern Canada. Condor 70: 149-153.

Enderson, J.H., G.R. Craig, W.A. Burnham and D.D. Berger. 1982. Eggshell thinning and organochlorine residues in Rocky Mountain peregrines, *Falco peregrinus*, and their prey. Canadian Field-Naturalist 96: 255-264.

Falk, K. and S. Møller. 1986. Eggshell thinning in Greenlandic peregrine falcons (*Falco peregrinus*), with a comparative analysis of eggshell thickness variation in the Greenlandic and European subspecies. Unpublished M.Sc. thesis (Ch.3). Roskilde University, Denmark.

Follinsbee, J. 1992. Activity of peregrine falcons in Edmonton, 1992. Unpublished report. Department of Environmental Protection, Division of Fish and Wildlife, Edmonton, Alberta.

Fyfe, R.W., S.A. Temple, and T.J. Cade. 1976. The 1975 North American Peregrine Falcon survey. Canadian Field-Naturalist 90: 228-273.

Fyfe, R.W. 1976. Rationale and success of the Canadian Wildlife Service Peregrine Breeding Project. Canadian Field-Naturalist 90: 308-319.

Fyfe, R.W., U. Banasch, V. Benavides, N. Hilgert de Benavides, T. Luscombe, and J. Sanchez. 1990. Organochlorine residues in potential prey of peregrine falcons, *Falco peregrinus*, in Latin America. Canadian Field-Naturalist 104: 285-292.

Henny, C.J., F.P. Ward, K.E. Riddle, and R.M. Prouty. 1982. Migratory peregrine falcons, *Falco peregrinus*, accumulate pesticides in Latin America during winter. Canadian Field-Naturalist 96: 333-338.

Hickey, J.J. Editor. 1969. Peregrine falcon populations: their biology and decline. University of Wisconsin Press, Madison.

Hickey, J.J. and D.W. Anderson 1968. Chlorinated hydrocarbons and eggshell changes in raptorial and fish eating birds. Science 165: 271-273.

Johnson-Beaver, L. 1979. Biology and management of peregrine falcons (*Falco peregrinus anatum*) in north-eastern Alberta. Alberta Oil Sands Environmental Research Program Report. N. 80.

Kiff, L.F. 1988. Changes in the status of the peregrine in North America: An overview. Pp. 123-139 *In* Peregrine Falcon populations: their management and recovery (Cade, T.J., J.H. Enderson, C.G. Thelander, and C.M. White, eds.). Proceedings of the 1985 International Peregrine Conference, Sacramento, Braun-Brumfeld, San Francisco, California.

Lincer, J.L., T.J. Cade, and J.M. Devine. 1970. Organochlorine residues in Alaskan peregrine falcons (*Falco peregrinus* Tunstall), rough-legged hawks (*Buteo lagopus* Pottoppidan), and their prey. Canadian Field-Naturalist 84: 253-255.

Murphy. J. 1990. The 1985-1986 Peregrine Falcon, *Falco peregrinus*, Survey. Canadian Field-Naturalist 104: 182-192.

Newton, I., J.A. Bogan, and M.B. Haas. 1989. Organochlorines and mercury in the eggs of British peregrines, *Falco peregrinus*. Ibis 131: 355-376.

Paetkau, P. 1990. Alberta Peregrine Falcon Management Plan. (Draft). Department of Environmental Protection, Fish and Wildlife Division, Edmonton, Alberta.

Peakall, D.B. 1976. The peregrine falcon (*Falco peregrinus*) and pesticides. Canadian Field-Naturalist 90: 301-307.

Peakall, D.B. and R.W. Fyfe. 1988. DDE contamination in peregrines and American kestrels and its effect on reproduction. Pp. 337-350 *In* Peregrine falcon populations: their management and recovery (Cade, T.J., J.H. Enderson, C.G. Thelander, and C.M. White, eds.). Proceedings of the 1985 International Peregrine

Conference, Sacramento, Braun-Brumfeld, San Francisco, California.

Peakall, D.B., T.J. Cade, C.M. White, and J.R. Haugh. 1975. Organochlorine residues in Alaskan peregrines. Pesticides Monitoring Journal 8: 255-260.

Peakall, D.B., D.G. Noble, J.E. Elliot, J.D. Somers, and G. Erickson. 1990. Environmental contaminants in Canadian peregrine falcons, *Falco peregrinus*: A toxicological assessment. Canadian Field-Naturalist 104: 244-254.

Ratcliffe, D.A. 1967. Decrease in eggshell weight in certain birds of prey. Nature 215: 208-210.

Ratcliffe, D.A. 1970. Changes attributable to pesticides in egg breakage frequency and eggshell thickness in some British birds. Journal of Applied Ecology 7: 67-115.

Sokal, R.R. and F.J. Rohlf. 1981. Biometry: the principles and practices of statistics and biological research. W.H. Freeman and Co., New York.

Stubbs, P. 1992. Southern Alberta Peregrine Falcon Reintroduction Project - 1992 Technical Report. Unpublished Report. Department of Environmental Protection, Fish and Wildlife Division, Edmonton, Alberta.

Walker, W.E., W.G. Mattox, and R.W. Risebrough. 1973. Pollutant and shell thickness determinations of peregrine eggs from West Greenland. Arctic 26: 256-258.

White, C.M., R.W. Fyfe, and D.B. Lemon. 1990. The 1980 North American Peregrine Falcon, *Falco peregrinus*, Survey. Canadian Field-Naturalist 104: 174-181.

Won, H. 1982. The Canadian Wildlife Service analytical manual. Environment Canada, Wildlife Toxicology Division, 100 Gamelin Boulevard, Hull, Quebec.

# STATUS OF BURROWING OWL AND OF RECOVERY EFFORTS IN CANADA

## Dale Hjertaas

*Department of Environment and Resource Management, Wildlife Branch,*
*3211 Albert Street, Regina, Saskatchewan S4S 5W6*

## INTRODUCTION

Thank you for the opportunity to speak about the conservation program for the burrowing owl (*Speotyto cunicularia*). The recovery team I chair has representatives from each of the 4 western provinces as well as Dr. Paul James and Elizabeth Haug. Dr. Josef Schmutz has also been a very valuable member of our team.

I wish I could give you a glowing report about the status of the burrowing owl, but I cannot. The population is in trouble across its Canadian range. Figure 1a (Wellicome & Haug 1994) shows the trend at Hanna and in Manitoba. The Manitoba population is down to 8 pairs, as recently as 1982 there were 76 known pairs. Figure 1b (Wellicome & Haug 1994) shows trends on the Regina, Avonlea and Hanna2 study areas, all are negative. Figure 2 (Wellicome & Haug 1994) shows the data from Operation Burrowing Owl in Saskatchewan. Again there is is a clear decline over the past several years in spite of increasing numbers of cooperating landowners.

The estimated number of pairs remaining in Canada is between 1,015 to 1,695 (Wellicome & Haug 1994) which compares with a recovery plan objective of 3,000 pairs across prairie Canada (Hjertaas *et al.* in press).

The recovery team is very concerned about this decline and commissioned a new status report to COSEWIC by Wellicome and Haug (1994). This document recommends the status be changed from threatened to endangered. The recovery team support this recommendation. COSEWIC will, of course, make the actual decision this spring.

## WHY IS THE BURROWING OWL DECLINING?

I will briefly offer **my own best guess** as to why the population is declining and present the issues I think are important to understanding the recovery path we are following.

## Land Use Change In Canada

Unfortunately burrowing owls seem to prefer areas which are good agricultural soils, the stone free lacustrine plains and similar areas. I think these areas may provide easier burrowing opportunities. As a result favoured areas for the burrowing owl, such as the Regina Plains, are also among the most intensively cultivated on the prairies. This intense cultivation has a number of potential effects on the burrowing owl.

The intensity of cultivation is greatest in the east side of the range while more grassland remains in the western part of the range. Although there are other possible explanations, this is one possible reason why the decline of the burrowing owl has been steeper in the eastern than in the western part of its range.

## Direct loss of breeding areas

In the past many actual nesting areas were cultivated and burrowing owls disappeared from these sites. That undoubtedly impacted the owl population. However due to excellent cooperation from the agricultural community, few nesting areas have been cultivated during the past 7 years. Nonetheless owls are disappearing from these former nest areas, suggesting other factors are impacting on the burrowing owl.

## Fragmentation

A characteristic of our prairie landscape in the cultivated areas is that areas of native vegetation and permanent cover are very fragmented. A colony of burrowing owls may be nesting on a small pasture several miles from the next grassland. From the burrowing owl perspective this intensively cultivated landscape with small fragments of grassland could affect survival and productivity in at least 5 ways.

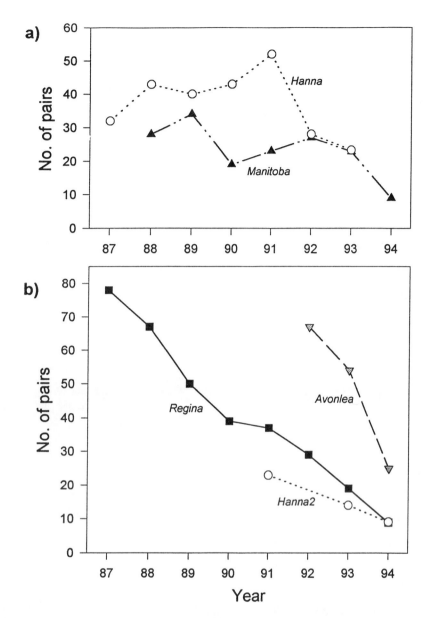

Figure 1. Number of owl pairs recorded in discrete research areas with at least 3 years of information. Survey methods varied within projects, but within each area investigators attempted complete owl counts and verified the presence of pairs by visiting individual nests. In the two studies shown in (a), search effort and or total area surveyed were not constant from year to year. Data from the Hanna site are only shown for years in which search effort was rated high. Search effort and knowledge of how and where to look for owls increased with time in the Manitoba site, so population decline is probably under estimated. Population changes in areas with constant search effort are shown in (b). (From Wellicome & Haug 1994)

## 1. Reduced food supply and productivity

The most important burrowing owl foods are voles, *Microtus* sp., and deer mice, *Peromyscus maniculatus*. The best areas for burrowing owls to hunt these rodents are areas of moderate height grassland, often a commodity in short supply. Wellicome (1992) showed that food is limiting productivity in some years. If the cultivated landscape provides fewer opportunities to capture

mice and voles than were formerly available, average productivity may be lowered by two or 3 chicks per year.

## 2. Road kills

Haug (1985) showed that burrowing owls did a lot of hunting in road ditches and tended to avoid cultivated fields. This probably reflects the greater availability of

269

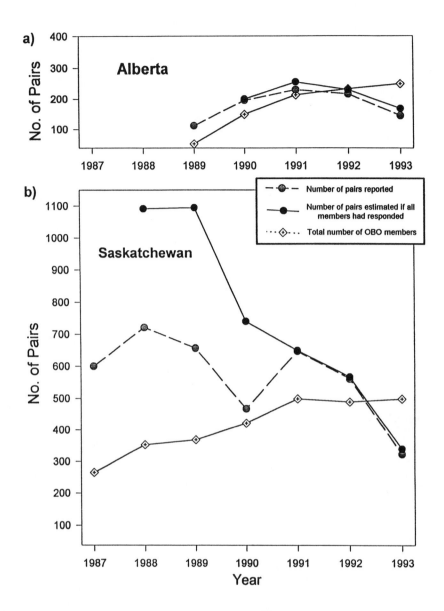

Figure 2. Number of owl pairs reported by Operation Burrowing Owl (OBO) members in Alberta (a) and in Saskatchewan (b). Because the percentage of members providing yearly census information was low in Saskatchewan, reports before 1991 under estimate the number of owls on OBO sites. A more accurate estimate of the total number of pairs on sites each year was obtained using a simple correction factor: average number of pairs per responding member x number of members not responding. Declines are apparent, despite a quadrupling of the number of cooperating members in Alberta and a doubling of members in Saskatchewan since the inception of the programs.

mice and voles in these grassed ditches. Unfortunately hunting these grassland fragments may lead to increased mortality from collisions with vehicles.

## 3. Increased predation

Predation is a normal occurrence. However it can accelerate population declines. We do not know if predation on burrowing owl adults and nests is higher now that it was presettlement. However it is possible that predators are attracted to the small remaining areas of prairie. At the same time burrowing owls are concentrated on these small areas. This may allow a predator to develop a search image for the burrowing owl nest.

## 4. Dispersal mortality

We know very little about where burrowing owls go after breeding. Young and adults gradually disappear from nest sites and presumably explore adjacent habitats until the southern migration. In a highly fragmented habitat dispersing young owls may not find suitable habitats and may therefore suffer high mortality in this period. This is an unanswered question.

### 5. Isolation and failure to recolonize

Isolated pastures may simply not be recolonized, or a male may settle on a site and fail to attract a female.

## PESTICIDES

Carbofuran flowable has been shown to impact burrowing owls when sprayed over or near nests (Fox *et al.* 1989). While this is not the main cause of the decline, the burrowing owl cannot afford any additional mortality. Because owls are concentrated on small areas of grassland, they may be more vulnerable to pesticide use.

## MIGRATION AND WINTER PROBLEMS

It is quite possible that changes along the migration route and on winter habitats have also affected burrowing owl survival. For example the substantial reduction in the number of prairie dog towns in parts of Mexico may have reduced an important winter habitat. However we have so far failed to confirm the winter areas used by burrowing owls and so are unable to determine which, if any, conservation issues may be important.

## MANAGEMENT ACTIONS

I perceive a series of affects on the burrowing owl most of which relate to the way we use the prairie landscape. These affects are complex and are not easily resolved. I will briefly explain some of the projects initiated by the recovery team following the headings of the 7 strategies identified in the National Recovery Plan (Hjertaas *et al.* 1995).

### 1. Reduce mortality on the breeding grounds

Environment Canada has lead environmental agencies seeking to have use of the pesticide Furadan eliminated in the burrowing owl to prevent accidental poisoning.

A decision on whether this pesticide will be restricted is pending from Agriculture Canada.

Use of nest boxes with wire bottoms and placing collars on entrance tunnels to restrict access of larger predators is reducing predation rates, but is only applicable to intensively managed sites. They are being used in the Regina - Moose Jaw area of Saskatchewan and in Manitoba.

Operation Burrowing Owl will offer warning signs to their members this year in an attempt to deal with road kills. Habitat management to offer hunting areas away from road ditches may also help and will be attempted in Saskatchewan as part of a strategy to improve productivity.

The issue of mortality after fledging has not yet been addressed although Dr. Schmutz has proposed to begin research on the question in 1995.

### 2. Increase productivity

Saskatchewan is planting grass and doing other habitat improvements in an effort to increase the mouse and vole population in owl territories. Supplemental feeding is now being used in Manitoba, Saskatchewan and B.C. to increase productivity. While this is not a sustainable long term strategy, it is an effective short term method to increase production while we seek to understand and deal with the larger problems.

Supplemental feeding has been combined with colour banding in Saskatchewan. Surveys of returning owls in 1995 should show if the increased productivity resulted in additional owls returning to our study area.

### 3. Protect and manage nesting habitat

Operation Burrowing Owl in Saskatchewan and Alberta continues to record good success in maintaining the actual nesting areas of the owls.

### 4. Monitor populations

Operation Burrowing Owl provides relatively cheap data from a wide area, but may have biases because is not random and has an unknown miss factor (Hjertaas in press). Small population size allow complete censuses annually in Manitoba and BC.

In 1994 Alberta initiated a randomized survey across the entire burrowing owl range. This survey will be completed in 1995, providing a population estimate for the province.

Long term data trends can also be provided by a series of randomly selected blocks surveyed in different years or long term studies of large study areas, usually as part of a larger research program. Random monitoring blocks have been established in Alberta and Saskatchewan, but low numbers of owls found create problems in identifying significant changes. Long term studies by James, Wellicome, De Smet and Schmutz have given annual population counts in study areas and data on productivity for modelling.

## 5. Management on migration and wintering areas

Dr. Holroyd of Environment Canada has been leading research in Mexico. His research is beginning to give a picture of the winter distribution of burrowing owls in Mexico and has identified the coastal lowlands as a possible area where Canadian burrowing owls may winter.

Banding studies are the traditional method of determining migration and winter areas for a population and continue, but we have not received any winter band returns.

DNA mapping offers a potential method to separate local burrowing owl populations and thus relate winter populations to breeding ranges. Team members have provided samples to two geneticists who are looking for DNA markers which could be used to separate populations.

## 6. Conduct release programs

When populations are very small, as in Manitoba, or had disappeared, as in British Columbia, releases may be able to reestablish populations. Both provinces release captive bred adult owls in the spring in the hope they will establish territories and breed that year.

## 7. Develop public support through education

The burrowing owl is dependent on private land for much of its habitat. Public support and sympathy is thus essential for its survival. A mixture of presentations, signs, newsletters to cooperators, pamphlets and a video are used in Canada to tell people about the burrowing owl.

The recovery team also hopes to increase awareness of the need for burrowing owl conservation in Mexico, for Mexicans. Environment Canada has translated pamphlets on the burrowing owl into Spanish and are developing a working relationship with Mexican biologists to continue studies and begin to address conservation issues in Mexico.

## LITERATURE CITED

Fox, G.A., P. Mineau, B. Collins, and P. C. James. 1989. The impact of the insecticide carbofuran (Furadan 480f) on the burrowing owl in Canada. Technical Report Series No. 72, Canadian Wildlife Service, Ottawa, Ontario.

Haug, E.A. 1985. Observations on the breeding ecology of burrowing owls in Saskatchewan. M.Sc. Thesis, University of Saskatchewan, Saskatoon, Saskatchewan

Hjertaas, D.G. 1995. Operation Burrowing Owl in Saskatchewan: The first 6 years. *In* Proceedings of the Burrowing Owl Symposium, Sacramento, California (J.L. Lincer, ed.). Journal of Raptor Research Special Publication. (In Press)

Hjertaas, D.G., S. Brechtel, K. De Smet, O. Dyer, E. Haug, G. Holroyd, P. James, and J. Schmutz. 1995. National Recovery Plan for the burrowing owl. Report #13, Ottawa: Recovery of Nationally Endangered Wildlife Committee.

Wellicome, Troy I. 1992. Reproductive performance of burrowing owls (*Athene cunicularia*): effects of supplemental food. Proceedings of the Burrowing Owl Symposium, Seattle. (In press).

Wellicome, Troy I. and Elizabeth A. Haug. 1994. Updated report on the status of the burrowing owl (*Speotyto cunicularia*) in Canada. Report to Committee On Status of Endangered Wildlife In Canada.

# THE RETURN OF THE SWIFT FOX TO THE CANADIAN PRAIRIES

## Ludwig N. Carbyn

*Canadian Wildlife Service, Environmental Conservation Branch, Prairie and Northern Region,*
*Room 200, 4999 - 98Avenue, Edmonton, Alberta T6B 2X3*

## INTRODUCTION

The mixed grasslands of western Canada, existing largely in Alberta and Saskatchewan, is among the most severely affected region by agriculture in Canada. Conversion of native vegetation to non-native vegetation suitable for grain growing and for livestock production went on at a time when little concern was shown for its effects on wildlife abundance, biodiversity or ecosystem stability.

A century of change on the prairies has affected wild canids differently (Sargeant *et al*. 1993). Coyote (*Canis latrans*) fared well and spread their range, while wolves were eliminated. Red foxes (*Vulpes vulpes*) became abundant in some areas, particularly around cultivated areas with farm buildings. The status of swift foxes paralleled that of wolves, that is, once common but disappeared in the first half of the 20th century. Habitat fragmentation and change from native to non-native grasslands, therefore, affected species differently.

The swift fox (*Vulpes velox*) once appeared to be more abundant throughout the Great Plains (Carlington 1980; Fauna West, 1991; Scott-Brown *et al.*, 1987). The species disappeared from the northern portion of its range and became rare in more southerly areas (Fig. 1).

The distribution of the species follows what, traditionally, has been considered the "normal" kind of distribution of a rare species namely, tendencies for populations to be lowest and less stable at the periphery of the range versus the centre (Brown 1984). Lomoline and Channell (1995) reviewed distribution changes of a range of non-volant terrestrial mammals and suggested that this pattern is not always applicable to population depletions in endangered mammals.

In southern Canada the swift foxes once were at the northern edge of its North American distribution. The last specimen collected in Canada was obtained as a museum skin in 1928 (COSEWIC 1978). After an absence of some 50 years swift foxes are now again present in small numbers but its ultimate fate in northern regions is still not certain. The closest northernmost record in the United States in recent years (prior to the Canadian reintroduction program) comes from North Dakota and is about 250 km south of the Canadian border (Pfeifer and Hibbard 1970). Cause for its widespread extirpation in some areas and decline in others is attributed to a number of factors (Table 1). A major cause may have been the ready acceptance by swift foxes of poisoned baits and vulnerability to trapping directed towards attempts to eliminate wolves from the great plains. However, if that were the sole cause one

Table 1. A review of potential factors that could have contributed to the decline of swift foxes in portions of its range and extirpation in other parts.

| Threats | Management options |
| --- | --- |
| Cultivation/habitat destruction | Habitat rehabilitation |
| Habitat fragmentation | Habitat rehabilitation |
| Ecosystem modification | |
| (loss of bison/wolves to the system) | Options limited/grazing |
| Predator control programs | No longer applicable |
| Trapping/hunting | Legal controls |
| Predation | Predator control |
| Road Mortalities | Signage/education |
| Pesticides/rodenticides | egal controls/biological controls |
| Winter food supplies | Grazing control/supplemental feeding |
| Canid diseases | None |

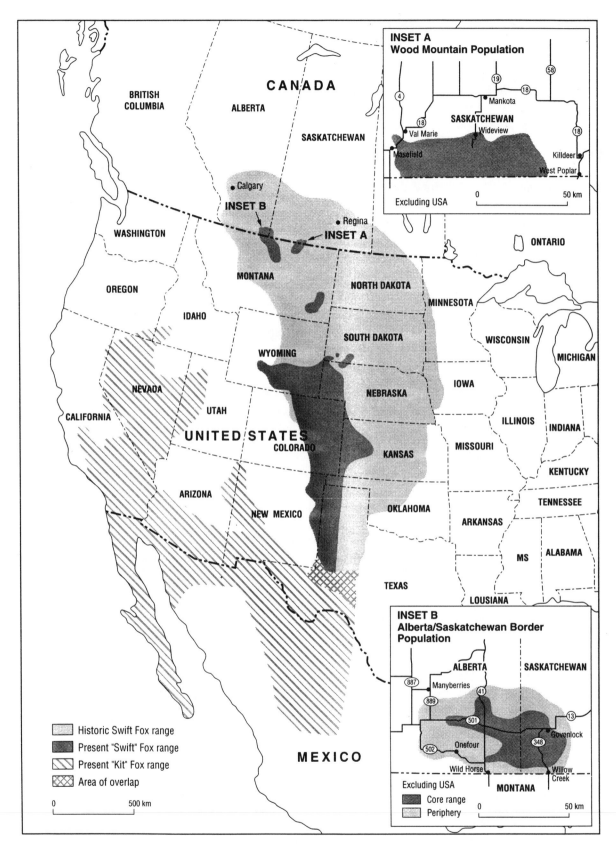

Figure 1. An approximate representation of the North American distribution of swift foxes on the continent. The northernmost distribution resulted from releases carried out in Alberta and Saskatchewan from 1983 to 1995.

would have expected the species to be eliminated in southern portions more so than in portions of its distribution in northern ranges. Wolf control began earlier and was more sustained in the United States than in Canada (Young and Goldman 1944; Carbyn 1983). Furthermore, it is highly unlikely that the demise can be attributed to any single factor. We are probably dealing with a suite of both anthropogenic and environmental factors, likely interacting in a combined manner to cause the declines. Loss of habitat to dry land agriculture, a changing prey base, and increased interspecific competition with coyotes and possibly red foxes have also been implicated. Added to this list is the possible impacts of habitat fragmentation, alteration of grazing regimes in which cattle replaced bison, the possible impacts of canid diseases and climatic change.

The reintroduction program in Canada began as a private project initiated when in 1973 the Smeeton family established a wildlife reserve near Calgary, Alberta, and imported two pairs of foxes from Colorado. This parent stock bred and raised young. That set in motion a lengthy process, which involved a large number of individuals and agencies (Herrero *et al.* 1991, Brechtel *et al.* 1993, Carbyn *et al.* 1994). Eventually four areas were chosen for releases. These were the Milk River Ridge area, the Lost River Ranch area, the Alberta-Saskatchewan border area and the Wood Mountain area in Saskatchewan.

## THE PLANNING PROCESS

Because of the evolution of the program through different stages, the project, from its inception, was not based on a single approved recovery plan. It had developed from a private initiative (1973), to a university project (1976) with some governmental support, to an interagency cooperative program (1984). Letters of agreement between provincial and federal governments had expired by 1989, were renewed to continue to 31 March 1994 and extended to 1997. Documents which placed the program into perspective initially were student thesis projects done through the University of Calgary under the direction of Stephen Herrero and subsequent agency reports. These included: 1) Carlington, B. 1978. Feasibility study: Reintroduction of the swift fox to southern Alberta; 2) Carlington, B. 1980. Reintroduction of the swift fox (*Vulpes velox*) to the Canadian prairies. M.Sc. thesis. Univ. of Calgary; 3) Reynolds, J. 1983. A plan for the reintroduction of swift fox to the Canadian prairies. M.Sc. thesis. Univ. of

Calgary; 4) Russell, R.H. and J. Zendran. 1983. A proposal to reintroduce the swift fox (*Vulpes velox*) to Alberta. Canadian Wildlife Service Report; 5) Carbyn, L.N. and C. Schroeder 1987. Preliminary recovery plan for the swift fox in Canada. Canadian Wildlife Service report.

By 1989 a considerable amount of field work had been carried out. However, a general framework for operation was still lacking. The then newly appointed Recovery Team set out to develop options and a management strategy. It is important to recognize that, without the lengthy trial and error period, none of the information we now have on the responses of the foxes to different release techniques and to different environmental conditions, would have been available. When the Recovery Team was established in April 1989, it had available to it a wealth of experience upon which to build a program. The Committee set out a schedule and maintained it throughout. From 1989 to 1992 the Committee held 17 meetings. The period was marked by an excellent spirit of cooperation among the agencies in carrying out, what at times, became a very difficult task. To this point much of the emphasis was on organizational structures (who does what) and policy. The recovery teams and the management authorities positions were that research should not be carried out in preference to "hands on management" activities. This resulted in a greater emphasis on practical aspects relating to captive breeding, acquisition of wild foxes and broad scale monitoring.

Results from an analysis of experimental releases of wild versus captive raised foxes, carried out from 1990 to 1992, indicated that wild caught foxes had a higher survival rate than captive raised spring released foxes (Brechtel *et al.* 1993). Similar experiments were not carried out in fall released foxes. Initial experimental work on survival of captive raised foxes immediately after release, can be increased by using portable protective shelters (Smeeton 1994). These shelters are boxes measuring about 40 x 20 x 20 cm.

The Canadian project had taken on a new dimension in 1994, as two research projects involving the Canadian Wildlife Service, universities and provincial agencies were initiated. This is a recognition that ecosystem management in Canada has been receiving higher priorities than before. Projects involve evaluating effects of radio collars on the behaviour of foxes. Another project is a study on the population dynamics of swift foxes at the northern extreme of their distribution and a study on food availability in winter (see Klausz *et al.* this volume). At the same time there was an emerging need for greater

Table 2. Summary of swift fox releases to reintroduce fox populations into southern Canada in an experimental reintroduction project (1983 to 1995).

| Year/Season of Release | Alta./Sask. Border | | Wood Mountain | | Milk River Ridge | |
|---|---|---|---|---|---|---|
| | # Released | # Collared | # Released | # Collared | # Released | # Collared |
| Fall 1987 | 57 | 18 | - | - | - | - |
| Fall 1988 | 53 | 12 | - | - | - | - |
| Spring 1989 | - | - | - | - | 28 | 14 |
| Fall 1989 | 35 | 13 | - | - | 33 | 13 |
| Spring 1990 | 28 | 27 | - | - | - | - |
| Fall 1990 | 38 | 0 | 51 | 20 | - | - |
| Spring 1991 | - | - | 29 | 28 | - | - |
| Fall 1991 | 35 | 0 | 46 | 10 | - | - |
| Fall 1992 | - | - | 87 | - | - | - |
| Fall 1993 | 15 | - | 35 | - | - | - |
| Fall 1994 | 43 | - | 19 | - | - | - |
| | | | | | | |
| Site Total | 304 | 70 | 267 | 58 | 61 | 27 |
| | | | | | | |
| Hard Release (1987-1995) | | | | | | 632 |
| | | | | | | |
| Soft Releases (between 1983 and 1987) | | | | | | 136 |
| | | | | | | |
| **Total** | | | | | | **768** |

cooperation among countries. This has become particularly important in recent years with the petition in the United States to declare the species, in at least part of its range, as an endangered species.

Earlier conservation issues regarding the species centred on the taxonomic status of northern populations (U.S. Fish and Wildlife Service 1979, 1982). The swift/kit fox complex should be looked at as a continental population and cooperation among Canada, United States and Mexico will be important. First efforts in that regard were made when in 1993 a swift fox workshop was held in Medicine Hat, Alberta. Further initiatives are underway. A Canadian/Mexican exchange project was initiated in 1994 and involves the Canadian Wildlife Service and two students from Oxford University in England.

## METHODS

From 1983 to the fall of 1987 all releases of mainly captive bred foxes had been done by the soft release technique, i.e., holding foxes over winter in field pens and releasing them into the prairies the following spring or summer. Foxes in soft releases were continued to be fed in release pens and had the option to stay in the pens or hunt for themselves. Through this method foxes became accustomed to the site and once released it was hoped that they would remain in the general area. In the fall of 1987 the first hard releases were attempted; releasing foxes directly into the natural prairie landscape, without subsequent feeding. Timing of hard releases from August to October—a period when young foxes normally disperse. Total number of foxes released are shown in Table 2.

About 30% of all swift foxes released were radio collared in both hard and soft releases. Survival data were obtained by monitoring collared foxes from the ground and from the air. The program was expanded in 1989 to include: 1) releasing more wild trapped foxes and comparing their survival with captive bred individuals; 2) releasing foxes in the spring rather than the fall to determine which time frame gives better survival; and 3) diversify release locations, choosing a release area which has more moisture and better habitat as a hedge against drought which had occurred in 1988 at the main release location. Swift foxes for the Canadian reintroduction program were obtained from the United States. They were caught in South Dakota, Wyoming and Colorado. Since the inception of the program, foxes were captured and used as breeding stock at 3 facilities and were released into the wild after a 30 day quarantine period (Carbyn et al. 1994). During the 1973-1995 period a total of 124 foxes were captured in the United States for the purpose of captive breeding and direct releases.

Population estimates of foxes were carried out in Alberta (Mamo 1994) and Saskatchewan (Hjertaas 1994) using a combination of live trapping, general track surveys (on foot, by skis and on skidoos), night lighting and scat counts.

A second source of information was interviews in 1995 with pasture managers, ranchers and riders at the Battle Creek, Govenlock and Nashlyn pastures (PFRA) and private run Lost River Ranch. This resulted in getting an overview and impressions of the sightability and presence of foxes within the 1994 and 1995 period.

Three community pastures are located east of the Alberta-Saskatchewan border. These are the Govenlock pasture (27,712 hectares of which 12.3 sections were ploughed), Nashlyn pasture (24,780 hectares of which 7.4 sections were ploughed) and the Battle Creek pasture (28,296 hectares of which 27 sections were ploughed). A large private land holding and associated crown lands, the Lost River Ranch (22,532 hectares, none of which has been broken) is located to the west of these community pastures.

## RESULTS AND DISCUSSION

After a total of 768 foxes had been released, it was found that foxes could survive and reproduce in an area they once flourished but had become extinct (Brechtel et al. 1993; Carbyn et al. 1994). Survival and reproduction to $F_1$, $F_2$ and subsequent generations was achieved. From 1984 to 1993, 55 pairs of free-roaming foxes produced a minimum of 183 young for an average of 3.3 pups per litter (Brechtel et al. 1993). Subsequent field work in the winter of 1993/94 indicated that foxes still had maintained their numbers in the core areas (W. Harris and C. Mamo pers. comm.), despite the fact that the winter was moderate to severe, both in terms of snow depths and low temperatures. One fox had survived for 6 years since it was first released. Clearly, on the short term it has been established that the niche is still present for the foxes.

The region identified as containing swift foxes in Alberta is shown in Figure 1. The region has been divided into the core area and the periphery area (Mamo 1994). Saturation trapping of one township in 1991 resulted in a density of eight swift foxes per township or 1 fox per 1,165 ha. The saturation trapping was followed in 1994 with another Survey (Mamo 1994). The second survey resulted in the capture of 13 foxes or 1 fox per 717 ha. Trapping in January 1995 resulted in the capture of 18 foxes in one township or 1 fox per 516 ha but not also in the immediate periphery bordering that township. (A. Moehrenschlager and J. Michie, preliminary data). Even though a preliminary assessment of the figures may lead one to conclude, that the population has increased, a study of current mortality rates trends suggest that this might be misleading. Studies currently in progress will evaluate the overall population dynamics of the recently established population. (A. Moehrenschlager).

The border population estimate for 1989 to 1991 was around 200 (Brechtel et al. 1993). The population estimate for 1994 (based on 8 captures) was about 120 foxes (Mamo, 1994). If we use the capture information for 1995 (18 foxes per township in the core area), the latest estimate would be about 300 foxes—an increase from 1994 to 1995. Foxes were captured in mid-winter and survival to spring was low, possibly indicating that food stress may be a factor in late winter.

In the process of monitoring foxes in the Alberta/ Saskatchewan area for 1995, one field worker estimated a population to be no more than 100 foxes at a time when the population is at its lowest, i.e. early spring a period prior to production of new litters (J. Michie pers. com.).

Mamo (1994) believed the decline from 1991 to 1994 may have been the result of two relatively severe winters and increased coyote populations. Two previously identified areas designated as core (in 1993) were devoid of foxes in 1994. Coyote activity and sightings had increased considerably. During track count surveys Mamo noted that at least 3 coyote tracks were observed for every swift fox track and it was not uncommon to observe from 6 - 12 coyotes per day. Mamo's ground observations substantiated reports from the division of Fish and Wildlife that coyote numbers had about doubled from the late 1980's to mid-1990's (G. Erickson pers. com.).

Community pasture managers at Govenlock, Battle Creek and Nashlyn all reported substantial increases in coyote numbers from 1990 to 1995. Similarly, Lost River Ranch owner, L. Piotrowski, noted substantial increase of coyotes and predation on calves. Presence of mange had been reported, but a consensus was that incidence appeared to have decreased within the 1994 to 1995 period.

Distribution of foxes in the southern Saskatchewan area is shown in Figure 1. Survival and establishment of foxes were lower in the Wood Mountain area than in the Alberta/Saskatchewan border area. One estimate places the 1993 border population at 25 foxes (Hjertaas, 1994). As with the Alberta population, the established Saskatchewan population is vulnerable and may disappear.

Swift foxes released at both release sites (Wood Mountain; Alberta-Saskatchewan border area) have moved into Montana (Carbyn and Killaby 1989; Hjertaas 1994; Craig Knowles pers. comm.). Because little monitoring has taken place not much is known about numbers. It is possible that small pockets of swift fox populations do exist. One such area is in the Fort Belknap Reservation. Three observations were made of swift foxes in the reserve during 1992-1994 (C. Knowles *et al.* in prep.).

The Canadian swift fox population in 1995, at peak numbers (in the fall period), probably ranges from 200 to 400 foxes. The most productive, core population exists along the Alberta/Saskatchewan border and occupies approximately 19 townships. Population in the core area in Saskatchewan (Grasslands National Park and adjacent areas) includes a more limited range (approximately 10 townships). Foxes are known to have ranged south into Montana for about 120 km from the U.S.-Canadian border (P. Knowles pers. com.) and as far north as Jenner, Alberta, about 190 km from the U.S.-Canadian border.

The results of the interviews with ranchers were revealing. The pasture manager for Govenlock PFRA

estimated that the area appeared to sustain a population of about 50 foxes. A rancher at Lost River Ranch noted more significant activities in winter (particularly around cattle guards), then in summer, but he knew of one den in an area immediately adjacent to his ranch (at the One-Four experimental station). The pasture manager at the Battle Creek site noted the presence of one fox in both 1994 and 1995. There were no reports of foxes from the Nashlyn community pasture. Correlation may not lead to cause and effect conclusions, however, one inference that can be made from the above is that the Govenlock fox population may benefit from some factors limited or absent from the other areas.

Mixed grass prairies, if not dissected by coulees, present a fairly uniform environment. Slope, moisture gradients, substrate, exposure to prevailing winds and animal disturbance create micro situations that enhances localized differences in the biotic community.

Roads are a major intrusion, as are coulees. They provide human access into the areas on a consistent basis, thus exposing species, such as coyote to human related mortality (shooting, highway kills). Some scavenging of road kills by both foxes and coyotes is possible (Hines and Case 1991). In 1994, 5 swift fox pups at one den site near a road were all killed by vehicles (L. Piotrowski pers. com.). Risk of foxes to being killed by vehicles is offset by the potential protection that roads could provide in reducing the presence of coyotes. Roads, therefore, could be looked upon as "linear refuge areas" for foxes if actual losses to vehicles is minimized. Roadsides may also provide micro environments that could be favourable to small mammal survival in that ditches adjacent to roads provide moister conditions than in surrounding areas.

## ECOSYSTEM RESEARCH

Short term success of fox survival does not guarantee long term establishment of populations as an integral part of the prairie ecosystem. Harsh northern environmental conditions, together with human impacts such as habitat fragmentation, prey base alterations through manipulation of grazing schedules, fence and road construction, killing of coyotes and provision of or removal of carrion can all affect fox survival and distribution. By establishing a network of research projects continent wide, north/south similarities and differences can provide information on a continental basis on the conservation needs of the species. Concerns have also been raised as to the continent wide status of the species. In 1993 a petition to classify the northern populations (possibly all the swift foxes in the United States as well) as an endangered species under U.S. Endangered Species Act was filed with the U.S. Fish and Wildlife Service. The petition is currently under review.

In 1993 the Wildlife Directors of Alberta, Saskatchewan and the Canadian Wildlife Service agreed that the reintroduction efforts in Canada should continue to 1997. The directors approved and supported a multi-agency approach, as it reduced costs to each stakeholder and increased effectiveness in getting a wider coverage of release sites and monitoring.

In order to advance from the present status to the recovery goal, the Canadian Recovery Plan outlined the following strategy: a) release sufficient swift foxes to ensure attainment of self sustaining population by the year 2000; b) identify, evaluate, manage and protect key habitat; c) protect wild swift foxes; d) monitor densities and distribution of wild swift foxes; e) maintain public administrative support; f) improve understanding of the demographics and ecological relationships of wild swift foxes. To date little emphasis was placed on research needs. The "who does what and how phase" was important to get the foxes out into the prairies. We have to now get into asking "what is going on and why?" phase. Can the species survive in the long term without constant supplementation of new foxes from captive and wild stocks?

## ACKNOWLEDGEMENTS

I would like to thank W. Harris, R. Longmuir, C. Mamo, J. Michie, A. Moehrenschlager (information supplied in unpublished reports) and K. Sturgess for the monitoring of fox survival in the field. H. Armbruster (Canadian Wildlife Service), S. Brechtel (Alberta), D. Hjertaas (Saskatchewan), A. Moehrenschlager (Oxford University), and C. Smeeton (Cochrane Wildlife Reserve) were active participants in many phases of the project. Without their involvement, this project would not have been possible to the degree it had developed. The staff of the various breeding facilities, particularly M. Curtis, J. Michie, P. Rhodes and C. Smeeton were enthusiastic participants and important to the program. Calgary Zoo staff, Sandy Black, Pam McDougall and Laurie McGivern provided much needed support. Staff of Wyoming Game and Fish, in particular Steve Dececco, provided important assistance in the capture of foxes in the United States within the last 5 years. Ranchers and managers L. Flaig, A. Frey, R. Jennett, R. Moorehead and L. Pietrowski gave generously of their information on the presence of foxes and coyotes in their areas. The program was funded by the Canadian Wildlife Service, Alberta Department of Environmental Protection, World Wildlife Fund Canada, Petro Canada, Esso Resources, Swift Fox Conservation Society and various other groups.

## LITERATURE CITED

Brechtel, S., L.N. Carbyn, D. Hjertaas, and C. Mamo. 1993. Canadian Swift Fox Feasibility Study: 1989 to 1992. Swift Fox Recovery Team Report.

Brown, J.H. 1984. On the relationship between distribution and abundance. The American Naturalist 124: 255-279.

Carbyn, L.N. 1983. Management of non-endangered wolf populations in Canada. Acta Zoologica Fennica 174: 239-243.

Carbyn, L.N. and M. Killaby. 1989. Status of the swift fox in Saskatchewan. Blue Jay 47: 41-52.

Carbyn, L.N., H.J. Armbruster, and C. Mamo. 1994. The swift fox reintroduction program in Canada from 1983 to 1992. Pp. 247-271 *In* Restoration of endangered species: Conceptual issues, planning and implementation (M.L. Bowles and C.J. Whelan eds.). Cambridge Univ. Press.

Carlington, B. 1980. Reintroduction of the swift fox (*Vulpes vulpes*) to the Canadian prairies. M.Sc. Univ. of Calgary.

COSEWIC. 1978. Committee On The Status Of Endangered Wildlife In Canada 1978. Status report and evaluations. Vol. 1. Official classification of the swift fox.

Fauna West Wildlife Consultants. 1991. An Ecological and taxonomic review of the swift fox (*Vulpes velox*) with a special reference to Montana. Montana Fish and Wildlife and Parks.

Herrero, S., C. Mamo, L. Carbyn, and M. Scott-Brown. 1991. Swift fox reintroduction into Canada. Pp. 246-252 *In* Proceedings of the 2nd Endangered Species and Prairie Conservation Workshop (G. Holroyd and H. Smith eds.). Provincial Museum of Alberta, Natural History Occasional Paper No. 15.

Hines, T.D. and R.M. Case. 1991. Diet, home range, movements and activity periods of swift fox in Nebraska. Prairie Naturalist. 23: 131-138.

Hjertaas, D. 1994. Reintroduction of the swift fox on the Wood Mountain Plateau in Saskatchewan. Saskatchewan Environment and Resource Management Report.

Lomoline, M.V. and R. Channell. 1995. Splendid isolation: Patterns of geographic range collapse in endangered mammals. Journal of Mammology 76: 335-347.

Mamo, C. 1994. Swift fox (*Vulpes velox*) population survey assessment (1994). Rocky Mountain Wildlife Research Report.

Pfeifer, W.K. and E.A. Hibbard. 1970. A recent record of the swift fox (*Vulpes velox*) in North Dakota. Journal of Mammalogy. 51: 835.

Sargeant, A.B., R.J. Greenwood, and M.A. Shaffer. 1993. Distribution and abundance of predators that affect duck production - prairie pothole region. U.S. Fish and Wildlife Resource Publication 194.

Scott-Brown, M., S. Herrero, and J. Reynolds. 1987. Swift foxes. Pp. 1168 *In* Wild furbearer management and conservation in North America (N.M. Novak, G.A. Baker, M.E. Obbard, and B. Mallock eds.). Ontario Trappers Association, Ministry of Natural Resources, Ontario.

Smeeton, C. 1994. Reintroducing the swift fox. Canid News. Pp. 13-16 *In* Newsletter of the Canid Specialist Group (D. Macdonald and I. Handoca, eds.). Wildlife Conservation Research Unit. Oxford University.

Young, S.P. and E.A. Goldman. 1944. The wolves of North America. American Wildlife Institute, Washington, D.C.

U.S. Fish and Wildlife Service. 1979. Federal Register, 17 June 1979. Washington, D.C., National Archives and Record Service.

U.S. Fish and Wildlife Service. 1982. Federal Register, 30 December 1982. Washington, D.C., National Archives and Record Service.

# INTERACTION OF VEGETATION STRUCTURE AND SNOW CONDITIONS ON PREY AVAILABILITY FOR SWIFT FOX IN THE NORTHERN MIXED-GRASS PRAIRIES: SOME HYPOTHESES

## Erika E. Klausz[1], Ross W. Wein[1], and L.N. Carbyn[2]

[1]*Department of Renewable Resources, University of Alberta, Edmonton, Alberta T6G 2H1*
[2]*Canadian Wildlife Service, 4999-98 Ave., Edmonton, Alberta T6B 2X3*

## ABSTRACT

Swift foxes (*Vulpes velox*) have been reintroduced to the Canadian Prairies since 1984: the present population is estimated at around 200. It is not clear what factors are the most critical in defining swift fox survival. Swift foxes utilize birds, insects, small mammals, lagomorphs and carrion for most of the spring, summer and fall months. As winter approaches, the prey source becomes much more limited including a few small mammal species, lagomorphs, and to a limited extent, birds and carrion. Small mammals appear to be the most available and accessible food item during the winter months. Small mammal numbers may be crucial in determining swift fox survival during the winter especially if snow depth and hardness prevent foxes from accessing the prey. It is hypothesized that the pattern of vegetation-snow-small mammal dynamics will determine overwintering success and therefore the long-term survival of the swift fox.

## INTRODUCTION

### Historical Range

The historical range of the swift fox *(Vulpes velox)* in Canada extended in Alberta north to the 53rd parallel and west to the edge of the Rocky Mountains. In Saskatchewan, the population reached to the North Saskatchewan River. There is some speculation that populations once existed in the southwestern region of Manitoba as well, but this is uncertain (Carbyn 1994). Numbers began to decline rapidly as European settlers arrived. The last documented swift fox record in Canada was in 1938 at Manyberries, Alberta (Soper 1964).

Factors that may have contributed to the eventual extirpation of the species from the Canadian Prairies include trapping, habitat destruction, disease, and inadvertent killing during predator control programs (Hines 1980; Carbyn *et al.* 1994). Some of these factors (trapping, predator control) are no longer relevant in all regions of swift fox habitat. Presently, mortalities may be attributed to rodenticide and pesticide use, an increased coyote population, which prey on the foxes, and vehicular traffic.

### Present Range and Numbers

Highest known population densities are found in two areas including Wood Mountain, Saskatchewan and the Alberta/Saskatchewan border region (Fig. 1). Since the initiation of efforts to reintroduce the swift fox to the Canadian Prairies in 1983, 768 captive-raised and wild-caught swift foxes have been released. Since then, numbers have reached about 200 (Carbyn *et al.* 994). There are many untested hypotheses as to why the population has not risen further.

### Objective

The objective of this paper is to raise several hypotheses as to how food might be a major limiting factor in the northern part of the swift fox range.

### The Cycle of Prey

Swift foxes are opportunistic predators and feed on a variety of available prey over the year. For much of the summer period, prey may include small mammals, birds, eggs, insects, reptiles, and carrion (Hines 1980). The importance of these prey items reflect the most available food type within the region (Rongstad *et al.* 1989). Studies in the central United States have indicated that lagomorphs are the major constituent of the swift fox diet (Egoscue 1962; Cutter 1958; Kilgore 1969). Hines (1980) stated that in Nebraska, rabbits are the primary food source in winter while in spring it is mice. Birds and insects are the major food source during the summer. Kilgore (1969) found that rabbits in the Oklahoma Panhandle comprised the major food source in early spring while rodents comprised the largest

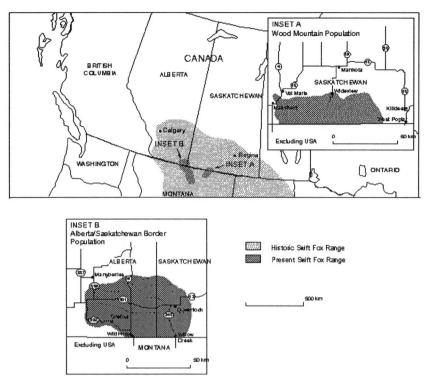

Figure 1. Present and historic swift fox range in Canada.

portion of the diet in fall. Hines and Case (1991) found that from January through August, the most frequently occurring prey items in swift fox scats collected in Nebraska were prairie voles and western harvest mice.

In the northern part of the swift fox range there is a lower density and diversity of alternative prey available. This is generally the trend observed as one goes northward in any region (Simpson 1964). Consequently, predators preying primarily on microtines are expected to decline after a crash in populations in these areas due to a shortage of alternative food. However, the seasonal cycle of prey capture of the swift fox is yet to be described. In the spring, a wider assortment of prey becomes available as birds return from their wintering grounds and ground squirrels resume activity after hibernation. In the summer, insects along with birds are abundant and become important in the diet. Hines and Case (1991) in Nebraska, observed that the frequency of occurrence of birds in the swift fox diet was highest during June-August, which probably reflected increased availability of birds. In autumn as birds move south again, insects become inactive, and ground squirrels prepare for hibernation, small mammals become increasingly important. Uresk and Sharps (1986) noted that there was a greater reliance on small mammals such as microtines and cricetines as winter approached. This

is probably the case in the Canadian Prairies as well. Scat samples collected around release sites in 1987, indicated that the highest frequency of prey occurrence in the diet during the winter months were microtines (Harry Armbruster and Charles Mamo, unpublished data). Preliminary analysis of stomach contents of one dead fox found in the Alberta/Saskatchewan border region in April consisted solely of voles (Axel Moehrenschlager, pers. comm.).

Although other potential prey may be present such as lagomorphs, snow buntings, grouse and Hungarian partridge, they are less available and accessible than the rodents. Zoellick and Smith (1992) observed that in the kit fox range of Arizona, lagomorphs (black-tailed jackrabbits and desert cottontails) were not abundant whereas nocturnal rodents were the most available throughout the year. Additionally, lagomorphs will concentrate in areas less preferred by the foxes such as in the coulees and brushy regions of high vegetation (Mamo 1994).

Prey may be limiting if foxes rely on small mammals as a major food source in winter. Over winter breeding of small mammals stops and the populations will decline naturally until early spring (Van Horne 1983; Erlinge 1987). Small mammal availability and accessibility will be governed by vegetation-snow characteristics of the wintertime decline in prey base.

## Suitable Habitats

Present fox population locations suggest that agricultural areas are poor swift fox habitat; it is hypothesized that there is a lack of suitable denning habitat, an insufficient prey base due to disturbance factors and the use of pesticides and rodenticides (Carbyn et al. 1994). River valleys, coulees and brushy areas are not favoured habitats either (Mamo 1994), at least for denning. The most suitable habitat appears to be native grasslands with short grass cover and flat to slightly rolling topography (Mamo 1994). There is considerable variability in habitats within the Canadian mixed-grass prairie and vegetation structure will vary depending on grazing pressure. Roadsides, ditches, and riparian habitats with abundant vegetation are a very small percentage of the landscape but may well prove to be important sites for a small mammal prey base. Close proximity to roads will serve as suitable hunting grounds (Hines and Case 1991). If swift fox rely on small mammals over the winter we need to know how closely species and populations are linked to vegetation and snow conditions.

## Vegetation and Small Mammals

A number of studies in the southern part of the swift fox range have indicated that alteration of vegetation influences small mammal populations (Rosenzweig and Winakur 1969; Rosenzweig 1973; Birney et al. 1976). O'Farrell (1983) found that overgrazing decreased prey diversity which resulted in a decline of kit fox densities in a hot desert environment. A similar scenario may be true for the swift fox in a cold desert environment. Rosenzweig (1973) observed that kangaroo rats (Dipodomys merriami) avoided areas with thick cover of vegetation heights between 8-45 cm, while pocket mice (Perognathus penicillatus) preferred areas that had cover over 45 cm (bushes). Whitford (1976) noted that the cotton rat (Sigmodon hispidus) preferred habitats with dense cover and had densities of 1 individual/ha under grazing and >14 individuals/ha when protected from cattle grazing. Furthermore, resident species of cotton rats, harvest mice (Reithrodontomys megalotis), and silky pocket mice (Perognathus flavus) responded to increased vegetation biomass by exhibiting increased recruitment and survivorship. The deer mouse (Peromyscus maniculatus) was more tolerant of shorter vegetation cover resulting from cattle grazing than microtine species that prefer areas of denser cover (LoBue and Darnell 1959; Birney et al. 1976) and required bushy growth (Rosenzweig and Winakur 1969). Taitt and Krebs (1983) showed that voles with extra vegetation cover had a significantly lower decline in numbers over the winter than populations with less vegetation cover. Quantitative studies of vegetation structure on small mammals are unavailable for the northern limits of the swift fox range.

Linear habitats such as roadsides and ditches often contain higher vegetation cover than adjacent fields grazed by cattle and often serve as protective havens for small mammal species under critical conditions. Mills et al. (1991) found that linear habitats along crop fields and undisturbed pasture in central Argentina generally supported higher relative densities of rodents especially during cultivation when these areas provided protective habitat. They found small mammal populations decreased abruptly or were completely absent following crop harvest while trap success in linear habitats was relatively stable with some increase as vegetation height increased in spring and some decrease as vegetation height decreased in winter. In Texas, Cutter (1958) observed that small mammals often concentrated along these corridors and swift foxes commonly foraged these areas. Zoellick et al. (1989) found that in Arizona, desert riparian habitats could be important foraging areas for kit foxes because of higher prey numbers in these productive and diverse areas. Indices of small mammal biomass were greatest in and near riparian areas as compared to more upland areas. Although foxes have been reported to den mostly on flat terrain where vegetation is sparse (Egoscue 1962), regions with higher vegetation cover and abundance of prey may well prove to be important hunting grounds.

## Snow and Small Mammals

Duration of snow cover, thickness, hardness and density are important features determining small mammal survival (Merritt 1984). Hardness and density of snow are governed by wind and winter freeze-thaw cycles. These factors will affect small mammal populations and swift fox accessibility to the prey.

Observations have indicated that at the beginning of the winter, when the snow is still shallow and temperatures do not fall below -5 to -10 degrees Celsius, activities of voles, mice, shrews, and even moles are apparent on the surface of the snow layer in Northern Russia. As snow depth increases and temperatures fall below -10 degrees, small mammals concentrate their activities under the snow cover and will rarely come to the surface, although voles will have ventilation holes (Formozov 1964). Peromyscus species are generally more active above the snow than vole species but are less preferred by the fox because of the ease with which voles are caught (Halpin and Bissonette 1988). With snow depths of 10-15 cm, runways beneath the snow remain relatively stable and do not collapse. During this time, vole species construct subnivean nests on the soil surface in the dead grassy cover and abandon their summer subterranean nests. This protects them from winter temperatures because of the low conductivity of the snow offering more protection than the frozen soil which has a greater conductivity (Formozov 1964). Small mammals will avoid places where the snow has been blown away (Formozov 1964). Hence, higher mortalities of rodents is likely to occur when there is less snow cover and where snow density is high which increases heat conductivity. Swift foxes have not been an intensively studied canid throughout their range (Hines and Case 1991) and northern studies are especially lacking. To our knowledge there are no studies that clarify the relations of vegetation and snow characteristics on small mammal species and populations in the northern range of the swift fox.

## Snow and Foxes

Red foxes detect prey under the snow with their keen sense of smell and hearing (Formozov 1964) and then pounce on their unsuspecting victims. Apparently, red foxes (*Vulpes vulpes*) are able to find the winter nests of voles under 30 to 40 cm of snow. Foxes have been observed to make as many as 20 to 25 diggings on their daily hunting routes (Formozov 1964). As the snow becomes deeper and more dense, prey are less available. A thin layer of snow with a hard crust can be more obstructive for hunting than relatively deep and fluffy snow. In low snowfall years, small mammals may concentrate in their burrows in the frozen soil and would be unavailable to foxes. Halpin and Bissonette (1988) observed, in eastern Maine, that red foxes preferred open areas for hunting, especially those areas with grass and sedge vegetation when snow was shallower. As snow depth increased, habitats with dense understorey vegetation were used. As snow depth and crusting of snow increased, the availability of small mammals in all habitats was restricted and the occurrence of hare in the diet increased. Foxes avoided deep soft snow for travel and favoured roads and trails and the wind-blown snow surfaces of open regions. Snow depths and structure reflected availability of predominant prey species and habitat use patterns by the fox. The proportion of small mammals in the diet decreased as snow depth increased or as crusting occurred. Pruitt (1978) also noted that small mammals are less accessible to predators as snow accumulates and forms crusts, resulting in snow conditions that are too difficult to penetrate.

There are no studies on the above subject for swift fox. Studies should be related specifically to the swift fox because of their morphology and their unique habitat.

## Climate

Winter snow fall, wind velocities and mean daily maximum temperatures for areas of swift fox habitat are given in Table 1. Although snowfall occurs in October, the snow does not begin to accumulate until November and then for the months of December to March roughly equal amounts of snow arrives per month. The extremely windy conditions (maximum hourly wind speeds) leads to relocation of snow into depressions and into dense drifts in the lee of obstructions such as shrubs and tall grasses. The daily average maximum temperatures in Table 1 suggest that temperatures reach well above the freezing point periodically in February and March; this can lead to snow crust formation.

## ASSUMPTIONS AND HYPOTHESES

It is assumed that microtines are the primary food source for the swift fox during winter and therefore dictate swift fox survival. In addition, late winter is the critical time for fox survival because food quantity declines and access to food source becomes increasingly limited by vegetation cover and snow conditions.

It is hypothesized that the general pattern of vegetation-snow-small mammal dynamics will be as follows, assuming there are sufficient prey numbers accessible to the foxes in early winter. As snow accumulates over the winter, and becomes more dense and crusted in areas with shorter grass cover (more heavily grazed and shorter vegetation types) because of wind action, the small mammals will aggregate in taller grass areas (ungrazed/lightly grazed and taller vegetation types) where snow is deeper and fluffier, providing them with better insulation and subnivean living space. In late winter, periodic temperatures above 0ºC will lead to crusting of the snow. This is an additional problem for foxes. Even though prey may be present they will not be accessible to the foxes.

Superimposed on this general pattern could be low or high snowfall years. In low snowfall years, under heavy wind action, snow is expected to be absent or at low levels in low vegetation areas and be very hard or dense. Small mammals will concentrate in areas where there is ample snow cover such as along roadsides with higher

Table 1. Selected climatic normals for the winter months at stations located in swift fox habitat.

| Measurement | Station | Oct. | Nov. | Dec. | Jan. | Feb. | Mar. | Apr. |
|---|---|---|---|---|---|---|---|---|
| Snow fall (cm) | Val-Marie | 6 | 12 | 15 | 19 | 12 | 15 | 7 |
| | Suffield | 7 | 14 | 20 | 21 | 13 | 15 | 14 |
| | Manyberries | 6 | 14 | 22 | 24 | 18 | 21 | 18 |
| | Foremost | 5 | 18 | 21 | 21 | 16 | 22 | 17 |
| | Aden | 9 | 14 | 24 | 24 | 15 | 26 | 23 |
| | Consul | 4 | 9 | 14 | 19 | 12 | 11 | 9 |
| | Mankota | 2 | 10 | 17 | 22 | 16 | 17 | 7 |
| Wind (km h$^{-1}$) | | | | | | | | |
| - daily average | Suffield | 19 | 18 | 18 | 18 | 18 | 18 | 19 |
| | Manyberries | — | 18 | 19 | — | 19 | 19 | 21 |
| - daily maximum | Suffield | 85 | 84 | 72 | 74 | 77 | 84 | 84 |
| | Manyberries | 77 | 76 | 92 | 85 | 95 | 89 | 85 |
| Temperature (°C) | Val-Marie | 13 | 3 | -5 | -6 | -4 | 3 | 12 |
| (daily maximum) | Suffield | 14 | 3 | -4 | -6 | -2 | 4 | 13 |
| | Manyberries | 13 | 3 | -4 | -6 | -2 | 3 | 12 |
| | Foremost | 14 | 4 | -3 | -4 | 0 | 4 | 12 |
| | Aden | 14 | 4 | 0 | -2 | 1 | 5 | 11 |
| | Mankota | 13 | 2 | -6 | -8 | -5 | 2 | 11 |

vegetation and in moister habitats. Under these conditions, small mammals are expected to have higher mortalities because of exposure to low temperatures and the higher conductivity of heat due to denser snow cover. Foxes will have more difficulty in digging out the prey from underneath this crusted, hard snow surface and must seek out areas with less dense and compacted snow such as around higher vegetation areas.

In high snowfall years, the snow covers both high and low vegetation areas. The small mammals will be more evenly distributed throughout the area and thus more available and accessible to the fox. If however, blowing winds and thaw-freeze cycles increase snow hardness or snow reaches extreme depths, small mammals will become inaccessible to the fox which must then hunt for alternative prey or find areas where the snow is less compacted and shallower if such areas exist within a reasonable distance.

The above hypotheses suggest how vegetation structure affects snow characteristics which in turn affects small mammal and swift fox hunting success through the winter. There are few data and even fewer studies that provide evidence. Hypotheses must be tested to help us understand if the winter period is the critical period for swift fox survival.

## ACKNOWLEDGEMENTS

We wish to recognize Dr. G.H. Coulter, Jasper Michie, Axel Moehrenschlager, Dr. Richard Moses, and Dr. Walter Willms for their help and discussions on many points that enabled us to better refine these hypotheses.

## LITERATURE CITED

Birney, E.C., W.E. Grant, and D.D. Baird. 1976. Importance of vegetative cover to cycles of *Microtus* populations. Ecology 57: 1043-1051.

Carbyn, L.N., H. Armbruster and C. Mamo. 1994. Reintroduction of the swift fox to the Canadian

Prairies. Pp. 247-271 *In* Symposium proceedings on restoration of endangered plants and animals (M. Bowles and C.J. Whelan, eds.). University of Cambridge Press.

Cutter, W.L. 1958. Food habits of the swift fox in northern Texas. Journal Mammalogy 39: 527-532.

Egoscue, H.J. 1962. Ecology and life history of the kit fox in Toole County, Utah. Ecology 43: 481-497.

Erlinge, S. 1987. Predation and noncyclicity in a microtine population in southern Sweden. Oikos 50: 347-352.

Formozov, A.N. 1964. Snow cover as an integral factor of the environment and its importance in the ecology of mammals and birds. Occasional Publication No.1. Boreal Institute for Northern Studies. University of Alberta, Edmonton, Alberta.

Halpin, M.A. and J.A. Bissonette. 1988. Influence of snow depth on prey availability and habitat use by red fox. Canadian Journal of Zoology 66: 587-592.

Hines, T.D. 1980. An ecological study of *Vulpes velox* in Nebraska. M.S. Thesis. Univ. of Nebraska, Lincoln, Nebraska.

Hines, T.D. and R.M. Case. 1991. Diet, home range, movements, and activity periods of swift fox in Nebraska. Prairie Naturalist 23: 131-138.

Kilgore, D.L. 1969. An ecological study of the swift fox *(Vulpes velox)* in the Oklahoma Panhandle. American Midland Naturalist 81: 512-534.

LoBue, J. and R.M. Darnell. 1959. Effects of habitat disturbance on a small mammal population. Journal Mammalogy 40: 425-437.

Mamo, C.C. 1994. Swift fox habitat survey. Alberta Fish and Wildlife Services. Rocky Mountain Wildlife Research.

Merritt, J.F. 1984. Winter ecology of small mammals. Special Publication of Carnegie Museum of Natural History. No.10. Pittsburgh.

Mills, J.N., B.A. Ellis, K.T. McKee, J.I. Maiztegui, and J.E. Childs. 1991. Habitat associations and relative densities of rodent populations in cultivated areas of central Argentina. Journal Mammalogy 72: 470-479.

O'Farrell, T.P. 1983. The San Joaquin kit fox recovery plan. U.S. Fish and Wildlife Service, Portland, Oregon.

Pruitt, W.O. 1978. Boreal ecology. Institute for Biological Studies, Biology No. 91. Camelot Press Ltd., Southampton, Great Britain.

Rongstad, O.J., T.R. Laurion, and D.E. Andersen. 1989. Ecology of swift fox on the Pinon Canyon Maneuver Site, Colorado. Final Report.

Rosenzweig, M.L. and J. Winakur. 1969. Population ecology of desert rodent communities: habitats and environmental complexity. Ecology 50: 558-572.

Rosenzweig, M.L. 1973. Habitat selection experiments with a pair of coexisting heteromyid rodent species. Ecology 54: 111-117.

Simpson, G.G. 1964. Species density of North American recent mammals. Systematic Zoology 13: 57-73.

Soper, J.D. 1964. The Mammals of Alberta. Edmonton. The Hamley Press Ltd.

Taitt, M.J. and C.J. Krebs. 1983. Predation, cover, and food manipulations during a spring decline of *Microtus townsendii*. Journal of Animal Ecology 52: 837-848.

Uresk, D.W. and J.C. Sharps. 1986. Denning habitat and diet of the swift fox in western South Dakota. Great Basin Naturalist 46: 249-253.

Van Horne, B. 1983. Density as a misleading indicator of habitat quality. Journal of Wildlife Management 47: 893-901.

Whitford, W.G. 1976. Temporal fluctuations in density and diversity of desert rodent populations. Journal of Mammalogy 57: 351-369.

Zoellick, B.W., N.S. Smith, and R.S. Henry. 1989. Habitat use and movements of desert kit foxes in western Arizona. Journal of Wildlife Management 53: 955-961.

Zoellick, B.W. and N.S. Smith. 1992. Size and spatial organization of home ranges of kit foxes in Arizona. Journal of Mammalogy 73: 83-88.

# STUDIES ON THE SWIFT FOX

## Axel Moehrenschlager

*Graduate Student, Department of Zoology, University of Oxford, England*

This study investigates the temporal utilization of space by swift fox (*Vulpes velox*) based on several ecosystem parameters. The effects of sex, season, disease prevalence, day period, topography, proximity to related or unrelated conspecifics, to coyotes, proximity to roads, prey base, and escape terrain are investigated.

Swift fox survival are expected to vary among adult/ juvenile and resident/captive-released populations. The study is designed to give some indication of how many swift foxes need to be released for a stable population to remain established in the area. Predator displacement will be tested by determining whether swift fox exist in areas of highest prey abundance or are displaced by coyotes to less favourable sites. This may hamper swift fox survival rates within the release sites. Factors affecting the dispersal success of resident and captive-bred juvenile swift fox will be monitored by radio-telemetry. The importance of different types of topographic, habitat, and structural aspects of the landscape will be identified. Release procedures could thus be modified according to the significance that these aspects have on survival.

Radio-tracking of animals has been used to investigate behavioral characteristics and interactive dynamics of wildlife populations. This study is designed to determine whether handling or the attachment of radio-collars on swift fox may cause significant behavioral differences among captive swift foxes in the short-term or the long term. Additionally, the study will determine adequate times of equilibration, should handling or collaring affect swift foxes in any way.

Behaviour of adult swift foxes in captivity are observed under three different treatment groups. The first are handled, inoculated, and radio-collared while the second placebo group are handled and inoculated only. The third group are not handled at all and serve as a control. Since swift foxes are an endangered species in Canada, it is crucial to verify that these actions do not significantly harm the animal.

# WHOOPING CRANE PRAIRIE HABITAT

## Brian W. Johns

*Canadian Wildlife Service, Saskatoon, Saskatchewan S7N 0X4*

## INTRODUCTION

Whooping Cranes typically spend 2 to 3 months each year in the prairie provinces, primarily Saskatchewan. Spring migration brings the birds through the prairie provinces between mid-April and mid-May, on their journey to the breeding grounds in Wood Buffalo National Park (Johns 1992). During fall migration early migrants may appear as early as mid August, with some birds lingering into November (Johns 1992). Regularly, but not each year, subadult whooping cranes may summer in the southern prairies. These areas used by the cranes were once a portion of their ancestral breeding grounds (Allen 1952).

## METHODS

Habitat use during migration through Saskatchewan was investigated between 1988 and 1990. Various habitat parameters were recorded at sites used by Whooping Cranes for feeding and roosting during the migration period.

## RESULTS

### Roost Site Characteristics

#### Wetland Type

Temporary and seasonal wetlands are used primarily during spring migration (71% of the time) when they are readily available, while during fall migration semi permanent and permanent wetlands are used (70% of the time).

#### Wetland Size

Mean wetland size used by the cranes varied by season. Mean wetland size used during spring migration was 37.8 hectares, while mean wetland size used during fall was 252 hectares.

### Ownership

Wetlands used were primarily in private ownership. Private ownership accounted for 85 (fall) to 96% (spring) of all wetlands used during migration. Provincial crown land accounted for 4 (spring) to 13 (fall) percent of all wetland use, while Federal crown lands (Last Mountain Lake National Wildlife Area) accounted for 2 percent (fall) of wetlands used.

### Land Use

Land use within 2 kilometres of the roost sites was: 71.3% cultivated lands; 15.5% wetlands; 9% pasture; 3.4% wooded and 0.6% occupied buildings.

### Disturbance

Mean distances to potential disturbance factors, such as buildings and roads, were less in spring than in fall. This may be due to the quantity of human disturbance that the birds were exposed to prior to migration. Human disturbance on the wintering grounds is greater, due to boat and barge traffic, than disturbance on the more remote breeding area.

### Feeding Site Characteristics

#### Habitat Type

Uncultivated and cultivated cereal crop stubble fields accounted for 99% of feeding sites in spring and 86% in fall.

#### Crop Type

Wheat fields made up the majority of feeding sites in spring (62%) and fall (59%). Barley stubble was used 27% of the time in spring and 36% of the time in fall. Durham and oat stubble fields were seldom used.

#### Disturbance

Distances to nearest buildings was less during spring migration than the fall.

## CURRENT POPULATION FIGURES

The Wood Buffalo population reached a high of 146 birds in 1989. Unusually high losses of birds during the winter and summer of 1991 reduced the population to 132. The population climbed back to 143 in 1993 but had since fallen to 133 by the end of 1994. During this same time period there have been record numbers of nesting pairs. In 1992 the number of breeding pairs equalled 40, up from the previous high of 33. During 1993 there were 45 nesting pairs. In 1994 the number of pairs breeding was 28, possibly due in part to poor habitat conditions caused by late spring thaw and low water levels in nesting ponds.

Chick survival on the breeding grounds since 1990 has been below average due to the poor habitat conditions. During years were water conditions are below average, chick survival is generally below average compared to years with abundant water conditions (Kuyt *et al.* 1992).

These recent population fluctuations demonstrate how precarious the recovery of the Whooping Crane can be and reinforces what a fragile balance we have between recovery and loss of a species.

## LITERATURE CITED

Allen, R.P. 1952. The whooping crane. National Audubon Society Research Report 3.

Johns, B.W. 1992. Preliminary identification of whooping crane staging areas in prairie Canada. Pp. 61-66 *In* Proceeding 1988 North American Crane Workshop (D.A. Wood ed.). Florida Game and Fresh Water Fish Commission, Tallahassee, Florida.

Kuyt, E., S.J. Barry, and B.W. Johns. 1992. Below average whooping crane production in Wood Buffalo National Park during drought years, 1990 and 1991. Blue Jay 50: 225-229.

# AN OVERVIEW OF SAGE GROUSE POPULATIONS IN ALBERTA

## Harold G. Vriend[1] and Leo D. Gudmundson[1]

[1]Alberta Environmental Protection, Natural Resources Service, Lethbridge, Alberta

## ABSTRACT

This paper provides a broad overview of sage grouse (*Centrocercus urophasianus*) inventory data obtained in Alberta for the period 1968 to 1994. Average male attendance at active leks in 1994 declined 64% from the 20 year average. Lek attendance has been below the long-term average since 1991 and depressed populations have been accompanied by abandonment of five of thirteen active leks. This rate of lek abandonment (9.6%/year) is substantially higher than the 2.7%/year rate recorded for the period 1968 to 1990. The direction for future management of sage grouse is discussed.

## INTRODUCTION

Sage grouse in Alberta occupy approximately 4,000 square kilometres of native rangelands in the extreme SE corner of the province (Fig. 1). Their distribution coincide with the occurrence and abundance of silver sage (*Artemesia cana*) (Carr 1972). Higher silver sage densities yield higher sage grouse populations and as a result most of the sage grouse in Alberta are associated with creek bottoms and drainage systems where sagebrush communities are common.

Sage grouse in Alberta are on the extreme northern edge of their North American range and their was between 3 and 6 thousand birds (Carr 1972). Current management goals suggest a sustainable spring population of 3,000 birds.

Much concern has been registered recently over a widespread decline in population levels throughout their North American range. Population declines have been recorded for Alberta. We have reviewed inventory data of sage grouse in Alberta and discuss possible factors influencing the decline. Future direction of management efforts are also indicated.

## Population Inventory

Inventories of sage grouse leks were initiated in 1967. Twenty-two leks were identified and monitoring of those leks has continued at irregular intervals since that time. The location of these leks is illustrated in Figure 1. Counts of males occupying the leks are taken in the first week of May. The number of males recorded on each lek and the average number of males per active lek are provided in Table 1.

High lek counts were recorded in 1968, 1969, 1980, 1981, 1987, 1988 and 1990. The 1990 count, however, is based on records obtained for only two leks. Low lek counts occurred in 1975, 1985 and for the last three years.

Since initiation of sage grouse lek counts, 21 of 29 leks have been abandoned. Sixteen leks were abandoned between 1968 and 1989. During this same period, seven new grounds were located. Using the original 22 leks located in 1968, the rate of abandonment (13 of 22 leks over a 21 year period) was 2.7% per year. During the last four years, five of the 13 remaining leks were abandoned for a rate of 9.6% per year.

In 1983 vegetation communities surrounding 25 of the 29 lek sites were inventoried (Clark and Dube 1984). These inventories covered a 6.4 kilometre square (4 mi²) area at each lek. A total of 102,304 hectares were mapped and major vegetation types were as follows:

| | | |
|---|---|---|
| Native grass prairie/Light sage | 47.3% | 3 to 10 plants/61 m line intercept |
| Native grass prairie/Heavy sage | 17.3% | >25 plants/61 m line intercept |
| Native grass prairie/Medium sage | 11.7% | 10 to 25 plants/61 m line intercept |
| Native grass prairie/Sparse sage | 9.2% | 0 to 3 plants/61 m line intercept |
| Cultivation | 6.7% | |
| Wet Meadow | 2.3% | |
| Miscellaneous | 5.5% | |

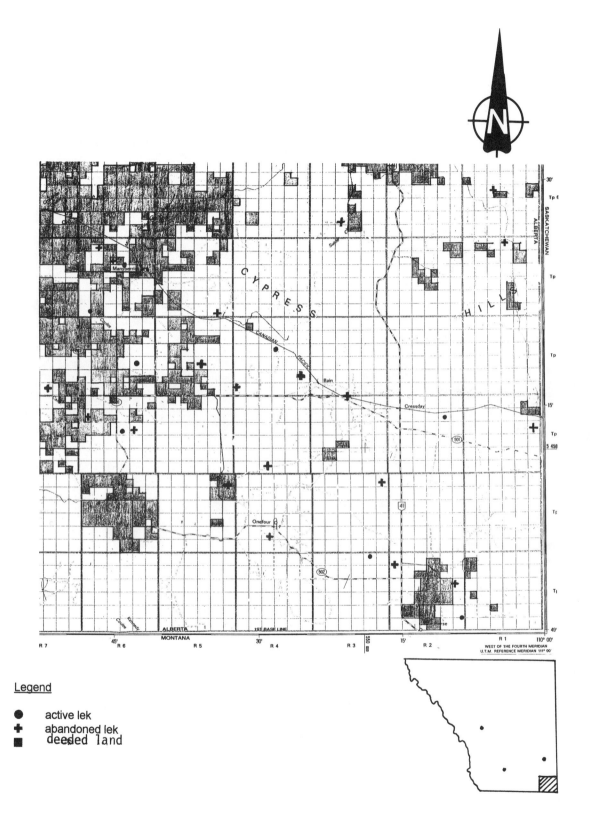

Legend

● active lek
✚ abandoned lek
■ deeded land

Figure 1. Sage grouse range in Alberta depicting the location of the leks and distribution of deeded lands.

Table 1. Male sage grouse occupancy on strutting grounds for the period of 1968-1995.

| Lek Number | Year | | | | | | | | | | | | | | | | | | | | |
|---|---|---|---|---|---|---|---|---|---|---|---|---|---|---|---|---|---|---|---|---|---|
| | 68 | 69 | 75 | 76 | 77 | 78 | 79 | 80 | 81 | 83 | 85 | 86 | 87 | 88 | 89 | 90 | 91 | 92 | 93 | 94 | 95 |
| 67-1 | 7 | 0 | 1 | 1 | a¹ | | | | | | | | | | | | | | | | |
| 67-2 | 36 | 30 | 15 | 18 | 13 | 11 | 9 | 19 | 28 | 16 | 7 | | 24 | 24 | 22 | a¹ | 28 | 12 | | 3 | 8 |
| 67-3 | 32 | 27 | 26 | 26 | | 13 | 8 | 14 | 15 | 15 | 14 | | 22 | 45 | 20 | | 5 | a¹ | | | |
| 67-4 | 85 | 83 | 8 | 44 | 36 | 34 | 51 | 54 | 54 | 50 | 23 | | 32 | | 11 | | | | | | |
| 67-5 | 14 | 14 | 11 | 12 | | 7 | 6 | 10 | 16 | 10 | 1 | a¹ | | | | | | | | | |
| 68-6/7 | 24 | 15 | 6 | 3 | | | | | | 1 | a¹ | | | | | | | | | | |
| 68-8 | 14 | 17 | 18 | 20 | 19 | 14 | | 6 | 5 | | | 20 | | | | | | | | | |
| 68-9 | 46 | 41 | 17 | 18 | 16 | 4 | | 24 | 27 | 23 | 16 | 18 | 35 | | 37 | 27 | 25 | 11 | | 11 | 4 |
| 68- | 58 | 38 | 26 | 30 | 30 | 35 | 18 | 57 | 53 | 44 | 24 | | 23 | | 27 | | 49 | 23 | 2 | 9 | 18 |
| 68-12 | 8 | 8 | 4 | 1 | a¹ | | | | | | | | | | | | | | | | |
| 68-13 | 43 | 39 | 7 | 15 | 8 | 5 | | 20 | 18 | 8 | 5 | | 8 | | 9 | | 1 | a¹ | | | |
| 68-14 | 12 | 0 | 4 | 8 | 16 | 2 | | 13 | 15 | 5 | a¹ | | | | | | | | | | |
| 68-15 | 12 | 14 | 5 | a¹ | | | | | | | | | | | | | | | | | |
| 68-16 | 38 | 44 | 16 | 27 | 15 | 13 | 13 | 26 | 27 | 24 | 13 | | 33 | | 32 | | 27 | 18 | 18 | 14 | 32 |
| 68-17 | 17 | 37 | 13 | 19 | 24 | 25 | 29 | 41 | 38 | 27 | 9 | | 29 | | 25 | | 2 | a¹ | | | |
| 68-18 | 22 | 16 | a¹ | | | | | | | | | | | | | | | | | | |
| 68-19 | 20 | 7 | 3 | a¹ | | | | | | | | | | | | | | | | | |
| 68-20 | 7 | 4 | 2 | a¹ | | | | | | | | | | | | | | | | | |
| 68-21 | 18 | 23 | a¹ | | | | | | | | | | | | | | | | | | 1² |
| 68-22 | 70 | 78 | 16 | 28 | 58 | 48 | 21 | 51 | 74 | 38 | 30 | | 69 | | 77 | 79 | 51 | | 26 | 9 | 7 |
| 68-23 | 30 | a¹ | | | | | | | | | | | | | | | | | | | |
| 69-24 | | 19 | 2 | a¹ | | | | | | | | | | | | | | | | | |
| 75-25 | | | 4 | 8 | | | | 9 | 2 | 3 | a¹ | | | | | | | | | | |
| 75-26 | | | 26 | 26 | 23 | | 20 | 32 | 66 | 17 | 18 | | 44 | | 31 | | 30 | | | 13 | 7 |
| 76-27 | | | | 14 | 1 | 11 | 8 | 30 | | 6 | 1 | | | | | | | | | | |
| 76-28 | | | | 29 | 27 | 17 | | 1 | 17 | 17 | 14 | a¹ | 25 | | 20 | | 12 | a¹ | | | |
| 79-29 | | | | | | | 15 | a¹ | | | | | | | | | | | | | |
| 80-30 | | | | | | | | 76 | 69 | 33 | 21 | | 31 | | 33 | | | | | 5 | 15 |
| 83-31 | | | | | | | | | | 21 | 13 | | 25 | | | | 11 | | 20 | 6 | 10 |
| 95-32 | | | | | | | | | | | | | | | | | | | | | 5**³ |
| 95-33 | | | | | | | | | | | | | | | | | | | | | 2** |
| Total | 613 | 554 | 214 | 347 | 286 | 239 | 198 | 483 | 524 | 358 | 209 | 38 | 400 | 95 | 344 | 106 | 241 | 46 | 66 | 70 | 110 |
| Avg.⁴ | 29.1 | 29.1 | 11.2 | 18.2 | 22.0 | 18.4 | 18.0 | 30.2 | 30.8 | 19.9 | 14.9 | 19.0 | 30.8 | 30.7 | 28.6 | 53.0 | 21.9 | 15.3 | 16.5 | 8.7 | 9.2 |

¹Abandoned
²Birds on abandoned grounds
³New Grounds
⁴20 year average - 23.3 males/ground

Table 2. Harvest and effort for sage grouse in Alberta.

| Year | Estimated Hunters | Estimated Harvest | No. of hunter-days | Birds per day |
|------|-------------------|-------------------|--------------------|--------------|
| 1992 | 150[1] | 103 | 288 | 0.4 |
|      | -[2,3] | - | - | - |
| 1991 | No data available | | | |
| 1990 | Insufficient data | | | |
| 1989 | 170 | 104 | 222 | 0.5 |
|      | - | - | - | - |
| 1988 | 446 | 452 | 821 | 0.6 |
|      | - | - | - | - |
| 1987 | 305 | 373 | 420 | 0.9 |
|      | 119 | 94 | 678h | 1.4 |
| 1986 | 183 | 180 | 280 | 0.6 |
|      | 67 | 24 | 324h | 0.7 |
| 1985 | No data available | | | |
|      | 41 | 20 | 216h | 0.9 |
| 1984 | - | - | - | - |
|      | 106 | 29 | 455h | 0.6 |
| 1983 | - | - | - | - |
|      | 57 | 45 | 455h | 0.6 |

[1] From harvest and effort by resident big game and bird game hunter telephone questionnaire.

[2] Data not available.

[3] Results of sage grouse hunter check stations - 1983-1987 (Moyles, D.L.J. 1989).

Recreational hunting of sage grouse in Alberta is limited. The season was first opened in 1967 and in the first year, 408 hunters harvested 272 birds during an October season. In 1983, the season was delayed to the last week of November. Limited information on the number of hunters suggest approximately 230 hunters harvest 250 birds annually. Success rates varied between 1.9 to 0.4 birds per hunter day (Table 2). This level of harvest represents less than 10% of the total population and is not considered detrimental to population levels.

# DISCUSSION

Population data for sage grouse in Alberta is limited. The data does indicate a population decline based on a lower than average number of males on active leks. However, extreme fluctuations in male occupancy of active leks are not unusual (Table 1). These fluctuations may or may not occur on all leks in a given year. For instance, male occupancy on two separate leks 68-10/11 and 68-22 (Table 1) illustrate that increases in male occupancy on one of the grounds was opposed by decreases on the other ground in 7 out of 20 years (1969,

Table 3. Precipitation data for southeast Alberta for the period 1968-1994 (One-Four Station) in millimetres.

| | | | | | | MONTH | | | | | | | |
|------|------|------|------|------|--------|--------|-------|---------|------|------|------|------|---------|
| YEAR | JAN | FEB | MAR | APR | MAY | JUN | JUL | AUG | SEP | OCT | NOV | DEC | TOTAL |
| 1968 | 22.4 | 4.6 | 18.0 | 25.2 | 26.3 | 64.5 | 9.7 | 52.2 | 50.7 | 6.6 | 6.8 | 33.6 | 320.6 |
| 1969 | 61.8 | 21.7 | 5.9 | 17.5 | 6.7 | 48.9 | 27.2 | 9.7 | 11.5 | 29.2 | 1.0 | 5.1 | 246.2 |
| 1970 | 22.1 | 12.7 | 17.1 | 20.3 | 15.0 | 139.3 | 44.7 | 17.3 | 6.2 | 6.3 | 16.5 | 35.1 | 352.6 |
| 1971 | 64.6 | 9.2 | 12.2 | 22.0 | 28.8 | 92.5 | 13.9 | 26.9 | 5.6 | 14.1 | 4.8 | 21.6 | 216.2 |
| 1972 | 44.9 | 24.2 | 16.3 | 8.6 | 45.2 | 36.6 | 35.1 | 40.4 | 44.5 | 15.7 | 2.8 | 19.4 | 333.7 |
| 1973 | 5.3 | 5.5 | 1.8 | 26.1 | 15.3 | 57.9 | 2.1 | 39.9 | 23.6 | 7.7 | 22.7 | 14.8 | 222.7 |
| 1974 | 18.2 | 22.6 | 24.0 | 47.2 | 98.1 | 26.1 | 45.2 | 53.9 | 5.7 | 1.0 | 7.8 | 33.3 | 383.1 |
| 1975 | 7.5 | 20.9 | 44.4 | 80.2 | 72.3 | 91.8 | 51.2 | 79.8 | 25.7 | 39.1 | 36.4 | 21.4 | 570.7 |
| 1976 | 7.7 | 10.3 | 30.6 | 28.0 | 12.9 | 116.8 | 17.6 | 41.2 | 7.9 | 8.1 | 12.5 | 7.1 | 300.7 |
| 1977 | 17.4 | 1.0 | 1.8 | 10.0 | 58.4 | 19.8 | 25.8 | 48.7 | 30.3 | 1.3 | 26.5 | 47.5 | 288.5 |
| 1978 | 51.3 | 55.9 | 13.5 | 70.0 | 51.8 | 29.1 | 69.9 | 18.1 | 60.9 | 8.6 | 43.5 | 45.8 | 518.4 |
| 1979 | 21.0 | 81.8 | 17.5 | 51.3 | 39.4 | 47.0 | 30.4 | 18.6 | 8.9 | 8.2 | 8.2 | 8.8 | 341.1 |
| 1980 | 38.2 | 13.2 | 14.6 | 31.1 | 43.0 | 62.8 | 25.0 | 25.6 | 13.4 | 41.2 | 8.4 | 22.4 | 338.9 |
| 1981 | 14.6 | 24.4 | 19.3 | 6.7 | 92.0 | 51.4 | 37.8 | 10.0 | 5.8 | 25.3 | 5.2 | 16.0 | 308.5 |
| 1982 | 64.1 | 23.0 | 57.0 | 20.8 | 111.2 | 27.2 | 29.8 | 51.5 | 35.2 | 13.0 | 4.4 | 11.2 | 448.4 |
| 1983 | 12.5 | 3.4 | 39.0 | 20.0 | 29.4 | 36.1 | 67.8 | 24.0 | 13.2 | 10.3 | 11.9 | 22.3 | 289.9 |
| 1984 | 16.9 | 3.0 | 33.4 | 11.4 | 36.6 | 20.8 | 1.2 | 43.4 | 43.6 | 38.0 | 9.4 | 14.9 | 272.6 |
| 1985 | 7.2 | 12.8 | 16.8 | 43.2 | 81.7 | 1.6 | 4.4 | 81.8 | 115.6 | 20.8 | 43.0 | 10.4 | 439.3 |
| 1986 | 10.6 | 15.6 | 26.6 | 15.8 | 81.2 | 98.4 | 36.6 | 3.2 | 179.0 | 19.0 | 20.0 | 7.0 | 513.0 |
| 1987 | 6.1 | 8.4 | 30.5 | 6.0 | 27.2 | 35.2 | 67.2 | 44.2 | 13.2 | 2.6 | 5.4 | 9.6 | 257.6 |
| 1988 | 0.0 | 0.0 | 0.0 | 0.0 | 5.2 | 24.0 | 15.5 | 18.8 | 29.1 | 3.3 | 0.0 | 1.0 | 96.9 |
| 1990 | 0.0 | 0.0 | 0.0 | 26.6 | 68.5 | 20.4 | 37.6 | 52.0 | 0.0 | 7.4 | 2.4 | 3.6 | 218.5 |
| 1991 | 0.0 | 0.2 | 6.2 | 26.9 | 84.1 | 129.8 | 17.2 | 43.6 | 6.8 | 2.8 | 7.6 | 1.0 | 326.2 |
| 1992 | 0.0 | 1.2 | 4.8 | 6.4 | 7.4 | 76.0 | 75.4 | 70.0 | 40.8 | 26.6 | 4.4 | 0.0 | 313.0 |
| 1993 | 0.0 | 0.0 | 24.7 | 45.0 | 28.2 | 86.2 | 128.6 | 79.9 | 23.6 | 11.5 | 4.8 | 0.2 | 432.7 |
| 1994 | 0.0 | 0.0 | 0.0 | 19.2 | 32.4 | 87.2 | 4.5 | 17.2 | 10.5 | 48.6 | 0.0 | 0.0 | 219.6 |
| TOTAL | 514.4 | 375.4 | 476.0 | 722.0 | 1256.3 | 1597.9 | 990.4 | 1,062.4 | 836.7 | 419.7 | 324.4 | 421.1 | 8,996.9 |
| Average | 19.1 | 13.9 | 17.6 | 26.7 | 46.6 | 59.2 | 36.7 | 39.3 | 31.0 | 15.5 | 12.0 | 15.6 | 333.2 |

1977, 1978, 1981, 1987, 1991 and 1994). Of more concern is the high rate of lek abandonment (9.6% per year) since 1991. Unfortunately the extent of decline is difficult to determined since inventories have been limited to traditional leks and field searches to identify new or relocated leks have not been carried out. Habitat inventories suggest that sage grouse habitat is relatively secure. The major portion of their range remains as crown land (Fig. 1) and grazing management over much of their range appears adequate. Eradication of sage brush, sod busting and use of pesticides do not appear to be major issues on this relatively pristine prairie environment.

What has impacted sate grouse populations in Alberta is uncertain. However, populations have been subjected to atypical climatic conditions within the last decade. A cursory review of precipitation obtained from the One Four station (Table 3) indicate higher than average annual precipitation in 1985, 1986 and 1993 and lower than average precipitation in 1988, 1990 and 1994. June precipitation has exceeded the long-term average of 57 mm in 5 of the last 6 years by a magnitude of 1.5 to 2 times. Excessive rainfall during the peak hatch of sage grouse could have had a substantial impact on chick survival and fall recruitment (Autenreith *et al.* 1979). Another complicating factor may be an increasing predator population. Trends in the coyote population

Table 4. Trends in coyote abundance in southeast Alberta (Aerial Surveys, 1977 to 1995).

| | Coyote observations | | | | |
|---|---|---|---|---|---|
| WMU | 1977-81 | 1985-89 | 1993-94 | 1993-94*[1] | 1995* |
| 102 | 14 | 16 | 32 | | |
| 104 | 8 | 16 | 28 | | |
| 106 | | | | 3 | 20 |
| 108 | 7 | 9 | 26 | 71 | 78 |
| 112 | | | | 9 | 30 |
| 116 | 23 | 12 | 33 | 60 | 81 |
| 118 | 14 | 19 | 14 | | |
| 119 | 3 | 5 | 12 | 38 | 58 |
| 124 | 14 | 10 | 32 | | |
| 128 | 5 | 7 | 2 | | |
| 130 | 17 | 8 | 16 | | |
| 134 | 45 | 18 | 41 | | |
| 148 | 16 | 22 | 18 | | |
| 150 | 13 | 13 | 17 | | |
| TOTAL | 179 | 155 | 271 | 202 | 306 |
| | | | (+62%)[2] | | (+51%) |

[1]Observations are not comparable to previous data.
[2]Percent change from previous survey results.

obtained from observations on deer survey blocks suggest at least a doubling of the coyote population since 1990. A 62% increase in coyote observations occurred from 1989 to 1994 and a further 51% increase was recorded from 1994 to 1995 (Table 4). Low recruitment in the pronghorn population since 1990 also suggest high predator populations. The addition of another predator, the swift fox, may also be impacting survival of young sage grouse. Most of these factors, however, are natural events which in our view are not serious and cause only short-term adjustments and, albeit, substantial fluctuations in the population of sage grouse.

The State of Oregon recently published a report on sage grouse in that state (Willis *et al.* 1993) and it appears that the Alberta situation may not be that different. The concluded the following:

1. The present range of sage grouse has not changed substantially in recent years and habitat conditions are relatively secure.

2. Earlier conversion of sagebrush to crested wheatgrass has reduced sage grouse capability on large areas of their range.

3. There has been no significant change in adult populations as indicated by males/lek since the 1950s however fluctuations in population indices are common and have been characteristic of sage grouse since the turn of the century. Long and short term climatic fluctuations and significant weather effects induce population fluctuations.

4. Productivity of sage grouse declined in the early 1970's and has persisted to present day. This decline in productivity coincides with the ban on 1,080 poison for coyote control in 1972. Coyote indices in Oregon remain high.

We have recognized that our information base for sage grouse is limiting. In 1995 we are initiating a project which will include:

1. Search for leks

2. Productivity studies

3. Updating habitat inventory

We expect this project to quantify limiting factors and assist us in our efforts to maintain the capability of sage grouse habitat in Southern Alberta.

## LITERATURE CITED

Autenreith, R.E., W. Moline, and C.E. Braun. 1979. Recommended sage grouse management strategies. Publication of Western States Sage Grouse Comm.

Carr, H.D. 1972. Status of sage grouse in Alberta in 1972. Alberta Dept. of Lands and Forests, Fish and Wildlife Division Report.

Clark, J. and L. Dube. 1984. An inventory of vegetative communities associated with sage grouse leks in southern Alberta. Alberta Energy and Natural Resources, Fish and Wildlife Division Report.

Moyles, D.L. 1989. Results of sage grouse hunter check stations. Alberta Dept. Forestry, Lands and Wildlife, Fish and Wildlife Division. Internal Report.

Willis, M.J., G.P. Keister, D.A. Immell, D.M. Jones, R.M. Powell, and K.R. Durbin. 1993. Sage grouse in Oregon. Oregon Dept. of Fish and Wildlife, Wildlife Research Section. Wildlife Research Report No. 15.

# SAGE GROUSE POPULATION STATUS, ITS MANAGEMENT AND FUTURE FOR THE WESTERN UNITED STATES WITH EMPHASIS ON MONTANA.

## Charles D. Eustace

*Montana Fish, Wildlife & Parks, 2300 Lake Elmo Drive, Billings, Montana 59105*

## POPULATION TRENDS IN WESTERN U.S.

The status of the sage grouse (*Centrocercus urophasianus*), in the United States is one of concern as indicated by the following analysis prepared by the Western States Sage Grouse Technical Committee (1995). Sage grouse historically occurred in at least 15 states and probably also in Arizona and Kansas although specimen records from those states are lacking (Fig. 1). They have been extirpated from Nebraska, New Mexico and Oklahoma and have greatly reduced distribution and abundance in all geographic areas of their former range. Population size as measured by counts of males on leks in spring has decreased at least 50 to 60% since

the early 1950's. This trend is evident across the range of sage grouse. Reasons for the demonstrated decreases in distribution and abundance relate to permanent loss of habitat (land conversion, roads, reservoirs, mining/oil and gas developments, etc.), degradation of habitat (spraying, reseeding, exotic plants, livestock grazing, powerlines, fences, dewatering, etc.), and fragmentation of habitat. Thus, the long-term trend in habitat quality and quantity of sagebrush (*Artemisia* spp.) rangelands used by sage grouse is markedly down even though quantitative data on historic conditions are lacking. Trends in numbers of livestock, especially sheep, on western rangelands are generally down but distribution of use appears to be more uniform and few areas are ungrazed. Cumulative totals of acres of sagebrush

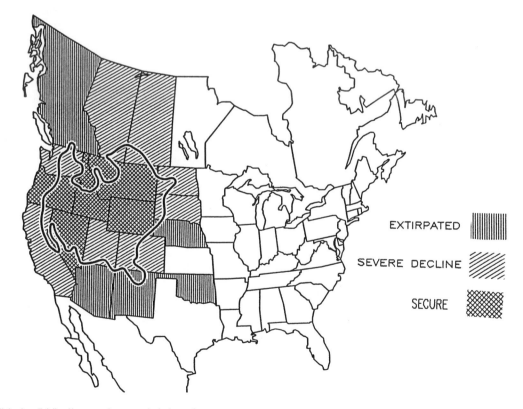

EXTIRPATED

SEVERE DECLINE

SECURE

Figure 1. Historic distribution and present status of sage grouse.

297

sprayed to enhance livestock forage production increased markedly in the 1960's but slowed in the last 10 to 15 years. The original vegetation composition of western rangelands is unknown. Thus, recreating presettlement vegetative conditions is unlikely. Management of western rangelands and sage grouse must proceed as a series of experiments designed to stabilize and then increase sage grouse abundance and distribution over time.

## MANAGEMENT SURVEYS

Montana Fish, Wildlife and Parks (MFWP), has used the harvest questionnaire method to survey resident and nonresident upland game bird (UGB), license holders since 1958. Results are tabulated for 56 counties, 7 MFWP administrative region's, and the state. Beginning in 1975, hunter days, a measure of hunter effort, was estimated for each UGB species. Prior to 1989 estimates of hunter numbers were made without regard to the species hunted. In 1989 we began to estimate hunter numbers for each UGB species. In 1993 UGB hunting and harvest statistics were estimated from a sample of 15,155 completed questionnaires representing about 19% of all UGB license holders (Lonner *et al.* 1993).

UGB wings are collected through hunter wing envelope surveys, hunter check stations, random field contacts and local hunting organizations. Based on feather replacement, shape and wear characteristics, we are able to record wings as male, female, juvenile or adult. Productivity is characterized as juveniles\100 adult hens. Date of hatching can also be determined for juveniles by measuring the last primary feather molted.

A third survey is the spring lek count. Each spring sage grouse return to the same breeding ground, or lek. This allows biologist to census males during and shortly after the peak of breeding, a period of maximum male attendance on the lek. Results are recorded as the average number of males/lek. It is assumed that changes in lek attendance provide an index to changes in the spring breeding population, and therefore, the fall population as well.

## SAGE GROUSE TRENDS IN MONTANA

### Harvest Trends

Sage grouse harvests increased during the late 1950's and early 1960's, remained relatively stable through 1979, then declined steadily through 1993 (Fig. 2). Harvests averaged 34,638 sage grouse during this 36 year period, ranging from 99,138 in 1964 to 7,716 in 1993.

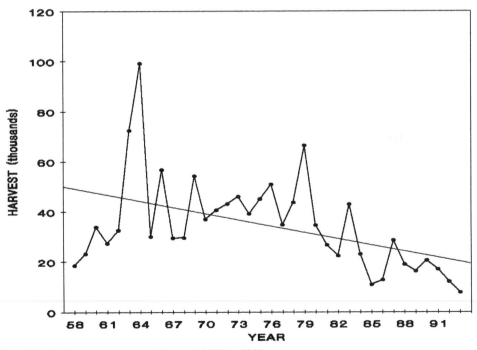

Figure 2. Trends in Montana sage grouse harvest, 1958 to 1993.

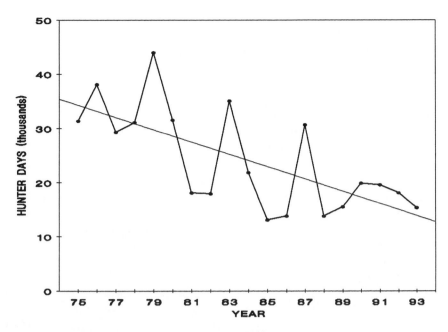

Figure 3. Trends in Montana sage grouse hunter days, 1975 to 1993.

By comparing two 5 year periods, 1975 to 1979 with 1989 to 1993, we see that some of this decline is a result of reduced numbers of hunters afield and hunter effort (Fig. 3). During this time the number of hunters afield for UGB hunters declined 34%, sage grouse hunter days declined 49% and sage grouse harvest declined 70%. The question that comes to mind is, are lower hunter numbers and reduced sage grouse hunter days responsible for declining harvests, or are lower sage grouse populations responsible for reduced hunter numbers and hunter effort?

The number of sage grouse a hunter takes per day is a measure of hunter success (Fig. 4). Success for 1975 to 1979, 1980 to 1984, 1985 to 1989 and 1990 to 1993 was 1.4, 1.2, 1.0 and 0.8 birds per hunter respectively. I believe a steady reduction in hunter success resulting from declining sage grouse populations is responsible

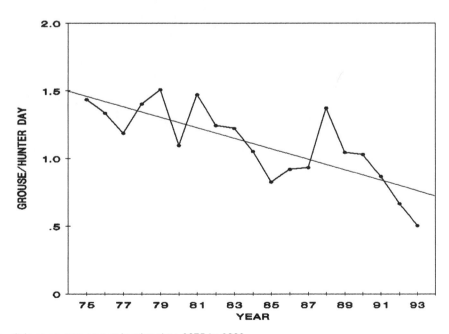

Figure 4. Trends in sage grouse per hunter day, 1975 to 1993.

for fewer hunters afield, and that those who did hunt spent fewer days hunting sage grouse.

## Productivity Trends

Production data is available from 1962 to 1993 (Fig. 5). From 1962 to 1979, a period of relatively stable harvest's, productivity averaged 263 juv./100 adult hens, then dropped to 202 juv./100 adult hens from 1980 to 1993. This difference is significant, P .≤ 02. I believe this statewide reduction of 23% in productivity explains much of the drop in sage grouse populations and harvest in Montana during the 1980's and 1990's. This can be illustrated by comparing harvest and hunter effort estimates with productivity data for 1975 to 1993. Although production was generally low between 1975 and 1993, there were 5 years when it averaged 348 juv./100 adult hens, (1978, 1979, 1983, 1987 and 1990) vs. 175 juv./100 adult hens for the other 14 years. The sage grouse harvest for the 5 high production years was 40,380 birds\year vs. 23,741 for the 14 low production years. Sage grouse bagged/hunter day increased very little, 1.2 vs. 1.1 for the high and low production years respectively. However, sage grouse hunter days averaged 32,200 vs. 21,300 for high and low production years respectively. While sage grouse hunter days increased by over 50% during high production years, the total number of UGB hunters were up only 18% when compared to low production years. This indicates that

good production does not improve shooting accuracy as much as it increase's the enjoyment of seeing more birds. As a result of seeing more birds, hunters spend more days afield when bird production is high. In short, the data suggests that harvest questionnaire information for Montana reflects actual changes in sage grouse populations.

To what can we attribute the decline in production? One possibility is a change in precipitation. The current years production of chicks correlates significantly with the previous years rainfall. The previous years rainfall influences residual cover for nesting and moisture reserves to start the current years growth of vegetation. More precipitation was recorded for the good production years (1962 to 1979) than for the poor production years (1980 to 1993) by 6.2, 6.0 and 3.2 cm./year for northeast, southeast and southcentral Montana respectively. Other sage grouse producing areas of Montana showed declines in rainfall, although to a lesser degree. While this appears to be a plausible explanation for low productivity in portions of Montana, it does not satisfactorily explain declines in other parts of the state.

## Breeding Population Trends

The total number of males recorded during the peak of breeding has ranged from 600+ to over 1,400 between 1978 and 1994. Lek attendance has dropped from 32

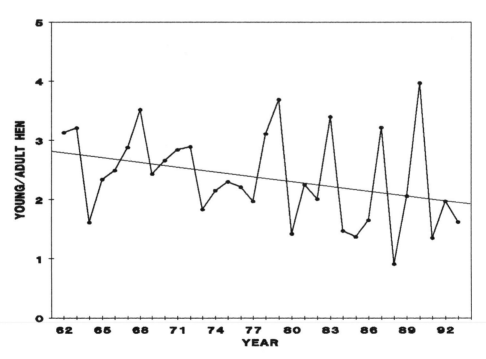

Figure 5. Trends in sage grouse productivity, 1962 to 1993.

300

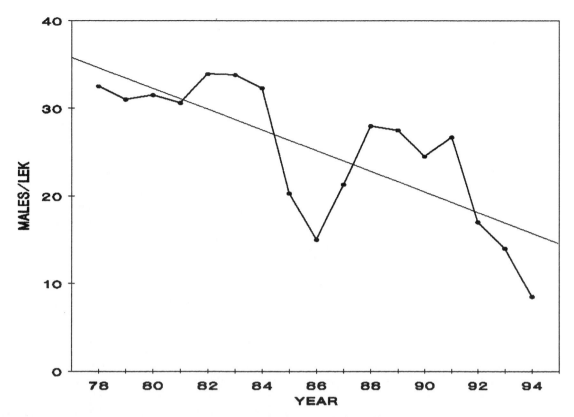

Figure 6. Trends in sage grouse males/lek, southcentral Montana, 1978 to 1994.

males/lek in 1978 to 8.5 males/lek in 1994 (Fig. 6). Using a linear regression to compare male lek attendance with fall harvest, it is my observation that fall harvests can be predicted with moderate accuracy from spring lek counts. Furthermore, the accuracy of the prediction is enhanced by including all leks that have been observed within the survey area, whether currently active or not. By including inactive leks we can account for 59% of all fluctuations in the fall harvest. Using the average number of males from active leks only accounts for 25% of the fluctuation in the fall harvest.

My assumption is that lek counts during periods of peak sage grouse populations represent the potential of an area to produce sage grouse. As populations decline some leks are abandoned. By including inactive leks in our survey, which adjusts the number of males/lek, we have a more accurate estimate of how close current lek attendance comes to the potential. This could possibly be improved by calculating the number of males/square kilometre, resulting in a spring breeding density index which I believe would be more meaningful than the average number of males/lek.

## THE FUTURE FOR SAGE GROUSE

While surveys are an important aspect of sage grouse management, they will not produce sage grouse or improve the sage grouse's lot in life. MFWP believes the best way to preserve and enhance wildlife populations is to preserve and enhance their habitat. MFWP currently has two habitat programs funded through sportsmen license dollars earmarked by the legislature for habitat preservation and enhancement. The upland game bird habitat enhancement program (UGBHEP), receives approximately $641,522 every year from a portion of the UGB license sales (Youmans 1995). This program develops upland game bird habitat on both private and public lands. Projects have a duration of one to fifteen years, depending on the land management practices involved. Over 575 contracts have been developed with individual land managers that include shelterbelt tree/shrub plantings, winter food/cover plots, nesting cover, range management and wetland restoration. As of December 1994, 321 square kilometres of upland game bird habitat has been established or improved. In my opinion the establishment of rotation grazing systems has the most promise to positively influence the largest land area for the greatest amount of time.

301

The second habitat program, receives approximately 2.8 million dollars a year from a portion of big game license sales earmarked for habitat. This program allows MFWP to acquire an interest in land for the purpose of protecting and enhancing wildlife habitat through the purchase of leases, conservation easements, or fee title. In this program emphasis is placed upon those areas where important habitat is seriously threatened by conversion to some use not beneficial to wildlife. To date 653 square kilometres of shrub grasslands have been protected through conservation easements which insure the land will remain in agriculture, which in this case is primarily livestock grazing. Rotation grazing systems have been established and public access for hunting and recreational purposes guaranteed. As a means of improving vegetation conditions on MFWP lands, agreements and leases have been developed with private landowners to utilize MFWP lands for rest-rotation grazing in return for like habitat management on private lands. These arrangements not only improve the capability of these areas to "produce," they also benefit everything that depends upon that land, including wildlife and their habitats, the sportsmen, the cooperator, neighbouring landowners and the local community.

## CONCLUSION

Concern has been expressed by many people and organizations in recent years regarding declines in sage grouse populations throughout its range. In Montana the sage grouse has been accompanied in its decline by all of the native UGB's; sharp-tailed grouse (*Tympanuchus phasianellus*), blue grouse (*Dendragapus obscurus*),

spruce grouse (*D. canadensis*) and ruffed grouse (*Bonasa umbellus*). All five species started a general harvest decline in 1980, and all recorded their lowest harvest in 36 years during 1993. All five occupy widely divergent habitats in both prairie and mountain environments. In past years sage grouse reached such low levels in Montana that hunting seasons were closed for periods of 1 to 7 years. The last closure, 1945 to 1951, was attributed to several years of low chick productivity. In short, populations have declined in the past and will again in the future. Our challenge is to concentrate on providing sufficient high quality shrub grasslands so that the sage grouse can concentrate on what they like to do best: be fruitful and multiply.

## LITERATURE CITED

Lonner, T., B. Hoskins, and C. Haskins. 1993. Upland game birds, waterfowl, and turkey hunting and harvest statistics. Montana Fish, Wildlife and Parks, Bozeman, Montana.

Western States Sage Grouse Technical Committee, 1995. Sage grouse population and habitat trends, 1950's-1990's: a long-term perspective. Wildlife Research Center, Ft. Collins, Colorado.

Youmans, H. 1995. Montana Department of Fish, Wildlife and Parks Upland Game Bird Habitat Enhancement Program, Legislative report. Montana Fish, Wildlife and Parks, Wildlife Division, Helena, Montana.

# ESTABLISHMENT OF A COLONY OF RICHARDSON'S GROUND SQUIRRELS IN SOUTHERN ALBERTA

## Gail R. Michener

*Department of Biological Sciences, University of Lethbridge, Lethbridge, Alberta T1K 3M4*

## ABSTRACT

A population of Richardson's ground squirrels was successfully re-established in a small (<2.5 ha) area of non-native grassland surrounded by irrigated farmland near Picture Butte, Alberta. Of 10 adult females released with their 57 offspring, 4 adult females released without litters, and 2 adult males released in 1985 and 1986, 9 adult females and 16 offspring (14 females and 2 males) survived for at least 1 year post-release. These survivors then founded a population that increased to a maximum of 193 adult females and 62 adult males by 1990 but thereafter declined as a result of predation, primarily by badgers and raptors, to 31 adult females and 10 adult males in 1995. A release of 15 adult females, 9 with litters, on native short-grass prairie in 1985 was not successful.

## INTRODUCTION

The first specimens of Richardson's ground squirrels (*Spermophilus richardsonii*) sent to Europe for scientific description were collected in Saskatchewan by the British surgeon-naturalist John Richardson in 1820 and named in his honour by Joseph Sabine (1822). With European settlement of the prairies, agricultural practices soon placed humans and ground squirrels in conflict. The burrowing activities of ground squirrels and their ability to substitute cereal grains and forage crops for the native plants destroyed by cultivation led to implementation of bounties for destruction of ground squirrels (Bailey 1893). Bell and Piper (1915) recommended the goal of exterminating Richardson's ground squirrels through use of poisoned baits. In Alberta, free distribution of poison and payment of cash bounties were mandated by provincial government statutes in 1907 and 1911 (Brown and Roy 1943). Although the bounty was removed in 1940, control of Richardson's ground squirrels with poison baits and fumigation continued (Brown and Roy 1943, Matschke *et al.* 1983).

The undesirable activities of Richardson's ground squirrels, as identified by Alberta Agriculture (1984), include direct effects such as damage to cereal crops, competition with livestock for forage, and damage to machinery by mounds of excavated soil and indirect effects such as attracting badgers (*Taxidea taxus*) that damage crops and pasture through excavations dug while preying on ground squirrels. In the 1970's, Alberta Agriculture investigated the possibility of reducing populations of Richardson's ground squirrels by using chemosterilants that reduce fertility. Although the steroid hormone mestranol, when administered to females shortly before or in early pregnancy, did inhibit reproduction, population reduction was often temporary because immigration, primarily by juveniles, offset the decreased production of resident females (Alsager and Yaremko 1972, Goulet and Sadleir 1974). The Crop Protection and Pest Control Branch in Alberta (Alberta Agriculture 1982) continued to recommend poisoning, trapping, fumigation, and shooting for control.

Whereas Richardson's ground squirrels are much vilified as pests by the agricultural community, biologists have long recognized their importance as an integral part of the prairie ecosystem, especially their role as prey for many predators. John Richardson (1829, p. 165) noted that "several species of falcon, that frequent the plains of the Saskatchewan, prey much on these (squirrels); but their principal enemy is the American badger". Hunt (1993) and Schmutz *et al.* (1980) reported that Richardson's ground squirrels are the most important item in the diets of prairie falcons (*Falco mexicanus*) and three species of *Buteo* in southern Alberta, often accounting for 89% of the prey biomass brought to nestlings. Preservation of remaining habitat for Richardson's ground squirrels, and preferably an increase in ground squirrel numbers, is an important aspect of maintaining breeding populations of prairie falcons on the Canadian prairies (Holroyd in press).

Because Richardson's ground squirrels have been the targets of control campaigns, populations in some regions of the Canadian prairies are sparse and sporadic, especially where cultivation has destroyed the natural habitat. Reintroduction of ground squirrels to historic sites or establishment of ground squirrels at new sites may be a means of creating a suitable prey base for native predators. California ground squirrels (*S. beecheyi*) and Columbian ground squirrels (*S. columbianus*) have been introduced to previously unoccupied habitat by initially placing them in wire-mesh cages, then opening the cages one to several months later to give them free access to the adjacent habitat (Salmon and Marsh 1981; Wiggett and Boag 1986). Here, I report a release technique for Richardson's ground squirrels, the fate of the transplanted populations, and the role of newly colonized sites in attracting predators.

## METHODS

### Release Sites

Two 1.25-ha sites, for convenience designated the prairie site and the farm site, were selected in spring 1985. These sites were located 1.25 km apart, approximately 5 km E and 1 km S of Picture Butte, Alberta. The prairie site was at the top of coulees associated with the Oldman River within a patch of native short-grass prairie that was subject to occasional light grazing by domestic cattle but was otherwise undisturbed by human activity. No evidence of recent use by ground squirrels was detected at the prairie site. The farm site was located on land that had been extensively modified by human activity. For example, aerial photographs taken in 1958 and 1961 showed that most of the site was fenced into several corrals holding cattle. With changes in land management and land ownership, the area was no longer used as a cattle feedlot by the early 1970's and the land revegetated, primarily to exotic grasses such as quack grass (*Agropyron repens*), tall wheat grass (*A. elongatum*), awnless brome (*Bromus inermis*), foxtail barley (*Hordeum jubatum*), and meadow fescue (*Festuca elatior*). Occasional grazing by cattle occurred up to 1977, but the area was not grazed from 1978 to 1985. When sampled 19 to 21 May 1978, 5 adult female, 6 juvenile female, and 8 juvenile male Richardson's ground squirrels were livetrapped and released. By 1980, no ground squirrels were resident on the farm site, probably because the tall vegetative cover was unsuitable habitat for Richardson's ground squirrels. Thus, at the time of the transplant in 1985, the farm site had not been occupied by Richardson's ground squirrels for at least 5 years and entrances to former burrow systems were silted in and difficult to locate. In spring 1985, the farm site was burned. From 1986 onwards, the vegetation on the farm release site was kept short by a combination of selective burning, mowing, and grazing by

either cattle (until 1990) or sheep (from 1991). By 1978, the farm site was bordered on two sides by cultivated fields, on one side by a gravel road with cultivated fields beyond, and on the fourth side by a farmyard with cultivated fields beyond; all fields were sown to annual crops and were under irrigation.

### Transplanted Animals

Richardson's ground squirrels to be transplanted were livetrapped from a pasture at which I had been conducting long-term behavioural and ecological studies since 1979 (e.g. Michener 1983, 1985, 1989). The source site was about 3.25 km from the release sites, with no intervening habitat suitable for ground squirrels because of intense land management for irrigated agriculture. The landowner of the source site indicated that, in advance of converting the pasture to annually cultivated crops, he would be poisoning the ground squirrels. In spring of 1985, I removed 22 pregnant females (17 yearlings, four 2-year-olds, and one 3-year-old) from the source population and transplanted 15 to the prairie site and 7 to the farm site. In spring of 1986, I removed the entire population of over 500 animals from the source site. Although most of these squirrels were killed for use in other studies (van Staaden *et al.* 1994, Dobson and Michener 1995), 4 pregnant females (3 yearlings and a 2-year-old), 3 non-pregnant females (2 yearlings and a 5-year-old), and 2 males (probably yearlings) were removed for transplantation to the farm site. Most females (22/29) were held captive (average 37 days; range 18-53 days) in plastic rodent cages in a building subject to natural light and temperature regimes before they were released; 7 pregnant females were transplanted directly from the source site to the prairie site.

### Release Cages and Release Technique

Release cages (Fig. 1) consisted of an arched metal hutch (radius 28 cm, length 44 cm), which provided shelter, with a run (length 58 cm) of expanded-metal mesh, and a floor of chicken-wire (2.54-cm mesh) under both the hutch and the run. The run, which extended from the open end of the hutch to a plywood wall, was reinforced with two metal rods and had a door (20 by 20 cm) in the roof. Before placing the cage on the ground, I used a soil-sample corer to dig a blind-ending starter tunnel approximately 7.5 cm in diameter, 1 m long, and angled at about 45° to the soil surface. The release cage was anchored to the ground with metal pins and positioned with the opening of the starter tunnel under a hole cut in the floor of the run. Release cages were spaced about 20 m apart.

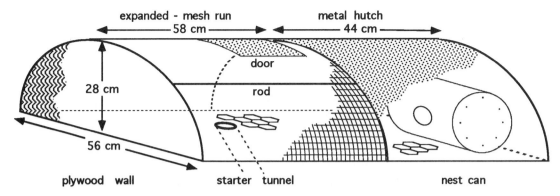

expanded - mesh run    metal hutch
— 58 cm —               — 44 cm —

door

28 cm                   rod

56 cm

plywood wall    starter tunnel    nest can

Figure 1. Schematic diagram of a release cage used to transplant Richardson's ground squirrels.

At least 12 h before release, I put the squirrel, the litter (if one had been born), and paper-towelling nest material into an unused 4.8-l metal paint can (17.5 cm diameter, 20.0 cm length) with a 5.5-cm entrance in the side wall and ventilation holes in each end. On the day of release, I placed the can containing the squirrel and nest within the hutch of the release cage. For a few releases, squirrels were given immediate access to the starter tunnel, but generally the starter tunnel was blocked for 1-4 days so that the animal first became familiar with viewing the above-ground surroundings. Once given access to the starter tunnel, most squirrels immediately dug a chamber and moved the nest underground within 48 h. They then extended the starter tunnel and ultimately gained their freedom by excavating a route to the surface. When a large quantity of excavated soil accumulated in the release cage, I scooped it out to ensure the squirrel always had plenty of space to pile soil. I dug at least one blind-ending tunnel, similar to the starter tunnel, near each release cage to provide additional refuge for released animals.

Until a squirrel was known to have excavated its way to freedom, food (rodent chow, sunflower seeds, and fresh leafy greens such as lettuce or dandelions) was added to the cage at least once daily; water requirements were met from the fresh greens. Provisioning of food ceased once the squirrel was confirmed to be foraging outside the release cage. I removed the cage shortly thereafter, usually 1 to 7 days after the animal had excavated its way out.

## RESULTS and DISCUSSION

### Fate of Prairie Release Site

The squirrels transplanted to the prairie site did not found a new population. Seven pregnant females were

released 4 to 10 April 1985. The day after release, 5 of these females were killed by a pack of domestic dogs that ripped the cages open; the females in the remaining two cages were not disturbed and subsequently gave birth and weaned litters. Between 2 and 23 May 1985, 1 post-lactation female without a litter and 7 lactating females with litters aged 19-40 days (average 31 days) were released. Eight females excavated a route out of the release cage 2 to 5 days after they were given access to the starter tunnel; although the other 2 females excavated soil they were still confined 9 and 13 days later, so I dug a tunnel from outside the release cage to interconnect with the starter tunnel. Of the 10 adult females and 56 juvenile offspring at the prairie site, only 1 adult female and 2 juveniles could be located 28 June 1985 and none were found in 1986. The burrow systems started by the transplanted animals soon fell into disuse.

Red foxes (*Vulpes vulpes*) may have contributed to the loss of the released squirrels at the prairie site; scats, urine, and shallow digs were noted and a red fox was seen at the site on 13 May 1985. However, the extent to which Richardson's ground squirrels dispersed from the prairie site was not assessable. Because I could find no evidence of previous use by ground squirrels, I suspect the habitat at the prairie site was unsuitable although it appeared similar to short-grass prairie commonly inhabited by Richardson's ground squirrels.

### Fate of Farm Release Site

In contrast to the undisturbed prairie site, the disturbed farm site was successfully recolonized. One 3-year-old post-lactation female without a litter and 6 females (3 yearlings and three 2-year-olds) with litters aged 19 to 39 days (average 30 days) were released 2 to 18 May 1985. The female without a litter escaped from her cage, apparently by squeezing under the mesh floor, and disappeared within 2 days. The 6 mothers dug routes to the surface in 2 to 5 days, thereby gaining freedom for themselves and their 33 juveniles (19 females and 14 males). Because the site was not grazed in 1985, the vegetation grew tall and censusing of squirrels was difficult after May. Tall vegetation facilitated a sit-and-wait hunting strategy by a domestic cat that, for example, was known to have killed at least 3 juveniles 16 to 20 May. The only ground squirrels that survived to 1986 were three of the transplanted adult females. On 25 and 28 March 1986, I transplanted 2 adult males to the farm site; although these males remained for only 1 or 2 days, the 3 surviving females were impregnated and subsequently weaned litters of 7, 7, and 10 offspring (12 females and 12 males) in 1986.

Because of the partial success of the release at the farm site in 1985, I stocked the area with 3 steers on 16 April 1986 to graze the vegetation and I captured an additional 7 adult females from the source population. The 3 non-pregnant females were released 21 April. The other 4 females gave birth in captivity 9-14 April, then were released 10-17 May when their litters were 31-33 days old. All females excavated routes to the surface within 3-6 days of access to the starter tunnel. One 5-year-old female without a litter disappeared within 3 days of leaving the release cage; her carcass was subsequently found near the site though cause of death could not be assessed. The other 6 females (5 yearlings and one 2-year-old) remained resident on the site for the summer. The 4 mothers released with litters in 1986 weaned 24 juveniles (16 females and 8 males).

Survival of females from 1986 to 1987 was remarkably high at the farm site. Seven of the 9 transplanted females alive in summer 1986 survived to spring 1987; one female originally transplanted in 1985 and one transplanted in 1986 did not survive to 1987. Of the 28 daughters born to females in 1986, 24 survived to 1987. Daughters born in captivity and released with their mothers in 1986 survived as successfully as daughters born in the field in 1986 (14 of 16 and 10 of 12, respectively). The two missing captive-born daughters were killed by a domestic cat shortly after release in 1986. The fates of the two missing field-born daughters were not known; their mother also did not survive.

As is usual for Richardson's ground squirrels (Michener 1989), recruitment of sons was low. Of the 12 sons born on the farm site in 1986 and the 8 captive-born sons released with their mothers in 1986, two (one field born and one captive born) were present on the site in early spring 1987. The field-born male disappeared on 6 March 1987, but the captive-born male remained

resident for the summer. On 14 March 1987, I released an adult male, that I found dispersing across short-grass prairie otherwise uninhabited by ground squirrels, 1-km from the farm site. This male became resident and survived to 1988 but he probably contributed little to reproduction in 1987 because most females had mated before he was released. The population at the farm site has been self-sustaining since this final release in March 1987.

## Population Growth and Predation at the Farm Site

The population of Richardson's ground squirrels at the farm site doubled in size annually for 3 years and attained a peak of 193 adult females in spring of 1990. The population then declined and stabilized at about 100 to 110 females for 3 years (1991 to 1993), before again declining in each of the next 2 years (Table 1). The population expanded beyond the original release site onto adjacent lawns, around farm buildings and granaries, and into the edges of cultivated fields. As a result of short-distance dispersal movements by females after the peak year, the colonized area expanded to about 2.2 ha in 1992. The decline in population was not matched by an equivalent decline in area, so in 1995 the population was sparsely spread over about 0.9 ha.

Badger predation on hibernating squirrels in the autumn and early winter of 1990 was largely responsible for the dramatic decline in population between 1990 and 1991, though hunting by Swainson's hawks (*Buteo swainsoni*) and prairie falcons shortly after litters came above ground in 1990 also contributed. The population remained at fewer than 110 adult females from 1991 to

Table 1. Numbers of adult (1-year-old) Richardson's ground squirrels that emerged from hibernation each spring on the farm release site.

| Year | Females | Males |
|------|---------|-------|
| 1987 | 31 | 2 |
| 1988 | 55 | 16 |
| 1989 | 101 | 28 |
| 1990 | 193 | 62 |
| 1991 | 103 | 32 |
| 1992 | 98 | 38 |
| 1993 | 109 | 51 |
| 1994 | 79 | 28 |
| 1995 | 31 | 10 |

1994, in part because of raptor predation but primarily because of badger predation both on infants in natal nests in 1991 and 1993 and on hibernating squirrels in autumn and early winter of 1991, 1992, and 1993. In the summer of 1994, predation by a female badger with 2 dependent young and by a long-tailed weasel (*Mustela frenata*), also thought to be a female with a litter, contributed to a further decline in population. Although a badger established residency on the site each autumn of the 4 consecutive years from 1990 to 1993, no badger became resident in autumn 1994, presumably because the population of Richardson's ground squirrels was substantially depleted by then.

Predators known to have killed adult and juvenile ground squirrels at the farm site, in decreasing order of their estimated impact on the population, were: badgers, Swainson's hawks, long-tailed weasels, domestic cats, prairie falcons, and domestic dogs. Prairie rattlesnakes (*Crotalus viridis*) occasionally killed juveniles. Coyotes (*Canis latrans*) were seen near the farm site but were not observed hunting ground squirrels. The deaths of 10% of juveniles, primarily males, in the summers of 1989, 1990, and 1991 were attributable to maggots of a parasitic Sarcophagid fly (*Neobellieria citellivora*; Michener 1993).

## Recommendations for Releasing Richardson's Ground Squirrels

Rapid growth of the population at the farm site, a disturbed area revegetated by non-native grasses, indicates that Richardson's ground squirrels are not dependent on native plant species for reproduction or survival. However, ground squirrels are dependent on burrow systems and underground chambers for sleeping, litter rearing, hibernation, and refuge both from predators and inclement weather. The success of the releases at the farm site and the failure at the prairie site were likely related to the differential availability of burrow systems. Although burrows at the farm site had not been used for at least 5 years, released animals soon located old entrances and renovated the systems. These old systems then provided a base from which squirrels excavated new systems as the population increased in size and expanded the area occupied. Short vegetation was important for long-term residency of Richardson's ground squirrels, a finding that concurs with the subjective observation that population densities are often high on over-grazed pastures. The combination of short vegetation and access to burrows presumably promotes survival by enabling ground squirrels to detect approaching predators and then seek refuge underground.

Based on my experience observing Richardson's ground squirrels, I chose to bias the transplants in favour of females with captive-born litters because I predicted that mothers would be unlikely to abandon the litter and that captive-born juveniles, with experience only of the new habitat, would have no tendency to home to the source site. I delayed most releases until the litter was old enough that juveniles could be eartagged before release (at about 25 days old) and could survive without the mother (from about 28-30 days of age). Possibly release of pregnant females or post-partum females with infants would be equally effective. Confinement to the release cage for several days before the starter tunnel was made accessible followed by 2 or more days to tunnel to the surface seemed sufficient for most squirrels to become familiar with the new site and to claim ownership of the incipient burrow system. With my technique, release cages became available for reuse within 7 to 10 days, in contrast to the techniques used by Salmon and Marsh (1981) and Wiggett and Boag (1986) that involved confinement of squirrels for a month or more.

In summary, access to sufficient underground refuges (which could be created artificially by excavation of numerous starter tunnels) and short vegetative cover (which could be achieved by burning, mowing, and grazing) appear to be minimal requirements for introduction of Richardson's ground squirrels to new habitat. Richardson's ground squirrels can survive and reproduce in disturbed habitat that has revegetated to non-native species.

## ACKNOWLEDGMENTS

I thank Dan Michener for building the release cages and for permitting me to release Richardson's ground squirrels on his farm

## LITERATURE CITED

Alberta Agriculture. 1982. The Richardson ground squirrel (prairie gopher) its importance and control. Agdex 684.

Alberta Agriculture. 1984. Control of pocket gophers and ground squirrels. Agdex 684-1.

Alsager D. E. and R. Yaremko. 1972. Experimental population suppression of Richardson's ground squirrels

(*Spermophilus richardsonii*) in Alberta. Vertebrate Pest Conference Proceedings 5: 93-100.

Bailey. V. 1893. The prairie ground squirrels or spermophiles of the Mississippi Valley. U. S. Department of Agriculture, Division of Ornithology and Mammalogy Bulletin 4: 1-69.

Bell, W. B. and S. E. Piper. 1915. Extermination of ground squirrels, gophers and prairie dogs in North Dakota. North Dakota Agriculture Experiment Station Circular 4: 1-11.

Brown, J. H. and G. D. Roy. 1943. The Richardson ground squirrel, *Citellus richardsonii* Sabine, in southern Alberta: Its importance and control. Scientific Agriculture 24: 176-197.

Dobson, F. S. and G. R. Michener. 1995. Maternal traits and reproduction in Richardson's ground squirrels. Ecology 76: 851-862.

Goulet, L. A. and R. M. F. S. Sadleir. 1974. The effects of a chemosterilant (mestranol) on population and behavior in the Richardson's ground squirrel (*Spermophilus richardsonii*) in Alberta. Vertebrate Pest Conference Proceedings 6: 90-100.

Holroyd, G. L. In press. Conservation of prairie raptors. Transactions of the 60th North American Wildlife and Natural Resources Conference, Wildlife Management Institute. Washington, D. C.

Hunt, L. E. 1993. Diet and habitat use of nesting prairie falcons (*Falco mexicanus*) in an agricultural landscape in southern Alberta. M. Sc. thesis. University of Alberta, Edmonton.

Matschke, G. H., M. P. Marsh, and D. L. Otis. 1983. Efficacy of zinc phosphide broadcast baiting for controlling Richardson's ground squirrels on rangeland. Journal of Range Management 36: 504-506.

Michener, G. R. 1983. Spring emergence schedules and vernal behavior of Richardson's ground squirrels: why do males emerge from hibernation before females? Behavioral Ecology and Sociobiology 14: 29-38.

Michener, G. R. 1985. Chronology of reproductive events for female Richardson's ground squirrels. Journal of Mammalogy 66: 280-288.

Michener, G. R. 1989. Sexual differences in interyear survival and life-span of Richardson's ground squirrels. Canadian Journal of Zoology 67: 1827-1831.

Michener, G. R. 1993. Lethal myiasis of Richardson's ground squirrels by the sarcophagid fly *Neobellieria citellivora*. Journal of Mammalogy 74: 148-155.

Richardson, J. 1829. Fauna Boreali-Americana; or the zoology of the northern parts of British America: containing descriptions of the objects of natural history collected on the late northern land expeditions, under command of Captain Sir John Franklin, R. N. Part first, containing the quadrupeds. John Murray, London.

Sabine, J. 1822. Account of the marmots of North America hitherto known, with notices and descriptions of three new species. Transactions of the Linnean Society London 13: 579-591.

Salmon, T. P. and R. E. Marsh. 1981. Artificial establishment of a ground squirrel colony. Journal of Wildlife Management 45: 1016-1018.

Schmutz, J. K., S. M. Schmutz, and D. A. Boag. 1980. Coexistence of three species of hawks (*Buteo* spp.) in the prairie-parkland ecotone. Canadian Journal of Zoology 58: 1075-1089.

van Staaden, M. J., R. K. Chesser, and G. R. Michener. 1994. Genetic correlations and matrilineal structure in a population of *Spermophilus richardsonii*. Journal of Mammalogy 75: 573-582.

Wiggett, D. R. and D. A. Boag. 1986. Establishing colonies of ground squirrels during their active season. Wildlife Society Bulletin 14: 288-291.

# ENDANGERED SPECIES: CONCLUDING SUMMARY

## Geoffrey Holroyd
*Theme Reporter*

The working sessions reiterated the concern that too much time was spent studying the problems and not enough time trying to implement solutions. I worked with two conservation groups in Guatemala during the past three years. These conservation groups do not have biologists on staff. They do not have agronomists, foresters and home economists working for them with the objective of solving local land conservation issues by making the local people three times more efficient on the land that they currently farm. If the local landowners can make a better living on the existing land, they will have no need to over-exploit the remaining natural habitats. With much more limited funding than in Canada, these Guatemalan conservation groups are tackling the land conservation issues head on rather than conducting more studies while the clearing of land continues. We should learn a lesson from this example by becoming more directly involved in the effect of land management practises on wildlife and modify current practises rather than just conducting more research. With billions of dollars in agricultural and social subsidies that could be redirected to conservation goals, lack of funding is not an acceptable excuse for no action.

In summary the recommendations of the endangered species working sessions were:

1. The requirements of endangered and other wildlife need to be integrated with human land uses on the prairie landscape.

2. Ecosystem teams should deal with broad issues of prairie conservation that affect the welfare of many species.

3. The RENEW committee should develop and approve recovery plans quickly.

4. International aspects of endangered species conservation need to be implemented through effective international communication and cooperation (existing or new agreements).

5. Endangered species recovery efforts should include a greater emphasis involving landowners in seeking solutions and on communication of information to landowners.

# 7.0 ABSTRACTS OF POSTERS AND DISPLAYS

# 7.1 PLANTS

## SEED PRODUCTION OF MIXED PRAIRIE FOR THE PURPOSE OF RESTORATION

**Geoff Clark and Bob Redmann**
*Department of Crop Science and Plant Ecology,
University of Saskatchewan, Saskatoon, Saskatchewan
S7N OW0*

Seed production and composition of three mixed grassland communities were studied within Grasslands National Park, Saskatchewan. These communities were the upland, slope, and lowland. Hand harvests were done on June 1, June 17, July 4, July 21, August 7, August 24, and September 10, 1994. Significant differences in standing crop seed yield (kg/ha) and standing crop seed numbers (# seeds/m²) occurred through the season in the slope and lowland, but not the upland community. Seed yields were greatest in the slope community, but seed numbers were greatest in the lowland community. Diversity of species producing seed was greatest in the slope, and least in the lowland at all harvest dates. Low seed fill of dominant species on the upland negatively affected production in this community. Seed yields for restoration from the upland community in 1994 would have been poor. Slope and lowland communities had better potential for seed harvests because the dominant species produced numerous seeds.

## SPRIGGING: AN EXPERIMENT IN RE-ESTABLISHING PLAINS ROUGH FESCUE AT RUMSEY, ALBERTA

**Heather S. Gerling**
*Public Land Management Branch, Alberta Agriculture
Food and Rural Development, 7000 - 113 Street,
Edmonton, Alberta T6H 5T6*

The Public Lands Branch of Alberta Agriculture Food and Rural Development, in partnership with Renaissance Energy, is experimenting with sprigging plains rough fescue (*Festuca hallii*). Sprigging is a method of transplanting grasses that involves the harvesting of small pieces of grass crowns, roots and rhizomes. These are subsequently replanted and sprout new plants from rhizome nodes and leaf meristem. In native grassland, sprigging may be one method of propagating rhizomatous native species like *F. hallii* that are difficult to grow from seed.

Part of a wellsite on the Rumsey Block was sprigged in September 1993. The site was monitored in 1994 to determine success and species composition. Early indications were that sprigging did not successfully transplant rough fescue. However, growth on the sprigs was observed in September. Introduced annuals dominated the site, but a number of early successional native species are colonizing e.g., blue lettuce, yarrow, vetch, hedge nettle, fowl bluegrass, tickle grass, sweetgrass, bearded wheatgrass.

There are plans to sprig again in the spring of 1995, when moisture conditions may be more favorable. Monitoring of succession will continue. It may be possible to leave native prairie sites in this area to revegetate on their own.

## SCULPTURED SEEDING - AN ECOLOGICAL APPROACH TO REVEGETATION

**Erling T. Jacobson[1], D. Brent Wark[2], Roy G. Arnott[2], Russell J. Haas[3], and Dwight A. Tober [3]
PRESENTER: Rick Andrews[4]**
*[1]USDA-Natural Resources Conservation Service,
Midwest National Technical Center, Federal Building,
Rm 152, 100 Centennial Mall North, Lincoln,
Nebraska 68508-3866
[2]Ducks Unlimited Canada, Stonewall P.O. Box 1160,
Oak Hammock Marsh, Manitoba R0C 2Z0
[3]USDA-Natural Resources Conservation Service,
Plants Materials Center, 3310 University Drive,
Bismarck, North Dakota 58504-7564
[4]Ducks Unlimited Canada, Box 8, R.R. #1, 2034
Currie Blvd., Brandon, Manitoba R7A 5Y1*

The sculptured seeding technique, an ecological approach to revegetation based on a knowledge and understanding of the natural vegetation of an area, establishes a diverse, effective native plant community capable of regeneration and plant succession. It is intended to match site capability with plant species known to thrive under particular conditions. Sculptured seeding is an option available to land managers interested in establishing and maintaining adapted native species and ecotypes within the limits of current technology and available seed sources.

## NATIVE GRASSES FOR RECLAMATION

**K. W. May, W. D. Willms, and Z. Mir**
*Agriculture and Agri-Food Canada, Lethbridge Research Centre, Lethbridge, Alberta TlJ 4B1*

One of the objectives of the Lethbridge Research Centre (LRC) program is to release ecovars and cultivars of native grass species for commercial production and conservation. Plant collections have been made from existing native stands in Alberta and selections have been made to maintain a genetically broad based population. The potential of three perennial brome species are being evaluated for revegetation of clear cut forest areas in Alberta and British Columbia. *Bromus anomalus* and *Bromus ciliatus* have a bunch growth habit, short plant height, resistance to lodging and other characteristics of which are of importance when planted among tree seedlings during reestablishment of a commercial forests. Native species of fescue are being evaluated for their potential in reclamation of land areas disturbed by construction, rights of way and other activities. Selections of Idaho fescue (*Festuca idahoensis*) from southern Albert exhibit a wide range of phenotypes in respect to straw strength, growth rates, seed production and other characteristics. New cultivars will include genotypes with characteristics to enable efficient seed production and plant establishment for reclamation purposes.

## EROSION CONTROL AND REVEGETATION AFTER PIPELINE CONSTRUCTION IN THE GREAT SAND HILLS REGION OF SASKATCHEWAN

**David Walker[1] and Laurier Kremer[2]**
*[1]David Walker and Associates Ltd., Calgary, Alberta*
*[2]TransCanada PipeLines, P.O. Box 1000, Station 'M', 111 - 5th Ave. S.W., Calgary, Alberta T2P 3Y6*

In 1990 and again in 1994, TransCanada PipeLines constructed a large diameter pipeline through 12 km of the Great Sand Hills region of southwestern Saskatchewan. Harsh environmental conditions necessitated extraordinary construction and mitigation measures to control wind erosion and successfully revegetate the highly erodible sand dunes and fragile plant communities. Generally, the mitigation measures included dormant season construction, topsoil salvage, placed fertilizer application, crimping flax straw, brush mulch wind barriers, fencing-out cattle and the use of a native grass seed mixture. Surface treatment with the Hodder Gouger and straw bale wind barriers were used as part of the reclamation program following 1990 construction. Subsequent to the 1990 construction, an ongoing environmental monitoring program was required until reclamation standards for plant density, canopy cover, erosion control, and species composition were met. The environmental monitoring program continued for four years (until 1994) at which time all criteria of the reclamation standards were met. The most successful of the sand stabilization treatments was crimping straw mulch applied at 6-9 t/ha. Brush mulch wind barriers composed of sagebrush salvaged from the right-of-way prior to construction was found to be an effective method of erosion control on very exposed sites. The monitoring program will resume as a result of the 1994 construction.

## CLONAL AND SEXUAL REPRODUCTION IN RIPARIAN COTTONWOODS ALONG THE OLDMAN RIVER AT LETHBRIDGE, ALBERTA

**Lori A. Gom[1], Stewart B. Rood[1]; and Andre Laroche[2]**
*[1]The University of Lethbridge and*
*[2]Agriculture and Agri-Food Canada Research Centre1, Lethbridge, Alberta*

Along the river valleys of the north western prairies, cottonwoods (*Populus deltoides*, *P. balsamifera*, and *P. angustifolia*) form the foundation for the riparian forest ecosystem. Consequently, conservation programs for riparian woodlands in Southern Alberta and elsewhere must consider cottonwood biology, and particularly mechanisms and requirements for cottonwood reproduction. It has often been assumed that cottonwoods reproduced primarily through sexual mechanisms involving seedling replenishment. It is now recognized that asexual (clonal) modes of reproduction are also involved. To assess the relative importance of sexual versus asexual reproductive strategies, confident methods are required to differentiate between seedlings and clonally originated individuals. The present study was conducted to develop such methods and then to apply these to determine the relative contribution of clonal recruitment in a riparian cottonwood grove. By analyzing spatial associations, phenotypes, and genotypes, it should be possible to recognize cottonwood clones. On an island of the Oldman River, 380 mature trees were mapped, and phenotypic characteristics were assessed. These included measures of leaf shape, tree sex, trunk architecture, and the timing of catkin emergence, bud flushing and leaf senescence. Based on these characteristics, clonal associations were proposed and these are now being evaluated with a genetic approach involving DNA 'fingerprinting', using random amplified polymorphic DNA (RAPD).

## ENVIRONMENTAL CONTROL OF SHOOT GROWTH OF RIPARIAN COTTONWOODS ALONG THE ST. MARY RIVER, ALBERTA

**John M. Mahoney[1], Jennifer Willms[2], and Stewart B. Rood[2]**

[1]Alberta Environmental Protection, Pincher Creek, Alberta T0K lW0
[2]Dept. Biological Sciences, Univ. Lethbridge, Alberta T1K 3M4

The shoot growth of plants is particularly sensitive to water status and may be useful for investigating instream flow needs of riparian cottonwoods. Riparian cottonwoods (*Populus deltoides*, *P. balsamifera* and *P. angustifolia*) were studied along the lower St. Mary River in southwestern Alberta to investigate correlations between both shoot growth and annual ring growth with environmental conditions relating to water supply (stream flow and precipitation) and demand (evaporation, temperature, sunshine and wind).

The two growth responses were correlated with different environmental factors. Annual ring width was significantly correlated with meteorological variables that determine the degree of water demand, indicating that the level of drought stress was limiting. Mid- and late-growing season (June to September) conditions influenced ring growth. In contrast, branch growth was correlated with late spring (May and June) conditions including stream flow.

This study demonstrates that the growth of riparian cottonwoods varies across years in southern Alberta in a manner that reflects the balance between water supply and water demand. Analysis of branch growth increments provides a useful indicator of cottonwood response to stream flow conditions over the previous 10 to 15 years, but has limited value for investigations of long term environmental influences. Analysis of tree rings investigates a longer period of record but provides a less sensitive growth measure.

## RIVER DAMMING AND RIPARIAN COTTONWOODS IN THE WESTERN PRAIRIES

**Stewart B. Rood[1], John M. Mahoney[2], Karen P. Zanewich[1], and Marie F. Wilfong[1]**

[1]The University of Lethbridge, Lethbridge, Alberta
[2]Alberta Environmental Protection

In prairie regions, native trees are restricted to riparian zones, river valley flood plains. In Alberta and Montana, three riparian cottonwoods occur, the prairie cottonwood, *P. deltoides*, the balsam poplar, *P. balsamifera* and the narrowleaf cottonwood, *P. angustifolia*. These species interbreed to produce a globally unique and biologically diverse, trispecific hybrid swarm.

Riparian cottonwood forests provide environmental, aesthetic and recreational relief from the treeless prairies. These woodlands are ecologically rich and generally provide the regional habitats with the greatest diversity and density of wildlife. However, riparian cottonwoods are also particularly vulnerable. Cottonwood forests have declined across western North America due to impacts of livestock grazing and clearing for crop production and various other uses.

River damming and diversion can also impose negative impacts. Flood control dams alter the pattern of downstream flow and attenuate flood flows. This prevents the creation and saturation of point bars that are seedling recruitment sites. Irrigation dams trap spring snow melt and allow water diversion offstream for crop watering. These dams reduce downstream flows and this imposes drought stress on riparian cottonwoods.

Impacts along dammed rivers in Alberta and Montana are demonstrated through photographs and data presentation. Dams on the Bow and Marias rivers attenuate flows, reducing seedling recruitment. Dams on the St. Mary and Waterton rivers reduce downstream flows, creating drought stress. Prospects for riparian cottonwoods along these rivers are described, along with possible conservation strategies.

## GRAZING IMPACTS ON THE BIODIVERSITY OF GRASSLAND RIPARIAN ECOSYSTEMS

**Astrid M. van Woudenberg.**
*288 Whiteshield Cres., Kamloops, British Columbia V2E 1G1*

Riparian habitats in dry grassland ecosystems are critical to both livestock and many species of wildlife. Conventional range management guidelines for uplands are unsuitable for mesic to hygric areas. Riparian borders surrounding ponds are not only used disproportionately by cattle and horses; they may also be more sensitive to disturbance. Livestock can reduce the integrity of riparian habitats by overgrazing, trampling, and waste production. The combination of soil compaction, decreased vegetation structure, and changes in vegetation species composition can reduce habitat suitability for indigenous wildlife species.

The objective of this research program is to derive sustainable management strategies for grassland riparian ecosystems. Fence exclosures will allow comparative analyses of grazed and ungrazed riparian ecosystems. A baseline inventory of wildlife and vegetation communities has been used to derive suitable pond pairs based on criteria of similar species, biophysical features, and historical grazing impact.

Long-term monitoring of paired fenced and unfenced ponds will include sampling of bird, small mammal, herpetofauna, and vegetation communities as well as soils and water quality. Grazing impact will be assessed after each pasture rotation. When species abundance and evenness in exclosures exhibits little or no further change over time, grazing treatments will be tested for impact. From these results management strategies specific to riparian habitats will be developed.

## THE EFFECTS OF FIRE ON SEXUAL REPRODUCTION OF ROUGH FESCUE (*Festuca scabrella* Torr.): PRELIMINARY FINDINGS

**M.D. Pahl**
*Alberta Environmental Centre, Vegreville, Alberta*

The aspen parkland and fescue grassland ecoregions cover approximately 9.8% of the province, however, little of the original vegetation remains in an unaltered form. This is largely due to cultivation of arable land, aspen/shrub encroachment onto rangelands, and invasion of exotics. Prior to European settlement, much of the aspen parkland was dominated by grassland vegetation which was maintained by frequent prairie fires. Restoration of these grasslands is limited by lack of reliable seed sources due largely to erratic seed production by rough fescue. Short-lived stimulation of flowering activity of native prairie after burning has often been observed, however, few studies have been conducted on fescue grassland. Spring burning and mowing treatments were carried out on a natural remnant and a cultivated stand of rough fescue located at the Alberta Environmental Centre (Vegreville, Alberta) and on a natural remnant located at Nose Hill Park (Calgary, Alberta). Preliminary findings indicate that prescribed spring burns have no deleterious effect on heading of rough fescue during the first growing season following applications in both native and cultivated stands. This is the initial stage of a larger research project, which will involve prescribed burns in several areas of the province over the next two to three years.

# 7.2 ANIMALS

## EFFECT OF LIVESTOCK GRAZING ON BUMBLE BEE POPULATIONS

**K.W. Richards and T.W. Myers**
*Agriculture and Agri-Food Canada, Lethbridge Research Centre Lethbridge, Alberta TlJ 4B1*

Recent advances in agricultural technology have focused on improving yield, increasing the number of crops grown, or increasing the area of harvestable crops. These advances have had impressive results, but have been applied indiscriminately to the majority of crop species with little regard to environmental sustainability. At the same time the technical advances and intensive farming practices evolved, a negative impact on crop pollination and native bee populations occurred. For example, clearing land of trees and increased cultivation practices have inadvertently eliminated many of the nesting areas previously used by native bees. Frequent applications of pesticides, planting cross-pollinated crops in large tracts of unbroken land, and irrigation practices have also reduced native bee populations. And overgrazing of rangelands and the use of herbicides has indirectly reduced the presence of pollinators by decreasing diversity of pollen-nectar resources. Thus one of the consequences of an increased food supply has been a depopulation of both numbers and species of pollinators within agricultural environments.

A current 5-yr study is attempting to quantify the effect of livestock grazing on bumble bee density and diversity and native flowering plants in southern Alberta. Three sites are being evaluated: Stavely substation (3 grazing pressures, 1.2, 2.4, 4.8 animal-unit-months), SW of Pincher Creek (historical information), and in Waterton Lakes National Park (control is grazed by only native fauna). The density/diversity of flowers is determined by using quadrants and counting bloom over the summer. Bumble bee density/diversity is determined using transects and observing the number and kind of bees visiting various flower species.

Preliminary analysis of data after 2 years indicates that grazing pressure does influence the flower species the bees visit and the general spectrum of plants available for them to visit. The density/diversity of plants and bumble bees at Pincher Creek and Waterton is higher than at Stavely.

## MANAGING LANDSCAPES TO ENHANCE HABITAT FOR THE THREATENED LOGGERHEAD SHRIKE
**Douglas M. Collister**
*URSUS Ecosystem Management Ltd., 3426 Lane Cr. SW, Calgary, Albert. T3E 5X2*

The loggerhead shrike (*Lanius ludovicianus excubitorides*) is designated as threatened in the southern prairie provinces by COSEWIC and the population has declined over the last twenty years at an average rate of -8.9%. Habitat loss is an important factor in this decline. Breeding territories in Alberta have been shown to consist of a diverse mixture of habitat types. Nesting bushes, heterogeneous foraging habitat and hunting perches are all important components. Loggerhead shrikes prefer thorny buffaloberry (*Shepherdia argentea*) and willow (*Salix spp.*) shrubs for nest sites. Shrub patches with limited areal extent are preferred. Relatively tall (ungrazed), dense vegetation acts as a source for invertebrate and small vertebrate prey while adjoining pastureland allows shrikes to observe and capture prey. The species is a visual predator and requires elevated hunting perches to effectively forage. In the arid southern prairie provinces tall dense vegetation, to complement heavily grazed native pasture, appears to be the primary factor limiting quality shrike breeding habitat. Landscapes providing optimum shrike habitat will consist of a mosaic of both grazed and ungrazed grassland along with thorny buffaloberry or willow bushes, greater than 2 metres tall, as potential nest sites and hunting perches.

## PIPING PLOVER (*Charadrius melodus*) HABITAT INITIATIVES WITHIN EAST-CENTRAL ALBERTA
**Brian E. Ilnicki**
*Ducks Unlimited Canada, Wainwright, Alberta*

The Piping Plover (*Charadrius melodus*) has been listed as an endangered species by the Committee on the Status of Endangered Wildlife in Canada (COSEWIC 1985). The continuing loss and degradation of suitable nesting habitat has been cited as the major reason for declining populations. The 1991 International Piping Plover Census recorded 180 adult piping plovers within Alberta. A total of 84 adults were recorded within the East-Central Alberta region during this same survey. Ducks Unlimited Canada, in conjunction with other NAWMP partners, has initiated a habitat securement program which in addition to addressing identified waterfowl habitat limitations is proactively engaged in the acquisition of nesting beaches and riparian habitat deemed critical to piping plovers within East-Central Alberta. A series of field investigations combined with a literature review has generated a prioritized ranking of wetlands with confirmed or suitable nesting habitat. Strategic plans, involving site specific securement and enhancement objectives, which integrate waterfowl and piping plover habitat requirements have been completed for many of these key wetlands.

Ducks Unlimited field staff are presently working with local landowners, municipalities, provincial and federal government agencies and other non-government organizations within this region. Continuing efforts are being made to resolve habitat limitations and to rectify these problems through upland and wetland management agreements. To date, high priority nesting and feeding habitats have already been obtained. The incentives for the local landowner are tailored to his/her specific needs and when coupled with the benefits to waterfowl and the many species of shorebirds, including the piping plover, the end result is a win-win situation.

## HABITAT SELECTION BY BAIRD'S SPARROW ON MANAGED GRASSLANDS IN SOUTHERN ALBERTA

**David R. C. Prescott[1] and Bob Goddard[2]**
[1]Alberta NAWMP Centre, 10011 109th Street, Edmonton, Alberta T5J 3S8
[2]Alberta Fish and Wildlife Services, 530 - 8th Street South, Lethbridge, Alberta T1J 2J8

The Baird's sparrow is a "threatened" species of songbird that prefers undisturbed or lightly-grazed native grasslands in the southern portions of the prairie provinces. Preliminary field work in 1993 suggested that the Medicine Wheel Landscape, a 20,000 ha rotational-grazing system managed by the North American Waterfowl Management Plan near Brooks Alberta, supports a large but patchily-distributed population of this species. We conducted a study in 1994 to better understand the habitat requirements of this species on the landscape, and to ensure that the current grazing regime being implemented to improve waterfowl nesting habitat does not adversely impact this sensitive species. We systematically located singing perches of all (57) male Baird's sparrows on a two-section (518 ha) study area. Nine vegetation measurements were taken at eight random locations around each perch, and compared to measurements taken at 480 random locations along transects through the study area. Stepwise and canonical discriminant function analyses identified 5 measurements that were potential discriminators of habitat selection in this species. Baird's sparrows preferred microhabitats that contain relatively tall and dense grass, a thick litter layer, and a large shrub component. Because such microhabitats result from an improved system of grazing, we believe that the current management regime on the Medicine Wheel Landscape is creating large expanses of suitable habitat for this sensitive species.

## EFFECTS OF HABITAT FRAGMENTATION ON BURROWING OWLS (*Speotyto cunicularia*) IN SASKATCHEWAN

**Robert Warnock[1] and Paul C. James[2]**
[1]Department of Biology, University of Regina, Regina, Saskatchewan S4S 0A2
[2] Saskatchewan Wildlife Branch, 3211 Albert Street, Regina, Saskatchewan S4S SW6

Habitat pattern around 152 burrowing owl (*Speotyto cunicularia*) sites and 250 random sites in Saskatchewan were manually recorded from 1990 Landsat-TM images. Persistent owl locations had owls for 4 or more years. The 1993 core area had an owl site density of 1.6/1000 km[2]. Habitat attributes were measured in two concentric circles based on the maximum owl foraging distance of 2.7 km and the median owl breeding dispersal of 20 km. Provincially, owl sites were less isolated than random locations and persistent owl sites had more nearby owl sites. The core owl sites were more persistent and less isolated but the habitat was more fragmented because of greater extent of cultivation than random locations. Non-core persistent owl locations were less fragmented than non-persistent owl sites. Stepwise multiple regression suggests one isolation measure and several spatial measures accounted for the length of persistence. Different and more numerous fragmentation measures accounted for owl persistence outside the core area. Stepwise discriminant function analysis suggests that owls are not nesting randomly across the landscape and low correct classification of persistent owl locations suggests that the best habitat is limited. Principal components analysis of habitat pattern around owl sites in 20 km circles suggests that there are two principal components based on extent and arrangement of habitat, isolation and patch dimensions explaining 57 percent of the variance. Isolation was more important outside the core area. The ideal habitat appears to the most fragmented and management should be focused on the core area.

## BURROWING OWL NEST SITE DISTRIBUTION IN THE PRAIRIE PROVINCES.

**James R. Duncan[1], Donna Derenchuk[1], Heather Dundas[2], Jeff Keith[3], Dave Scobie[4], Ken DeSmet[5], Ken Donkersloot[1], and Bob Bruce[6]**
[1]Manitoba Conservation Data Centre, 1007 Century St., Winnipeg, Manitoba R3H 0W4
[2] Nature Saskatchewan (Operation Burrowing Owl), Box 4348, Regina, Saskatchewan S4P 3W6
[3] Saskatchewan Conservation Data Centre, Room 326, 3211 Albert St., Regina, Saskatchewan S4S 5W6
[4] Operation Grassland Community, Alberta Fish and Game Association, Box 1829, Brooks, Alberta T1R 1C6
[5] Endangered Grassland Bird Project, Manitoba natural Resources, Box 511, Melita, Manitoba R0M 1L0
[6] Land information Services, Land Information Centre, 1007 Century St., Winnipeg, Manitoba R3H 0W4

Burrowing owl nest site data were computerized, mapped and reviewed to document this threatened grassland species' current distribution in Canada to assist with a review of the species' status and recovery plan. Standard methods employed by the Manitoba and Saskatchewan Conservation Data Centres and The Nature Conservancy were used for Manitoba and Saskatchewan Data. Variations of these methods were employed by Operation Grassland Community for Alberta data. Data sources included the Prairie Nest Records Scheme cards (Manitoba Museum of Man and Nature & Canadian Wildlife Service), Nature Saskatchewan's Operation Burrowing Owl data base, Alberta Fish and Game Association's Operation Grassland Community data base, and provincial wildlife biologists field notes. Use of NOAA Satellite Imagery (with 1 km habitat classification resolution) as a basemap provides a visual interpretation of habitat associations on a prairie ecosystem scale. Some clumping of dense nesting is apparent. Owl nest sites are not present (or reported) in some areas with extensive and contiguous grassland or rangeland. Potential exists for analysis such as nest site/soil type associations, cluster analysis of burrowing owl nest sites, owl distribution in relation to protected areas, national population trend estimates and others.

This effort would have been impossible without the dedication of participating landowners, field naturalists, and biologists who compiled the data at all stages. The Manitoba Remote Sensing Centre kindly donated the NOAA satelite image base map.

## SHARING THE PEACE PARKLANDS: HOW THE TRUMPETER SWAN (*Cygnus buccinator*) AND OTHER WILDLIFE COEXIST WITH AGRICULTURAL DEVELOPMENT IN CANADA'S MOST NORTHERLY PARKLAND HABITAT
### Michael J. Williams[1] and Reginald G. Arbuckle[2]

[1]*Ducks Unlimited Canada, Grande Prairie, Alberta*
[2]*Alberta Environmental Protection, Fish and Wildlife Services, Grande Prairie, Alberta*

The Peace Parkland Biome of north-west Alberta is comprised of some 2 million ha of flat to rolling terrain characterized by numerous large molting/staging wetlands and isolated areas of pothole habitat. Recent Ducks Unlimited research and surveys conducted by the U.S. Fish and Wildlife Service/Canadian Wildlife Service indicate that the Peace parklands possess some extremely productive waterfowl habitat. This area is also the breeding grounds for Canada's largest breeding population of trumpeter swans (*Cygnus buccinator*). Other features of this biome include long-toed salamander (*Ambystoma macrodactylum*) habitat, shorebird breeding/staging areas and a vast boreal forest zone surrounding the parkland habitat.

With its productive soils and good moisture conditions the Peace River region has been attractive to agricultural development. As a result, wetland drainage and intensive cultivation have had a negative impact on the habitat of the trumpeter swan and other wildlife. Ducks Unlimited under the auspices of the North American Waterfowl Management Plan and in partnership with Alberta Environmental Protection, Fish and Wildlife Services is implementing a multi-faceted management plan to address the impacts of agricultural development on waterfowl and other wildlife in the Peace River parklands. This plan, while improving waterfowl recruitment, will create greater biological diversity in our targeted landscapes resulting in benefits to many other wildlife species.

## NORTHERN LEOPARD FROG PROJECT - RESEARCH ON A THREATENED SPECIES
### Leslie Yaremko

*11631 - 51 Ave., Edmonton, Alberta T6H 0M4*

In Alberta, the Northern Leopard Frog (*Rana pipiens*), is absent from much of its former range due to fairly recent population declines. Because of the Leopard Frog's importance to wetland ecosystems, and because of concern for its status, a research project was initiated to investigate various aspects of Leopard Frog ecology, and to monitor this species at Cypress Hills, and Empress, Alberta. At suspected locations, breeding activity and reproductive success were determined, using a combination of calling surveys, egg mass counts, tadpole identification and young-of-the-year (YOY) censuses. Three sites in Cypress Hills, and two sites in Empress were found to have successful reproduction in 1994. Considering that yearly differences in densities are common in amphibians, the data collected this year were not that different from previous years. Based on a mark-recapture experiment, overwinter mortality of a cohort of YOY frogs was found to be 93%, which has important implications for overall population status. Efforts were also made to identify overwintering sites. However, this was unsuccessful, and in the future better methods must be employed. Several limiting factors for the Northern Leopard frog were observed throughout the study. For example, livestock activity, road kills, development, fluctuating water levels, and predation were all noted. Many of these limiting factors directly relate to land-use issues. Finally, a rare yellow Northern Leopard Frog was sighted in the Cypress Hills, which is unique, as the predominant color of these frogs is green or brown.

## ALBERTA'S AMPHIBIAN MONITORING PILOT PROJECT
**Leslie Yaremko**

*11631 - 51 Ave., Edmonton, Alberta T6H 0M4*

In response to recent worldwide declines in amphibian populations in both developed and pristine areas, the International Union for the Conservation of Nature (IUCN) established the Declining Amphibian Population Task Force (DAPTF). As part of the Canadian effort, the province of Alberta developed an amphibian monitoring project that was piloted in 1994. Within Alberta, there are 10 species of amphibians: 4 frogs, 4 toads, and 2 salamanders, all of which are important to ecosystems and are potential indicators of environmental health. The monitoring project is designed to gather basic presence/absence data on these animals using volunteers. The monitoring techniques are simple. The presence of vocal frogs and toads is determined by calling surveys; nonvocal salamanders must be seen to document. Several trips to potential breeding sites are required in the spring. Presence/ absence data will lead to a better understanding of amphibian distribution; whereas, information on population status will be determined by more intense research at specific sites. Because amphibian populations fluctuate, long-term monitoring of sites is ultimately needed to distinguish short-term fluctuations from the more meaningful trends. Prior to monitoring, volunteers receive the Handbook for Monitoring Amphibians of Alberta, which contains species descriptions, range maps, an identification key, life stage tables, monitoring protocol, and a tape of amphibian calls. Overall, response has been favourable. Because 1994 was a trial year, Alberta's Amphibian Monitoring Project will be modified and expanded, and more volunteers will be needed to make the project a continued success.

# 7.3 CONSERVATION INITIATIVES

## SENSITIVE AREAS IN SOUTHERN ALBERTA: BIOPHYSICAL INFORMATION ASSISTING PRAIRIE CONSERVATION
**D. Bradshaw[1] and J. Clark[2]**

*[1]GEOWEST Environmental Consultants Ltd., Edmonton and*
*[2]Fish and Wildlife Services, Alberta Environmental Protection, Lethbridge, Alberta*

Eight sensitive areas have been identified in southern Alberta. These areas are largely located on public land and are considered sensitive due to the presence of biological and physical features that are sensitive to disturbance. Increased petroleum exploration activity and associated disturbances in southeastern Alberta have put pressure on these sensitive areas. Fish and Wildlife Services require oil and gas proponents to prepare Land Surface Management Plans prior to the commencement of exploration activity within portions of sensitive areas where such activity may be allowed. Each plan must address wildlife, access and reclamation concerns, as well as outline mitigation measures for the impacts of exploration activities on sensitive and/or special features in the area. In support of this initiative, GEOWEST Environmental Consultants Ltd. provided a biophysical overview of the Lost River Sensitive Area and identified significant, sensitive and disturbance features present within the study area. The study is intended to serve as an initial source for use by the petroleum industry and by government agencies to help "red-flag" areas where detailed site specific study may be necessary prior to any proposed land use activity.

The Lost River Sensitive Area is located in the extreme southeast corner of the province, and is part of one of the few contiguous and relatively large areas of native prairie remaining in Alberta. The study area has many unique biological and geological features, many of which are restricted in Alberta to the Lost River - Milk River Canyon area, and some of which are not found elsewhere in Canada.

## NATIVE PRAIRIE VEGETATION BASELINE INVENTORY

**Ian Dyson**

*Regional Environmental Coordinator, Prairie Region, Alberta Environmental Protection, Lethbridge T1J 2J8*

The purpose of the project is to classify and map, at a quarter section resolution, native vegetation within the department's previous Southern Region boundaries. Native vegetation is classified as tree, shrub, graminoid, riparian, or wetland. The products are generated through the interpretation of recent (1991) aerial photography and the subsequent creation of a digital attribute file for each quarter section. An interim display map at a scale of 1:350,000 of the area was generated depicting vegetation cover classes (the total percentage native vegetation in all native vegetation classes) for 80,000 of the 85,000 quarter sections that had been interpreted to date. The cover class intervals are 76 to 100, 51 to 75, 26 to 50, and 1 to 25 percent. The map was generated by converting a dBASE attribute file to ASCII file format and merging it with digital quarter section base map data. Work continues on finalizing the database and assessing the overall accuracy of the interpreted results.

## SOUTHERN REGION LAND STANDING MAP

**Ian Dyson**

*Regional Environmental Coordinator, Prairie Region, Alberta Environmental Protection, Lethbridge T1J 2J8*

The purpose of the project is to improve on existing manual methods of producing quarter section resolution Land Status Maps. A colour Land Standing Map at a scale of 1:250,000 of the Southern Region was produced, and procedures and standards were documented for the new process. The study area includes 66,000 square kilometres, of which 12,000 square kilometres are provincially owned lands and 5,500 square kilometres are Federal Lands. The product will be finalized after regional staff complete their review of the product. The next phase of the project will be to expand the map area to include all lands in the new Prairie region.

## NATIVE HABITAT LOSS TRENDS IN SASKATCHEWAN NAWMP KEY PROGRAM AREAS

**Kim Eskowich**

*Ducks Unlimited Canada, Box 2139, Melfort, Saskatchewan S0E 1A0*

Agricultural expansion into the prairie and parkland regions of Saskatchewan during the 20th century has been the single most important factor contributing to native habitat loss and degredation. Awareness of the importance of remaining native habitat has increased dramatically over the last decade as a higher value is placed on the need for preserving native plants, animals and overall biodiversity. Conservation organizations such as Ducks Unlimited have also realized the benefits of securing native prairie and parkland. Under the auspices of the North American Waterfowl Management Plan (NAWMP) and through traditional wetland enhancement projects, Ducks Unlimited has secured over 50,000 acres of idled native habitat in Saskatchewan. Approximately 70% of these acres have been secured under the NAWMP since 1989. Overall securement has been accomplished through conservation easements (42.6%) as well as purchase (23.2%), lease (30.4%), and management agreements (3.8%) under the Saskatchewan Prairie CARE program.

Although the majority of habitat loss has occurred prior to 1980, annual loss of remaining native habitat to agriculture is still occurring. In order to quantify the degree of threat to remaining habitat, Ducks Unlimited has analyzed annual habitat loss from 1979-1994 in numerous townships (36 square miles) throughout NAWMP Key Program Areas of delivery in Saskatchewan. Data was collected by comparison of current false colour infrared photography to historical black and white coverage from 1979-1981. Preliminary data indicate that annual losses of upland habitat alone can reach 2-3% in some areas. The analysis only included native upland habitat >5 acres so overall annual habitat loss including wetlands and smaller areas is undoubtedly much higher. Data on habitat loss, annual loss and remaining habitat for selected townships will be presented.

## A MULTISPECIES INVENTORY OF FLORA AND FAUNA ON A DUCKS UNLIMITED/NORTH AMERICAN WATERFOWL MANAGEMENT PLAN PROJECT IN THE PRAIRIE PARKLAND OF EAST-CENTRAL SASKATCHEWAN

**Mark Kornder[1], Ken Belcher[2], and Warren Hjertaas[3]**

[1]*Ducks Unlimited Canada, #4 - Fifth Avenue N., Yorkton, Saskatchewan S3N 0Y9*
[2]*1121 7th Street E., Saskatoon, Saskatchewan S7H 0Y9*
[3]*Nature Saskatchewan, 510 Circlebrook Dr., Yorkton, Saskatchewan S3N 2Y3*

The staff of Ducks Unlimited Canada, Yorkton, and volunteers from the local chapter of Nature Saskatchewan conducted plant and animal surveys on a North American Waterfowl Management Plan (NAWMP) project, in the spring of 1994. The purpose of these surveys was to identify the multispecies use of a Ducks Unlimited Canada/NAWMP Prairie Care program area and to promote interagency cooperation. Ducks Unlimited Canada has secured a 480 acre block of wildlife habitat in a larger area called the Barvas Marsh complex, near Yorkton, Saskatchewan. Agricultural use is limited in this area. The Barvas marsh complex is a mosaic of native grass, forb, shrub and tree species interspersed with numerous wetlands. Baseline checklists have identified 72 species of migratory birds, 109 plant species and several mammalian species. The multispecies inventory will be expanded in the future to include amphibian, small mammal and insect surveys. Similar inventories are planned for other Ducks Unlimited Canada/NAWMP projects. The accumulation of this baseline data is critical to the understanding of the biodiversity of the prairie environment. It will help to assess the impact of NAWMP programs on the prairie land base and enable resource managers to make better informed decisions. Baseline inventories are cost effective when the talents of volunteers from different groups or agencies are utilized.

## INVENTORY OF NATIVE PRAIRIE WITHIN THE BOW RIVER IRRIGATION DISTRICT USING LANDSAT DATA

**Al J. Richard**
*Ducks Unlimited Canada, Edmonton, Alberta*

The native prairie is widely recognized as one of Canada's most degraded and vulnerable habitats. The first objective of the Prairie Conservation Action Plan is to inventory the remaining native areas across the prairies.

For several years Ducks Unlimited's (DU) Habitat Inventory (HI) program has been generating a digital inventory of various upland and wetland cover types using ELAS image analysis software and Landsat 5 TM imagery. The inventory is used to help meet the habitat information requirements in planning and implementing habitat protection programs throughout the settled area of the province under the auspices of the NAWMP

Throughout certain areas of Alberta's Prairie Biome, remaining tracts of native grass cover have been identified. One such area is the Bow River Irrigation District (BRID) where various agricultural land-use practices exist. The inventory of the native grass along with other upland and wetland cover types within the BRID is from 1986 & 1987 imagery. In the BRID, DU is able to identify the area (ac), location, and distribution of the native grass cover. Numerous digital and hardcopy products are generated in both visual and statistical formats. Accuracies are deemed to be very high with respect to the inventory of the native grass. With future repeat coverage, DU will be able to monitor the change in native cover within the BRID over time.

An inventory of native prairie in the BRID allows managers to more effectively plan and manage this vulnerable habitat. DU's goal is to inventory the native prairie throughout southern Alberta by 1997.

## THE ALBERTA ENVIRONMENTAL CENTRE PRAIRIE DATABASE INFORMATION SYSTEM

**Delinda Ryerson**
*Wildlife Ecology Branch, Alberta Environmental Centre, Postal Bag 4000, Vegreville, Alberta T9C 1T4*

In order to adopt an ecosystem level approach to managing grassland systems, resource managers will need to integrate knowledge obtained through research to obtain a more complete understanding of prairie ecosystems.

The purpose of the Prairie Database Information System is to collect, compile, store, and disseminate information concerning grassland ecology. This will enable Alberta's resource managers to access information quickly. In addition, the Database Information System will assist in accomplishing the goals outlined in the Prairie Conservation Action Plan.

The electronic Prairie Database Information System consists of the following:

1) A bibliographic database containing North American references addressing the ecology of grassland associated plant and wildlife species, and the effects of various land use practices on wildlife habitat.

2) Wildlife databases, comprised of the habitat requirements and life history characteristics of select grassland species. These data have been extracted from the existing scientific literature.

3) A contact database identifying authorities in grassland ecology and ongoing grassland related studies throughout the great plains of North America.

The databases will be useful alternatives to conventional time consuming and costly literature searches. As the databases become more robust, their value as information management tools will increase. This will result in the identification of knowledge gaps which may encourage research in required areas. Because they reflect the information compiled in response to information requests, the databases will be dynamic indicators of the current atmosphere in grassland management and research.

## SOUTH COUNTRY PROTECTED AREAS PROJECT

**Cheryl Bradley**
*625-18 St. S., Lethbridge, Alberta TlJ 3E9*

The South Country Protected Areas project, begun in June 1993, is a cooperative initiative of five conservation organizations based in Lethbridge. The objectives of the project are, through a cooperative and consultative approach, to:

- compile and synthesize information on significant natural areas in the prairies of south-central Alberta;

- raise awareness among community residents about the significance of the areas; and

- determine protection issues and options and work to address these.

In 1993, project participants determined that less than 1% of the 30,720 km$^2$ study region has protective designation. Using Environmentally Significant Area Reports for each county and municipal district and provincial-level gap analysis, the project's advisory committee identified fourteen priority prairie areas for further work. Over 20 protective mechanisms available in Alberta were also identified. Upon the recommendation of the project participants, stakeholder contacts were undertaken in two priority areas, Purple Springs Dunes and Ross Lake Unglaciated. In 1994, sixteen owners of private land or lessees of public land were visited and interviewed as well as government land managers. Over thirty mineral rights holders also were identified and contacted. General findings were that, although resident landholders appreciate the areas' natural features and wish to maintain these, they are concerned that official protective designation by government would threaten current use for grazing and attract motorized public use. Oil and gas industry contacts stated that protection decisions are the responsibility of the provincial government and should be made prior to sale of mineral rights in significant areas. A recommended approach to reaching agreement on protected area needs among key stakeholders (government and non-government) is to get agreement on the area's significance, define management objectives, and identify appropriate mechanisms to realize management objectives.

Reports on both phases of the project are available at cost by contacting the author.

## THE QUILL LAKES/MOUNT HOPE HERITAGE MARSH COMPLEX: A NEW WESTERN HEMISPHERE SHOREBIRD RESERVE
**Chuck Deschamps**

*Ducks Unlimited Canada, Box 670, Waden, Saskatchewan S0A 4J0*

Located in east central Saskatchewan in the centre of a North American Waterfowl Management Plan's Key Program Area are the Quill Lakes. This Saskatchewan Heritage Marsh and RAMSAR site is a major staging area for hundreds of thousands of ducks, geese, and cranes. The lakes support a breeding colony of white pelicans as well as being ranked as having North America's 6th largest breeding population of endangered piping plovers.

Ground and aerial surveys by the Canadian Wildlife Service since 1987 have also shown these large saline lakes to be of major importance to migrating shorebirds. Thirty-seven species are found here, many of which breed in the Arctic and winter in South America. The shallow mud flats and marshy bays of the Quill Lakes richly supplied with invertebrates and submergent vegetation, make this an excellent feeding and resting stop.

In 1994 the Governments of Canada and Saskatchewan, Wetlands For The Americans, and Ducks Unlimited Canada, designated the Quill Lakes an international shorebird reserve under the Western Hemispheric Shorebird Reserve Network (WHSRN). This is only the second site in Canada to receive international recognition.

WHSRN is an international conservation initiative aimed at protecting key shorebird habitats throughout their migration ranges. Surveys estimate the Quill Lakes support over 200,000 shorebirds annually. Since the 1950s Ducks Unlimited Canada has been actively managing wetlands at the Quill Lakes. Currently Ducks Unlimited Canada manages 19 separate wetland projects in the area totalling approximately 14,600 acres.

## "PRAIRIE SPACES": A NORTHERN FESCUE PRAIRIE RESTORATION PROJECT
**Vernon Barford Junior High School Grade 8 students, with assistance from Terry Gerling (teacher), Heather Gerling (AAFRD), and Diana Brierley**

*Edmonton, Alberta*

The Public Lands Branch of Alberta Agriculture, Food and Rural Development has an interest in maintaining the integrity of native prairie and is actively engaged in trying to find ways to restore disturbed native prairie to its original condition. Most of the remaining northern fescue prairie is found in east-central Alberta on public land.

Vernon Barford Junior High School in Edmonton has assisted Public Lands in setting up a pilot prairie restoration project. Native seed from 25 northern fescue prairie plants was donated by Enviroscapes (Lethbridge) and planted by students on a 100 sq. m. plot in October. Shrubs donated by Eagle Lake Nursuries (Strathmore) were also planted. Another plot will be seeded in the spring.

The objectives of this pilot project are:

1. To promote public awareness of the value and importance of prairie ecosystems (Prairie Conservation Action Plan Goal #9);

2. To provide an opportunity for students to practise stewardship of the earth;

3. To encourage conservation and responsible use of native prairie;

4. To further knowledge about prairie restoration;

5. To increase species diversity in local landscapes.

There are plans to develop curriculum materials for teachers and a video for use by those interested in creating their own "Prairie Space". Information sheets are available.

Contact:

Terry Gerling
Vernon Barford Junior High School
32 Fairway Drive
Edmonton, Alberta T6J 2C1

Heather Gerling
Public Land Management Branch
Alberta Agriculture Food and
Rural Development
7000 - 113 Street
Edmonton, Alberta T6H 5T6

Corporate Sponsors:
    Renaissance Energy Ltd.
    Pinnacle Resources

## THE DEER MEADOW WOLF PROJECT: COEXISTENCE BETWEEN WOLVES AND HUMANS IN THE RIDING MOUNTAIN BIOSPHERE RESERVE

**Gloria D. Goulet and Tim A. Sallows**
*Riding Mountain Park Plus People, Box 9, Wasagaming, Manitoba R0J 2H0*

The denning and survival of the Deer Meadow wolf pack on agricultural land 4 km south of Riding Mountain National Park (RMNP), MB, during 1994, has provided a unique opportunity to monitor: (A) the ecology of a wolf pack living outside the protection of RMNP, (B) human/livestock/wolf interactions in the Riding Mountain Biosphere Reserve and (C) transboundary movements of wolves and other wildlife. RMNP is a relatively small (2,976 km2) "island" reserve in southwestern Manitoba surrounded by farmland interspersed with fragmented, unmodified habitat (rolling hills, spruce bogs, sloughs and thick woodlands). Wolves are fully protected within National Parks, but can be legally harvested for almost 10 months of the year outside RMNP. The nearest viable wolf population to RMNP is located in the Duck Mountains, approximately 45 km northwest of RMNP. The problem is that long-term survival for wolves inhabiting the RMNP ecosystem is threatened due to isolation (that can result in extensive inbreeding), human attitudes (fear for personal safety and loss of livestock, and competition for game animals) and an extensive wolf hunting season. These issues are being addressed by documenting the movements, resource use and survivability of the Deer Meadow wolf pack, education (sharing knowledge with schools and interest groups in the communities that surround RMNP), landowner involvement, fiscal support (wolf depredation fund) and cooperation with the provincial Dept. of Natural Resources to examine removing the wolf as a Big Game Species, in southern Manitoba.

## REGINA SOUTH NATIVE HABITAT SECUREMENT

**Andrew Hak and Brian Hepworth**
*Ducks Unlimited Canada, P.O. Box 4465, 1606 4th Ave, Regina, Saskatchewan S4P 3W7*

Through the cooperative efforts of the North American Waterfowl Management Plan (NAWMP) and Ducks Unlimited Canada, the Regina South Area Office has secured 39 parcels of native prairie habitat. The securement methods afford three levels of protection for important habitat. The first level is the purchase of native habitat which is set aside solely for the benefit of wildlife in perpetuity. We currently hold title to 1,076 acres of native habitat. The second level of securement involves an annual payment to set aside land for the benefit of wildlife. An agreement between Ducks Unlimited Canada and the private landowner is signed for a term not less than 10 years. To date, 2,199 acres are being leased to Ducks Unlimited Canada. The final level of securement does not remove agricultural use of the land but manages the grazing impact on large tracts of land. To date, grazing management techniques have been implemented on over 73,610 acres. To accomplish this, Ducks Unlimited Canada provides necessary fencing materials and water development to private landowners and government agencies. Properly managed grazing systems attain the goal of providing waterfowl habitat by controlling grazing on key nesting areas and in addition, provides multi-species habitat and improved grazing conditions for the patrons. Our field observations on these native parcels of land indicate breeding and foraging are by the following groups of species: passerines, game birds, birds of prey, small and large mammals, amphibians, insects and reptiles.

## PRAIRIE ECOSYSTEM MANAGEMENT - NAWMP IN ACTION

**E.W. Houck[1], K.K. Kaczanowski[1], G. R. Kindrat[2], and D.M. Watson[3]**
*[1]Ducks Unlimited Canada, Box 818, Brooks, Alberta, T1R 0C8*
*[2]NAWMP, Strathmore, Alberta*
*[3]Ducks Unlimited Canada, Lethbridge, Alberta*

Integrating water and grassland habitat on the mixed grass prairie of southern Alberta is an aggressive initiative to secure thousands of hectares of prime waterfowl and wildlife habitat in the Prairie Biome. At present over 1 million acres of land (65% of the total irrigated land in Canada) are under irrigation development in southern Alberta. The infrastructure created by this irrigation system enables the creation of "drought proofed" wetland habitat. Multi-basin projects have been developed to create a wetland complex approach to habitat development in order to diversify habitat types. Complexes include a number of wetland basins (as many as 60) which range in size and type from ephemeral wetlands less than 1 ha in size to permanent basins averaging 20 ha or more. The second major resource integrated into prairie ecosystem management are grasslands. Although cultivation has occurred on irrigable lands, a significant amount (4 million ha) remains in native ground cover and provides a significant grazing resource. Habitat programs in the Prairie Biome secure from 4 to to 20 thousand ha of upland habitat in single management units. Integrating habitat development into grazing systems that enable both wildlife and agriculture to benefit is a priority of program implementation in Southern Alberta. One such development is the Medicine Wheel Intensive Management Unit in the Brooks area. This project creates long-term water and upland management programs which will benefit prairie wildlife populations. By cooperating with irrigation, ranching, energy industry and other interest groups, a mutually beneficial integrated resource plan has been implemented on the prairie landscape.

## ALBERTA PRAIRIE CARE: AN APPROACH TO ECOSYSTEM MANAGEMENT IN THE ASPEN PARKLAND BIOME OF ALBERTA

**John W. Martin, Ian M. McFarlane, and Michael T. Barr**

*Ducks Unlimited Canada, Camrose, Alberta*

In response to drastic declines in waterfowl populations, the North American Waterfowl Management Plan (NAWMP) is executing an aggressive and widespread habitat initiative to maintain, restore and enhance waterfowl habitat within major production areas of the Aspen Parkland Biome of Alberta. Alberta Prairie CARE (APC) is the major component of the waterfowl habitat programs offered under the NAWMP and is delivered on behalf of the Plan's partners by Ducks Unlimited Canada and Alberta Environmental Protection, Fish and Wildlife Services.

The expansion and intensification of agriculture in the Aspen Parkland has produced extensive changes to the waterfowl habitat base. The NAWMP seeks to restore waterfowl breeding populations to levels experienced

during the mid-1970s as well as provide habitat benefits to a wide array of other wildlife species. Planning and delivery of the APC program involves the delineation and prioritization of homogeneous habitat landscapes within the biome. Within priority landscapes, factors limiting waterfowl production are identified and appropriate habitat initiatives are prescribed. Limiting factors typically include the quantity, diversity and distribution of wetland habitat and associated nesting cover. Wetland developments are integrated with complimentary upland habitat initiatives to restore landscape heterogeneity and ultimately maximize benefits for waterfowl and other wildlife species.

Although improved waterfowl recruitment is the major impetus for the APC program, the approach used will provide tangible benefits to numerous other wildlife species through increased biological diversity within delivery landscapes. We suggest that this methodology may serve as a working model of an ecosystem approach to habitat restoration and management.

## PRAIRIE CONSERVATION: WE ARE NOT JUST WORRYING ABOUT IT; WE ARE NOT JUST TALKING ABOUT IT; WE ARE DOING IT!

**Ruth M. Powell**

*Helen Schuler Coulee Centre, City of Lethbridge, 910 - 4 Ave. S., Lethbridge, Alberta T1J 0P6*

Teen Naturalists is an action oriented group of teens, aged 12 -16 years, who are committed to helping the environment. A core group meets twice a month for two hours, while other Teens help out with the projects that are of particular interest to them. Our group is responsible for two mountain bluebird trails. We researched, built and now continue to clean and monitor the nest boxes. Seeing the baby bluebirds is definitely a reward for our efforts.

Our muscles have been put to the test during work on our reclamation project. Hauling in loads of top soil, hammering in protective snow fencing and planting native grasses and bushes in hopes that they will one day stabilize the eroding coulee slope. We have helped the city in protecting cottonwood trees from excessive beaver damage and participate in the annual Coulee Clean Up and information gathering at the Christmas Bird Count. We continually expand our experiences with nature and other naturalists by visiting a variety of sites and natural areas within Lethbridge. Some of our field trips have included a pheasant farm, an agricultural research station, an astronomy observatory, Six Mile Coulee and, of course, the nature reserve adjacent to the Helen Schuler Coulee Centre.

## ALBERTA CHAPTER OF THE WILDLIFE SOCIETY
**M.J. Pybus**
*Box 4990, Edmonton, Alberta T6E SG8*

The Alberta Chapter of The Wildlife Society is a non-profit organization comprised of professionals and students who share interests and activities in wildlife-related fields. In 1988, the Chapter received its charter from The Wildlife Society, an organization with a long history of outstanding achievements in wildlife research, management, and education. Our Chapter is dedicated to maintaining such standards through programs and opportunities for members and non-members to exchange information, share ideas, and have a voice in the wise stewardship of natural resources in Alberta. The Chapter hosts an annual meeting and publishes a quarterly newsletter that keeps members informed about current wildlife research and management programs in Alberta as well as topical issues in wildlife management. Students are an integral component of the Chapter. Our annual Chapter meeting includes a student award competition and the announcement of the Alberta Chapter of the Wildlife Society student scholarship winner. The Chapter is thriving and provides an expanding forum to learn new techniques, influence management and policy, and network with colleagues. New members are always welcome.

## PRAIRIE CONSERVATION IN AN URBAN SETTING - LETHBRIDGE, ALBERTA
**Elizabeth Savoy**
*City of Lethbridge, 910 - 4th Ave South, Lethbridge, Alberta T1J 0P6*

The City of Lethbridge is fortunate in that it encompasses large tracts of relatively undisturbed natural areas ( about 4,000 ha). These represent diverse habitats ranging from dry coulee slopes and grasslands to cottonwood forests and wetlands found along in the Oldman River Valley. More than 260 species of birds, 40 species of mammals, 10 species of herptiles, and numerous plants and insects have been recorded in the City limits.

Over the past two years the City of Lethbridge, in conjunction with a wildlife steering committee, has developed wildlife management guidelines to:

1. Identify opportunities for enhancing and protecting wildlife and wildlife habitats;

2. Develop parameters for dealing with wildlife issues; and

3. Involve the public in wildlife conservation.

The guidelines identify five challenges and recommend strategies for working towards meeting these challenges. In 1995, a wildlife management team was established to oversee the implementation of the guidelines over the next three years.

The City is also initiating the incorporation of natural resource information into the City's geographical information system with a pilot project in 1995. In 1996 work will begin towards developing a vegetation management plan. The poster presents these initiatives and highlights of cooperative conservation projects that are ongoing in the City of Lethbridge.

## CONSERVATION EASEMENTS: AN IMPORTANT PRIVATE LAND PRESERVATION TOOL FOR THE PRAIRIES
**Thea M. Silver**
*Delta Waterfowl Foundation, R.R.#1, Portage la Prairie, Manitoba R1N 3A1*

Much of the remaining wildlife habitat in the Prairies is on private lands. Currently, there are two habitat protection mechanisms being used by non-governmental organizations to protect these lands; outright acquisition and short-term leases. Both approaches have significant disadvantages which limit their utility for achieving the objectives of private conservancy. The solution to this problem in other jurisdictions has been the creation by legislation of a statutory conservation easement.

Conservation easements are a statutory adaptation of two familiar legal tools, the restrictive covenant and the easement. A conservation easement is a written agreement negotiated by a conservation agency with a private landowner, under which the owner agrees with a qualified private conservation organization to protect his/her land or specified aspects of it. The conservation easement is registered against title to the land and binds successor owners.

These agreements are voluntary and are established by negotiation with willing landowners.

Most existing provincial easement legislation is limited in its application for preserving natural areas as it is targeted to heritage or historic sites. Currently, none of the Prairie Provinces has legislation in place that would allow for the broad use of conservation easements for natural area preservation. However, the situation is changing and the governments of all three of the Prairie Provinces are examining the need for legislative change. This poster paper provides an overview of the state of conservation easement legislation in Canada and discusses the importance of conservation easements for preserving private lands in the Prairies.

# 8.0 CONCLUSION

# HUMAN/NATURE TRANSACTIONS SURVEY

## Don Gayton

*723 Robson St., Nelson, British Columbia V1L 5A9*

We are moving into a new era of land and resource management that is more sensitive to nature, and changing paradigms always generates uncertainty and confusion. Often the biggest uncertainty stems not from the lack of right answers, but the lack of right questions. This self-survey poses a series of choices and situations—to which there is no "right" or "wrong" response—that may help you decide what the right questions are for you.

Remember, this is NOT a skill-testing questionnaire—there are no right or wrong answers, and no "trick" questions. You do not need to sign your name. Results will be collated and reported back to stimulate thought and discussion.

1. Is there such a thing as a truly "native" or "natural" landscape, or do all sites reflect some degree of disturbance?

|   |   |
|---|---|
| a. Yes, truly natural landscapes do exist | **45%**[1] |
| b. No, all landscapes reflect some disturbance | **55%** |

2. Is it actually possible to construct or reconstruct a natural ecosystem?

|   |   |
|---|---|
| a. Yes, it is possible | **34%** |
| b. No, it is not possible | **66%** |

3. Could any of the species extinctions that have occurred in the last hundred years be considered "natural" extinctions, that would have occurred even if humans were not present?

|   |   |
|---|---|
| a. Yes, there were natural extinctions | **11%** |
| b. No, all extinctions were man-caused | **17%** |
| c. There were both natural and man-caused extinctions | **72%** |

4. If you were faced with a deteriorating site and had the choice of A), seeding it to introduced or cultivated plant species, with the short-term prospect of successful establishment and a halt to the site deterioration, but with poor long-term chances of ever getting the site restored to the original native plant species, or B), seeding it to a mix of local native species, with a good chance deterioration would continue on the short term, but on the long term, good prospects for reestablishing native vegetation. Which option would you choose?

|   |   |
|---|---|
| a. Option A | **7%** |
| b. Option B | **93%** |

5. Are there species of wildlife (other than rare or endangered types) that can be considered "managed" in the sense of domestic livestock or fowl—that is, humans exercise significant control over their population size, breeding, habitat, food sources etc.?

|   |   |
|---|---|
| a. Yes, there are managed populations | **91%** |
| b. No, there are no managed populations | **9%** |

---

[1]Results to questionnaire from about 190 respondents.

6. Are there situations where it can be appropriate to provide winter feed supplements on a permanent basis to maintain a particular wildlife population?

    a. Yes, it can be appropriate                                              **64%**
    b. No, it is never appropriate                                        **36%**

7. Is it possible to interrupt a particular natural fish spawning cycle but maintain the population indefinitely through fish hatchery releases?

    a. Yes, it is possible    **41%**
    b. No, it is not possible    **59%**

8. Is the use of a manmade chemical, such as a herbicide or poison, ever appropriate in an ecological restoration project?

    a. Yes, it can be appropriate    **78%**
    b. No, it is never appropriate    **21%**

9. Would selective or partial cutting of forests be preferable to clearcutting, if the selective cutting required more roads and skidtrails over the landbase than did clearcutting, for the same volume of timber?

    a. Yes, partial cutting would still be preferred    **68%**
    b. No, partial cutting would not be preferred    **32%**

10. Are there any kinds of disturbances made by humans that can be considered "natural" disturbances?

    a. All human disturbances are natural    **13%**
    b. Some human disturbances are natural    **69%**
    c. No human disturbance is natural    **18%**

11 Is it technically possible to remove significant numbers of seeds, plants or animals from a natural ecosystem, without permanently altering that ecosystem?

    a. Yes, it is possible    **44%**
    b. No, it is not possible    **56%**

12. In collecting species of plants and/or animals for use in ecological restoration, can a maximum distance be specified between the collection site and the restoration site that, if exceeded, would mean the transplanted species would no longer be a "native," but an "introduction?"

    a. Yes, a distance can be specified    **58%**
    b. No, a distance cannot be specified    **42%**

13. Can the natural vegetation on a site evolve toward one of several different final plant assemblages (polyclimax) or is there a single, specific climax plant assemblage for each site?

    a. Polyclimax    **65%**
    b. Single climax    **9%**
    c. Climax is never achieved    **26%**

14. If seed is collected from an undisturbed natural landscape, planted in a multiplication plot, and the resulting seed harvested again, is that seed still considered "native," or is it "cultivated ?"

|   |   |
|---|---|
| a. Native | **71%** |
| b. Cultivated | **29%** |

15. If lightning starts a wildfire in a wilderness or protected area, is it proper to put it out or let it burn?

|   |   |
|---|---|
| a. Put it out | **17%** |
| b. Let it burn | **83%** |

16. If wild plants are removed from a natural ecosystem and used in landscaping, public parks, etc., is it possible the resulting increased public awareness can more than offset the damage caused by their removal?

|   |   |
|---|---|
| a. Yes, public awareness can compensate | **64%** |
| b. No, public awareness cannot compensate | **36%** |

17. What seems to you to be the best single definition of a site in "natural" condition (choose one only):

|   |   |
|---|---|
| a. Maximum biodiversity (that is, largest possible number of species present) | **7%** |
| b. Vegetation is assessed at the "climax" or at "100% of potential natural community" level | **10%** |
| c. Species numbers on the site and their distribution are as they were prior to European contact | **32%** |
| d. Existing species are at the ideal known parameters of population growth, reproduction, and longevity | **20%** |
| e. Site has never been disturbed by humans | **31%** |

18. Should the concept of "nature" be defined as:

|   |   |
|---|---|
| a. Separate from humankind | **14%** |
| b. Including humankind | **86%** |

19. Can the scientific approach to nature coexist with a spiritual, mystical approach, or are the two incompatible?

|   |   |
|---|---|
| a. Yes, they can coexist | **92%** |
| b. No, they cannot coexist | **8%** |

20. You are asked to divide a region into three land use zones. Each zone has a different purpose:

Protect (wilderness area: no economic activity)
Integrate (economic and ecosystem values must coexist)
Dedicated (economic activity dominates)

|   | Option a | Option b | Option c |
|---|---|---|---|
| Protected | 10%[2] | 20% | 40% |
| Integrated | 80% | 60% | 20% |
| Dedicated | 10% | 20% | 40% |

[2]Percentages refer to the regional land base occupied by each zone

|   |   |   |   |
|---|---|---|---|
| Which Option would you choose? | **26%** | **55%** | **19%** |

# COMMENTARY ON RESPONSES TO SURVEY - by Don Gayton

1. A precise, as well as a philosophical, understanding of what is "natural" will be critical to successful ecosystem management.

2. If we cannot reconstruct a natural ecosystem, then we need to be clear what it is we are doing when we are practicing "ecosystem restoration." Some theorists think that it is important for us to not only know how to reconstruct ecosystems, but also learn how to create totally new landscapes and ecosystems.

3. To admit that natural extinctions occur is to acknowledge that nature, ecosystems, and climax are not static entities.

4. This is a very real and difficult choice that land managers face. I am pleased to see the practicality of the audience—they see preservation of the soil as a paramount concern. Plant breeders could do wonders for us if they could develop aggressive, easily-established cover crop mixtures that leave open the "ecological window" for subsequent reinvasions of native species.

5. Interesting result. I would speculate in saying that those who said yes to this question were referring to deer, elk, ducks, and geese. Another reason why the boundaries between the rancher and the wildlife manager are beginning to break down.

6. If we do contemplate long-term feeding arrangements, are we potentially upsetting a natural balance, or worse yet, compensating for our destruction of the species habitat or natural food source?

7. No comment.

8. The issue here is can we use unnatural means to achieve natural ends, and can we synthesize chemicals that the earth simply does not have the ability to neutralize and break down.

9. In many cases, the worst environmental damage in timber harvesting is from the roads and skidtrails, not the cutting itself, and clearcuts do tend to minimize the kilometres of road per cubic meter of wood harvested.

10. As in question 1, the definition of what is "natural" is central to the concept of ecosystem management, and "disturbance" is central to the concept of "natural".

11. This may be more of a philosophical question than a technical one.

12. If John Morgan is in the audience, he might be willing to comment on this.

13. It is interesting that a significant proportion of us have thrown out the concept of "climax" altogether.

14. Again, if there are native seed growers in the audience, they might want to comment.

15. I was happy to see these results.

16. Examine your hearts on this one and decide if you would have answered the same way if the questions were about plants instead of animals.

17. Quite a range on this one. As for "e", is there a difference between the precontact aboriginal human and the European human, and if so, why?

18. My own personal answer is that we were once part of nature, but now have largely stepped outside of it, because of our willingness to kill our own kind, our willingness to exceed our carrying capacity, and our tool-making ability. We have crossed a Rubicon, so to speak.

19. 1 am surprised at this much consensus, when I rarely see examples of where these two approaches are integrated in practice.

20. Interesting spread. we are beginning to develop a sense of the mix of different landscapes that we want as a society.

# 4TH PRAIRIE CONSERVATION AND ENDANGERED SPECIES WORKSHOP AWARDS

## Cheryl Bradley, Awards subcommittee Chair

Awards presented at the PCES workshop recognize exceptional commitment to the conservation and understanding of native prairie or endangered species within the grassland and parkland regions of western Canada. Three awards are presented, one for each of the three prairie provinces. Past award recipients have included: Dr. Stewart Houston, accomplished naturalist and conservationist (Sask. 1989); Dianne Pachal and Vivian Pharis, long-standing environmental activists working for protected areas (Alta., 1989); Art Alan, volunteer for Manitoba Wildlife Federation and Habitat Foundation Incorporated (Man., 1992); Donald Hooper, farmer and outstanding naturalist (Sask., 1992) and Cliff Wallis, outstanding naturalist and dedicated conservation advocate (Alta., 1992).

Award recipients for the 1995 workshop were chosen, in Manitoba, by Bob Sopuck; in Saskatchewan, by the Wilderness Strategy Committee, facilitated by Alan Appleby; and in Alberta, by the workshop organizing committee, facilitated by Cheryl Bradley. Awards (plaques carved by Julie Winkler of Twin Butte) were presented by Monte Hummel, President of World Wildlife Fund Canada, at the banquet. The names of award recipients and a brief description of their accomplishments follow.

## MANITOBA: LOCAL GOVERNMENT DISTRICT OF STUARTBURN (Representative: Ed Dolynchuk)

The 4th PCES award for exceptional commitment to prairie conservation in the province of Manitoba goes to a local government. The Local Government District of Stuartburn has been chosen from among several worthy nominees in Manitoba for their donation of 800 acres of tall grass prairie to the province for protection in perpetuity. Tall grass prairie is our most endangered ecosystem with less than 1% remaining. Eight hundred acres added to the tall grass prairie preserve in south eastern Manitoba is a lot! Not only have councillors and staff with the Local Government District made the donation of land, they also have worked to convey an appreciation and understanding among their electorate of the tall grass prairie initiative. The donated lands will be designated a provincial Wildlife Management Area. The Local Government District of Stuartburn's cooperation and support for the tall grass prairie initiative is appreciated, not only by those working in Manitoba's Critical Wildlife Habitat Program, but by all Canadians concerned with prairie conservation and endangered species.

Other conservation efforts by the Local Government District in the diverse area they administer in southeastern Manitoba are to promote and develop:

- the Rat River Swamp Wetlands Restoration Project, a co-operative effort with Ducks Unlimited Canada, the Manitoba Habitat heritage Corporation, Manitoba Natural Resources and local wildlife associations; and,

- a sharptail grouse enhancement project with Sharptails Plus.

Here to receive the award on behalf of the LGD of Stuartburn is Reeve, Ed Dolynchuk. Ed was elected the first reeve in 1975 and served for five years. He was re-elected reeve in 1986 and continues to hold that position. Ed is a beef producer and also involved in forage marketing. I am asking Ed to pass on our appreciation to councillors, Roman Bodz, who presently serves on the Tall Grass Prairie Local Advisory Committee, John Korchak, Paul Horobec and Matt Drewniak as well as resident administrator, since 1979, Judy Reimer. Those who have worked with you speak highly of you, Ed, and it is a great honour to meet you and to present this award for exceptional commitment to prairie conservation in Canada. Your efforts serve as a fine example for other local and municipal governments.

## SASKATCHEWAN: DALE GEORGE HJERTAAS

The 4th PCES award for exceptional commitment to prairie conservation in Saskatchewan goes to a biologist with the Government of Saskatchewan. Dale Hjertaas is professionally known and respected by many of us here this evening. He has played a key role in organizing previous PCES workshops and served on the subcommittee which wrote the Prairie Conservation Action Plan. Dale has been selected from among several worthy nominees for his enduring commitment to endangered species on the prairies, both through his work and volunteer activities.

For over 12 years, Dale has been the endangered species biologist with the Government of Saskatchewan. Of necessity, his work has focused on the prairies. Not only has he undertaken direct studies and management of endangered species, but also has worked to find cooperators. In 1988, Dale negotiated creation of a $300,000 Saskatchewan Endangered Species Fund with World Wildlife Fund and Saskatchewan Environment and Renewable Resources.

Dale initiated Operation Burrowing Owl, and has involved more than 500 landowners in voluntarily protecting habitat. He has worked on the Swift Fox reintroduction, protection of Ferruginous Hawk nest sites and habitat, and identification of Piping Plover habitat in Saskatchewan; as well as nine other species recovery teams, acting as chair for three of these. The first projects largely oriented to nongame to be funded by NAWMP—that is the Prairie Pothole Project and Prairie Shores Program—were initiated by Dale. He introduced the very successful wildlife education program called Project Wild to Saskatchewan Schools.

For over 20 years, Dale also has worked on prairie conservation as a volunteer, most notably through the Saskatchewan Natural History Society (Nature Saskatchewan), where he has served as Editor, Conservation Director, Membership Director, Secretary and President. As President he led the society in a period of rapid growth, including hiring its first staff and initiation of a series of conservation projects.

Contributions of dedicated government employees too often go unrecognized. Many groups and individuals, provincially and nationally, value the work that Dale has done for prairie conservation and endangered species. I understand this is the first award he has ever received. Dale, it is a great honour to present you this ever-so-well-deserved award.

## ALBERTA: FRANCIS AND BONNIE GARDNER

The 4th PCES award for exceptional commitment to prairie conservation in Alberta goes to a ranching couple. Francis and Bonnie Gardner, are third-generation ranchers managing the 8500-acre Mount Sentinel Ranch in the foothills fescue grassland and aspen parkland near Nanton, Alberta. They own 3,400 acres and lease another 5,100 acres for grazing. Francis and Bonnie were chosen from among several worthy nominees for not only practising prairie conservation while maintaining a profitable ranching operation, but also for promoting conservation and sustainable use among a wide range of people.

The Mount Sentinel Ranch is a model of sound range management. Through careful application of range management principles and practices, such as conservative stocking rates and a planned grazing system that recognizes the seasonal needs of plants and wildlife, the Gardners maintain range productivity, minimize yield losses during drought and maintain high quality wildlife habitat. The ranch encourages responsible use by recreationists by limited motorized access and assisting those who hunt on foot.

The Gardners have dedicated a quarter section of deeded land and other ranch resources to a breeding program for the Mongolian Wild horse restoration program in co-operation with the Calgary Zoo and World Wildlife Fund. Francis has served on Alberta's Land Conservation and Reclamation Council, promoting progressive reclamation techniques using native species and using the ranch for a demonstration project. Francis and a neighbour, Gordon Cartwright, initiated a co-operative research program to demonstrate the use of fire and grazing as an alternative method of brush management. As well, Francis has made numerous presentations sharing his knowledge, perspectives and personal philosophy of rangelands and ranching to a wide range of groups and individuals. The Alberta Prairie Conservation Coordinating Committee's first occasional paper, published in 1993, is based on a speech by Francis Gardner - *The Rules of the World* - in which Francis argues for preservation of prairie through working with producers. Some of you may have seen Francis featured in a 30-minute television film, *The Nature Connection: Grasslands,* sharing a positive message about responsible range management with David Suzuki and three school children. Francis was so convincing that David Suzuki concludes, "So Francis, with proper management, we <u>can</u> raise livestock and maintain our natural ecosystems at the same time!"

The Gardners are down-to-earth, well-respected folks who are helping to show us the way to a sustainable future on the prairies. Francis and Bonnie, it is a great honour to present you with this award.

# CONCLUDING REMARKS

## Ian W. Dyson, Chair of the Organizing Committee

*Alberta Environmental Protection, Bag 3014, YPM Place, 530 - 8th Street South,*
*Lethbridge, Alberta T1J 4C7*

Over the past several days you have experienced the warm blush of spring, observed the Chinook arch, etched like a geomorphological feature in the western sky, endured a bitter, biting east wind, and now its snowing! Ah, the joys of southern Alberta in February.

Thank you all for making this workshop a special event. The organizing committee put the shell in place, but only you could breath life into it. Thank you to all the presenters and all registrants for a super level of participation.

Enduring images from "Sharing the Prairies' include Charles Kay's brilliant fulminations - turning peoples' world views upside down, Jerome Martin's 'Being Rural on the Prairies' session with barely a dry eye in the house, and the Alberta Wilderness Association's Cliff Wallis and the Alberta Cattle Commission's Chris Mills with their arms around one another in the 'Crown Land Conflicts' session! Magic moments all.

Looking back over the last few days I am struck by the individuality and diversity of the experience we have all had. Given the way the workshop was structured, few of us, if any, will have attended all the same sessions and events. Yet I believe we leave this workshop with a common sense of a positive experience and a special event shared. We need to bring that dual sense of diversity and commonality to our lives and work in the environmental field. As individuals our world views are shaped by our different life experiences and the value baggage we have accumulated over the years, but we share more than we differ.

There are two rather trite, but rather fundamental messages I would like you to take away and remember Lethbridge by. Firstly, respect for our environment and natural resources, a sense of obligation to take our stewardship responsibilities for this good earth seriously. Secondly, respect for each other, and a commitment to take our responsibilities towards each other seriously.

With 399 registrants, some 50 volunteers and guest speakers and the participation of 100 or so Lethbridgians in the public sessions, this has been the biggest Prairie Conservation and Endangered Species workshop yet. I have also been impressed by the breadth of participation with agricultural and environmental interests, academia and professionals from the public and private sector all well represented. We have got healthy contingents from Saskatchewan and Manitoba and the workshop has also been enriched both intellectually and in terms of energy, by the enthusiastic participation of our U.S. guests.

(At this point there was some general discussion about the possibility of expanding workshops into the United States. There was general consensus that they are enhanced by U.S. participation, but concern that the period between jurisdictions hosting the event would grow to long and that the opportunity for prairie provinces to get together would be lost. Participants agreed to keep workshops in Canada, but encourage U.S. participation. If sufficient interest exists Stateside to get a similar event in motion there, organizers of this workshop would be pleased to share our experiences.)

The metaphorical torch was passed to Lorne Scott, Dale Hjertaas, Bob Clark, and Phil Taylor. The Fifth Prairie Conservation and Endangered Species Workshop will be held in Saskatoon, 19 - 22 February 1998.

Goodbye. Thank you. Travel safely. See you in Saskatoon in 1998.